INVESTIGATING BIOLOGY
Fourth Edition

Of Related Interest from the Benjamin Cummings Series in the Life Sciences

General Biology

N. A. Campbell, L. G. Mitchell, and J. B. Reece
Biology, Concepts & Connections Third Edition (2000)

N. A. Campbell and J. B. Reece
Biology, Sixth Edition (2002)

R. A. Desharnais and J. R. Bell
BiologyLabs On-Line (2000)

J. Dickey
Laboratory Investigations for Biology (1995)

J. B. Hagen, D. Allchin, and F. Singer
Doing Biology (1996)

R. Keck and R. Patterson
Biomath: Problem Solving for Biology Students (2000)

A. E. Lawson and B. D. Smith
Studying for Biology (1995)

J. Lee
The Scientific Endeavor (2000)

J. A. Pechenik
A Short Guide to Writing about Biology, Fourth Edition (2001)

G. I. Sackheim
An Introduction to Chemistry for Biology Students, Seventh Edition (2002)

R. M. Thornton
The Chemistry of Life CD-ROM (1998)

Biotechnology

D. Bourgaize, T. Jewell, and R. Buiser
Biotechnology: Demystifying the Concepts (2000)

Cell Biology

W. M. Becker, L. J. Kleinsmith, and J. Hardin
The World of the Cell, Fourth Edition (2000)

Biotechnology

R. F. Boyer
Modern Experimental Biochemistry, Third Edition (2000)

C. K. Mathews, K. E. van Holde and K. G. Ahern
Biochemistry, Third Edition (2000)

Genetics

R. J. Brooker
Genetics: Analysis and Principles (1999)

J. P. Chinnici and D. J. Matthes
Genetics: Practice Problems and Solutions (1999)

P. J. Russell
iGenetics (2002)

P. J. Russell
Fundamentals of Genetics, Second Edition (2000)

Human Biology

M. D. Johnson
Human Biology: Concepts and Current Issues (2001)

Molecular Biology

M. V. Bloom, G. A. Freyer, and D. A. Micklos
Laboratory DNA Science (1996)

J. D. Watson, N. H. Hopkins, J. W. Roberts, J. A. Steitz, and A. M. Weiner
Molecular Biology of the Gene, Fourth Edition (1987)

Microbiology

G. J. Tortora, B. R. Funke, and C. L. Case
Microbiology: An Introduction, Seventh Edition (2001)

Anatomy and Physiology

W. J. Germann and C. L. Stanfield
Principles of Human Physiology (2002)

E. N. Marieb
Anatomy and Physiology (2002)

E. N. Marieb
Essentials of Human Anatomy and Physiology, Sixth Edition (2000)

E. N. Marieb
Human Anatomy and Physiology, Fifth Edition (2001)

E. N. Marieb and J. Mallatt
Human Anatomy, Third Edition (2001)

Ecology and Evolution

C. J. Krebs
Ecological Methodology, Second Edition (1999)

C. J. Krebs
Ecology: The Experimental Analysis of Distribution and Abundance, Fifth Edition (2001)

J. W. Nybakken
Marine Biology: An Ecological Approach, Fifth Edition (2001)

E. R. Pianka
Evolutionary Ecology, Sixth Edition (2000)

R. L. Smith
Ecology and Field Biology, Sixth Edition (2001)

R. L. Smith and T. M. Smith
Elements of Ecology, Fourth Edition Update (2000)

Plant Ecology

M. G. Barbour, J. H. Burk, W. D. Pitts, F. S. Gilliam, and M. W. Schwartz
Terrestrial Plant Ecology, Third Edition (1999)

INVESTIGATING BIOLOGY

Fourth Edition

Judith Giles Morgan
Emory University

M. Eloise Brown Carter
Oxford College of Emory University

Benjamin
Cummings

San Francisco   Boston   New York
Cape Town   Hong Kong   London   Madrid   Mexico City
Montreal   Munich   Paris   Singapore   Sydney   Tokyo   Toronto

Senior Editor: Beth Wilbur
Project Editor: Evelyn Dahlgren
Biology Marketing Manager: Josh Frost
Production Editor: Steven Anderson
Production Service: Matrix Productions
Copy Editors: Anna Reynolds Trabucco, Betty Duncan
Cover and Insert Designer: Roy Neuhaus
Cover Photograph: Tony Stone Images/Chicago Inc.
Production Artists: Karl Miyajima, Nea Bisek, Barbara Cousins, Terry Toyama, Valerie Felts, John Norton
Photo Editors: Travis Amos, Feldman and Associates
Manufacturing Buyer: Vivian McDougal
Composition: Omegatype Typography, Inc.
Printer: Banta Book Group

Benjamin
Cummings

Preface

It is not the answer that enlightens, but the question.

Eugène Ionesco

Our knowledge of the biological world is based on the scientific enterprise of asking questions and testing hypotheses. An important aspect of learning biology is participating in the process of science and developing creative and critical reasoning skills. Our goal in writing this laboratory manual is to present a laboratory curriculum that encourages participation in the scientific process. We want students to experience the excitement of discovery and the satisfaction of solving problems and connecting concepts. For us, investigating biology is more than just doing experiments; it is an approach to teaching and learning.

The laboratory exercises are designed to encourage students to ask questions, to pose hypotheses, and to make predictions before they initiate laboratory work. Students are required to synthesize results from observations and experiments, then draw conclusions from evidence. Finally, whenever possible, students apply their results to new problems and are encouraged to pursue open-ended investigations of their own design. Scientific writing is emphasized throughout the laboratory manual.

We are convinced that involving students in the process of science through their investigating of biological phenomena is the best way to teach. The organization of this laboratory manual complements this approach to teaching and learning.

New in the Fourth Edition

Throughout the fourth edition, we have incorporated current biological research and issues. For example, you will find new questions and problems in the Applying Your Knowledge sections of most lab topics. In Lab Topic 1, Scientific Investigation, we have included new questions and examples as well as improved the instructions for creating effective tables and figures. For open-ended investigations (Lab Topic 5, Cellular Respiration and Fermentation; Lab Topic 20, Plant Growth; and Lab Topic 27, Animal Behavior), we have provided new and interesting ideas for designing student investigations.

We have modified several lab topics (Lab Topic 14, Protists and Fungi; and Lab Topic 15, Plant Diversity I: Bryophytes and Seedless Vascular Plants) based on new evidence in molecular biology. At the present time, there is still no consensus among scientists concerning the classification and evolutionary relationships in the protists. Our treatment reflects a traditional approach to protists: animal-like protists (protozoa), plantlike protists (algae), and slime molds. However, we have included within the text the current grouping of organisms to taxa that correspond to the sixth edition of Campbell and Reece (2002). Lab Topic 14 allows students to view the exciting although sometimes frustrating process of ongoing scientific research. The relationships in the plant kingdom have also changed with horsetails and whisk ferns now recognized as members of the Pterophyta. Whisk ferns have returned to the demonstration materials for Lab Topic 15. In this laboratory manual, we utilize the three domain systems of classification but remain open to the number and names of kingdoms.

We have provided an investigative case study as part of Lab Topic 26, Ecology II: Computer Simulations of a Pond Ecosystem. Teaching with case studies has been part of many instructors' teaching methods in the lecture component of introductory biology. We have provided a factual case on invasive species for students to model in the laboratory. In the teaching plans for instructors, we have included suggestions for teaching with a case plus resource information for writing a case tailored to your region and interests (Lab Topic 26 and Lab Topic 25, Ecology I: Terrestrial Ecology). We encourage you to incorporate case-based teaching and learning with these lab topics.

Other changes are more subtle but represent fine-tuning based on our experiences and those of instructors and students who used the first three editions. Figures and photos have been revised, and new ones added where needed for visualization of procedures, structures, or organisms. Several procedures have been modified for clarity and completeness.

Throughout the manual we have updated the References sections to include recent publications and relevant websites.

The Preparation Guide and Annotated Instructor's Edition have also been revised to coordinate with and support the laboratory manual. In the Preparation Guide we have updated catalog numbers, clarified procedures, added more suggestions for success, and incorporated many suggestions from our reviewers.

Laboratory Exercises

The laboratory exercises are arranged by topic and in some cases build on information and techniques in previous exercises. The laboratory exercises incorporate a combination of directed procedures and investigative processes for both experimental and observational exercises. There are basically three types of lab topics included in the manual.

1. **Directed investigations** in which traditional exercises have been reconstructed to involve students in the process of science. We have reorganized traditional lab topics to include introductory information from which students develop hypotheses and then predict the results of their experiments. They collect their data and summarize it in tables and figures of their own construction. The students must then accept or reject their hypotheses, based on their results. Examples of these directed investigations include Lab Topic 2, Enzymes; Lab Topic 4, Diffusion and Osmosis; and Lab Topic 6, Photosynthesis.

2. **Thematic investigations** in which traditional laboratory exercises have been reconstructed to incorporate unifying themes in biology. These exercises have been the most challenging to write, to teach, and to do.

We are convinced that observational exercises can be investigative if we provide the evolutionary themes of biology to assist students in summarizing and synthesizing their observations. Students can use their observations as evidence in support of these major concepts and apply their understanding to new problems. Examples of these laboratories (and their underlying concepts) include Lab Topic 3, Microscopes and Cells (Unity and Diversity of Life); Lab Topics 15 and 16, Plant Diversity (Adaptation to the Land Environment); and Lab Topics 21 to 23, Vertebrate Anatomy (Form and Function).

3. **Open-ended investigations** in which students generate their own hypotheses and design their own experiments. These exercises begin with an introduction and a simple experiment that demonstrates procedures. Then students are given suggestions for further investigation and a framework for performing these experiments. Examples of these open investigations include Lab Topic 5, Cellular Respiration and Fermentation; Lab Topic 20, Plant Growth; Lab Topic 26, Ecology II; and Lab Topic 27, Animal Behavior.

Lab Topics are designated as *Directed, Thematic,* or *Open-Ended Investigations* in the table of contents.

Scientific Communication—Writing and Speaking

Scientists must communicate their results in writing and in presentations to research groups and at meetings. Undergraduates need instruction in writing and an opportunity to practice these skills; however, instructors do not have the time to critique hundreds of student research reports for each exercise. Throughout this lab manual, teams of students work together on improving their skills. They are asked to organize and present their results to their peers during the discussion and summary sessions in the laboratory. Students are also required to write as part of each laboratory. They summarize and discuss their results and then apply information to new problems in the questions at the end of the laboratory.

We have also incorporated scientific writing into our lab manual in a stepwise fashion. Students must answer questions and summarize results within the context of the laboratory exercises. For directed investigations, students are required to submit one section of a scientific paper. For example, they might submit the Results section for one experiment in Lab Topic 2, and the Discussion section for one experiment in Lab Topic 4. Once students have experience writing each section, they write at least one complete scientific paper for an open-ended investigation, for example, Lab Topics 20 and 27. Instructions for writing a scientific paper are included in Appendix A, which also contains suggestions for developing an organized writing program.

See Appendix A and the Teaching Plans for additional information on scientific writing.

Integration of Other Sciences and Mathematics

Students often view biology as a separate and isolated body of knowledge. We have attempted to integrate biology, chemistry, some physics, and geology whenever possible. We provide opportunities for students to quantify observations, analyze and summarize results in tables and figures, and, ultimately, to use these data to construct arguments in support of their hypotheses.

Special Features

Questions for Review: Students review basic content and terminology at the end of each lab topic.

Applying Your Knowledge: As instructors, we want our students to be challenged to think and to develop critical thinking skills. Throughout this manual, students are asked to work logically through problems, critique results, and modify hypotheses. To emphasize these skills further, we have developed a section in each laboratory topic called Applying Your Knowledge, in which students are asked to apply their knowledge to other aspects of biology, to medicine, or to daily life.

  Safety considerations: Safety concerns are noted in the text by the use of icons for general safety and for biohazards. Laboratory safety is also addressed in the teaching plans at the end of each lab topic in the Instructor's Edition.

 Notes to students: To assure student success, cautionary reminders and notes of special interest are also highlighted in the text.

Appendixes: Information needed in several laboratory topics is included in the appendixes: scientific writing, using chi-square analysis, and dissection terminology.

Color insert: Color photographs are particularly helpful in the study of cells and organisms. Photos and illustrations in the color insert are cross-referenced to the text.

Instructional Support

Preparation Guide: A detailed Preparation Guide accompanies the laboratory manual. It contains materials lists, suggested vendors, instructions for preparing solutions and constructing materials, schedules for planning advance preparation, and organization of materials in the lab. The Preparation Guide is *essential* for successfully preparing and teaching these investigative laboratories.

Annotated Instructor's Edition: Teaching biology using an investigative approach requires that instructors guide students in posing questions and hypotheses from which they can predict the results of their experiments. We have included additional support for the instructor in the form of instructor's annotations in each lab topic. These annotations are intended to guide the instructor in responding to students, not to provide the right answers to every student question. We encourage instructors to become the guide to discovery rather than the repository of correct answers. Features of the Annotated Instructor's Edition include:

- **Margin notes** with simple suggestions, such as accepting hypotheses as long as they are testable, hints for success, and additional explanations appropriate for the instructor.
- **Suggested answers** to student questions.
- **Appendix D** with calculations and answers to questions in Lab Topic 12, Population Genetics II: Determining Genetic Variation.
- **Typical results.**
- **Explanatory figures.**
- **Teaching Plans.**

Teaching plans: The teaching plans are the instructor's guide to organizing and teaching each laboratory, and they reflect our objective to systematically develop more effective ways to engage students in the study of biology. The teaching plans have been particularly useful for instructors initiating investigative approaches to lab programs. Instructors should feel free to modify these plans to meet their specific needs. The teaching plan for each lab topic includes:

- **Detailed objectives,** both for content and for development of skills in problem solving and scientific methodology.
- **A list of activities** that correspond to specific objectives for the laboratory so that instructors can integrate concept objectives with features of the laboratory topic.
- **Suggested order of the lab.**
- **Estimated time requirements** for each portion of the lab.
- **Suggested options for organizing the activities for a 2-hour lab period.**
- **Hints on how to manage groups of students** and involve them in investigations that might otherwise become passive learning experiences.

 The Teaching Plans in the Annotated Instructor's Edition and the Preparation Guide provide valuable suggestions and essential information for the successful implementation of the laboratory topics.

Acknowledgments

The development of our ideas, the realization of those ideas in laboratory exercises, and the preparation of this laboratory manual are the result of the effort of many colleagues over many years. We are indebted to our many teaching assistants whose critical evaluations and insightful suggestions helped shape the exercises. Many colleagues made especially helpful or critical contributions to our efforts, including: Evelyn Bailey, Steve Baker, Jim Brown, Joy Budensiek, Walter Escobar, Katie Dew Floyd, Beth Haines, Kitty McNeill, and Theodosia Wade. We are grateful for the support and guidance provided by the editorial and production group at Benjamin/Cummings. Our thanks to Beth Wilbur, Frank Ruggirello, Evelyn Dahlgren, Steve Anderson, Merrill Peterson, Betty Duncan, Anna Reynolds Trabucco and Travis Amos. We are especially indebted to all the laboratory educators who have shared their ideas, hints for success, and philosophies of teaching with us, particularly our friends in the Association for Biology Laboratory Education (ABLE). We are grateful to our reviewers for sharing their words of encouragement and criticism, which were essential to the success of our work. We thank our students who, over the years, have provided the ultimate test for these exercises and our ideas. Finally, we extend special appreciation to our families for their perseverance, love, and encouragement.

Reviewers for the First Edition

Phyllis Baudoin, *Xavier University of Louisiana*
Carol Bernson, *University of Illinois*
Charles Biggers, *Memphis State University*
Neil Campbell, *University of California, Riverside*
Charles Creutz, *University of Toledo*
Jean DeSaix, *University of North Carolina, Chapel Hill*
Rebecca Diladdo, *Suffolk University*
John Doherty, *Villanova University*
Regina Guiliani, *Saint Peter's College*
John Hare, *Linfield College*
Laurie Henderson, *Sam Houston State University*
Alan Jaworski, *University of Georgia*
Virginia A. Johnson, *Towson State University*
Raymond Lynn, *Utah State University*
Presley Martin, *Drexel University*
Dawn McGill, *Virginia Western Community College*
Greg Paulson, *Washington State University*
Nanci Smith, *University of Texas, San Antonio*
Gerald Summers, *University of Missouri*
Roberta Williams, *University of Nevada, Las Vegas*
Dan Wivagg, *Baylor University*

Reviewers for the Second Edition

Mitch Albers, *Minneapolis Community College*
Carol Alia, *Sarah Lawrence College*
Connie L. Allen, *Edison Community College*
Daniel Hoffman, *Bucknell University*
Brian T. Livingston, *University of Missouri, Kansas City*
Jacqueline McLaughlin, *Pennsylvania State University, Lehigh Campus*
Charles W. Mims, *The University of Georgia*
Michael R. Schaefer, *University of Missouri, Kansas City*
Daniel C. Scheirer, *Northeastern University*
Geraldine W. Twitty, *Howard University*
Carol Yeager, *The University of Alabama*

Reviewers for the Third Edition

Jerry Bricker, *Laramie County Community College*
Linda Burroughs, *Rider University*
Sunita Cooke, *Montgomery College*
April Fong, *Portland Community College*
William Garnett, *Raymond Walters College*
Teresa Hanlon, *Washington and Lee University*
Daniel Hoffman, *Bucknell University*
Jacqueline McLaughlin, *Pennsylvania State University, Lehigh Campus*
Alison Mostrom, *Philadelphia College of Pharmacy and Science*

Reviewers for the Fourth Edition

Sandra Bobick, *Community College of Allegheny County*
Jerry Bricker, *Cameron University*
Jeffrey T. Burkhart, *University of LaVerne*
Deborah Clark, *Oregon State University*
Caitlin Gabor, *Southwest Texas State University*
Patricia S. Glas, *The Citadel*
Michelle F. Gaudette, *Tufts University*
Tracy Halward, *Colorado State University*
Nikolai Kirov, *New York University*
George Krasilovsky, *Rockland Community College*
Barbara J. Maynard, *Colorado State University*
Jane Rasco, *University of Alabama*

To Mary, Bill, Rob, Laura, and dear Tori, with love.

J.G.M.

To Elizabeth, Stefanie, and Cindy, with love and gratitude.

M.E.B.C.

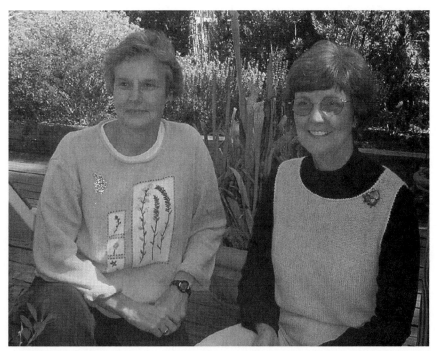

M. Eloise Brown Carter   Judith Giles Morgan

About the Authors

Judith Giles Morgan received her M.A. degree from the University of Virginia and her Ph.D. from the University of Texas, Austin. She teaches in the coastal biology program and the introductory biology program at Emory University. She has revised the general biology laboratory curriculum for majors to incorporate an investigative approach and has developed a TA training program for multisection investigative laboratories. She has long emphasized the importance of writing and computer simulations in the lab.

M. Eloise Brown Carter earned her Ph.D. from Emory University and is Professor of Biology at Oxford College of Emory University. With expertise in plant ecology, she has incorporated independent and team research into lecture and laboratory courses in introductory and advanced biology. Dr. Carter also teaches in the Oxford Institute for Environmental Education, a summer program of Oxford College for precollege teachers.

Contents

Preface v

1 Scientific Investigation 1

Laboratory Objectives 1

Introduction 1

Exercise 1.1 Questions and Hypotheses 2

Exercise 1.2 Designing Experiments to Test Hypotheses 4

Exercise 1.3 Designing an Experiment 9

Exercise 1.4 Presenting and Analyzing Results 14

Exercise 1.5 Interpreting and Communicating Results 18

Questions for Review 20

Applying Your Knowledge 22

References 27

2 Enzymes 31

Laboratory Objectives 31

Introduction 31

Exercise 2.1 Experimental Method and the Action of Catechol Oxidase 32

Exercise 2.2 Inhibiting the Action of Catechol Oxidase 35

Exercise 2.3 Influence of Concentration, pH, and Temperature on the Activity of Amylase 38

Questions for Review 49

Applying Your Knowledge 50

Investigative Extensions 52

Reference 52

3 **Microscopes and Cells 57**

Laboratory Objectives 57

Introduction 57

Exercise 3.1   Parts of the Microscope 58

Exercise 3.2   Basic Microscope Techniques 61

Exercise 3.3   The Stereoscopic Microscope 65

Exercise 3.4   The Electron Microscope 67

Exercise 3.5   The Organization of Cells 69

Questions for Review 76

Applying Your Knowledge 77

References 78

4 **Diffusion and Osmosis 81**

Laboratory Objectives 81

Introduction 81

Exercise 4.1   Diffusion of Molecules 83

Exercise 4.2   Osmotic Activity in Cells 88

Exercise 4.3   Estimating the Osmolarity of Plant Cells 92

Questions for Review 101

Applying Your Knowledge 101

References 102

5 **Cellular Respiration and Fermentation 107**

Laboratory Objectives 107

Introduction 107

Exercise 5.1   Alcoholic Fermentation 110

Exercise 5.2   Cellular Respiration 117

Exercise 5.3   Designing and Performing Your Independent Investigation 124

Questions for Review 125

Applying Your Knowledge 126

References   127

6   **Photosynthesis   131**

Laboratory Objectives   131

Introduction   131

Exercise 6.1   The Wavelengths of Light for Photosynthesis   132

Exercise 6.2   Pigments in Photosynthesis   136

Exercise 6.3   Separation and Identification of Plant Pigments by Paper Chromatography   138

Exercise 6.4   Determining the Absorption Spectrum for Leaf Pigments   141

Questions for Review   146

Applying Your Knowledge   147

References   148

7   **Mitosis and Meiosis   153**

Laboratory Objectives   153

Introduction   153

Exercise 7.1   Modeling the Cell Cycle and Mitosis in an Animal Cell   154

Exercise 7.2   Observing Mitosis and Cytokinesis in Plant Cells   159

Exercise 7.3   Observing Chromosomes, Mitosis, and Cytokinesis in Animal Cells   162

Exercise 7.4   Modeling Meiosis   165

Exercise 7.5   Meiosis in *Sordaria fimicola*: A Study of Crossing Over   171

Questions for Review   175

Applying Your Knowledge   176

References   177

8 **Mendelian Genetics: Fast Plants   183**

Laboratory Objectives   183

Introduction   183

Overview of Exercises   188

General Procedures for All Exercises   188

Exercise 8.1   Inheritance of Anthocyanin Gene   192

Exercise 8.2   Inheritance of Plant Color: Green, Yellow-Green, and Purple (Anthocyanin Present)   196

Exercise 8.3   Inheritance of Variegated and Nonvariegated Leaf Color   202

Questions for Review   207

Applying Your Knowledge   207

References   208

9 **Mendelian Genetics: *Drosophila*   213**

Laboratory Objectives   213

Introduction   213

Exercise 9.1   Establishing the Enzyme Reaction Controls   214

Exercise 9.2   Determining the Pattern of Inheritance of the Aldox Gene   220

Exercise 9.3   Determining Parental Genotypes Using Evidence from Progeny   224

Exercise 9.4   Mapping Genes   227

Questions for Review   231

Applying Your Knowledge   231

References   232

10 **Molecular Biology   239**

Laboratory Objectives   239

Introduction   239

Exercise 10.1   Mapping DNA Using Restriction Enzymes and Electrophoresis   241

Exercise 10.2   Practice Problem for Mapping DNA   256

Questions for Review   260

Applying Your Knowledge   260

References   261

11 Population Genetics I: The Hardy-Weinberg Theorem   265

Laboratory Objectives   265

Introduction   265

Exercise 11.1   Testing Hardy-Weinberg Equilibrium Using a Bead Model   268

Exercise 11.2   Simulation of Evolutionary Change Using the Bead Model   271

Exercise 11.3   Investigating the Evolution of Populations Using Computer Simulations   287

Questions for Review   288

Applying Your Knowledge   289

References   290

12 Population Genetics II: Determining Genetic Variation   295

Laboratory Objectives   295

Introduction   295

Exercise 12.1   Interpreting Banding Patterns in a Gel   296

Exercise 12.2   Interpreting Results of Gels of a Hypothetical Population   310

Questions for Review   314

Applying Your Knowledge   315

References   317

13 Bacteriology   321

Laboratory Objectives   321

Introduction   321

Exercise 13.1 Investigating Characteristics of Bacteria 322

Exercise 13.2 Ecological Succession of Bacteria in Milk 331

Exercise 13.3 Bacteria in the Environment 334

Exercise 13.4 Controlling the Growth of Bacteria 341

Questions for Review 346

Applying Your Knowledge 347

Investigative Extensions 348

References 349

14 Protists and Fungi 353

Laboratory Objectives 353

Introduction 353

Exercise 14.1 The Protists 355

Exercise 14.2 The Kingdom Fungi 372

Exercise 14.3 Designing Your Independent Investigation 381

Questions for Review 383

Applying Your Knowledge 385

References 386

15 Plant Diversity I: Bryophytes and Seedless Vascular Plants 391

Laboratory Objectives 391

Introduction 391

Exercise 15.1 Bryophytes 395

Exercise 15.2 Seedless Vascular Plants 401

Questions for Review 411

Applying Your Knowledge 412

References 413

16 Plant Diversity II: Seed Plants 417

Laboratory Objectives 417

Gymnosperms 417

Angiosperms   418

Exercise 16.1   Gymnosperms   419

Exercise 16.2   Angiosperms   425

Questions for Review   437

Applying Your Knowledge   438

Investigative Extensions   439

References   440

17   **Animal Diversity I   445**

Laboratory Objectives   445

Introduction   445

Exercise 17.1   Phylum Porifera—Sponges (*Scypha*)   449

Exercise 17.2   Phylum Cnidaria—Hydras (*Hydra*)   451

Exercise 17.3   Phylum Platyhelminthes—Planarians (*Dugesia*)   454

Exercise 17.4   Phylum Nematoda—Roundworms (*Ascaris*)   457

Exercise 17.5   Phylum Annelida—Clamworms (*Nereis*) and
Earthworms (*Lumbricus terrestris*)   461

Applying Your Knowledge   465

References   466

18   **Animal Diversity II   467**

Exercise 18.1   Phylum Mollusca—Clams   467

Exercise 18.2   Phylum Arthropoda   470

Exercise 18.3   Phylum Chordata   477

Results   484

Results Summary   484

Applying Your Knowledge   484

References   490

19   **Plant Anatomy   497**

Laboratory Objectives   497

Introduction   497

Summary of Basic Plant Tissues and Cell Types 498

Exercise 19.1 Plant Morphology 499

Exercise 19.2 Plant Primary Growth and Development 501

Exercise 19.3 Cell Structure of Primary Tissues 502

Exercise 19.4 Cell Structure of Tissues Produced by Secondary Growth 516

Exercise 19.5 Grocery Store Botany: Modifications of Plant Organs 519

Questions for Review 521

Applying Your Knowledge 521

Investigative Extensions 524

References 525

20 Plant Growth 529

Laboratory Objectives 529

Introduction 529

Germinating Seeds and Growing Plants for Independent Investigations 530

Exercise 20.1 Factors Influencing Seed Germination 533

Exercise 20.2 Plant Growth Regulators: Auxin 535

Exercise 20.3 Plant Growth Regulators: Gibberellins 540

Exercise 20.4 Designing Your Independent Investigation 544

Questions for Review 545

Applying Your Knowledge 546

References 546

21 Vertebrate Anatomy I: The Skin and Digestive System 551

Overview of Vertebrate Anatomy Labs (Lab Topics 21, 22, and 23) 551

Laboratory Objectives 552

Introduction to Tissues 552

Exercise 21.1 Histology of the Skin 556

Exercise 21.2   Introduction to the Fetal Pig   559

Exercise 21.3   The Digestive System in the Fetal Pig   563

Applying Your Knowledge   571

References   572

22   Vertebrate Anatomy II: The Circulatory and Respiratory Systems   577

Laboratory Objectives   577

Introduction   577

Exercise 22.1   Glands and Respiratory Structures of the Neck and Thoracic Cavity   578

Exercise 22.2   The Heart and the Pulmonary Blood Circuit   579

Exercise 22.3   The Heart and the Systemic Circuit in the Thorax   582

Exercise 22.4   The Systemic Circuit in the Abdominal Cavity   585

Exercise 22.5   Fetal Pig Circulation   590

Exercise 22.6   Details of the Respiratory System   591

Applying Your Knowledge   594

References   596

23   Vertebrate Anatomy III: The Excretory, Reproductive, and Nervous Systems   599

Laboratory Objectives   599

Introduction   599

Exercise 23.1   The Excretory System   600

Exercise 23.2   The Reproductive System   603

Exercise 23.3   Nervous Tissue, the Reflex Arc, and the Vertebrate Eye   612

Applying Your Knowledge   618

References   619

24   Animal Development   623

Laboratory Objectives   623

Introduction   623

Overview of Stages in Early Development   624

Exercise 24.1   Development in an Echinoderm: The Sea Star   628

Exercise 24.2   Development in an Amphibian   632

Exercise 24.3   Development in the Zebra Fish   635

Exercise 24.4   Development in a Bird: The Chicken   639

Questions for Review   646

Applying Your Knowledge   647

References   649

25   Ecology I: Terrestrial Ecology   653

Laboratory Objectives   653

Introduction   653

Stating the Problem   655

Exercise 25.1   Biotic Components   656

Exercise 25.2   Abiotic Components   669

Exercise 25.3   Data Analysis   673

Questions for Review   683

Applying Your Knowledge   684

Optional Exercise 25.1   Biotic Components: Weedy Lots or Fields   686

References   686

26   Ecology II: Computer Simulations of a Pond Ecosystem   697

Laboratory Objectives   697

Introduction   697

The Pond Ecosystem   698

Exercise 26.1   Computer Model of the Pond Ecosystem   699

Exercise 26.2   Effects of Disturbance on the Pond Ecosystem   709

Questions for Review   722

Applying Your Knowledge   723

Investigative Extension   724

References   724

27 Animal Behavior   729

Laboratory Objectives   729

Introduction   729

Exercise 27.1   Taxis in Brine Shrimp   731

Exercise 27.2   Kinesis in Pill Bugs   734

Exercise 27.3   Agonistic Display in Male Siamese Fighting Fish   737

Exercise 27.4   Reproductive Behavior in Fruit Flies   742

Questions for Review   746

Applying Your Knowledge   746

References   747

A Scientific Writing   751

B Chi-Square Test   761

C Terminology and Techniques for Dissection   765

List of Color Plates   775

Color Plates   777

Credits

Photo Credits

Page xi photo of authors: Kay Hinton, ©Emory University Photography. 3.1: Eloise Carter. 3.2: Judith Morgan. 4.7a,b: Eloise Carter. Page 183: ©Carolina Biological Supply/Phototake NYC. 7.3a: ©David M. Phillips/Visuals Unlimited. 7.3c: Micrograph by B. A. Palevitz. Courtesy of E. H. Newcomb, University of Wisconsin. 7.7: From Bold, Alexopoulos, and Delevoryas, *Morphology of Plants and Fungi*, 5th ed., Harper Collins, 1980, p. 677. 11.5a, b: ©M. W. F. Tweedie/Photo Researchers, Inc. 11.6a: ©Photo Researchers, Inc. 11.6b: ©Nigel Calder/Photo Researchers, Inc. UN12.1: Courtesty of Helena Laboratories, Beaumont TX USA and Paul Herbert and Margaret Beaton, University of Guelph, Ontario Canada/Helena Laboratories. 13.2a, b: CDC/BPS. 14.1b: ©Biophoto Associates/Science Source/Photo Researchers, Inc. 14.2b: Courtesy of John Mansfield, University of Wisconsin, Madison. 14.3a: Courtesy of the Virginia Institute of Marine Science/William and Mary. 14.3b: Courtesy of Jean-Marie CAVANIHAC/Jean-Marie CAVANIHAC. 14.3c: Courtesy of JoAnn Burkholder, North Carolina State University. 14.3d: ©Eric Grave/Photo Researchers, Inc. 14.3c: ©Michael Abbey/Photo Researchers, Inc. 14.3d: ©Cabisco/Visuals Unlimited. 14.5a: ©Gary Robinson/Visuals Unlimited. 14.5b: ©D. P. Wilson/Eric and David Hosking/Photo Researchers, Inc. 14.5c: Courtesy of Wayne Armstrong/Wayne's World. 14.6a: ©Kim Taylor/Bruce Coleman, Inc. 14.6c: ©Kerry A. Dressler/Biological Photo Service. 14.7: ©R. R. Degginger/Earth Scenes/Animals Animals. 15.5b: ©James W. Richardson/Visuals Unlimited. 19.2b: ©John Cunningham/Visuals Unlimited. 19.4b: ©Ed Reschke. 19.4c: ©Richard Gross/Biological Photography. 19.5b: ©Ed Reschke/Peter Arnold, Inc. 19.5c: ©John Cunningham/Visuals Unlimited. 19.7b: Courtesy of Ray Evert, University of Wisconsin. 19.9b: ©Runk Schoenberger/Grant Heilman Photography. 20.6: ©Grant Heilman/Grant Heilman Photography. 21.1a, b, c, d, 21.2a, b, c: Marian Rice. 21.2d: Biophoto Associates/Science Source/Photo Researchers, Inc. 21.3a, b, c: Marian Rice. 21.4b: Victor Eroschenko. 21.5a: ©Ed Reschke. 23.7a, b: Photograph by Esther Kutnick, ©1985 The Exploratorium. 24.6a, b, c, d, e: ©Dr. Walter Metcalfe. 24.8a, 24.9a, 24.10a, 24.11: From Matthews and Schoenwolf, *Atlas of Descriptive Embryology*, 5th ed., ©1998. Reprinted by permission of Prentice-Hall, Inc., Upper Saddle River, NJ. 27.1: ©Bruce Taylor/Bruce Coleman. 27.2: ©M. W. F. Tweedie/Photo Researchers, Inc.

Color Insert

Plate 1: ©M.Abbey/Visuals Unlimited. Plate 2: ©Eric Grave/Phototake NYC. Plate 3: ©Runk Schoenberger/Grant Heilman Photography, Inc. Plate 4: ©Philip Sze/Visuals Unlimited. Plate 5: ©Manfred Kage/Peter Arnold, Inc. Plate 6: ©Runk Schoenberger/Grant Heilman Photography, Inc. Plate 7: ©Bruce Iverson/SPL/Photo Researchers, Inc. Plate 8: ©CNRI/SPL/Photo Researchers, Inc. Plate 9: Campbell et al, 5th ed. Plate 10: Judith Morgan. Plate 11: Judith Morgan. Plate 12: Mike Clayton. Plate 13: ©Phototake. Plate 14: ©Phototake. Plate 15: Eloise Carter. Plate 16: ©Christine Case. Plate 17: ©Runk Schoenberger/Grant Heilman Photography, Inc. Plate 18: ©John Durham/SPL/Photo Researchers, Inc. Plate 19: Courtesy of Carol Rehkugler, Cornell University. Plate 20: Courtesy of Barry L.Batzing, Department of Biological Sciences, SUNY Cortland. Plate 21: ©Eric Grave/Phototake NYC. Plate 22: ©Carolina Biological Supply/Phototake NYC. Plate 23: Courtesy of J.R.Waaland, University of Washington/BPS. Plate 24: ©W. Lewis, Trusty/Animals Animals. Plate 25: ©Laurie Campbell/NHPA. Plate 26: Heather Angel/Natural Visions. Plate 27: George Barron. Plate 28: ©William Crowder/National Geographic Image Collection. Plate 29: ©ENP Images. Plate 30: ©James W. Richardson/Visuals Unlimited. Plate 31: ©Science VU. Plate 32: ©Pat Lynch/Photo Researchers, Inc. Plate 33: ©Jane Gushow/Grant Heilman Photography, Inc. Plate 34: Michel Viard/Peter Arnold, Inc. Plate 35: ©D. Newman/Visuals Unlimited. Plate 36: ©Glenn Oliver/Visuals Unlimited. Plate 36 inset: ©Walter H. Hodge/Peter Arnold, Inc. Plate 37: ©Visuals Unlimited. Plate 37 inset: Fred Spiegel. Plate 38: Eloise Carter. Plate 38 inset: Eloise Carter. Plate 39: ©Ken Brate/Photo Researchers, Inc. Plate 40: Eloise Carter. Plate 41: ©Biophoto Associates/Photo Researchers, Inc. Plate 42: ©Keith Gunnar/Bruce Coleman, Inc. Plate 43: ©M.E.Warren/Photo Researchers, Inc. Plate 44: Stephen Dalton/Oxford Scientific Films. Plate 45: ©D. Wilder. Plate 46: ©Anthony Mercieca/Photo Researchers, Inc. Plate 47: ©Merlin D.Tuttle/Bat Conservation International/Photo Researchers, Inc. Plate 48: ©Ed Reschke. Plate 49: Eloise Carter. Plate 50: ©Robert Brons/BPS. Plate 51: ©Fred Bavendam/Minden Pictures. Plate 52: ©Biophoto Associates/Science Source/Photo Researchers, Inc. Plate 53: Eloise Carter. Plate 54: ©S.Stephanowicz/SPL/Photo Researchers, Inc. Plate 55: ©Robert Dunne/Photo Researchers, Inc. Plate 56: ©Kjell Sandved/Photo Researchers, Inc. Plate 57: ©Kjell Sandved/Bruce Coleman, Inc. Plate 58: Luis Castaneda Inc./Image Bank. Plate 59: ©Runk Schoenberger/Grant Heilman Photography, Inc. Plate 60: ©Ed Reschke/Peter Arnold, Inc. Plate 61: ©Grant Heilman/Grant Heilman Photography. Plate 62: Richard Gross/Biological Photography. Plate 63: ©Triarch/Visuals Unlimited. Plate 64: ©Martin Dohrn/Royal College of Surgeons/SPL/Photo Researchers, Inc. Plate 65: George Von Dassow, Friday Harbor Laboratory. Plate 66: George Von Dassow, Friday Harbor Laboratory. Plate 67: Courtesy of Nancy Hopkins, MIT. Plate 68: ©Jane Burton/Bruce Coleman, Inc.

Trademarks

Clorox is a registered trademark of the Clorox Company.
FlyNap is a registered trademark of Carolina Biological Supply Company.
Kimwipes is a registered trademark of Kimberly Clark Corporation.
Listerine is a registered trademark of Warner-Lambert Company.
Lysol is a registered trademark of Sterling Drug Inc.
Parafilm is a registered trademark of American National Can Company.
Protoslo is a registered trademark of Carolina Biological Supply Company.
Roquefort is a registered trademark of Roquefort Brand.
Windows is either a registered trademark or a trademark of Microsoft Corporation in the United States and/or other countries.

Art Credits

1.2: From *Your Guide to Getting Fit,* by Ivan Kusinitz and Morton Fine, by permission of Mayfield Publishing Company. Copyright ©1987, 1991, 1995 by Mayfield Publishing Company. 1.3: Adapted from *Full House,* by Stephen Jay Gould. Copyright ©1996 by Stephen Jay Gould. Reprinted by permission of Harmony Books, a division of Crown Publishers, Inc. 1.4: Adapted from J. E. Schwegman, "Some aspects of the life history and population dynamics of *Astralagus tennesseensis* A. Gray in Illinois," *Castanea* 63 (1998):64, fig. 1. 1.5: Adapted from J. E. Schwegman, "Some aspects of the life history and population dynamics of *Astralagus tennesseensis* A. Gray in Illinois," *Castanea* 63 (1998):65, fig. 2. 2.3, 2.4: Adapted from Neil Campbell, Jane Reece, and Larry Mitchell, *Biology,* 5th ed. (Menlo Park, CA: Benjamin/Cummings, 1999), ©1999 The Benjamin/Cummings Publishing Company. 3.4: Adapted from Neil Campbell, *Biology,* 3rd ed. (Redwood City, CA: Benjamin/Cummings, 1993), ©1993 The Benjamin/Cummings Publishing Company. 4.2, 5.2, 5.5, 7.2: Adapted from Neil Campbell, Jane Reece, and Larry Mitchell, *Biology,* 5th ed. (Menlo Park, CA: Benjamin/Cummings, 1999), ©1999 The Benjamin/Cummings Publishing Company. 7.4: Adapted from Neil Campbell, *Biology,* 3rd ed. (Redwood City, CA:

Benjamin/Cummings, 1993), ©1993 The Benjamin/Cummings Publishing Company. 8.1, 8.2: Adapted from Neil Campbell, Jane Reece, and Larry Mitchell, *Biology,* 5th ed. (Menlo Park, CA: Benjamin/Cummings, 1999), ©1999 The Benjamin/Cummings Publishing Company. 8.3, 8.4, 8.5, 8.6, 8.7: Reproduced from *Wisconsin Fast Plants Manual* with permission of Carolina Biological Supply, Burlington, NC 27215, and Wisconsin Alumni Research Foundation, Madison WI 53707. 9.2, 9.3: From Demerec and Kaufman, *Drosophila Guide,* 9th ed. (Washington, DC: Carnegie Institution of Washington, 1986), ©1986 Carnegie Institution of Washington. Reprinted by permission. 10.1, 10.2, 10.3, 11.1: Adapted from Neil Campbell, Jane Reece, and Larry Mitchell, *Biology,* 5th ed. (Menlo Park, CA: Benjamin/Cummings, 1999), ©1999 The Benjamin/Cummings Publishing Company. 11.6c: Adapted from C. Starr and R. Taggart, *Biology Concepts and Applications* (Belmont, CA: Wadsworth Publishing, 1991), ©1991 Wadsworth Publishing. Reprinted by permission. 12.1: Adapted from F. Ayala, *Population and Evolutionary Genetics: A Primer* (Menlo Park, CA: Benjamin/Cummings, 1982), ©1982 The Benjamin/Cummings Publishing Company. 13.6: Adapted from E. Alcamo, *Fundamentals of Microbiology,* 5th ed., figure 3.11 (Menlo Park, CA: Benjamin/Cummings, 1997), ©1997 The Benjamin/Cummings Publishing Company. 14.6c: From Bold et al., *Morphology of Plants and Fungi,* 5th ed. (New York: Harper and Row, 1987), ©1987 by Harper and Row Publishers, Inc. Reprinted by permission of Addison Wesley Longman, Inc. 14.9, 14.10: Adapted from illustrations by Miguel Ulloa, Departamento de Botanica, Instituto de Biologia, Universidad Nacional Autonoma de Mexico. 14.11, 4.12: ©Miguel Ulloa. 15.3, 15.7: Adapted from James D. Mauseth, *Botany: An Introduction to Plant Biology,* fig. 23.3, p. 667 (Sudbury, MA: Jones and Bartlett Publishers, 1991), www.jbpub.com. Reprinted with permission. 16.3: Adapted from Neil Campbell, Jane Reece, and Larry Mitchell, *Biology,* 5th ed. (Menlo Park, CA: Benjamin/Cummings, 1999), ©1999 The Benjamin/Cummings Publishing Company. 17.1: Adapted from Neil Campbell, *Biology,* 4th ed. (Menlo Park, CA: Benjamin/Cummings, 1996), ©1996 The Benjamin/Cummings Publishing Company. 17.2, 17.3: Adapted from Larry Mitchell, John Mutchmor, and Warren Dolphin, *Zoology* (Menlo Park, CA: Benjamin/Cummings, 1988), ©1988 The Benjamin/Cummings Publishing Company. 17.4: Adapted from Neil Campbell, Jane Reece, and Larry Mitchell, *Biology,* 5th ed. (Menlo Park, CA: Benjamin/Cummings, 1999), ©1999 The Benjamin/Cummings Publishing Company. 17.5: Adapted from Larry Mitchell, John Mutchmor, and Warren Dolphin, *Zoology* (Menlo Park, CA: Benjamin/Cummings, 1988), ©1988 The Benjamin/Cummings Publishing Company. 17.7: Adapted from Neil Campbell, Jane Reece, and Larry Mitchell, *Biology,* 5th ed. (Menlo Park, CA: Benjamin/Cummings, 1999), ©1999 The Benjamin/Cummings Publishing Company. 18.2, 18.3, 18.4, 18.6: Adapted from Larry Mitchell, John Mutchmor, and Warren Dolphin, *Zoology* (Menlo Park, CA: Benjamin/Cummings, 1988), ©1988 The Benjamin/Cummings Publishing Company. 20.1, 20.2, 20.3, 20.4: Reproduced from *Wisconsin Fast Plants Manual* with permission of Carolina Biological Supply, Burlington, NC 27215, and Wisconsin Alumni Research Foundation, Madison WI 53707. 21.1a1: Adapted from Elaine Marieb, *Human Anatomy and Physiology Laboratory Manual,* Cat Version, 6th ed. (Menlo Park, CA: Benjamin/Cummings, 1999), © 1999 The Benjamin/Cummings Publishing Company. 21.1a2: Adapted from Elaine Marieb, *Human Anatomy and Physiology Laboratory Manual,* Cat Version, 4th ed. (Menlo Park, CA: Benjamin/Cummings, 1993), ©The Benjamin/Cummings Publishing Company. 21.1b1, 21.1c1: Adapted from Elaine Marieb, *Human Anatomy and Physiology Laboratory Manual,* Cat Version, 6th ed. (Menlo Park, CA: Benjamin/Cummings, 1999), ©1999 The Benjamin/Cummings Publishing Company. 21.1d1: Adapted from Neil Campbell, Jane Reece, and Larry Mitchell, *Biology,* 5th ed. (Menlo Park, CA: Benjamin/Cummings, 1999), ©1999 The Benjamin/Cummings Publishing Company. 21.1d2: Adapted from Elaine Marieb, *Human Anatomy and Physiology Laboratory Manual,* Cat Version, 4th ed. (Menlo Park, CA: Benjamin/Cummings, 1993), ©1993 The Benjamin/Cummings Publishing Company. 21.2a1: Elaine Marieb, *Human Anatomy and Physiology Laboratory Manual,* Cat Version, 5th ed. (Menlo Park, CA: Benjamin/Cummings, 1996), ©1996 The Benjamin/Cummings Publishing Company. 21.2b1: Elaine Marieb, *Human Anatomy and Physiology Laboratory* Manual, Cat Version, 6th ed. (Menlo Park, CA: Benjamin/Cummings, 1999), ©1999 The Benjamin/Cummings Publishing Company. 21.2c1: Elaine Marieb, *Human Anatomy and Physiology Laboratory Manual,* Cat Version, 3rd ed. (Menlo Park, CA: Benjamin/Cummings, 1989), ©1989 The Benjamin/Cummings Publishing Company. 21.2d1: Elaine Marieb, *Human Anatomy and Physiology Laboratory Manual,* Cat Version, 4th ed.

(Menlo Park, CA: Benjamin/Cummings, 1993), ©1993 The Benjamin/Cummings Publishing Company. 21.3a1: Elaine Marieb, *Human Anatomy and Physiology Laboratory Manual,* Cat Version, 6th ed. (Menlo Park, CA: Benjamin/Cummings, 1999), ©1999 The Benjamin/Cummings Publishing Company. 21.3c1: Elaine Marieb, *Human Anatomy and Physiology Laboratory Manual,* Cat Version, 6th ed. (Menlo Park, CA: Benjamin/Cummings, 1999), ©1999 The Benjamin/Cummings Publishing Company. 21.4a: Adapted from Elaine Marieb, *Human Anatomy and Physiology Laboratory Manual,* Cat Version, 6th ed. (Menlo Park, CA: Benjamin/Cummings, 1999), ©1999 The Benjamin/Cummings Publishing Company. 21.7: Adapted from Stephen Gilbert, *Pictorial Anatomy of Fetal Pig,* 2nd ed. ©1966 University of Washington Press. Reprinted by permission of the University of Washington Press. 22.8: Adapted from Elaine Marieb, *Human Anatomy and Physiology Laboratory Manual,* Fetal Pig Version, 6th ed. (Menlo Park, CA: Benjamin/Cummings, 1999), ©1999 The Benjamin/Cummings Publishing Company. 23.5: Elaine Marieb, *Human Anatomy and Physiology Laboratory Manual,* Cat Version, 4th ed. (Menlo Park, CA: Benjamin/Cummings, 1993), ©The Benjamin/Cummings Publishing Company. 24.1, 24.2, 24.3, 24.4: Larry Mitchell, John Mutchmor, and Warren Dolphin, *Zoology,* figure 16.2 (Menlo Park, CA: Benjamin/Cummings, 1988), ©1988 The Benjamin/Cummings Publishing Company. 24.7: From Goodenough, *Laboratory Collection* (Redwood City, CA: Benjamin/Cummings, 1990), ©1990 The Benjamin/Cummings Publishing Company. 26.IA.1: E. C. Odum, H. T. Odum, and N. S. Peterson, *Environmental Decision Making: A Project BioQUEST Simulation.* The Academic Software Development Group, Computer Science Center, University of Maryland, College Park, 1993. 26.1: Adapted from Miller, *Living in the Environment,* 7th ed., figure 4.13, p. 88 (Belmont, CA: Wadsworth, 1992), ©1992 Wadsworth Publishing Company. Reprinted by permission. 26.2, 26.3, 26.4, 26.5, 26.6, 26.7, 26.8: E. C. Odum, H. T. Odum, and N. S. Peterson, *Environmental Decision Making: A Project BioQUEST Simulation.* The Academic Software Development Group, Computer Science Center, University of Maryland, College Park, 1993. 27.4: Illustration by Suzanne Barnes.

Text Credits

Lab Topics 1, 20, 21: Adapted from Neil A. Campbell, *Biology,* 4th ed. (Menlo Park, CA: Benjamin/Cummings, 1996), ©1996 The Benjamin/Cummings Publishing Company. Lab Topic 4: Experiment B adapted from D. R. Helms and S. B. Miller, *Principles of Biology: A Laboratory Manual for Biology 110* (Apex, NC: Contemporary Publishing, 1978), by permission. Lab Topic 8: Procedure for exercises adapted from *Wisconsin Fast Plants Manual* with permission of Carolina Biological Supply, Burlington, NC 27215, and Wisconsin Alumni Research Foundation, Madison WI 53707. Lab Topic 9: First published as Morgan, J. G., and V. Finnerty, "Inheritance of aldehyde oxidase in *Drosophila melanogaster*" in *Tested Studies for Laboratory Teaching,* Volume 12, Proceedings of the 12th Workshop/Conference of the Association for Biology Laboratory Education (ABLE), Corey A. Goldman, Editor. Used by permission. Lab Topic 10: Adapted from the original version written by Dr. Arri Eisen, Assistant Professor of Biology at Emory University, by permission. Lab Topic 11: Adapted from Glase, J. C. 1993. "A laboratory on population genetics and evolution: A physical model and computer simulation." In *Tested Studies for Laboratory Teaching,* Volume 7/8, pp. 29–41, Proceedings of the 7th and 8th Workshop/Conference of the Association for Biology Laboratory Education (ABLE), C. A. Goldman and P. L. Hauta, Editors. Used by permission. Lab Topic 14: Excerpt from William Crowder, "Marvels of Mycetozoa" *National Geographic Magazine,* April 1926. Copyright ©1926 National Geographic Society. Reprinted by permission. Lab Topic 24: Adapted from an exercise by John Pilger, Professor of Biology, Agnes Scott College, Decatur, GA, and a workshop presented by Robert R. Cohen, Professor of Biology, Metropolitan State College, Denver, at a meeting of the American Society of Zoologists, by permission. Lab Topic 26: Adapted from E. C. Odum, H. T. Odum, and N. S. Peterson, *Environmental Decision Making: A Project BioQUEST Simulation.* The Academic Software Development Group, Computer Science Center, University of Maryland, College Park, 1993, by permission. Appendix A: Adapted from L. S. Gray, J. Dickey, and R. Kosinski, *Writing Guide* (Clemson, SC: Clemson University, 1988), by permission. Appendix B, Table B.2: From R. A. Fisher and F. Yates, *Statistical Tables for Biological, Agricultural and Medical Research,* 6th ed, Table IV. Reprinted by permission of Addison Wesley Longman Ltd.

Scientific Investigation

Before going to lab, read the Introduction and Exercises 1.1 and 1.2. Be prepared to answer all questions and contribute your ideas in a class discussion.

Laboratory Objectives

After completing this lab topic, you should be able to:

1. Identify and characterize questions that can be answered through scientific investigation.
2. Define *hypothesis* and explain what characterizes a good scientific hypothesis.
3. Identify and describe the components of a scientific experiment.
4. Summarize and present results in tables and graphs.
5. Discuss results and critique experiments.
6. Design a scientific experiment.
7. Interpret and communicate results.

Introduction

Biology is the study of the phenomena of life, and biological scientists—researchers, teachers, and students—observe living systems and organisms, ask questions, and propose explanations for those observations. Scientific investigation is a way of testing those explanations. Science assumes that biological systems are understandable and can be explained by fundamental rules or laws. Scientific investigations share some common elements and procedures, which are referred to as the *scientific method*. Not all scientists follow these procedures in a strict fashion, but each of the elements is usually present. Science is a creative human endeavor that involves asking questions, making observations, developing explanatory hypotheses, and testing those hypotheses. Scientists closely scrutinize investigations in their field, and each scientist must present his or her work at scientific meetings or in professional publications, providing evidence from observations and experiments that supports the scientist's explanations of biological phenomena.

In this lab topic, you will not only review the process that scientists use to ask and answer questions about the living world, but you will develop the skills to conduct and critique scientific investigations. Like scientists, you will work in research teams in this laboratory and others, collaborating as you ask questions and solve problems. Throughout this laboratory manual, you will be investigating biology using the methodology of scientists, asking questions, proposing explanations, designing experiments, predicting results, collecting and analyzing data, and interpreting your results in light of your hypotheses.

EXERCISE 1.1
Questions and Hypotheses

This exercise explores the nature of scientific questions and hypotheses. Before going to lab, read the explanatory paragraphs and then be prepared to present your ideas in the class discussion.

Lab Study A. Asking Questions

Scientists are characteristically curious and creative individuals whose curiosity is directed toward understanding the natural world. They use their study of previous research or personal observations of natural phenomena as a basis for asking questions about the underlying causes or reasons for these phenomena. For a question to be pursued by scientists, the phenomenon must be well defined and testable. The elements must be measurable and controllable.

There are limits to the ability of science to answer questions. Science is only one of many ways of knowing about the world in which we live. Consider, for example, this question: Do excessively high temperatures cause people to behave immorally? Can a scientist investigate this question? Temperature is certainly a well-defined, measurable, and controllable factor, but morality of behavior is not scientifically measurable. We probably could not even reach a consensus on the definition. Thus, there is no experiment that can be performed to test the question. Which of the following questions do you think can be answered scientifically?

1. Does binge drinking cause more brain damage in teenagers than in adults?
2. Is genetically modified corn safe to eat?
3. Do children who wash their hands often and bathe daily have a greater risk of asthma than those who wash their hands less often and bathe every other day?
4. Should endangered species be cloned to prevent extinction?
5. What is the function of spines on cacti?
6. Did the 19-year-old college student develop ulcers because of his stress and fast-food diet?

How did you decide which questions can be answered scientifically?

Lab Study B. Developing Hypotheses

As questions are asked, scientists attempt to answer them by proposing possible explanations. Those proposed explanations are called **hypotheses.** A hypothesis tentatively explains something observed. It proposes an answer to a question. Consider question 5, preceding. One hypothesis based on this question might be "Spines on cacti prevent animals from eating the cacti." The hypothesis has suggested a possible explanation for the observed spines.

A scientifically useful hypothesis must be testable and falsifiable (able to be proved false). To satisfy the requirement that a hypothesis be falsifiable, it must be possible that the test results do not support the explanation. In our example, if spines are removed from test cacti and the plants are not eaten by animals, then the hypothesis has been falsified. *Even though the hypothesis can be falsified, it can never be proved true.* The evidence from an investigation can only provide support for the hypothesis. In our example, if cacti without spines were eaten, the hypothesis has not been proved, but has been supported by the evidence. Other explanations still must be excluded, and new evidence from additional experiments and observations might falsify this hypothesis at a later date. In science seldom does a single test provide results that clearly support or falsify a hypothesis. In most cases, the evidence serves to modify the hypothesis or the conditions of the experiment.

Science is a way of knowing about the natural world (Moore, 1993) that involves testing hypotheses or explanations. The scientific method can be applied to the unusual and the commonplace. You use the scientific method when you investigate why your once-white socks are now blue. Your hypothesis might be that your blue jeans and socks were washed together, an assertion that can be tested through observations and experimentation.

Students often think that controlled experiments are the only way to test a hypothesis. The test of a hypothesis may include experimentation, additional observations, or the synthesis of information from a variety of sources. Many scientific advances have relied on other procedures and information to test hypotheses. For example, James Watson and Francis Crick developed a model that was their hypothesis for the structure of DNA. Their model could only be supported if the accumulated data from a number of other scientists were consistent with the model. Actually, their first model (hypothesis) was falsified by the work of Rosalind Franklin. Their final model was tested and supported not only by the ongoing work of Franklin and Maurice Wilkins but also by research previously published by Erwin Chargaff and others. Watson and Crick won the Nobel Prize for their scientific work. They did not perform a controlled experiment in the laboratory but tested their powerful hypothesis through the use of existing evidence from other research. Methods other than experimentation are acceptable in testing hypotheses. Think about other areas of science that require comparative observations and the accumulation of data from a variety of sources, all of which must be consistent with and support hypotheses or else be inconsistent and falsify hypotheses.

The information in your biology textbook is often thought of as a collection of facts, well understood and correct. It is true that much of the knowledge of biology has been derived through scientific investigations, has been thoroughly tested, and is supported by strong evidence. However, scientific knowledge is always subject to novel experiments and new technology, any aspect of which may result in modification of our ideas and a better understanding of biological phenomena. The structure of the cell membrane is an example of the self-correcting nature of science. Each model of the membrane has been modified as new results have negated one explanation and provided support for an alternative explanation.

Application

Before scientific questions can be answered, they must first be converted to hypotheses, which can be tested. For each of the following questions, write an explanatory hypothesis. Recall that the hypothesis is a statement that explains the phenomenon you are interested in investigating.

1. Does regular interaction with pets improve the health of the elderly?

2. What effect do high concentrations of the industrial pollutant PCB (polychlorinated biphenyl) have on killer whale reproduction?

Scientists often propose and reject a variety of hypotheses before they design a single test. Discuss with your class which of the following statements would be useful as scientific hypotheses and could be investigated using scientific procedures. Give the reason for each answer by stating whether it could possibly be falsified and what factors are measurable and controllable.

1. The number of fungiform papillae (bumps on the tongue) affects taste sensitivity.
2. Inflated self-esteem in young males increases the odds of aggression.
3. Anglers catch more bass during a full moon.
4. Exposure to environmental pollutants produces feminization in newly hatched male alligators.
5. Birds are the living descendants of dinosaurs.

EXERCISE 1.2
Designing Experiments to Test Hypotheses

The most creative aspect of science is designing a test of your hypothesis that will provide unambiguous evidence to falsify or support a particular explanation. Scientists often design, critique, and modify a variety of experiments and other tests before they commit the time and resources to perform a single experiment. In this exercise, you will follow the procedure for experimentally testing hypotheses, but it is important to remember that other methods, including observation and the synthesis of other sources of data, are acceptable in scientific investigations. An experiment involves defining variables, outlining a procedure, and determining controls to be used as the experiment is performed. Once the experiment is defined, the investigator predicts the outcome of the experiment based on the hypothesis.

Read the following description of a scientific investigation of the effects of sulfur dioxide on soybean reproduction. Then in Lab Study A you will determine the types of variables involved, and in Lab Study B, the experimental procedure for this experiment and for others.

INVESTIGATION OF THE EFFECT OF SULFUR DIOXIDE ON SOYBEAN REPRODUCTION

Agricultural scientists were concerned about the effect of air pollution, sulfur dioxide in particular, on soybean production in fields adjacent to coal-powered power plants. Based on initial investigations, they proposed that sulfur dioxide in high concentrations would reduce reproduction in soybeans. They designed an experiment to test this hypothesis (Figure 1.1). In this experiment, 48 soybean plants, just beginning to produce flowers, were divided into two groups, treatment and no treatment. The 24 treated plants were divided into four groups of 6. One group of 6 treated plants was placed in a fumigation chamber and exposed to 0.6 ppm (parts per million) of sulfur dioxide for 4 hours to simulate sulfur dioxide emissions from a power plant. The experiment was repeated on the remaining three treated groups. The no-treatment plants were placed similarly in groups of 6 in a second fumigation chamber and simultaneously exposed to filtered air for 4 hours. Following the experiment, all plants were returned to the greenhouse. When the beans matured, the number of bean pods, the number of seeds per pod, and the weight of the pods were determined for each plant.

Lab Study A. Determining the Variables

Read the description of each category of variable; then identify the variable described in the preceding investigation. The variables in an experiment must be clearly defined and measurable. The investigator will identify

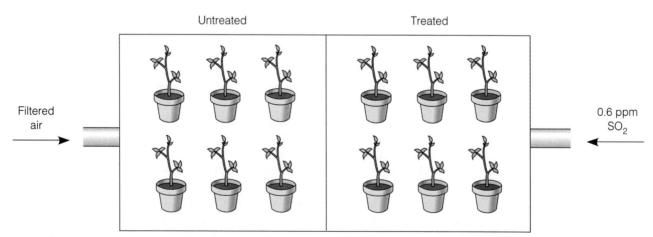

Figure 1.1.
Experimental design for soybean experiment. The experiment was repeated four times. Soybeans were fumigated for 4 hours.

and define *dependent, independent,* and *controlled variables* for a particular experiment.

The Dependent Variable

Within the experiment, one variable will be measured or counted or observed in response to the experimental conditions. This variable is the **dependent variable.** For the soybeans, several dependent variables are measured, all of which provide information about reproduction. What are they?

The Independent Variable

The scientist will choose one variable, or experimental condition, to manipulate. This variable is considered the most important variable by which to test the investigator's hypothesis and is called the **independent variable.** What was the independent variable in the investigation of the effect of sulfur dioxide on soybean reproduction?

Can you suggest other variables that the investigator might have changed that would have had an effect on the dependent variables?

Although other factors, such as light, temperature, time, and fertilizer, might affect the dependent variables, only one independent variable is usually chosen. Why is it important to have only one independent variable?

Why is it acceptable to have more than one dependent variable?

The Controlled Variable

Consider the variables that you identified as alternative independent variables. Although they are not part of the hypothesis being tested in this investigation, they would have significant effects on the outcome of this experiment. These variables must, therefore, be kept constant during the course of the experiment. They are known as the **controlled variables.** The underlying assumption in experimental design is that the selected independent variable is the one affecting the dependent variable. This is only true if all other variables are controlled. What are the controlled variables in this experiment? What variables other than those you may have already listed can you now suggest?

Lab Study B. Choosing or Designing the Procedure

The **procedure** is the stepwise method, or sequence of steps, to be performed for the experiment. It should be recorded in a laboratory notebook before initiating the experiment, and any exceptions or modifications should be noted during the experiment. The procedures may be designed from research published in scientific journals, through collaboration with colleagues in the lab or other institutions, or by means of one's own novel and creative ideas. The process of outlining the procedure includes determining control treatment(s), levels of treatments, and numbers of replications.

Level of Treatment

The value set for the independent variable is called the **level of treatment.** For this experiment, the value was determined based on previous research and preliminary measurements of sulfur dioxide emissions. The scientists may select a range of concentrations from no sulfur dioxide to an extremely high concentration. The levels should be based on knowledge of the system and the biological significance of the treatment level. What was the level of treatment in the soybean experiment?

Replication

Scientific investigations are not valid if the conclusions drawn from them are based on one experiment with one or two individuals. Generally, the same procedure will be repeated several times (**replication**), providing consistent results. Notice that scientists do not expect exactly the same results inasmuch as individuals and their responses will vary. Results from replicated experiments are usually averaged and may be further analyzed using statistical tests. Describe replication in the soybean experiment.

Control

The experimental design includes a **control** in which the independent variable is held at an established level or is omitted. The control or control treatment serves as a benchmark that allows the scientist to decide whether the predicted effect is really due to the independent variable. In the case of the soybean experiment, what was the control treatment?

What is the difference between the control and the controlled variables discussed previously?

Lab Study C. Making Predictions

The investigator never begins an experiment without a prediction of its outcome. The **prediction** is always based on the particular experiment designed to test a specific hypothesis. Predictions are written in the form of if/then statements: "If the hypothesis is true, then the results of the experiment will be . . ."; for example, "if cactus spines prevent herbivory, then removal of the spines will result in cacti being eaten by animals." Making a prediction provides a critical analysis of the experimental design. If the predictions are not clear, the procedure can be modified before beginning the experiment. For the soybean experiment, the hypothesis was: "Exposure to sulfur dioxide reduces reproduction." What should the prediction be? State your prediction.

To evaluate the results of the experiment, the investigator always returns to the prediction. If the results match the prediction, then the hypothesis is supported. If the results do not match the prediction, then the hypothesis is falsified. Either way, the scientist has increased knowledge of the process being studied. Many times the falsification of a hypothesis can provide more information than confirmation, since the ideas and data must be critically evaluated in light of new information. In the soybean experiment, the scientist may learn that the prediction is true (sulfur dioxide does reduce reproduction at the concentration tested). As a next step, the scientist may now wish to identify the particular level at which the effect is first demonstrated.

Return to page 4 and review your hypotheses for the numbered questions. Consider how you might design an experiment to test the first hypothesis. For example, you might measure "health" by determining blood pressure before and after interactions with a rabbit. The prediction might be:

> **If** regular interaction with pets improves the health of the elderly (*a restatement of the hypothesis*), **then** blood pressure will be lowered in elderly people who spend 15 minutes daily with a pet rabbit (*predicting the results from the experiment*).

Now consider an experiment you might design to test the second hypothesis on page 4. How will you measure killer whale "reproduction"?

State a prediction for this hypothesis and experiment. Use the if/then format:

The actual test of the prediction is one of the great moments in research: No matter the results, the scientist is not just following a procedure but truly testing a creative explanation derived from an interesting question.

Discussion

1. From this exercise, list the components of scientific investigations from asking a question to carrying out an experiment.

2. From this exercise, list the variables that must be identified in designing an experiment.

3. What are the components of an experimental procedure?

EXERCISE 1.3

Designing an Experiment

Materials

steps or platform, 8 in. high
clock with a second hand
metronome

Introduction

In this exercise, your entire class, working together, will practice investigating a question using what you have learned so far about the scientific process.

Question

Cardiovascular fitness can be determined by measuring a person's pulse rate and respiration rate before and after a given time of aerobic exercise. A person who is more fit may have a relatively slower pulse rate and a lower respiratory rate after exercise, and his or her pulse rate should return to normal more quickly than that of a person who is less fit. Your assignment is to investigate the effect of a well-defined, measurable, controllable independent variable on cardiovascular fitness.

In your research teams, take about 10 minutes to discuss several *specific* questions that you can ask about an independent variable related to the *broad* topic of cardiovascular fitness. List your questions in the space provided. For example, your question might be "Does cigarette smoking have an effect on cardiovascular fitness?" Choose your best question and propose a testable hypothesis. Contribute your question and hypothesis to a class list recorded by the instructor.

 The entire class decides on the hypothesis, the experimental design, and the predicted results. The same experiment is performed by all teams.

Hypothesis

Record the hypothesis chosen by the class.

The Experiment

If you were performing an independent investigation, at this time you would go to the library and read relevant scientific articles or texts to determine an accepted procedure used by scientists to test cardiovascular fitness. You might discover that there is a test, called the *step test,* that is used for this purpose (Kusinitz and Fine, 1987). Here are the basic elements of this test:

1. The subject steps up and down on a low platform, approximately 8 in. from the ground, for 3 minutes at a rate of 30 steps per minute. (Using a metronome to count steps ensures that all subjects maintain a constant step rate.) The subject should step up and then step down again, keeping the rate constant (Figure 1.2).

2. The subject's pulse rate is measured before the test and immediately after the test. The subject should be sitting quietly when the pulse is counted. Use three fingers to find the pulse in the radial artery (the artery in the wrist, above the thumb). Count the number of beats per minute. (Count the beats for 30 seconds and multiply by 2.)

3. Additionally, the pulse rate is measured at 1-minute intervals after the test until the pulse rate returns to normal (recovery time). Count the pulse for 30 seconds, rest 30 seconds, count 30 seconds, and rest 30 seconds. Repeat this procedure until the pulse returns to normal. Record the number of minutes to return to the normal pulse rate. (Do not record the pulse rate.)

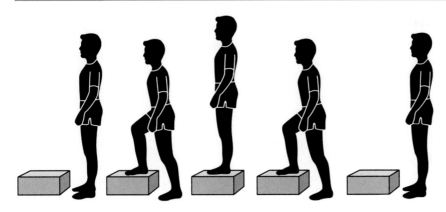

Figure 1.2.
The step test. Step up on the platform, and then step down again, keeping the rate constant.

As a class, design the experiment. Record the components of your experiment by completing the information below.

Dependent variable(s):

Independent variable:

Controlled variables:

Control:

Level of treatment:

Replication:

Summarize the experiment designed by your class:

Prediction

Predict the results of the experiment based on your hypothesis (if/then).

Procedure

Two students in each student team will serve as subjects. All other students in the team will be the investigators. The investigators will record the data for the two subjects.

 Students with respiratory or circulatory disorders should not be the subjects in this experiment.

List in numerical order each exact step of your procedure. Begin with recruitment of the subjects in each treatment category. Refer to the description of the experimental test. Remember to designate persons to time the experiment and record the measurements.

Performing the Experiment

Following the procedures established by your investigative team, perform the experiment and record your results.

Results

Record the results for your team in Table 1.1. Record total class results in Table 1.2. Identify the treatment conditions at the top of the table.

Table 1.1
Results of Step Test for Your Team (Pulse rates are beats per minute.)

	Treatment 1: _____	**Treatment 2:** _____
Before step test Pulse rate		
After step test Pulse rate		
Recovery time (min)		

Table 1.2
Results of Step Test for All Teams (Pulse rates are beats per minute.)

Treatment 1: _____

Subject	**1**	**2**	**3**	**4**	**5**	**6**	**Average**
Before step test Pulse rate							
After step test Pulse rate							
Recovery time (min)							

Treatment 2: _____

Subject	**1**	**2**	**3**	**4**	**5**	**6**	**Average**
Before step test Pulse rate							
After step test Pulse rate							
Recovery time (min)							

EXERCISE 1.4

Presenting and Analyzing Results

Once the data are collected, they must be organized and summarized so that the scientists can determine if the hypothesis has been supported or falsified. In this exercise, you will design **tables** and graphs; the latter are also called **figures.** Tables and figures have two primary functions. They are used (1) to help you analyze and interpret your results and (2) to enhance the clarity with which you present the work to a reader or viewer.

Lab Study A. Tables

You have collected data from your experiment in the form of a list of numbers that may appear at first glance to have little meaning. Look at your data. How could you organize the data set to make it easier to interpret? You could *average* the data set for each treatment, but even averages can be rather uninformative. Could you use a summary table to convey the data (in this case, averages)?

Table 1.3 is an example of a table using data averages of the number of seeds per pod and number of pods per plant as the dependent variables and exposure to sulfur dioxide as the independent variable. Note that the number of replicates and the units of measurement are provided in the table and table legend.

Table 1.3
Effects of 4-Hour Exposure to 0.6 ppm Sulfur Dioxide on Average Seed and Pod Production in Soybeans

Treatment	Number	Seeds per Pod	Pods per Plant
Control	24	3.26	16
SO_2	24	1.96	13

Tables are used to present results that have a few to many data points. They are also useful for displaying several dependent variables. For example, average number of bean pods, average number of seeds per pod, and average weight of pods per plant for treated and untreated plants could all be presented in one table.

The following guidelines will help you construct a table:

* All values of the same kind should read down the column, not across a row. Include only data that are important in presenting the results and for further discussion.

* Information and results that are not essential (for example: test-tube number, simple calculations, or data with no differences) should be omitted.

* The headings of each column should include units of measurement, if appropriate.

- Tables are numbered consecutively throughout a lab report or scientific paper. For example: Table 4 would be the fourth table in your report.

- The **title,** which is located at the top of the table, should be clear and concise, with enough information to allow the table to be understandable apart from the text. Capitalize the first and important words in the title. Do not capitalize articles (a, an, the), short prepositions, and conjunctions.

- Refer to each table in the written text. Summarize the data and refer to the table; for example, "The plants treated with sulfur dioxide produced an average of 1.96 seeds per pod (Table 3)." Do not write, "See the results in Table 3."

- If you are using a database program, such as Excel, you should still sketch your table on paper before constructing it on the computer.

Application

1. Using the data from your experiment, design a summary table to present the results for *one* of your dependent variables, pulse rate. Your table need not be the same size or design as the sample. In your table, provide units of the dependent variable (pulse rate). Tell the reader how many replications (if any) were used to calculate the averages.

2. Compose a title for your table. Refer to the guidelines in the previous section.

Lab Study B. Graphs

The results of an experiment usually are presented graphically, showing the relationships among the independent and dependent variable(s). A graph or figure provides a visual summary of the results. Often, characteristics of the data are not apparent in a table but may become clear in a graph. By looking at a graph, then, you can visualize the effect that the independent variable has on the dependent variable and detect trends in your data. Making a graph may be one of the first steps in analyzing your results.

The presentation of your data in a graph will assist you in interpreting and communicating your results. In the final steps of a scientific investigation, you must be able to construct a logical argument based on your results that either supports or falsifies your starting hypothesis. Your graph should be accurately and clearly constructed, easily interpreted, and well annotated. The following guidelines will help you to construct such a graph.

- Use graph paper and a ruler to plot the values accurately. If using a data-base program, you should first sketch your axes and data points before constructing the figure on the computer.

- The independent variable is graphed on the x axis (horizontal axis, or abscissa), and the dependent variable, on the y axis (vertical axis, or ordinate).

- The numerical range for each axis should be appropriate for the data being plotted. Generally, begin both axes of the graph at zero (the extreme left corner). Then choose your intervals and range to maximize the use of the graph space. Choose intervals that are logically spaced and therefore will allow easy interpretation of the graph, for example, intervals of 5s or 10s. To avoid generating graphs with wasted space, you may signify unused graph space by two perpendicular tic marks between the zero and your lowest number on one or both axes.

- Label the axes to indicate the variable and the units of measurement. Include a legend if colors or shading is used to indicate different aspects of the experiment.

- Choose the type of graph that best presents your data. Line graphs and bar graphs are most frequently used. The choice of graph type depends on the nature of the variable being graphed.

- Compose a title for your figure, and write it below your graph. Graphs, diagrams, drawings, and photographs are all called *figures* and should be numbered consecutively throughout a lab report or scientific paper. Each figure is given a caption or title that describes its contents, giving enough information to allow the figure to be self-contained. Capitalize only the first word in a figure title and place a period at the end.

The Line Graph

Line graphs show changes in the quantity of the chosen variable and emphasize the rise and fall of the values over their range. Use a line graph to present continuous data. For example, changes in the dependent variable pulse rate, measured over time, would be depicted best in a line graph.

- Plot data as separate points.

- Whether to connect the dots on a line graph depends on the type of data and how they were collected. To show trends, draw smooth curves or straight lines to fit the values plotted for any one data set. Connect the points dot to dot when emphasizing meaningful changes in values on the x axis.

- If more than one set of data is presented on a graph, use different colors or symbols and provide a key or legend to indicate which set is which.

- A boxed graph, instead of one with only two sides, makes it easier to see the values on the right side of the graph.

Note the features of a line graph in Figure 1.3., which depicts the increase in gray whale populations along the California coast over 35 years.

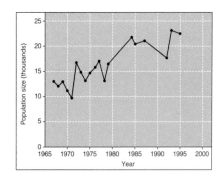

Figure 1.3.
Population size. Eastern North Pacific gray whales observed off the coast of California, 1965–2000. (After Gerber et al., 2000.)

The Bar Graph

Bar graphs are constructed following the same principles as for line graphs, except that vertical bars, in a series, are drawn down to the horizontal axis. Bar graphs are often used for data that represent separate or discontinuous groups or non-numerical categories, thus emphasizing the discrete differences between the groups. For example, a bar graph might be used to depict differences in number of seeds per pod for treated and untreated soybeans. Bar graphs are also used when the values on the *x* axis are numerical but grouped together. These graphs are called histograms.

Note the features of a bar graph in Figure 1.4., which indicates the area of cropland used for genetically modified crops.

You will be asked to design graphs throughout this laboratory manual. Remember, the primary function of the figure is to present your results in the clearest manner to enhance the interpretation of your data.

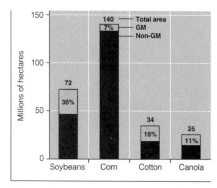

Figure 1.4.
Global area of genetically modified (GM) crops and non-GM crops grown in 2000. (After Brown, 2001.)

Application

1. Using data from your experiment and the grid provided below, design a bar graph that shows the relationship between the dependent and independent variables in this experiment. Discuss with your teammates how to design this figure so that it includes the data for pulse rate before and after exercise for the treatments selected for your experiment. Draw and label the figure, and compose a title for it.

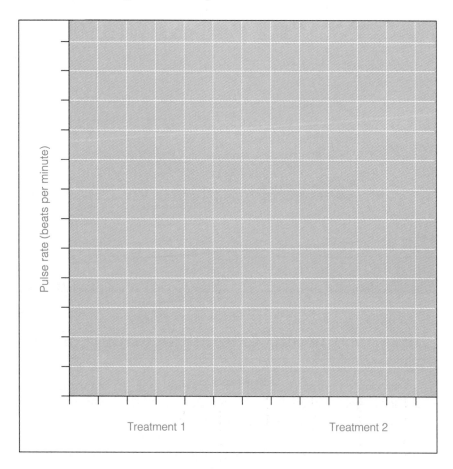

Figure 1.

a. What was your independent variable (treatment)?

b. Write the dependent variable on the appropriate axis. Write the independent variable on the appropriate axis.

2. Design an additional figure that will assist with interpreting the results of your experiment. You might use the data for recovery time or the difference in pulse rate before and after the step test for each treatment.

3. Draw, label, and compose a title for that figure using the grid provided below.

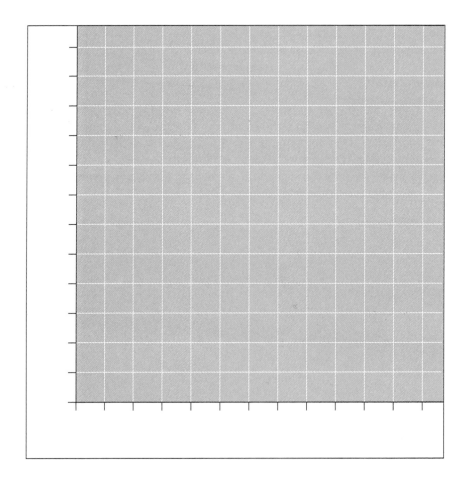

EXERCISE 1.5

Interpreting and Communicating Results

The last component of a scientific investigation is to interpret the results and discuss their implications in light of the hypothesis and its supporting literature. The investigator studies the tables and graphs and determines if the hypothesis has been supported or falsified. If the hypothesis has been falsified, the investigator must suggest alternate hypotheses for testing. If the hypothesis has been supported, the investigator suggests additional experiments to strengthen the hypothesis, using the same or alternate methods.

Scientists will thoroughly investigate a scientific question, testing hypotheses, collecting data, and analyzing results, until they are satisfied that they can explain the phenomenon of interest. The final phase of a scientific investigation is the communication of the results to other scientists. Preliminary results may be presented within a laboratory research group and at scientific meetings where the findings can be discussed. Ultimately, the completed project is presented in the form of a scientific paper that is reviewed by scientists within the field and published in a scientific journal. The ideas, procedures, results, analyses, and conclusions of all scientific investigations are critically scrutinized by other scientists. Because of this, science is sometimes described as *self-correcting,* meaning that errors that may occur are usually discovered within the scientific community.

Scientific communication, whether spoken or written, is essential to science. During this laboratory course, you often will be asked to present and interpret your results at the end of the laboratory period. Additionally, you will write components of a scientific paper for many lab topics. In Appendix A at the end of the lab manual, you will find a full description of a scientific paper and instructions for writing each section.

Application

1. Using your tables and figures, analyze your results and discuss your conclusions with your group.
2. Write a summary statement for your experiment. Use your results to support or falsify your hypothesis. Be prepared to present your conclusions to the class.

3. Critique your experiment. What weaknesses do you see in the experiment? Suggest improvements.

Weaknesses in Experiment	Improvement
1.	
2.	
3.	
4.	
5.	

4. Suggest additional and modified hypotheses that might be tested. Briefly describe your next experiment.

5. Refer to Appendix A at the end of your lab manual. Briefly describe the four major parts of a scientific paper. What is the abstract? What information is found in a References Cited section?

Questions for Review

1. Review the major components of an experiment by matching the following terms to the correct definition: *control, controlled variables, level of treatment, dependent variable, replication, procedure, prediction, hypothesis, independent variable.*

   a. Variables that are kept constant during the experiment (variables not being manipulated)

   b. Tentative explanation for an observation

   c. What the investigator varies in the experiment (for example, time, pH, temperature, concentration)

   d. Process used to measure the dependent variable

   e. Appropriate values to use for the independent variable

   f. Treatment that eliminates the independent variable or sets it at a standard value

g. What the investigator measures, counts, or records; what is being affected in the experiment

h. Number of times the experiment is repeated

i. Statement of the expected results of an experiment based on the hypothesis

2. Identify the dependent and independent variables in the following experiments. (*Circle* the dependent variable and *underline* the independent variable.)

   a. The rate of oxygen production for yeast cells growing with and without cyanide, a respiratory inhibitor.

   b. Number of colorectal tumors for patients taking aspirin twice a day.

   c. Number of gray whales observed for 35 years.

3. Suggest a control treatment for each of the following experiments.

   a. Subjects ingest candied ginger (a spice) and then spin in chairs for 10 minutes. Bouts of nausea are recorded at the end of each treatment.
   Control treatment:

   b. Bean plants are sprayed with a water-based mist containing the growth hormone auxin. The length of the stem is measured after 2 weeks.
   Control treatment:

   c. Alligators are captured as they hatch from nests maintained at 22°C, 30°C, and 37°C. The number of males and females is recorded from each nest.
   Control treatment:

4. What is the essential feature of science that makes it different from other ways of understanding the natural world?

Applying Your Knowledge

Interpreting Graphed and Tabular Data

1. The winning times for men and women competing in the Boston Marathon from 1972 to 1990 are presented in Figure 1.5. Women were allowed to compete for the first time in 1972. Write a statement summarizing these results.

   a. For men:

   b. For women:

   c. Compare the slope of the two lines from 1972 to 1980. What possible explanation can you suggest for the rapid improvement in women's times compared to men's during this time period? During the 1980s, why did women's times level off?

Figure 1.5.
Winning times for the Boston Marathon for men and women from 1972 to 1990. (After Gould, 1996.)

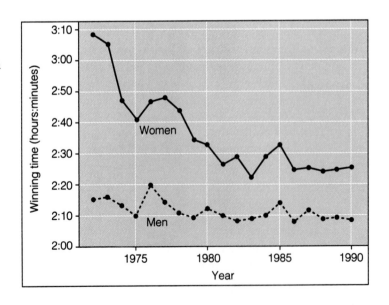

d. What is the independent variable?

What is the dependent variable?

2. Sherman and Billing (1999), investigating the uses of spices (plant products that flavor food), hypothesized that spices have been and are used to reduce foodborne illnesses and food poisoning. They predicted that if spices reduce these illnesses, then spices should have antibacterial activity. They reviewed the results of research by many scientists who documented bacterial inhibition for 30 spices commonly found in food. The spices were tested on foodborne bacteria, such as *Salmonella*, *Escherichia*, and *Listeria*. The number of bacterial species tested ranged from 4 to 31. The proportions of bacteria inhibited by each spice are presented in Figure 1.6.

a. Which spices inhibited or killed all species of bacteria tested?

b. How many spices inhibited at least 75% of the bacteria?

c. Which spices inhibited 30–40% of the bacteria?

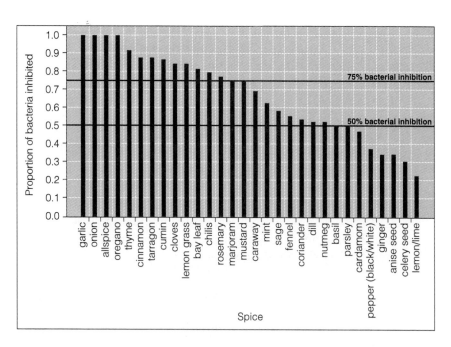

Figure 1.6.
Bacterial inhibition by 30 spices tested in the laboratory. The number of bacterial species tested ranged from 4 to 31. (After Sherman and Billing, 1999.)

3. Review the guidelines for graphs on pages 15–17 and critique Figure 1.7 below. This figure illustrates the changes in risk factors that are important in chronic diseases such as coronary heart disease, lung cancer, diabetes, and stroke.

Figure 1.7.
RISK-FACTOR PREVALENCE IN U.S.

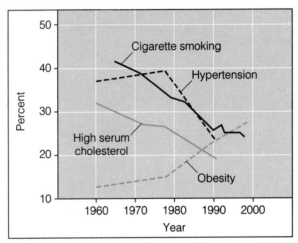

Source: Centers for Disease Control and Prevention. (After Doyle, 2001.)

4. Non-native invasive species are considered a serious threat to biodiversity and in particular to species already threatened by extinction. The percentage of threatened vertebrate species affected by invasive species differs on the continental mainlands versus the islands of the world (Table 1.4).

a. Make a general statement about the effect of invasive species on threatened animals on the mainland compared to those on islands.

b. Which taxonomic category has a higher percentage of mainland species affected than island species?

c. Is there a greater number of threatened species among birds or mammals?

Table 1.4
Percentage of Threatened Terrestrial Vertebrate Species on Continental
Mainlands and Islands Affected by Invasive Species (The number of
threatened species is in parentheses.)

Taxonomic Group	Mainland Areas		Insular Areas	
	%	(n)	%	(n)
Mammals	19.4	(283)	11.5	(61)
Birds	5.2	(250)	38.2	(144)
Reptiles	15.5	(84)	32.9	(76)
Amphibians	3.3	(30)	30.8	(13)
Total for all groups considered	12.7	(647)	31.0	(294)

(After McNeely, 2000.)

Practicing Experimental Design

1. Students are interested in investigating the effect of temperature on the
    time needed for metamorphosis for caterpillars of the Eastern swal-
    lowtail butterfly. They design an experiment to test their hypothesis that
    increasing temperature will reduce the time needed for metamorpho-
    sis to take place. They predict that the time of metamorphosis will
    decrease as the temperature increases. The students collect eight cater-
    pillars from the butterfly garden on campus over a 1-week period. They
    place pairs of caterpillars in four different temperature environments: the
    refrigerator, the laboratory, outdoors, and an incubator at 37°C. They
    record the time it takes for the caterpillars to become pupae (form a
    chrysalis) and then to emerge as butterflies. They are dismayed by their
    results. Three of the caterpillars died. The other data are inconclusive.

    Critique their experiment and suggest improvements. Your comments
    should address all aspects of the scientific method and reflect your
    understanding of experimental design.

2. Scientists have successfully moved genes from one species to another,
    resulting in genetically engineered organisms referred to as transgenic
    species. For example, plant breeders have transferred a gene from the
    bacterium *Bacillus thuringiensis* into corn and cotton, causing these plants
    to produce a compound called *Bt* toxin. These plants now have a built-
    in insecticide. As part of the environmental review of *Bt* cotton, researchers
    investigated the effect of the *Bt* toxin on soil invertebrates (Marvier,
    2001).

    Can you state a hypothesis for this investigation?

They tested their hypothesis that there would be no significant effect on soil invertebrates by measuring the survival and weight of earthworms cultivated in soil containing ground leaves of *Bt* cotton. The experimental design called for batches of ten worms to be weighed and then placed in each of four cups containing the soil and leaf mixture. After 14 days the worms were removed from the cups, counted, and weighed again. The percent change in weight was calculated.

For this experiment, what is the independent variable?

What is the dependent variable?

Can you suggest a control treatment for this experiment?

What controlled variables might need to be considered in designing this experiment?

How many replicates were used?

Write a prediction for this experiment. (Remember that the prediction is written in the form of an if/then statement.)

The results from the experiment were the following:

There was no difference in survival for the two treatments; only one worm died during the entire experiment. The average weight increase for the worms in each cup is shown in Figure 1.8. The worms in the treated soil increased in weight on average 49%, and the worms in the control soil increased in weight 78.5%. In other words, the worms in soil with transgenic cotton gained 29.5% less weight than those in soil with nontransgenic cotton. Because of the small sample size and variation from cup to cup, these results were not statistically significant and the researchers supported the hypothesis that *Bt* cotton had no significant negative effect on the soil invertebrates, specifically worms.

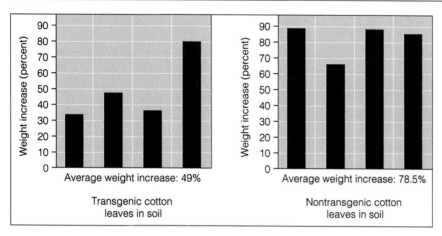

Figure 1.8.
The effect of soil mixed with crushed leaves of transgenic cotton or nontransgenic cotton on weight increase in earthworms. (From Marvier 2001—"Ecology of Transgenic Crops." *American Scientist,* vol. 89, pp. 160–167. Figure 6, p. 165.)

Given these results, what suggestions might you make for designing additional investigations?

References

Brown, K. "Seeds of Concern," 2001, *Scientific American,* vol. 284, pp. 52–57.

Campbell, N., and J. Reece. *Biology,* 6th ed. San Francisco, CA: Benjamin/Cummings, 2002.

Doyle, R. "Lifestyle Blues," *Scientific American,* vol. 284 (2001) p. 30.

Gerber, L., D. P. DeMaster, and S. P. Roberts. "Measuring Success in Conservation." *American Scientist,* 2000, vol. 88, pp. 316–324.

Gould, S. *Full House.* New York: Random House, 1996.

Kusinitz, I., and M. Fine. *Your Guide to Getting Fit,* 3rd ed. Palo Alto, CA: Mayfield, 1995.

Marvier, M. "Ecology of Transgenic Crops," *American Scientist,* 2001, vol. 89, pp. 160–167. (This article is an excellent model illustrating the scientific process.)

McNeely, J. A. "The Future of Alien Invasive Species: Changing Social Views." In *Invasive Species in a Changing World,* eds. H. A. Mooney and R. J. Hobbs. Washington, D.C.: Island Press, 2000.

Moore, J. *Science as a Way of Knowing.* Cambridge, MA: Harvard University Press, 1993.

Pechenik, J. *A Short Guide to Writing about Biology,* 4th ed. San Francisco, CA: Addison Wesley Longman, 2001.

Sherman, P. W., and J. Billing. "Darwinian Gastronomy: Why We Use Spices," *Bioscience,* 1999, vol. 49, pp. 453–463. (The second author contributed to this work through undergraduate research.)

The format and many ideas in this lab topic were based on an exercise written by Jean Dickey, published in J. Dickey, *Laboratory Investigations for Biology,* Menlo Park, CA: Addison Wesley Longman, 1995.

Websites

Good Science:
http://www.ucmp.berkeley.edu/diapsids/buzz/dinoscience.html

Information on Scientific Process:
http://koning.ecsu.ctstateu.edu/plants_human/scimeth.html

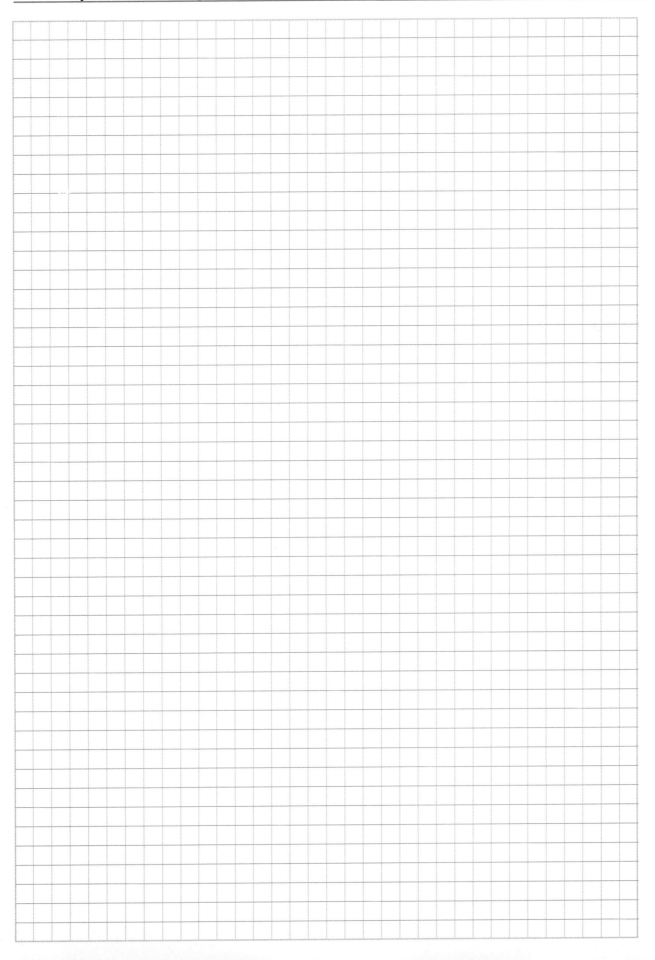

Enzymes

Laboratory Objectives

After completing this lab topic, you should be able to:

1. Define *enzyme* and describe the activity of enzymes in cells.
2. Differentiate competitive and noncompetitive inhibition.
3. Discuss the effects of varying environmental conditions such as pH and temperature on the rate of enzyme activity.
4. Discuss the effects of varying enzyme and substrate concentrations on the rate of enzyme activity.
5. Discuss the scientific process, propose hypotheses, and make predictions based on hypotheses.
6. Practice scientific persuasion and communication by constructing and interpreting graphs of enzyme activity.

Introduction

Living cells perform a multitude of chemical reactions very rapidly because of the participation of enzymes. **Enzymes** are biological **catalysts**, compounds that speed up a chemical reaction without being used up or altered in the reaction. The material with which the catalyst reacts, called the **substrate**, is modified during the reaction to form a new product (see Figure 2.1). But because the enzyme itself emerges from the reaction unchanged and ready to bind with another substrate molecule, a small amount of enzyme can alter a relatively enormous amount of substrate.

The **active site** of an enzyme will bind with the substrate, forming the **enzyme-substrate complex.** It is here that catalysis takes place, and when it is complete, the complex dissociates into enzyme and product or products.

Enzymes are, in part or in whole, proteins and are highly specific in function. Because enzymes lower the energy of activation needed for reactions to take place, they accelerate the rate of reactions. They do not, however, determine the direction in which a reaction will go or its final equilibrium.

Enzyme activity is influenced by many factors. Varying environmental conditions, such as pH or temperature, may change the three-dimensional shape of an enzyme and alter its rate of activity. Specific chemicals may also bind to an enzyme and modify its shape. Chemicals that must bind for the enzyme to be active are called **activators. Cofactors** are nonprotein substances that usually bind to the active site on the enzyme and are essential for the enzyme to work. Organic cofactors are called **coenzymes,** but other cofactors may

31

Figure 2.1.
Enzyme activity. A substrate or substrates bind to the active site of the enzyme, forming the enzyme-substrate complex, which then dissociates into enzyme and product(s). The enzyme may catalyze the addition or removal of a molecule or a portion of a molecule from the substrate to produce the product (a), or the enzyme may catalyze the splitting of a substrate into its component subunits (b).

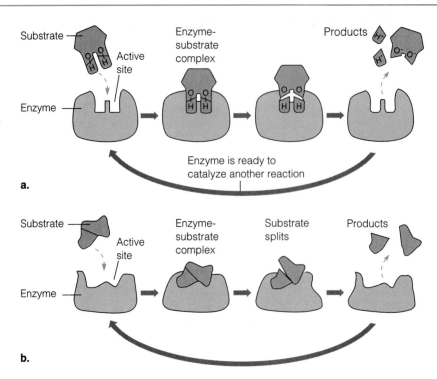

simply be metal ions. Chemicals that shut off enzyme activity are called **inhibitors,** and their action can be classified as **competitive** or **noncompetitive inhibition.**

Review Figure 2.1, illustrating enzyme activity. There are two ways to measure enzyme activity: (1) Determine the rate of disappearance of the substrate, and (2) determine the rate of appearance of the product.

In this laboratory, you will use both methods to investigate the activity of two enzymes, **catechol oxidase** and **amylase.** You will use an inhibitor to influence the activity of catechol oxidase and determine if it is a competitive or noncompetitive inhibitor. Additionally, you will investigate the effect of changing environmental conditions on the rate of amylase activity.

EXERCISE 2.1

Experimental Method and the Action of Catechol Oxidase

Materials

test-tube rack	pipette filler
3 small test tubes	pipette bulb
small Parafilm™ squares	distilled or deionized (DI) water
calibrated 5-mL pipette	potato extract
3 calibrated 1-mL pipettes	catechol
disposable pasteur pipettes	disposable gloves (optional)

Introduction

This exercise will investigate the result of catechol oxidase activity. In the presence of oxygen, catechol oxidase catalyzes the removal of electrons and hydrogens from **catechol**, a phenolic compound found in plant cells. Catechol is converted to benzoquinone, a pigment product. The hydrogens combine with oxygen, forming water (Figure 2.2). The pigment products are responsible for the darkening of fruits and vegetables, such as apples and potatoes, after exposure to air.

In this exercise you will use an extract of potato tuber to test for the presence of catechol oxidase and to establish the appearance of the products when the reaction takes place.

Figure 2.2.
The oxidation of catechol. In the presence of catechol oxidase, catechol is converted to benzoquinone. Hydrogens removed from catechol combine with oxygen to form water.

Question

Remember that every experiment begins with a question. Review the information given above about the activity of catechol oxidase. You will be performing an experiment using potato extract.

Formulate a question about catechol oxidase and potato extract. The question may be broad, but it must propose an idea that has measurable and controllable elements.

Hypothesis

Construct a hypothesis for the presence or absence of catechol oxidase in potato extract. Remember, the hypothesis must be testable. It is possible for you to propose one or more hypotheses, but all must be testable.

Prediction

Predict the result of the experiment based on your hypothesis. To test for the presence or absence of catechol oxidase in potato extract, your prediction would be what you expect to observe as the result of this experiment (if/then).

Catechol is a poison! Avoid contact with all solutions. Do not pipette any solutions by mouth. Wash hands thoroughly after each experiment. If a spill occurs, notify the instructor. If the instructor is unavailable, wear disposable gloves and use dry paper towels to wipe up the spill. Follow dry towels with towels soaked in soap and water. Dispose of all towels in the trash.

Procedure

1. Using Table 2.1, prepare the three experimental tubes. Note that all tubes should contain the same total amount of solution. Do not cross-contaminate pipettes! After each tube is prepared, use your finger to hold a Parafilm™ square securely over the tube mouth and then rotate the tube to mix the contents thoroughly. Use a fresh square for each tube.

Table 2.1
Contents of the Three Experimental Tubes

Tube	Distilled Water	Catechol	Distilled Water	Potato Extract
1	5 ml	0.5 ml	0.5 ml	—
2	5 ml	0.5 ml	—	0.5 ml
3	5 ml	—	0.5 ml	0.5 ml

2. Explain the experimental design: What is the purpose of each of the three test tubes? Which is the control tube? Is more than one control tube necessary? Explain. Which is the experimental tube?

3. Observe the reactions in the tubes, and record your observations in the Results section below. Explain your conclusions in the Discussion section.

Results

Design a simple table to record results (Table 2.2).

Table 2.2
Results of Catechol Oxidation Experiment

Discussion

Explain your results in terms of your hypothesis.

EXERCISE 2.2
Inhibiting the Action of Catechol Oxidase

Materials

test-tube rack	pipette bulb
3 small test tubes	distilled water
small Parafilm™ squares	potato extract
calibrated 5-mL pipette	catechol
4 calibrated 1-mL pipettes	phenylthiourea (PTU)
disposable pasteur pipettes	disposable gloves (optional)

Introduction

This exercise will investigate the inhibition of enzyme activity by specific chemicals called **inhibitors.** The specific inhibitor used will be **phenylthiourea (PTU).** To be active, catechol oxidase requires copper as a cofactor. PTU is known to combine with the copper in catechol oxidase and inhibit its enzymatic activity.

An inhibitor molecule affects an enzyme in one of two ways. **Competitive inhibition** takes place when a molecule that is structurally similar to the substrate for a particular reaction competes for a position at the active site on the enzyme. This ties up the enzyme so that it is not available to the substrate. Competitive inhibition can be reversed if the concentration of substrate is raised to sufficiently high levels while the concentration of the inhibitor is held constant (Figure 2.3).

In **noncompetitive inhibition,** the inhibitor binds to a site that is *not* the active site. In so doing, it changes the nature of the enzyme so that its

Figure 2.3.
Action of a competitive inhibitor.
(a) Substrate normally can bind to the active site of an enzyme.
(b) A competitive inhibitor mimics the substrate and competes for the position at the active site on the enzyme.

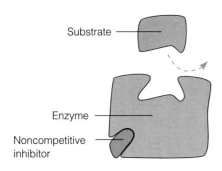

Substrate

Enzyme

Noncompetitive inhibitor

Figure 2.4.
Action of a noncompetitive inhibitor. The noncompetitive inhibitor binds to the enzyme at a location away from the active site, either blocking access to the active site or changing the conformation of the enzyme, rendering it inactive.

catalytic properties are lost. This can happen in two ways. Either the noncompetitive inhibitor itself physically blocks the access to the active site, or it causes a conformational change in the protein, thus inactivating the active site. In noncompetitive inhibition the inhibitor can become unbound, reversing the inhibition. However, unlike competitive inhibition, adding additional substrate will not reverse the inhibition. (Figure 2.4.)

In the following experiment, you will determine if PTU is a competitive or noncompetitive inhibitor.

Question

Pose a question about the activity of PTU.

Hypothesis

Hypothesize about the nature of inhibition by PTU.

Prediction

Predict the results of the experiment based on your hypothesis (if/then).

Procedure

 PTU and catechol are poisons! Avoid contact with solutions. Do not pipette any solutions by mouth. Wash hands thoroughly after the experiment. If a spill occurs, notify the instructor. If the instructor is unavailable, wear disposable gloves and use dry paper towels to wipe up the spill. Follow dry towels with towels soaked in soap and water. Dispose of all towels in the trash.

1. Using Table 2.3, prepare three experimental tubes. Be sure to add solutions in the sequence given in the table (water first, potato extract next, PTU next, etc.). Cover each tube with a fresh Parafilm™ square and mix.

Table 2.3
Contents of the Three Experimental Tubes

Tube	Distilled Water	Potato Extract	PTU	Distilled Water	Catechol
1	5 mL	0.5 mL	0.5 mL	0.5 mL	0.5 mL
2	5 mL	0.5 mL	0.5 mL	—	1 mL
3	5 mL	0.5 mL	—	1 mL	0.5 mL

2. Which test tube is the control?

3. Why was the concentration of catechol increased in test tube 2?

4. Why should the catechol be added to the test tubes last?

5. Record your observations in the Results section, and explain your results in the Discussion section.

Results

Design a table to record your results (Table 2.4).

Table 2.4
Results of Inhibition Experiment

Discussion

Explain your results in terms of your hypothesis.

EXERCISE 2.3

Influence of Concentration, pH, and Temperature on the Activity of Amylase

Introduction

In the following exercise, you will investigate the influence of enzyme concentration, pH, and temperature on the activity of the enzyme **amylase**. Amylase is found in the **saliva** of many animals, including humans, that utilize **starch** as a source of food. Starch, the principal reserve carbohydrate stores of plants, is a polysaccharide composed of a large number of glucose monomers joined together. Amylase is responsible for the preliminary digestion of starch. In short, amylase breaks up the chains of glucose molecules in starch into maltose, a two-glucose-unit compound. Further digestion of this disaccharide requires other enzymes present in pancreatic and intestinal secretions. To help us follow the digestion of starch into maltose by salivary amylase, we will take advantage of the fact that starch, but not maltose, turns a dark purple color when treated with a solution of I_2KI (this solution is normally yellow-amber in color). Draw equations to help you remember these reactions in the margin of your lab manual.

In the following experiments, the **rate of disappearance** of starch in different amylase concentrations allows a quantitative measurement of reaction rate. Recall that the rate of appearance of the product (in this case, maltose) would give the same information, but the starch test is simpler.

You will be assigned to a team with three or four students. Each team will carry out only one of the experiments. However, each student is responsible for understanding all experiments and results. Be prepared to present your results to the entire class. Your instructor may require you to write a component of a scientific paper. (See Appendix A.)

Experiment A. The Influence of Enzyme Concentration on the Rate of Starch Digestion

Materials

test-tube rack	2 1-mL calibrated pipettes
8 standard test tubes	calibrated 5-mL pipette
wax pencil	disposable pasteur pipettes
test plate	pipette bulb
flask of distilled or DI water	buffer solution (pH = 6.8)
beaker of distilled or DI rinse water	I_2KI solution
	1% starch solution
5-mL graduated cylinder	0.5% amylase solution

Introduction

In this experiment you will vary the concentration of the enzyme amylase to determine what effect the variation will have on the rate of the reaction.

You will make serial dilutions of the amylase resulting in a range of enzyme concentrations. For serial dilutions, you will take an aliquot (sample) of the original enzyme and dilute it with an equal amount of water for a 1:1 dilution (50% of the original concentration). You will then take an aliquot of the resulting 1:1 solution and add an equal amount of water for a 1:3 dilution of the original concentration. You will continue this series of dilutions until you have four different amylase concentrations.

Question

Pose a question about enzyme concentration and reaction rate.

Hypothesis

Hypothesize about the effect of changing enzyme concentration on the rate of reaction.

Prediction

Predict the results of the experiment based on your hypothesis (if/then).

Procedure

1. Prepare the amylase dilution (test-tube set 1):
   a. Number four standard test tubes 1 through 4.
   b. Using the 5-mL graduated pipette, add 5 mL distilled water to each test tube.
   c. Make serial dilutions as follows (use the graduated cylinder):

      Tube 1: Add 5 mL amylase and mix by rolling the tube between your hands. (Dilution: 1:1; 0.25% amylase)

      Tube 2: Add 5 mL amylase solution from tube 1 and mix. (Dilution: 1:3; 0.125% amylase)

      Tube 3: Add 5 mL amylase solution from tube 2 and mix. (Dilution: 1:7; 0.063% amylase)

      Tube 4: Add 5 mL amylase solution from tube 3 and mix. (Dilution: 1:15; 0.031% amylase)

      Rinse the graduated cylinder thoroughly.

2. Prepare the experimental test tubes (test tube set 2):
   a. Number a second set of four standard test tubes 1 through 4.
   b. Beginning with tube 4 of the first set, transfer 1 mL of this dilution into tube 4 of the second set. Use the 1-mL pipette for the transfer. Rinse the pipette in distilled water, and repeat the procedure for tubes

3, 2, and 1, transferring 1 mL of tube 3 (first set) into tube 3 (second set), etc. After these transfers have been carried out, test-tube set 1 will no longer be used.

c. Add 20 drops of pH 6.8 buffer solution to each of the tubes in the second set. Mix by rolling the tubes between your hands. Set these tubes aside.

d. Add 1 or 2 drops of I_2KI to each compartment of four rows of a test plate. You will use a separate row for each concentration of amylase.

e. Using the second set of tubes, proceed with the tests beginning with tube 4.

(1) Using a clean 1-mL pipette, add 0.5 mL of the 1% starch solution to tube 4 and mix by rolling the tube between your hands. One team member should immediately record the time. This is time 0.

(2) Quickly remove 1 drop of the mixture with a disposable pasteur pipette, and add it to a drop of I_2KI in the first compartment on the test plate (time 0).

 Remember, when the enzyme and substrate are together, the reaction has begun!

---

(3) Sample the reaction mixture at 10-second intervals, each time using a new compartment of the test plate. Continue until a blue color is no longer produced and the I_2KI solution remains yellow-amber (indicating the digestion of all the starch). Record the time required for the digestion of the starch in Table 2.5.

(4) Repeat steps 1 through 4 for the other three concentrations (tubes 3, 2, and 1 of set 2).

3. Finish recording your findings in the Results section, and state your conclusions in the Discussion section.

Results

1. Complete Table 2.5 as you determine rates of digestion (time of starch disappearance) in different enzyme concentrations.

Table 2.5
Time of Starch Disappearance in Different
Concentrations of the Enzyme Amylase

Tube	% Amylase	Time of Starch Disappearance (in seconds)
1	0.25	
2	0.125	
3	0.063	
4	0.031	

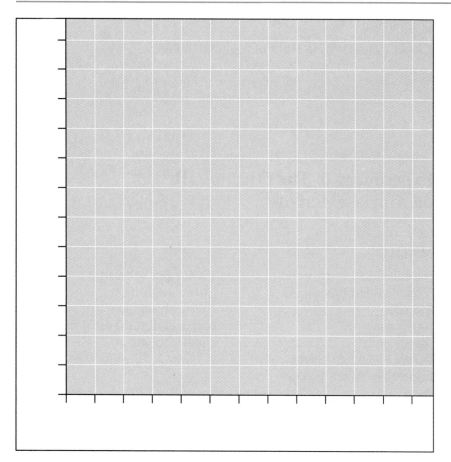

Figure 2.5.
Enzyme reaction rate (time of starch disappearance) for different concentrations of amylase.

2. Construct a graph (Figure 2.5) to illustrate your results. See Lab Topic 1 for assistance in graph construction.

   a. What is the independent variable? Which is the appropriate axis for this variable?

   b. What is the dependent variable? Which is the appropriate axis for this variable?

   c. Label the axes of the graph. Using Table 2.5, note the maximum number of seconds in your results, and choose an appropriate scale for the dependent variable. Reaction rate, the dependent variable, was measured as time of starch (product) disappearance. The data must, therefore, be graphed in reverse order because the highest values indicate the slowest reaction rate. You should place "0" at the end of the axis and write "fast" by your 0. Place your highest number near the origin (where the x and y axes cross). Write "slow" near the origin. Choose an appropriate scale for the independent variable (% amylase), and label this axis.

Discussion

Explain your results in terms of your hypothesis.

Experiment B. The Effect of pH on Amylase Activity

Materials

test-tube rack	1% amylase solution
7 standard test tubes	I_2KI solution
test plate	1% starch solution
wax pencil	beaker of distilled or DI rinse water
pipette bulb	7 buffer solutions
3 5-mL calibrated pipettes	(pH = 5, 5.5, 6, 6.5, 7, 7.5, 8)
disposable pasteur pipettes	

Introduction

The environmental factor pH can influence the three-dimensional shape of an enzyme. Every enzyme has an optimum pH at which it is most active. In this experiment you will determine the optimum pH for the activity of amylase. What was the source of the amylase used in this experiment? (Check the Introduction to this exercise.)

Question

Pose a question about pH and reaction rate.

Hypothesis

Hypothesize about the rate of activity of amylase at various pHs.

Prediction

Predict the results of the experiment based on your hypothesis (if/then).

Procedure

Buffers can burn skin! Avoid contact with all solutions. Do not pipette any solutions by mouth. Wash hands thoroughly after each experiment. If a spill occurs, notify the instructor. If the instructor is unavailable, wear disposable gloves and use dry paper towels to wipe up the spill. Follow dry towels with towels soaked in soap and water. Dispose of all towels in the trash.

1. Using a wax pencil, number seven standard test tubes 1 through 7. Beginning with tube 1 and pH 5, mark one tube for each pH of buffer (5, 5.5, 6, 6.5, 7, 7.5, 8). After you mark the test tubes, use a 5-mL graduated pipette to add 5 mL of the appropriate buffer to each test tube (5 mL buffer 5 to tube 1, 5 mL buffer 5.5 to tube 2, etc.). Rinse the pipette with distilled water after dispensing each buffer.

2. Using a clean 5-mL graduated pipette, add 1.5 mL amylase solution to each tube and mix by rolling the tubes in your hands.

3. Introduce 1 or 2 drops of I_2KI into the compartments of several rows of the test plate.

4. Using only tube 1, add 2.5 mL of the 1% starch solution with a clean 5-mL pipette. Leave the pipette in the starch solution. Mix by rolling the tube in your hands. One team member should immediately record the time. This is time 0. Start testing immediately (next step).

Remember, when the enzyme and substrate are together, the reaction has begun!

5. Using a disposable pasteur pipette, remove a drop of the reaction mixture from tube 1. Add to a drop of I_2KI on the test plate.

6. Sample the reaction mixture at 10-second intervals, each time using a new compartment of the test plate. Continue until a blue color is no longer produced and the I_2KI solution remains yellow-amber (indicating the digestion of all the starch).

7. Record the time required for the digestion of the starch in Table 2.6. If after 7 minutes there is no color change, terminate the experiment with that reaction mixture.

8. Repeat steps 4 through 7 using the other six test tubes. Use separate rows on the test plate for each pH. Rinse the pipette between uses. Record results in Table 2.6.

9. Graph your observations in the Results section, and explain your results in the Discussion section.

Results

1. Complete Table 2.6 as rates of digestion (time of starch disappearance) in different pHs are determined.

Table 2.6
Time of Starch Disappearance in Different
pH Environments for the Enzyme Amylase

Tube	pH	Time of Starch Disappearance (in minutes)
1	5	
2	5.5	
3	6	
4	6.5	
5	7	
6	7.5	
7	8	

2. Construct a graph using Figure 2.6 to illustrate your results. See Lab
    Topic 1 for assistance in graph construction.

    a. What is the independent variable? Which is the appropriate axis for
        this variable?

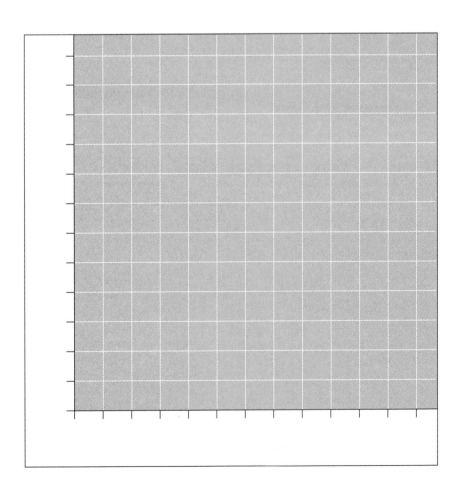

Figure 2.6.
Reaction rate (time of starch
disappearance) of amylase in
different pH environments.

b. What is the dependent variable? Which is the appropriate axis for this variable?

c. Label the axes of the graph. Using Table 2.6, note the maximum number of minutes in your results, and choose an appropriate scale for the dependent variable. Reaction rate, the dependent variable, was measured as time of starch (product) disappearance. The data must, therefore, be graphed in reverse order because the highest values indicate the slowest reaction rate. You should place "0" at the end of the axis and write "fast" by your 0. Place your highest number near the origin (where the x and y axes cross). Write "slow" near the origin. Choose an appropriate scale for the independent variable (pH) and label the axis.

Discussion

Explain your results in terms of your hypothesis.

Experiment C. The Effect of Temperature on Amylase Activity

Materials

8 standard test tubes
test-tube rack
2 5-mL calibrated pipettes
2 1-mL calibrated pipettes
disposable 7.5-inch pasteur
   pipettes
pipette bulb
wax pencil
1% starch solution
I_2KI solution

buffer solution (pH = 6.8)
1% amylase solution
flask of DI water
On the demonstration table:
   water bath at 80°C
   water bath at 37°C
   test-tube rack at room
      temperature
   beaker of crushed ice for
      ice bath

Introduction

Chemical reactions accelerate as temperature rises, partly because increased temperatures speed up the motion of molecules. This means that substrates collide more frequently with enzyme active sites. Generally, a 10° rise in temperature results in a two- to threefold increase in the rate of a particular reaction. However, at high temperatures, the integrity of proteins can be irreversibly denatured. The activity of enzymes is dependent on the proper tertiary and quaternary structures; the optimum temperature for activity, therefore, may vary, depending on the structure of the enzyme.

What was the source of the amylase used in this experiment? (Check the Introduction to this exercise.)

Question

Pose a question about temperature and reaction rate.

Hypothesis

Hypothesize about the rate of activity of amylase at various temperatures.

Prediction

Predict the results of the experiment based on your hypothesis (if/then).

Procedure

1. Number four standard test tubes 1 through 4.
2. Using the 5-mL calibrated pipette, add 2 mL of the 1% starch solution to each tube.
3. Using a clean 5-mL pipette, add 4 mL DI water to each tube.
4. Add 1 mL of 6.8 buffer to each tube.
5. Place the test tubes as follows:

   Tube 1: 80°C water bath

   Tube 2: 37°C water bath

   Tube 3: test-tube rack (room temperature, or about 22°C)

   Tube 4: beaker of crushed ice (4°C)

6. Number and mark a second set of standard test tubes 1A through 4A. Use the 1-mL calibrated pipette to add 1 mL amylase to each tube, and place as follows (do not mix together the solutions in the two sets of tubes until instructed to do so):

   Tube 1A: 80°C water bath

   Tube 2A: 37°C water bath

   Tube 3A: test-tube rack (room temperature, or about 22°C)

   Tube 4A: beaker of crushed ice (4°C)

7. Let all eight tubes sit in the above environments for 10 minutes. You should have one tube of amylase and one of starch at each temperature.

8. Fill several rows of the test plate with 1 or 2 drops of I_2KI per compartment.

Remember, when the enzyme and substrate are together, the reaction has begun!

9. Leaving the tubes in the above environments as they are being tested, mix tubes 1 and 1A, record the time (this is time 0), and use a disposable pipette to immediately add 1 or 2 drops of the mixture to a drop of I_2KI on the test plate.

10. Continue adding mixture drops to new wells of I_2KI at 30-second intervals until a blue color is no longer produced and the I_2KI solution remains yellow-amber (indicating that all the starch is digested). If within 10 minutes there is no color change, terminate the experiment with that particular reaction mixture. Record your results in Table 2.7.

11. Repeat steps 9 and 10 for the other reaction mixtures (mix tubes 2 and 2A and test, mix 3 and 3A and test, etc.).

12. If time permits, transfer tube 4 (in ice, containing the enzyme and substrate) into the 37°C water bath. After 2 minutes, test the contents of the tube at 10-second intervals. Record these results in the margin of your lab manual and refer to them as you answer Discussion Question 2 below.

13. Finish recording and graphing your observations in the Results section, and explain your results in the Discussion section.

Results

1. Complete Table 2.7 as rates of digestion (time of starch disappearance) in different temperatures are determined.

Table 2.7
Time of Starch Disappearance in Different
Temperatures for the Enzyme Amylase

Tube	Temp. °C	Time of Starch Disappearance (in minutes)
1	80°	
2	37°	
3	22°	
4	4°	

2. Construct a graph using Figure 2.7 on the next page to illustrate your results. See Lab Topic 1 for assistance in graph construction.

   a. What is the independent variable? Which is the appropriate axis for this variable?

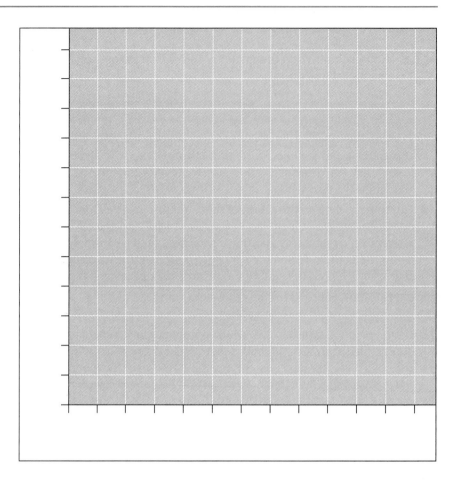

Figure 2.7.
Reaction rate (time of starch
disappearance) of amylase in
various temperatures.

b. What is the dependent variable? Which is the appropriate axis for this variable?

c. Label the axes of the graph. Using Table 2.7, note the maximum number of minutes in your results, and choose an appropriate scale for the dependent variable. Reaction rate, the dependent variable, was measured as the time of starch disappearance. The data must, therefore, be graphed in reverse order because the highest values indicate the slowest reaction rate. You should place "0" at the end of the axis and write "fast" by your 0. Place your highest number near the origin (where the x and y axes cross). Write "slow" near the origin. Choose an appropriate scale for the independent variable (temperature) and label the axis.

Discussion

1. Explain your results in terms of your hypothesis.

2. What do you think would happen to reaction rate in the tube incubated in ice if this tube, with enzyme and substrate already mixed, were placed in the 37°C water bath?

Explain your answer in terms of the effect of various temperatures on enzyme structure and the rate of enzyme activity.

Questions for Review

1. Define and use the following terms, providing examples if appropriate: *catalyst enzyme, substrate, active site, cofactor, coenzyme, competitive inhibition, noncompetitive inhibition.*

2. a. Compare and contrast competitive and noncompetitive inhibition.

   b. Why does adding additional substrate overcome competitive but not noncompetitive inhibition?

Applying Your Knowledge

1. a. In the first experiment, the enzyme catechol oxidase was extracted from potato. However, this was not a purified preparation; it contained hundreds of enzymes. What evidence supports the assumption that catechol oxidase was the enzyme studied?

    b. Design an experiment to determine whether amylase was also present in the extract.

2. Suggest a reason why canned acidic fruits and vegetables (such as tomatoes) have a longer shelf life than those with more neutral pH (such as green beans).

3. The PSA (prostate-specific antigen) test is the most widely used test to detect prostate cancer. The PSA marker is a protease that is manufactured specifically in the prostate gland. Cancer in the prostate gland will cause PSA to be expelled into the bloodstream. How could a researcher devise a test to detect this prostate-specific protease in the lab?

4. Well-preserved mammoths have been found in ice and frozen soil in northern Siberia. Using information about enzyme activity learned in this lab, explain why these animal carcasses have survived all of these years.

5. A researcher discovers that an antibiotic, sulfanilamide, can be used to treat infections caused by a particular bacterial species. He finds out that the structure of sulfanilamide is almost identical to that of para-aminobenzoic acid (PABA), one of the compounds in the metabolic pathway leading to folic acid, a vitamin required for bacterial growth and survival.

Speculate about the mechanism of drug action in controlling the bacterial growth. *Hint:* Enzymes catalyze all reactions in metabolic pathways.

6. There is an enzyme that catalyzes the production of the pigment responsible for dark fur color in Siamese cats and Himalayan rabbits. This enzyme is *thermolabile,* meaning that it does not function at higher temperatures. Rabbits raised at 5°C are all black. If raised at 20°C, they are white with black paws, ears, and noses; they are all white when raised at 35°C. Which of the following best represents an activity curve for this enzyme?

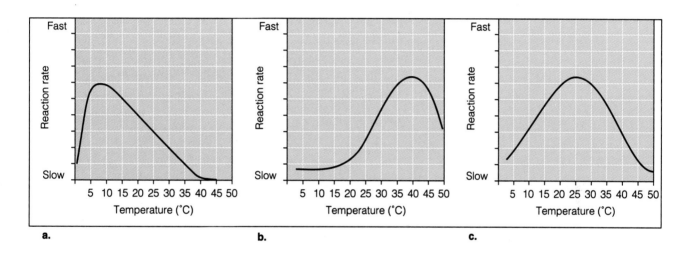

a.   b.   c.

7. Under what conditions are enzymes denatured? Is denaturation reversible?

8. Why doesn't the rate of reaction continue to increase proportionally as the concentration of enzyme increases?

Investigative Extension

The experiments using catechol oxidase may be quantified by measuring results using a Spectronic 20. Modify the instructions in Exercises 2.1 and 2.2 according to the following instructions.

1. Rather than using three experimental tubes, use four cuvettes, and label them B (the blank), 1, 2, and 3.

2. Prepare the solutions in cuvettes as directed for test tubes 1, 2, and 3, omitting catechol until ready to take the reading. The blank will contain 5 mL of distilled water, 20 drops of distilled water, and 10 drops of potato extract only. Do not add catechol to the blank.

3. Design a table to record your data.

4. Record absorbance of the solutions in the four cuvettes. (For steps a–c, following, see the diagram of the Spectronic 20 and details of its operation in Lab Topic 6: Photosynthesis. Steps d–f are self-explanatory.)

    a. Set the wavelength at 540 nm.

    b. Zero the instrument.

    c. Calibrate the instrument.

    d. Add the catechol to the appropriate cuvettes.

    e. Insert cuvette 1 into the sample holder and record absorbance in your data table. Immediately repeat with cuvettes 2 and 3.

    f. Continue to take readings at 5-minute intervals for 30 minutes or an appropriate time.

References

Matthews, H. R., R. A. Freedland, and R. L. Miesfeld. *Biochemistry: A Short Course.* New York: Wiley-Liss, 1997.

Voet, D., J. G. Voet, and C. W. Pratt. *Fundamentals of Biochemistry.* New York: John Wiley and Sons, Inc., 1999. Discussion of enzyme inhibition, pp. 335–342.

Website

Factors Affecting Enzymes. Describes how temperature, pH, and substrate concentration affect enzyme activity: http://ntri.tamuk.edu/cell/enzyme2.html

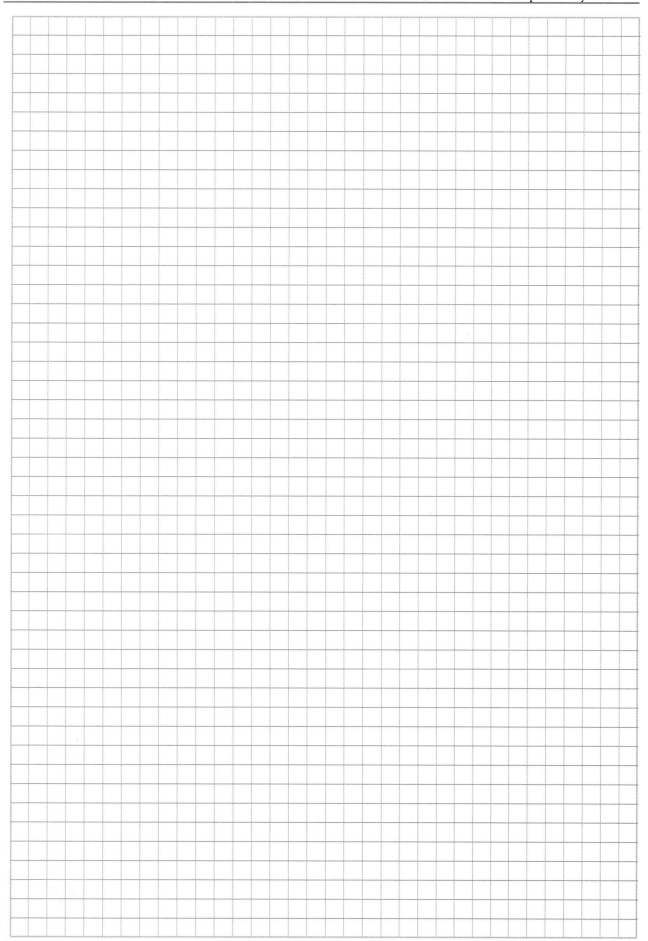

Microscopes and Cells

Laboratory Objectives

After completing this lab topic, you should be able to:

1. Identify the parts of compound and stereoscopic microscopes and be proficient in their correct use in biological studies.

2. Describe procedures used in preparing materials for electron microscopy and compare these with procedures used in light microscopy.

3. Identify cell structures and organelles from electron micrographs and state the functions of each.

4. Describe features of specific cells and determine characteristics shared by all cells studied.

5. Discuss the evolutionary significance of increasing complexity from unicellular to multicellular organization and provide examples from the lab.

Introduction

According to cell theory, the *cell* is the fundamental biological unit, the smallest and simplest biological structure possessing all the characteristics of the living condition. All living organisms are composed of one or more cells, and every activity taking place in a living organism is ultimately related to metabolic activities in cells. Thus, understanding the processes of life necessitates an understanding of the structure and function of the cell.

The earliest known cells found in fossilized sediments 3.5 billion years old (called **prokaryotic** cells) lack nuclei and membrane-bound organelles. Cells with a membrane-bound nucleus and organelles (**eukaryotic** cells) do not appear in the fossil record for another 2 billion years. But the eventual evolution of the eukaryotic cell and its internal compartmentalization led to enormous biological diversity in single cells. The evolution of loose aggregates of cells ultimately to colonies of connected cells provided for specialization, so that groups of cells had specific and different functions. This early division of labor included cells whose primary function was locomotion or reproduction. The evolution of multicellularity appears to have originated more than once in eukaryotes and provided an opportunity for extensive adaptive radiation as organisms specialized and diversified, eventually giving rise to fungi, plants, and animals. This general trend in increasing complexity and specialization seen in the history of life will be illustrated in Lab Topic 3.

Given the fundamental role played by cells in the organization of life, one can readily understand why the study of cells is essential to the study of life. Cells, however, are below the limit of resolution of the human eye. We cannot study them without using a microscope. The microscope has probably contributed more than any other instrument to the development of biology as a science. Two types of microscopes are named according to the source of illumination used: light microscopes and electron microscopes. We will be using light microscopes exclusively in our study of cells, and we will view electron micrographs of cell structures not visible with the light microscope.

Microscopes of one kind or another are used by all biologists in numerous subdisciplines: genetics, molecular biology, neurobiology, cell biology, evolution, and ecology. The knowledge and skills you develop today will be used and enhanced throughout this course and throughout your career in biology. It is important, therefore, that you take the time to master these exercises thoroughly.

EXERCISE 3.1

Parts of the Microscope

Materials

compound microscope

Introduction

The microscope is designed to make objects visible that are too difficult or too small to see with the unaided eye. There are many different kinds of light microscopes, including phase-contrast, darkfield, polarizing, and UV. These differ primarily in the source and manner in which light is passed through the specimen to be viewed.

The microscopes in biology lab are usually compound binocular or monocular light microscopes, some of which may have phase-contrast attachments. **Compound** means that the scopes have a minimum of two magnifying lenses (the ocular and the objective lenses). **Binocular microscopes** have two eyepieces, **monoculars** have only one eyepiece, and **light** refers to the type of illumination used, that is, visible light from a lamp.

Your success in and enjoyment of a large portion of the laboratory work in introductory biology will depend on how proficient you become in the use of the microscope. When used and maintained correctly, these precision instruments are capable of producing images of the highest quality.

Although there are many variations in the features of microscopes, they are all constructed on a similar plan (Figure 3.1). In this exercise you will be introduced to the common variations found in different models of compound microscopes and asked to identify those features found on your microscope.

 Please treat these microscopes with the greatest care!

a.

b.

Figure 3.1.

a. **The compound binocular light microscope.** Locate the parts of your microscope described in Exercise 3.1 and label this photograph. Indicate in the margin of your lab manual any features unique to your microscope.

b. **Enlarged photo of compound light microscope as viewed from under the stage.** This microscope is equipped with phase-contrast optics. Locate the condenser, condenser adjustment knob, phase-contrast revolving turret, and iris diaphragm on your microscope (if present) and label them on the diagram.

Procedure

1. Obtain a compound light microscope, following directions from your instructor. To carry the microscope correctly, hold the arm with one hand, and support the base with your other hand. Remove the cover, but do not plug in the microscope.

2. Locate the parts of your microscope, and label Figure 3.1. Refer to the following description of a typical microscope. In the spaces provided, indicate the specific features related to your microscope.

a. The **head** supports the two sets of magnifying lenses. The **ocular** is the lens in the eyepiece, which typically has a magnification of 10×. If your microscope is binocular, the distance between the eyepieces (**interpupillary distance**) can be adjusted to suit your eyes. Move the eyepieces apart, and look for the scale used to indicate the distance between the eyepieces. Do not adjust the eyepieces at this time. A pointer has been placed in the eyepiece and is used to point to an object in the **field of view,** the circle of light that one sees in the microscope.

Is your microscope monocular (one eyepiece) or binocular (two eyepieces)?

What is the magnification of your ocular(s)?

 Although the eyepiece may be removable, it should not be removed from the microscope.

b. **Objectives** are the three lenses on the **revolving nosepiece.** The shortest lens is typically 4× and is called the **scanning lens.** The **intermediate lens** is 10×, and the longest, the **high-power lens,** is 40× (the fourth position on the nosepiece is empty). It is important to clean both the objective and ocular lenses before each use. Dirty lenses will cause a blurring or fogging of the image. Always use lens paper for cleaning! Any other material (including Kimwipes®) may scratch the lenses.

What is the magnification of each of your objectives? List them in order of increasing magnification.

c. The **arm** supports the stage and condenser lens. The **condenser lens** is used to focus the light from the **lamp** through the specimen to be viewed. The height of the condenser can be adjusted by an **adjustment knob.** The **iris diaphragm** controls the width of the circle of light and, therefore, the amount of light passing through the specimen.

If your microscope has phase-contrast optics, the condenser may be housed in a **revolving turret.** When the turret is set on 0, the normal optical arrangement is in place. This condition is called **brightfield microscopy.** Other positions of the turret set phase-contrast optics in place. To use phase-contrast, the turret setting must correspond to the magnifying power of the objective being used.

Is your microscope equipped with phase-contrast optics?

The **stage** supports the specimen to be viewed. A mechanical stage can be moved right and left and back and forth by two **stage adjustment knobs.** With a stationary stage, the slide is secured under **stage clips** and moved slightly by hand while viewing the slide. The distance between the stage and the objective can be adjusted with the **coarse** and **fine focus adjustment knobs.**

Does your microscope have a mechanical or stationary stage?

d. The **base** acts as a stand for the microscope and houses the lamp. In some microscopes, the intensity of the light that passes through the specimen can be adjusted with the **light intensity lever.** Generally, more light is needed when using high magnification than when using low magnification. Describe the light system for your microscope.

EXERCISE 3.2
Basic Microscope Techniques

Materials

clear ruler	lens paper
coverslips	blank slides
prepared slides: letter	Kimwipes®
and crossed thread	dropper bottle with distilled water

Introduction

In this exercise, you will learn to use the microscope to examine a recognizable object, a slide of the letter *e*. Recall that microscopes vary, so you may have to omit steps that refer to features not available on your microscope. Practice adjusting your microscope to become proficient in locating a specimen, focusing clearly, and adjusting the light for the best contrast.

Procedure

1. Clean microscope lenses.

   Each time you use the microscope, you should begin by cleaning the lenses. Using lens paper moistened with a drop of distilled water, wipe the ocular, objective, and condenser lenses. Wipe them again with a piece of dry lens paper.

 Use only lens paper on microscope lenses. Do not use Kimwipes®, tissues, or other papers.

---

2. Adjust the focus on your microscope:
   a. Plug your microscope into the outlet.
   b. Turn on the light. Adjust the light intensity to mid-range if your microscope has that feature.

c. Rotate the 4X objective into position using the revolving nosepiece ring, not the objective itself.

d. Take the letter slide and wipe it with a Kimwipe® tissue. Each time you study a prepared slide, you should first wipe it clean. Place the letter slide on the stage, and center it over the stage opening.

Slides should be placed on and removed from the stage only when the 4X objective is in place. Removing a slide when the higher objectives are in position may scratch the lenses.

e. Look through the ocular and bring the letter into rough focus by slowly focusing upward using the coarse adjustment.

f. For binocular microscopes, looking through the oculars, move the oculars until you see only one image of the letter *e*. In this position, the oculars should be aligned with your pupils. In the margin of your lab manual, make a note of the **interpupillary distance** on the scale between the oculars. Each new lab day, before you begin to use the microscope, set this distance.

g. Raise the condenser to its highest position, and fully close the iris diaphragm.

h. Looking through the ocular, slowly lower the condenser just until the graininess disappears. Slowly open the iris diaphragm just until the entire field of view is illuminated. This is the correct position for both the condenser and the iris diaphragm.

i. Rotate the 10X objective into position.

j. Look through the ocular and slowly focus upward with the coarse adjustment knob until the image is in rough focus. Sharpen the focus using the fine adjustment knob.

Do not turn the fine adjustment knob more than two revolutions in either direction. If the image does not come into focus, return to 10X and refocus using the coarse adjustment.

k. For binocular microscopes, cover your left eye and use the fine adjustment knob to focus the fixed (right) ocular until the letter *e* is in maximum focus. Now cover the right eye and, using the diopter ring on the left ocular, bring the image into focus. The letter *e* should now be in focus for both of your eyes. Each new lab day, as you begin to study your first slide, repeat this procedure.

l. You can increase or decrease the contrast by adjusting the iris diaphragm opening. Note that the maximum amount of light provides little contrast. Adjust the aperture until the image is sharp.

m. Move the slide slowly to the right. In what direction does the image in the ocular move?

n. Is the image in the ocular inverted relative to the specimen on the stage?

o. Center the specimen in the field of view; then rotate the 40✕ objective into position while watching from the side. *If it appears that the objective will hit the slide, stop and ask for assistance.*

Most of the microscopes have parfocal lenses, which means that little refocusing is required when moving from one lens to another. If your scope is *not* parfocal, ask your instructor for assistance.

p. After the 40✕ objective is in place, focus using the fine adjustment knob.

Never focus with the coarse adjustment knob when you are using the high-power objective.

q. The distance between the specimen and the objective lens is called the **working distance.** Is this distance greater with the 40✕ or the 10✕ objective?

3. Compute the total magnification of the specimen being viewed. To do so, multiply the magnification of the ocular lens by that of the objective lens.

a. What is the total magnification of the letter as the microscope is now set?

b. What would be the total magnification if the ocular were 20✕ and the objective were 100✕ (oil immersion)? This is the magnification achieved by the best light microscopes.

4. Measure the diameter of the field of view. Once you determine the size of the field of view for any combination of ocular and objective lenses, you can determine the size of any structure within that field.

a. Rotate the 4✕ objective into position and remove the letter slide.

b. Place a clear ruler on the stage, and focus on its edge.

c. The distance between two lines on the ruler is 1 mm. What is the diameter (mm) of the field of view?

      d. Convert this measurement to micrometers, a more commonly used unit of measurement in microscopy (1 mm = 1,000 μm).

      e. Measure the diameters of the field of view for the 10X and 40X objectives, and enter all three in the spaces below to be used for future reference.

          4X ≈ _____   10X ≈ _____   40X ≈ _____

      f. What is the relationship between the size of the field of view and magnification?

5.   Determine spatial relationships. The **depth of field** is the thickness of the specimen that may be seen in focus at one time. Because the depth of focus is very short in the compound microscope, focus up and down to clearly view all planes of a specimen.

      a. Rotate the 4X objective into position and remove the ruler. Take a slide of crossed threads, wipe it with a Kimwipe, and place the slide on the stage. Center the slide so that the region where the two threads cross is in the center of the stage opening.

      b. Focus on the region where the threads cross. Are both threads in focus at the same time?

      c. Rotate the 10X objective into position and focus on the cross. Are both threads in focus at the same time?

         Does the 4X or the 10X objective have a shorter depth of field?

      d. Focus upward (move the stage up) with the coarse adjustment until both threads are just out of focus. Slowly focus down using the fine adjustment. Which thread comes into focus first? Is this thread lying under or over the other thread?

      e. Rotate the 40X objective into position and slowly focus up and down, using the fine adjustment only. Does the 10X or the 40X objective have a shorter depth of field?

6.   At the end of your microscope session, use these procedures to store your microscope:

      a. Rotate the 4X objective into position.

      b. Remove the slide from the stage.

c. Return the phase-contrast condenser to the 0 setting if you have used phase-contrast.

d. Set the light intensity to its lowest setting and turn off the power.

e. Unplug the cord and wrap it around the base of the microscope.

f. Replace the dust cover.

g. Return the microscope to the cabinet using two hands; one hand should hold the arm, and the other should support the base.

These steps should be followed every time you store your microscope.

EXERCISE 3.3

The Stereoscopic Microscope

Materials

stereoscopic microscope   microscope slides
dissecting needles   droppers of water
living *Elodea*   coverslips

Introduction

The stereoscopic (dissecting) microscope has relatively low magnification, 7X to 30X, and is used for viewing and manipulating relatively large objects. The binocular feature creates the stereoscopic effect. The stereoscopic microscope is similar to the compound microscope except in the following ways: (1) The depth of field is much greater than with the compound microscope, so objects are seen in three dimensions, and (2) the light source can be directed down onto as well as up through an object, which permits the viewing of objects too thick to transmit light. Light directed down on the object is called **reflected** or **incident light.** Light passing through the object is called **transmitted light.**

Procedure

1. Remove your dissecting microscope from the cabinet and locate the parts labeled in Figure 3.2. Locate the switches for both incident and transmitted light. In the margin of your lab manual, note any features of your microscope that are not shown in the figure. What is the range of magnification for your microscope?

2. Prepare a wet mount of *Elodea.* Living material is often prepared for observation using a wet mount. (The material is either in water or covered with water prior to adding a coverslip.) You will use this technique to view living material under the dissecting and compound microscopes (Figure 3.3).

   a. Place a drop of water in the center of a clean microscope slide.

   b. Remove a single leaf of *Elodea,* and place it in the drop of water.

   c. Using a dissecting needle, place a coverslip at a 45° angle above the slide with one edge of the coverslip in contact with the edge of the water droplet, as shown.

Oculars

Magnification control knob

Movable binocular head

Incident light

Focus knob

Objective

Figure 3.2.
The stereoscopic (dissecting) microscope. Locate the parts of your microscope by referring to this photograph. Note in the margin any features of your microscope that are not shown in the photograph.

Transmitted light

Stage

Light adjustment knob

Figure 3.3.
Preparation of a wet mount. Place a drop of water and your specimen on the slide. Using a dissecting needle, slowly lower a coverslip onto the slide, being careful not to trap air bubbles in the droplet.

d. Lower the coverslip slowly onto the slide, being careful not to trap air bubbles in the droplet. The function of the coverslip is threefold: (1) to flatten the preparation, (2) to keep the preparation from drying out, and (3) to protect the objective lenses. Over long periods of time, the preparation may dry out, at which point water can be added to one edge of the coverslip.

✳ Specimens can be viewed without a coverslip using the stereoscopic microscope, but a coverslip must always be used with the compound microscope.

3. Observe the structure of the *Elodea* leaf at increasing magnification.

    a. Place the leaf slide on the stage, and adjust the interpupillary distance (distance between the oculars) by gently pushing or pulling the oculars until you can see the object clearly as a single image.

    b. Change the magnification and note the three-dimensional characteristic of the leaf.

    c. Sketch the leaf in the margin of your lab manual and list, in the space below, the structures that are visible at low and high magnification.

    Low:

    High:

    Is it possible to see cells in the leaf using the stereoscopic microscope?

    Organelles?

    d. Save your slide for later study. In Exercise 3.5, Lab Study C, you will be asked to compare these observations of *Elodea* with those made while using the compound microscope.

EXERCISE 3.4
The Electron Microscope

Materials

demonstration resources for the electron microscope
electron micrographs

Introduction

The electron microscope magnifies objects approximately 1,000X larger than a light microscope can (up to 1,000,000X). This difference depends on the **resolving power** of the electron microscope, which allows the viewer to see two objects of comparable size that are close together and still be able to recognize that they are two objects rather than one. Resolving power, in turn, depends on the wavelength of light passed through the specimen: the shorter the wavelength, the greater the resolution. Because electron microscopes use electrons as a source of illumination and electrons have a much shorter wavelength than does visible light, the resolving power of electron microscopes is much greater than that of light microscopes. Both the electron and light microscopes can be equipped with lenses that allow for tremendous magnification, but only the electron microscope has sufficient resolving power to make these lenses useful.

Procedure

1. Compare the features of the light and electron microscopes (Figure 3.4).
    a. Name three structures found in both microscopes.

    b. What is the energy source for the electron microscope?

    For the compound microscope?

    c. Describe how the lenses differ for the two microscopes.

2. Using the resources provided by your instructor, review the procedures and materials for preparing a specimen for electron microscopy.

a. Light microscope

b. Electron microscope

Figure 3.4.
Comparison of light microscope and electron microscope. The source of illumination is light for the light microscope and electrons for the electron microscope. The image is magnified by glass objectives in light microscopy and by electromagnets in electron microscopy.

3. Define the following terms on separate paper or in the margin of your lab manual:

fixation	*staining with heavy metals*
embedding	*electromagnetic lenses*
ultramicrotome	*fluorescent screen*
boat on diamond or glass knife	*vacuum*
copper grids	*electron micrographs*

4. Observe the electron micrographs on demonstration in the laboratory. Use these and your textbook to complete Table 3.1.

EXERCISE 3.5

The Organization of Cells

In this exercise, you will examine the features common to all eukaryotic cells that are indicative of their common ancestry. However, you will observe that all cells are not the same. Some organisms are **unicellular** (single-celled), with all living functions (respiration, digestion, reproduction, and excretion) handled by that one cell. Others form random, temporary **aggregates,** or clusters, of cells. Clusters composed of a consistent and predictable number of cells are called **colonies.** Simple colonies have no physiological connections but maintain a predictable multicellular structure. Complex colonies have physiological connections and specialization of groups of cells. **Multicellular** organisms have large numbers of cells with specialized structure and function, and no one cell can exist successfully by itself.

In this exercise, you will examine selected unicellular, aggregate, colonial, and multicellular organisms. (See Color Plates 1–7.)

Lab Study A. Unicellular Organisms

Materials

microscope slides	coverslips
culture of *Amoeba*	dissecting needles
living termites	insect Ringers
forceps	

Introduction

Unicellular eukaryotic organisms may be **autotrophic** (photosynthetic) or **heterotrophic** (deriving food from other organisms or their by-products). These diverse organisms, called protists, will be studied in detail in Lab Topic 14.

Table 3.1
Characteristics of Cellular Organelles; EM = Electron Microscope, LM = Light Microscope

Organelle	Size (μm); Visualization	Function	Where Present:	
			Plants and Autotrophic Protists	Animals and Heterotrophic Protists
Plasma membrane	$7-9 \times 10^{-3}$ (thickness); EM			
Cell wall	Variable; a single fibril is as thick as the plasma membrane; LM, EM			
Nucleus	4–10 (diameter); LM, EM			
Chloroplast	8 (length); LM, EM			
Mitochondria	0.5–10 (diameter); EM			
Vacuole	Variable; LM, EM			
Golgi apparatus	Variable; EM			
Peroxisomes	0.2–1.5 (diameter); EM			
Lysosomes	0.2–0.5 (diameter); EM			
Endoplasmic reticulum	0.005–0.01 (tube diameter); EM			
Ribosomes	$1.7-2.3 \times 10^{-3}$ (diameter); EM			
Flagella, cilia	0.2 (diameter); 2–150 (length); LM, EM			

Procedure

1. Examine a living *Amoeba* (Figure 3.5) under the compound microscope. Amoebas are aquatic organisms commonly found in ponds. To transfer a specimen to your slide, follow these procedures:

   a. Place the culture dish containing the amoeba under the dissecting microscope, and focus on the bottom of the dish. The amoeba will appear as a whitish, irregularly shaped organism attached to the bottom.

   b. Using a clean pipette (it is important not to interchange pipettes between culture dishes), transfer a drop with several amoebas to your microscope slide. To do this, squeeze the pipette bulb *before* you place the tip under the surface of the water. Disturbing the culture as little as possible, pipette a drop of water with debris from the *bottom* of the culture dish. You may use your stereoscopic microscope to scan the slide to locate amoebas before continuing.

   c. Cover your preparation with a clean coverslip.

   d. Under low power on the compound scope, scan the slide to locate an amoeba. Center the specimen in your field of view; then switch to higher powers.

   e. Identify the following structures in the amoeba:

   Cell membrane is the boundary that separates the organism from its surroundings.

   Ectoplasm is the thin, transparent layer of cytoplasm directly beneath the cell membrane.

   Endoplasm is the granular cytoplasm containing the cell organelles.

   The **nucleus** is the grayish, football-shaped body that is somewhat granular in appearance. This organelle, which directs the cellular activities, will often be seen moving within the endoplasm.

   Contractile vacuoles are clear, spherical vesicles of varying sizes that gradually enlarge as they fill with excess water. Once you've located a vacuole, watch it fill and then empty its contents into the surrounding environment. These vacuoles serve an excretory function for the amoeba.

   Food vacuoles are small, dark, irregularly shaped vesicles within the endoplasm. They contain undigested food particles.

   Pseudopodia ("false feet") are fingerlike projections of the cytoplasm. They are used for locomotion as well as for trapping and engulfing food in a process called **phagocytosis.**

2. Examine *Trichonympha* under a compound microscope. You will first have to separate the *Trichonympha* (Figure 3.6) from the termite with which it lives in a symbiotic relationship. *Trichonympha* and other organisms occupy the gut of the termites, where they digest wood particles eaten by the insect. Termites lack the enzymes necessary to digest wood and are dependent on *Trichonympha* to make the nutrients in the wood available to them. *Trichonympha* has become so well adapted to the environment of the termite's gut that it cannot survive outside of it.

   To obtain a specimen:

   a. Place a couple of drops of **insect Ringers** (a saline solution that is isotonic to the internal environment of insects) on a clean microscope slide.

   b. Using forceps or your fingers, transfer a termite into the drop of Ringers.

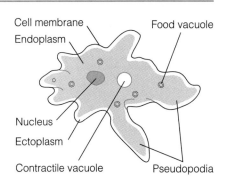

Figure 3.5.
Amoeba. An *Amoeba* moves using pseudopodia. Observe the living organisms using the compound microscope. (See Color Plate 1.)

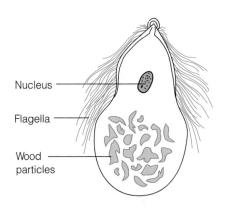

Figure 3.6.
Trichonympha. A community of microorganisms, including *Trichonympha,* inhabits the intestine of the termite. Following the procedure in Exercise 3.5, Lab Study A, disperse the microorganisms and locate the cellular structures in *Trichonympha.* (See Color Plate 2.)

c. Place the slide under the dissecting microscope.

d. Place the tips of dissecting needles at either end of the termite and pull in opposite directions.

e. Locate the long tube that is the termite's intestine. Remove all the larger parts of the insect from the slide.

f. Using a dissecting needle, mash the intestine to release the *Trichonympha* and other protozoa and bacteria.

g. Cover your preparation with a clean coverslip.

h. Transfer your slide to the compound microscope and scan the slide under low power. Center several *Trichonympha* in the field of view and switch to higher powers.

 Several types of protozoans and bacteria will be present in the termite gut.

i. Locate the following structures under highest power:

Flagella are the long, hairlike structures on the outside of the organism. The function of the flagella is not fully understood. Within the gut of the termite, the organisms live in such high density that movement by flagellar action seems unlikely and perhaps impossible.

The **nucleus** is a somewhat spherical organelle near the middle of the organism.

Wood particles may be located in the posterior region of the organism.

Lab Study B. Aggregate and Colonial Organisms

Materials

microscope slides
dissecting needles
forceps
coverslips

broken glass chips
cultures of *Protococcus*,
    Scenedesmus, and *Volvox*

Introduction

Unlike unicellular organisms, which live independently of each other, colonial organisms are cells that live in groups and are to some degree dependent on one another. The following organisms show an increasing degree of interaction among cells.

— Cell wall

Figure 3.7.
Protococcus. *Protococcus* is a terrestrial green alga that forms loose aggregates on the bark of trees. (See Color Plate 3.)

Procedure

1. Examine *Protococcus* under the compound microscope. *Protococcus* (Figure 3.7) is a terrestrial green alga that grows on the north sides of trees and is often referred to as "moss."

a. To obtain a specimen, use a dissecting needle to brush off a small amount of the green growth on the piece of tree bark provided into a drop of water on a clean microscope slide. Avoid scraping bark onto the slide. Cover the preparation with a clean coverslip.

b. Observe at highest power that these cells are **aggregates:** The size of the cell groupings is random, and there are no permanent connections between cells. Each cell is surrounded by a cell membrane and an outer **cell wall.**

c. Observe several small cell groupings and avoid large clumps of cells. Cellular detail may be obscure.

2. Examine living *Scenedesmus* under the compound microscope. *Scenedesmus* (Figure 3.8) is an aquatic green alga that is common in aquaria and polluted water.

a. To obtain a specimen, place a drop from the culture dish (using a clean pipette) onto a clean microscope slide, and cover it with a clean coverslip.

b. Observe that the cells of this organism form a **simple colony:** The cells always occur in groups of from four to eight cells, and they are permanently united.

c. Identify the following structures:

The **nucleus** is the spherical organelle in the approximate middle of each cell.

Vacuoles are the transparent spheres that tend to occur at either end of the cells.

Spines are the transparent projections that occur on the two end cells.

Cell walls surround each cell.

3. Examine living *Volvox* under the compound microscope. *Volvox* (Figure 3.9) is an aquatic green alga that also is common in aquaria, ponds, and lakes.

a. To obtain a specimen, prepare a wet mount as you did for *Scenedesmus* with the following addition: Before placing a drop of the culture on your slide, place several glass chips on the slide. This will keep the coverslip from crushing these spherical organisms.

b. Observe that the cells of this organism form a large **complex colony.** Approximately 500 to 50,000 cells (depending on the species) are permanently united, there are cytoplasmic connections between cells, and some cells are specialized for reproduction.

c. Identify the following structures:

Individual cells all possess the following structures: **cell wall, nucleus, vacuole, chloroplasts, flagella** (two per cell).

Cytoplasmic strands form connections between adjacent cells.

Daughter colonies are smaller spheres within the larger colony. These are produced asexually, and when they are large enough, they will be discharged from the parent colony into the surrounding environment.

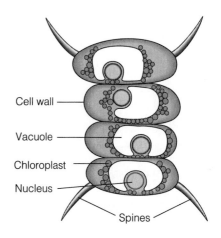

Figure 3.8.
Scenedesmus. *Scenedesmus* is an aquatic alga that usually occurs in simple colonies of four cells connected by an outer cell wall. (See Color Plate 4.)

Figure 3.9.
Volvox. In this complex colony, the individual cells are interconnected by cytoplasmic strands to form a sphere. Small clusters of cells, called daughter colonies, are specialized for reproduction. (See Color Plate 5.)

Lab Study C. Multicellular Organisms

Materials

microscope slides	coverslips
dropper bottles of water	*Elodea*
toothpicks	methylene blue
	finger bowl with disinfectant

Introduction

Multicellular organisms are composed of groups of specialized cells, called **tissues**, that together perform particular functions for the organism. Tissues, in turn, may be grouped to form **organs**, and organs may be grouped into **organ systems**. In this lab study, you will examine some of the cells that compose the basic tissue types of plants and animals.

Procedure

Plant Cells

1. The major characteristics of a typical plant cell are readily seen in the leaf cells of *Elodea,* a common aquatic plant (Figure 3.10). Prepare a wet mount and examine one of the youngest (smallest) leaves from a sprig of *Elodea* under the compound microscope.

2. Identify the following structures:

   The **cell wall** is the rigid outer framework surrounding the cell. This structure gives the cell a definite shape and support. It is not found in animal cells.

   Protoplasm is the organized contents of the cell, exclusive of the cell wall.

   Cytoplasm is the protoplasm of the cell, exclusive of the nucleus.

   The **central vacuole** is a membrane-bound sac within the cytoplasm that is filled with water and dissolved substances. This structure serves to store metabolic wastes and gives the cell support by means of turgor pressure. Animal cells also have vacuoles, but they are not as large and conspicuous as those found in plants.

   Chloroplasts are the green, spherical organelles often seen moving within the cytoplasm. These organelles carry the pigment chlorophyll that is involved in photosynthesis. As the microscope light heats up the cells, cytoplasm and chloroplasts may begin to move around the central vacuole in a process called *cytoplasmic streaming,* or *cyclosis.*

   The **nucleus** is the usually spherical, transparent organelle within the cytoplasm. This structure controls cell metabolism and division.

3. What three structures observed in *Elodea* are unique to plants?

Cytoplasmic strands

Nucleus

Chloroplast

Figure 3.10.
Elodea. *Elodea* is an aquatic plant commonly grown in freshwater aquaria. The cell structures may be difficult to see because of the three-dimensional cell shape and the presence of a large central vacuole. (See Color Plate 6.)

4. Compare your observations of *Elodea* using the compound scope with those made in Exercise 3.3 using the stereoscopic scope. List the structures seen with each:

Stereoscopic:

Compound:

Animal Cells

1. Animals are multicellular heterotrophic organisms that ingest organic matter. They are composed of cells that can be categorized into four major tissue groups: epithelial, connective, muscle, and nervous tissue. In this lab study, you will examine epithelial cells. Similar to the epidermal cells of plants, **epithelial cells** occur on the outside of animals and serve to protect the animals from water loss, mechanical injury, and foreign invaders. In addition, epithelial cells line interior cavities and ducts in animals. Examine the epithelial cells (Figure 3.11) that form the lining of your inner cheek. To obtain a specimen, follow this procedure:

   a. With a clean toothpick, gently scrape the inside of your cheek several times.

   b. Roll the scraping into a drop of water on a clean microscope slide, add a small drop of methylene blue, and cover with a coverslip. Discard the used toothpick in disinfectant.

   c. Using the compound microscope, view the cells under higher powers.

2. Observe that these cells are extremely flat and so may be folded over on themselves. Attempt to locate several cells that are not badly folded, and study their detail.

3. Identify the following structures:

   The **cell membrane** is the boundary that separates the cell from its surroundings.

   The **nucleus** is the large, circular organelle near the middle of the cell.

   Cytoplasm is the granular contents of the cell, exclusive of the nucleus.

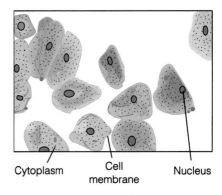

Cytoplasm   Cell   Nucleus
                membrane

Figure 3.11.
Human epithelial cells. The epithelial cells that line your cheek are thin, flat cells that you can remove easily from your cheek by scraping it with a toothpick. (See Color Plate 7.)

Lab Study D. Unknowns

Materials

microscope slides
coverslips
pond water or culture of unknowns

Introduction

Use this lab study to see if you have met the objectives of this lab topic. As you carry out this lab study, (1) think carefully about using correct microscopic techniques; (2) distinguish organisms with different cellular organization or configuration; (3) note how the different organisms are similar yet different; and (4) note cell differences.

Procedure

1. Examine several drops of the culture of pond water that you col-
    lected, or examine the unknown culture provided by the instructor.
2. Record in Table 3.2 the characteristics of at least four different
    organisms.

Table 3.2
Characteristics of Organisms Found in Pond Water

Tube Unknown	Means of Locomotion	Cell Wall (+/–)	Chloroplasts (+/–)	Organization
1				
2				
3				
4				
5				

Questions for Review

1. List several organelles that are visible with the electron microscope but
    that were not visible with your microscope.

2. Describe at least two types of materials or observations that would neces-
    sitate the use of the stereoscopic microscope.

3. What characteristics do all eukaryotic cells have in common?

4. a. What cellular features differentiate plants from animals?

    b. How are the structures that are unique to plants important to their
       success?

Applying Your Knowledge

1. In your own words, describe the evolutionary trend for increasing organismal complexity, using examples from this lab to illustrate your answer.

2. We often imply that multicellular organisms are more advanced (and therefore more successful) than unicellular or colonial organisms. Explain why this is not true, using examples from this lab or elsewhere.

3. Following is a list of tissues that have specialized functions and demonstrate corresponding specialization of subcellular structure. Match the tissue with the letter of the cell structures and organelles listed to the right that would be abundant in these cells. (Refer to Table 3.1.)

Tissues

Cell Structures and Organelles

*   Enzyme (protein)-secreting cells of the pancreas

    a.   plasma membrane

    b.   mitochondria

    c.   Golgi apparatus

*   Insect flight muscles

    d.   chloroplast

    e.   endoplasmic reticulum

*   Cells lining the respiratory passages

    f.   cilia and flagella

    g.   vacuole

    h.   ribosome

*   White blood cells that engulf and destroy invading bacteria

    i.   lysosome

    j.   peroxisomes

*   Leaf cells of cacti

4. One organism found in a termite's gut is *Mixotricha paradoxa*. This strange creature looks like a single-celled swimming ciliate under low magnification. However, the electron microscope reveals that it contains spherical bacteria rather than mitochondria and has on its surface, rather than cilia, hundreds of thousands of spirilla and bacilla bacteria. You are the scientist who first observed this organism. How would you describe this organism—single-celled? aggregate? colony? multicellular? Review definitions of these terms on page 69. Can the structure of this organism give you any insight into the evolution of eukaryotic cells? (*Hint:* See the discussion of the endosymbiosis hypothesis in your text.)

References

Alberts, B., D. Bray, J. Lewis, M. Raff, K. Roberts, and J. Watson. *Molecular Biology of the Cell,* 3rd ed. New York: Garland, 1994.

Becker, W. M., J. B. Reece, and M. F. Poenie. *The World of the Cell,* 3rd ed. Redwood City, CA: Benjamin/Cummings, 1996.

Cooper, G. M. *The Cell: A Molecular Approach,* 2nd ed. Sunderland, MA: ASM Press/Sinauer Associates, 2000.

Margulis, L., and D. Sagan. "The Beast with Five Genomes," *Natural History,* 2001, vol. 110, pp. 38–41.

Website

Cells Alive:
http://www.cellsalive.com

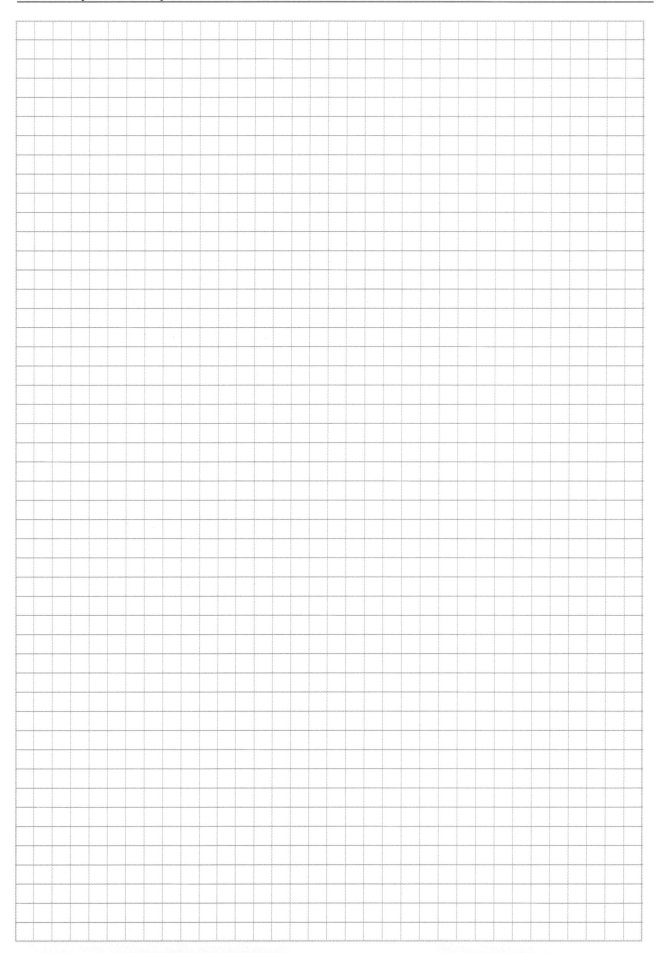

Diffusion and Osmosis

Laboratory Objectives

After completing this lab topic, you should be able to:

1. Describe the mechanism of diffusion at the molecular level.
2. List several factors that influence the rate of diffusion.
3. Describe a selectively permeable membrane, and explain its role in osmosis.
4. Define *hypotonic, hypertonic,* and *isotonic* in terms of relative concentrations of osmotically active substances.
5. Discuss the influence of the cell wall on osmotic behavior in cells.
6. Explain how incubating plant tissues in a series of dilutions of sucrose can give an approximate measurement of osmolarity of tissue cells.
7. Explain why diffusion and osmosis are important to cells.
8. Apply principles of osmotic activity to medical, domestic, and environmental activities.

Introduction

Maintaining the steady state of a cell is achieved only through regulated movement of materials through cytoplasm, across organelle membranes, and across the plasma membrane. This regulated movement facilitates communication within the cell and between cytoplasm and the external environment. The cytoplasm and extracellular environment of the cell are aqueous solutions. They are composed of water, which is the **solvent,** or dissolving agent, and numerous organic and inorganic molecules, which are the **solutes,** or dissolved substances. Organelle membranes and the plasma membrane are **selectively permeable,** allowing water to freely pass through but regulating the movement of solutes.

The cell actively moves some dissolved substances across membranes, expending adenosine triphosphate (ATP) (biological energy) to accomplish the movement. Other substances move passively, without expenditure of ATP from the cell, but only if the cell membrane is permeable to those substances. Water and selected solutes move passively through the cell and cell membranes by **diffusion,** a physical process in which molecules move from an area where they are in high concentration to one where their concentration is lower. The energy driving diffusion comes only from the intrinsic kinetic energy in all atoms and molecules. If nothing hinders the movement, a solute will diffuse until it reaches equilibrium.

Osmosis is a type of diffusion, the diffusion of water through a selectively permeable membrane from a region where it is highly concentrated to a region where its concentration is lower. The difference in concentration of water occurs if there is an unequal distribution of at least one dissolved substance on either side of a membrane and the membrane is impermeable to that substance. In this situation, the substance is called an **osmotically active substance (OAS).** For example, if a membrane that is impermeable to sucrose separates a solution of sucrose from distilled water, water will move from the distilled water, where it is in higher concentration, through the membrane into the sucrose solution, where it is in lower concentration. In this case, sucrose is the osmotically active substance.

Three terms, **hypertonic, hypotonic,** and **isotonic,** are used when referring to two solutions separated by a selectively permeable membrane (Figure 4.1). The hypertonic solution (Figure 4.1a) has a greater concentration of OAS than the solution on the other side of the membrane. It is described, therefore, as having a greater **osmolarity** (solute concentration expressed as molarity). The hypotonic solution (Figure 4.1b) has a lower concentration of OAS, or a lower osmolarity, than the solution on the other side of the membrane. When the two solutions are in equilibrium, the concentration of OAS being equal on both sides of the membrane, the osmolarities are equal and the substances are said to be isotonic (Figure 4.1c). The *net flow* of water is from the hypotonic to the hypertonic solution. When the solutions are isotonic, there is no net flow of water across the membrane.

The concept of osmotic pressure must be understood when studying osmosis. The movement of water from a hypotonic solution through the membrane into a hypertonic solution can be prevented by applying force or pressure on the hypertonic side (Figure 4.2). The force that must be applied to prevent osmotic movement of water from hypotonic to hypertonic, measured in atmospheres, is referred to as **osmotic pressure.** Solutions with greater concentrations of OAS have greater osmotic pressures because greater

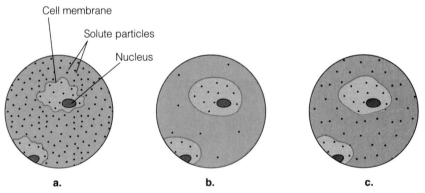

Cell membrane

Solute particles

Nucleus

a.   b.   c.

Figure 4.1.
Diagrammatic representation of cells in (a) hypertonic, (b) hypotonic, and (c) isotonic solutions. The hypertonic solution has a greater concentration of OAS than the solution on the other side of the membrane, the hypotonic solution has a lower concentration of OAS than the solution on the other side of the membrane, and the concentration of OAS is equal on both sides of the membrane in isotonic solutions.

Figure 4.2.
Applying the correct pressure to the hypertonic side of two osmotically active solutions will prevent water movement into that solution.

force is required to prevent water movement into them. Distilled water has an osmotic pressure of zero.

EXERCISE 4.1
Diffusion of Molecules

In this exercise you will investigate characteristics of molecules that facilitate diffusion, factors that influence diffusion rates, and diffusion of solutes through a selectively permeable membrane.

Experiment A. Kinetic Energy of Molecules

Materials

dropper bottle of water
carmine powder
dissecting needle

slide and coverslip
compound microscope

Introduction

Molecules of a liquid or gas are constantly in motion because of the intrinsic kinetic energy in all atoms and molecules. In 1827, Robert Brown, a Scottish botanist, noticed that pollen grains suspended in water on a slide appeared to move by a force that he was unable to explain. In 1905, Albert Einstein, searching for evidence that would prove the existence of atoms and molecules, predicted that this type of motion must exist, although he did not realize that it had been studied for many years. Only after the kinetic energy of molecules was understood did scientists ask if the motion observed by Brown and predicted by Einstein could be the result of molecular kinetic energy being passed to larger particles. In this lab study, you will observe this movement, called **Brownian movement**, which we now know is the driving force of diffusion.

Procedure

Work in pairs. One person should set up the microscope while the other person makes a slide as follows:

1. Place a drop of water on the slide.
2. Touch the tip of a dissecting needle to the drop of water and then into the dry carmine.
3. Add the carmine on the needle to the drop of water on the slide, mix, cover with a coverslip, and observe under the compound microscope.
4. Observe on low power and then high power. Focus as much as possible on one particle of carmine.
5. Record your findings in the Results section, and draw conclusions based on your results in the Discussion section.

Results

Describe the movement of single carmine particles.

1. Is the movement random or directional?
2. Does the movement ever stop?
3. Do smaller particles move more rapidly than larger particles? Other observations?

Discussion

1. Are you actually observing molecular movement? Explain.

2. How can the movement being observed bring about diffusion?

3. Speculate about the importance of diffusion in cell metabolism.

Experiment B. Diffusion of Molecules
Through a Selectively Permeable Membrane

Materials

string or rubber band	500-mL beaker one-third filled with water
wax pencil	handheld test tube holder
30% glucose solution	3 standard test tubes
starch solution	disposable transfer pipettes
I_2KI solution	2 400-mL beakers to hold dialysis bag
Benedict's reagent	30-cm strip of moist dialysis tubing
hot plate	

Introduction

Dialysis tubing is a membrane made of regenerated cellulose fibers formed into a flat tube. If two solutions containing dissolved substances of different molecular weights are separated by this membrane, some substances may readily pass through the pores of the membrane, but others may be excluded.

Working in teams of four students, you will investigate the selective permeability of dialysis tubing. You will test the permeability of the tubing to glucose (molecular weight 180), starch (a variable-length polymer of glucose), and iodine potassium iodide (I_2KI). You will place a solution of glucose and starch into a dialysis tubing bag and then place this bag into a solution of I_2KI. Sketch and label the design of this experiment in the margin of your lab manual to help you develop your hypotheses.

You will use two tests in your experiment:

1. *I_2KI test for presence of starch.* When I_2KI is added to the unknown solution, the solution turns purple or black if starch is present. If no starch is present, the solution remains a pale yellow-amber color.

2. *Benedict's test for reducing sugar.* When Benedict's reagent is added to the unknown solution and the solution is heated, the solution turns green, orange, or orange-red if a reducing sugar is present (the color indicates the sugar concentration). If no reducing sugar is present, the solution remains the color of Benedict's reagent (blue).

Hypothesis

Hypothesize about the selective permeability of dialysis tubing to the substances being tested.

Prediction

Predict the results of the I_2KI and Benedict's tests based on your hypothesis (if/then).

Procedure

1. Prepare the dialysis bag with the initial solutions:

   a. Fold over 3 cm at the end of a 25- to 30-cm piece of dialysis tubing that has been soaking in water for a few minutes, pleat the folded end "accordion style," and close the end of the tube with the string or a rubber band, forming a bag. This procedure must secure the end of the bag so that no solution can seep through.

   b. Roll the opposite end of the bag between your fingers until it opens, and add 4 pipettesful of 30% glucose into the bag. Then add 4 pipettesful of starch solution to the glucose in the bag.

   c. Hold the bag closed and mix its contents. Record its color in Table 4.1 in the Results section. Carefully rinse the outside of the bag in tap water.

   d. Add 300 mL of water to a 400- to 500-mL beaker. Add several droppersful of I_2KI solution to the water until it is visibly yellow-amber. Record the color of the H_2O + I_2KI solution in Table 4.1.

   e. Place the bag in the beaker so that the untied end of the bag hangs over the edge of the beaker (Figure 4.3). *Do not allow the liquid to spill out of the bag!* If the bag is too full, remove some of the liquid and rinse the outside of the bag again. If needed, place a rubber band around the beaker, holding the bag securely in place. If some of the liquid spills into the beaker, dispose of the beaker water, rinse, and fill again.

2. Leave the bag in the beaker for about 30 minutes. (You should go to another lab activity and then return to check your setup periodically.)

3. After 30 minutes, carefully remove the bag and stand it in a dry beaker.

4. Record in Table 4.1 the final color of the solution in the bag and the final color of the solution in the beaker.

5. Perform the Benedict's test for the presence of sugar in the solutions.

   a. Label three clean test tubes: control, bag, and beaker.

   b. Put 2 pipettesful of water in the control tube.

   c. Put 2 pipettesful of the bag solution in the bag tube.

   d. Put 2 pipettesful of the beaker solution in the beaker tube.

   e. Add 1 dropperful of Benedict's reagent to each tube.

   f. Heat the test tubes in a boiling water bath for about 3 minutes.

   g. Record your results in Table 4.1.

Figure 4.3.

Setup for Exercise 4.1, Experiment B. The dialysis tubing bag, securely closed at one end, is placed in the beaker of water and I_2KI. The open end of the bag should drape over the edge of the beaker.

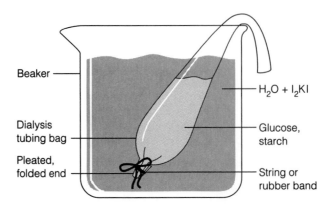

6. Review your results in Table 4.1 and draw your conclusions in the Discussion section.

Results

Complete Table 4.1 as you observe the results of Experiment B.

Table 4.1
Results of Experiment Investigating the Permeability of
Dialysis Tubing to Glucose, I_2KI, and Starch

Solution Source	Original Contents	Original Color	Final Color	Color After Benedict's Test
Bag				
Beaker				
Control				

Discussion

1. What is the significance of the final colors and the colors after the Benedict's tests? Did the results support your hypothesis? Explain, giving evidence from the results of your tests.

2. How can you explain your results?

3. From your results, predict the size of I_2KI molecules relative to glucose and starch.

4. What colors would you expect if the experiment started with glucose and I_2KI inside the bag and starch in the beaker? Explain.

EXERCISE 4.2
Osmotic Activity in Cells

All organisms must maintain an optimum internal osmotic environment. Terrestrial vertebrates must take in and eliminate water using internal regulatory systems to ensure that the environment of tissues and organs remains in osmotic balance. Exchange of waste and nutrients between blood and tissues depends on the maintenance of this condition. Plants and animals living in fresh water must control the osmotic uptake of water into their hypertonic cells.

In this exercise, you will investigate the osmotic behavior of plant and animal cells placed in different molar solutions. What happens to these cells when they are placed in hypotonic or hypertonic solutions? This question will be investigated in the following experiments.

Experiment A. Osmotic Behavior of Animal Cells

Materials

4 clean microscope slides and coverslips
wax pencil
dropper bottle of ox blood
dropper bottles with three solutions of unknown osmolarity

Introduction

Mature red blood cells (erythrocytes) are little more than packages of hemoglobin bound by a plasma membrane permeable to small molecules, such as oxygen and carbon dioxide, but impermeable to larger molecules, such as proteins, sodium chloride, and sucrose. In mammals these cells even lack nuclei when mature, and as they float in isotonic blood plasma, their shape is flattened and pinched inward into a biconcave disk. Oxygen and carbon dioxide diffuse across the membrane, allowing the cell to carry out its primary function, gas transport, which is enhanced by the increased surface area created by the shape of the cell. When water moves into red blood cells placed in a hypotonic solution, the cells swell and the membranes burst, or undergo **lysis.** When water moves out of red blood cells placed in a hypertonic solution, the cells shrivel and appear bumpy, or **crenate.** In this experiment, you will investigate the behavior of red blood cells when the osmolarity of the environment changes from isotonic to hypertonic or hypotonic. (See Color Plate 8.)

Hypothesis

Hypothesize about the behavior of red blood cells when they are placed in hypertonic or hypotonic environments.

Prediction

Predict the results of the experiment based on your hypothesis (if/then).

Procedure

 Have your microscope ready, and observe slides immediately after you have prepared them. Do one slide at a time.

1. Label four clean microscope slides A, B, C, and D.
2. Place a drop of blood on slide D, cover with a coverslip, and observe the shape of red blood cells with no treatment. Record your observations in Table 4.2 in the Results section.
3. Put a drop of solution A on slide A and add a coverslip. Place the slide on the microscope stage and carefully add a small drop of blood to the edge of the coverslip. The blood cells will be drawn under the coverslip by capillary action.
4. As you view through the microscope, carefully watch the cells as they come into contact with solution A; record your observations in Table 4.2.
5. Repeat steps 3 and 4 with solutions B and C.
6. Record your observations in Table 4.2. Draw your conclusions in the Discussion section.

Results

Record your observations of red blood cell behavior in Table 4.2.

Table 4.2
Appearance of Red Blood Cells in Test Solutions

Solution	Appearance/Condition of Cells
D (blood only)	
A	
B	
C	

Discussion

Explain your results in terms of your hypothesis.

1. Based on your hypothesis and predictions, which of the three solutions is hypertonic to the red blood cells?

   Hypotonic?

   Isotonic?

   Verify your conclusions with the laboratory instructor.

2. What conditions might lead to results other than those expected?

Experiment B. Osmotic Behavior in Cells with a Cell Wall

Materials

On demonstration: 2 compound microscopes labeled A and B
1 slide of *Elodea* in a hypertonic salt solution
1 slide of *Elodea* in distilled water

Introduction

In their natural environment, cells of freshwater plants and algae are bathed in water with little OAS. The net flow of water is from the surrounding medium into the cells. To understand this process, review the structure of *Elodea* cells from Lab Topic 3.

The presence of a cell wall and a large fluid-filled central vacuole in a plant or algal cell will affect the cell's response to solutions of differing molarities. When a plant cell is placed in a hypertonic solution, water moves out of the cell; the protoplast shrinks and may pull away from the cell wall. This process is called **plasmolysis,** and the cell is described as **plasmolyzed** (Figure 4.4). In a hypotonic solution, as water moves into the cell and ultimately into the cell's central vacuole, the cell's **protoplast** (the plant cell exclusive of the cell wall—the cytoplasm enclosed by plasma membrane) expands. The cell wall, however, restricts the expansion, resulting in **turgor pressure** (pressure of the protoplast on the cell wall owing to uptake of water). A high turgor pressure will prevent further movement of water into the cell. This process is a good example of the interaction between pressure and osmolarity in determining the direction of the net movement of water. The hypertonic condition in the cell draws water into the cell until the membrane-enclosed cytoplasm presses against the cell wall. Turgor pres-

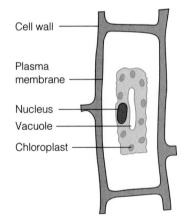

Cell wall

Plasma membrane

Nucleus

Vacuole

Chloroplast

Figure 4.4.
Plant cell placed in a hypertonic solution. Water leaves the central vacuole and the cytoplasm shrinks, a process called plasmolysis.

sure begins to force water through the membrane and out of the cell, changing the direction of net flow of water (Figure 4.5).

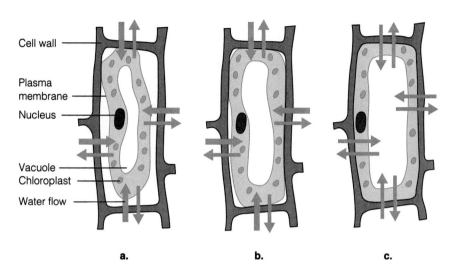

Cell wall

Plasma membrane

Nucleus

Vacuole
Chloroplast

Water flow

a.   b.   c.

Figure 4.5.
The effect of turgor pressure on the cell wall and the direction of net flow of water in a plant cell. A plant cell undergoes changes in a hypotonic solution. (a) Low turgor pressure. The net flow of water comes into the cell from the surrounding hypotonic medium. (b) Turgor pressure increases. The protoplast begins to press on the cell wall. (c) Greatest turgor pressure. The tendency to take up water is ultimately restricted by the cell wall, creating a back pressure on the protoplast. Water enters and leaves the cell at the same rate.

For this experiment, two slides have been set up on demonstration microscopes. On each slide, *Elodea* has been placed in a different molar solution: One is hypotonic (distilled water) and one is hypertonic (concentrated salt solution).

Hypothesis

Hypothesize about the movement of water in cells with a cell wall when they are placed in hypertonic or hypotonic environments.

Prediction

Predict the appearance of *Elodea* cells placed in the two solutions (if/then).

Procedure

1. Observe the two demonstration microscopes with *Elodea* in solutions A and B.
2. Record your observations in Table 4.3 in the Results section, and draw your conclusions in the Discussion section.

Results

Describe the appearance of the *Elodea* cells in Table 4.3.

Table 4.3
Appearance of *Elodea* Cells in Unknown Solutions A and B

Solution	Appearance/Condition of Cells
A	
B	

Discussion

1. Based on your predictions and observations, which solution is hypertonic?

   Hypotonic?

2. Which solution has the greatest osmolarity?

3. Would you expect pond water to be isotonic, hypertonic, or hypotonic to *Elodea* cells? Explain.

4. Verify your conclusions with your laboratory instructor.

EXERCISE 4.3
Estimating the Osmolarity of Plant Cells

Frequently, plant scientists need to determine the optimum water content for normal physiological processes in plants. They know that for normal activities to take place, the amount of water relative to osmotically active substances in cells must be maintained within a reasonable range. If plant cells have a reduced water content, all vital functions slow down.

In the following experiments, you will estimate the osmolarity of potato tuber cells using two methods, change in weight and change in volume.

You will incubate pieces of potato tuber in sucrose solutions of known molarity. The object is to find the molarity at which weight or volume of the potato tuber tissue does not change, indicating that there has been no net loss or gain of water. This molarity is an indirect measure of the osmolarity of the potato tuber.

Work in teams of four. Each team will measure either weight change or volume change. Time will be available near the end of the laboratory period for each team to present its results to the class for discussion and conclusions.

Experiment A. Estimating Osmolarity by Change in Weight

Materials

1 large potato tuber
7 250-mL beakers (disposable
   cups may be substituted)
wax marking pencil
forceps
balance that weighs to the
   nearest 0.01 g
aluminum foil
petri dish

sucrose solutions: 0.1, 0.2, 0.3,
   0.4, 0.5, 0.6 molar (M)
razor blade
cork borer
deionized (DI) water (0 molar)
paper towels
metric ruler
calculator

Introduction

In this experiment, you will determine the weight of several potato tuber cylinders and incubate them in a series of sucrose solutions. After the cylinders have incubated, you will weigh them and determine if they have gained or lost weight. This information will enable you to estimate the osmolarity of the potato tuber tissue.

Hypothesis

Hypothesize about the osmolarity of potato tuber tissue.

Prediction

Predict the results of the experiment based on your hypothesis (if/then).

Procedure

1. Obtain 100 mL of DI water and 100 mL of each of the sucrose solutions. Put each solution in a separate, appropriately labeled 250-mL beaker or paper cup.

Cork borers and razor blades can cut! Use them with extreme care! To use the cork borer, hold the potato in such a way that the borer will not push through the potato into your hand.

2. Use a sharp cork borer to obtain seven cylinders of potato. Push the borer through the length of the potato, twisting it back and forth. When the borer is filled, remove from the potato and push the potato cylinder out of the borer. You must have seven complete, undamaged cylinders at least 5 cm long.

3. Line up the potato cylinders and, using a sharp razor blade, cut all cylinders to a uniform length, about 5 cm, removing the peel from the ends.

4. Place all seven potato samples in a petri dish, and keep them covered to prevent their drying out.

 In subsequent steps, treat each sample individually. Work quickly. To provide consistency, each person should do one task to all cylinders (one person wipe, another weigh, another slice, another record data).

5. Remove a cylinder from the petri dish, and place it between the folds of a paper towel to blot sides and ends.

6. Weigh it to the nearest 0.01 g on the aluminum sheet on the balance. Record the weight in Table 4.4 in the Results section.

7. Immediately cut the cylinder lengthwise into two long halves.

8. Transfer potato pieces to the water beaker.

9. Note what time the potato pieces are placed in the water beaker. Time: _____.

10. Repeat steps 5 to 8 with each cylinder, placing potato pieces in the appropriate incubating solution from 0.1 to 0.6 M.

 Be sure that the initial weight of the cylinder placed in each test solution is accurately recorded.

11. Incubate 1.5 to 2 hours. (As this takes place, you will be performing other lab activities.)

12. Swirl each beaker every 10 to 15 minutes as the potato pieces incubate.

13. At the end of the incubation period, record the time when the potato pieces are removed. Time: _____.
    Calculate the approximate incubation time in Table 4.4.

14. Remove the potato pieces from the first sample. Blot the pieces on a paper towel, removing excess solution only.

15. Weigh the potato pieces and record the final weight in Table 4.4.

16. Repeat this procedure until all samples have been weighed in the chronological order in which they were initially placed in the test solutions.

17. Record your data in the Results section, and complete the questions in the Discussion section.

Results

1. Complete Table 4.4. To calculate percentage change in weight, use this formula:

$$\text{Percentage change in weight} = \frac{\text{weight change}}{\text{initial weight}} \times 100$$

If the sample gained in weight, the value should be positive. If it lost in weight, the value should be negative.

Table 4.4
Data for Experiment Estimating Osmolarity by Change in Weight

Approximate time in solutions: _____							
Sucrose Molarity							
	0.0	**0.1**	**0.2**	**0.3**	**0.4**	**0.5**	**0.6**
Final weight (g)							
Initial weight (g)							
Weight change (g)							
% change in weight							

2. Plot percentage change in weight as a function of the sucrose molarity in Figure 4.6.
    a. Place a 0 in the middle of the y axis. Choose appropriate scales.
    b. Label the axes of the graph: Determine dependent and independent variables, and place each on the appropriate axis (see Lab Topic 1 for assistance in graphing).
    c. Graph your results. Weight increase (positive values) should be above the zero change line on the "percentage change in weight" axis. Weight decrease should be below the zero change line.
    d. Construct a curve that best fits the data points. Use this curve to estimate the osmolarity of the potato tuber.
    e. Compose an appropriate figure title.

Discussion

1. At what sucrose molarity does the curve cross the zero change line on the graph?

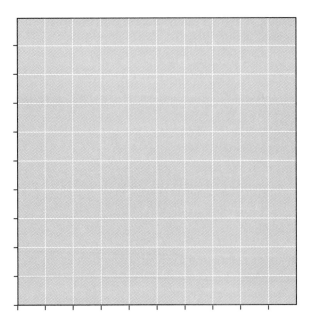

Figure 4.6.

_____

_____

_____

2. Explain how this information can be used to determine the osmolarity of the potato tuber tissue.

3. Estimate the osmolarity of the potato tuber tissue.

Experiment B. Estimating Osmolarity by Change in Volume

Materials

1 large potato tuber	cork borer (0.5-cm diameter)
vernier caliper	sucrose solutions: 0.1, 0.2, 0.3,
7 250-mL beakers (disposable	0.4, 0.5, 0.6 _M_
cups may be substituted)	DI water (0 _M_)
wax marking pencil	metric ruler
forceps	paper towels
petri dish	calculator
razor blade	

Introduction

In this experiment, you will determine the volume of several potato tuber cylinders by measuring the length and diameter of each. You will then incubate them in a series of sucrose solutions. After the cylinders have incubated, you will again measure their length and diameter and determine if they have increased or decreased in size. This information will enable you to estimate the osmolarity of the potato tuber tissue.

Hypothesis

Hypothesize about the osmolarity of potato tuber tissue.

Prediction

Predict the results of the experiment based on your hypothesis (if/then).

Procedure

1. Practice measuring with the vernier caliper (Figure 4.7a, b).

   a. Identify the following parts of the caliper and add these labels on Figure 4.7a: *stationary arm, movable arm, ruler, vernier scale*. Notice that the numbers on the bottom ruler scale are centimeters; each graduated line is 1 mm.

   b. Choose a small object (a coin will work) and place it between the two arms, adjusting the movable arm until both arms just touch the object.

   c. Note the 0 mark on the vernier scale (Figure 4.7b). The graduated line on the ruler just to the left of the 0 mark is the distance between the caliper arms measured in whole millimeters. In Figure 4.7b, that number is 22 mm. Write that number for your object as the answer in blank (1), on the next page.

   d. Look at the graduated lines between 0 and 10 on the vernier scale. Note the line on the vernier scale that exactly matches with a line on the ruler. That line on the vernier scale is the measurement in tenths of a millimeter, which should be added to the whole-millimeter reading.

Figure 4.7a.
Vernier caliper. Identify the stationary arm, movable arm, ruler, and vernier scale.

Figure 4.7b.
Enlarged vernier scale. The correct measurement is 22.4 mm.

In Figure 4.7b, that number is 4. Write the measurement in tenths of a millimeter for your object as the answer in blank (2) below.

What is the size of your object?

(1) _____

(2) _____

Total measurement: _____

When you know how to measure using the caliper, proceed to the next step.

2. Obtain 100 mL of DI water and 100 mL of each of the sucrose solutions. Put each solution in a separate, appropriately labeled 250-mL beaker or paper cup.

 Use cork borers and razor blades with extreme care! To use the cork borer, hold the potato in such a way that the borer will not push through the potato into your hand.

3. Use a sharp cork borer to obtain seven cylinders of potato. Push the borer through the length of the potato, twisting it back and forth. When the borer is filled, remove it from the potato and push the potato cylinder out of the borer. You must have seven complete, undamaged cylinders at least 5 cm long.

4. Line up the potato cylinders and, using a sharp razor blade, cut all cylinders to a uniform length, about 5 cm, removing the peel from the ends.

5. Place all seven potato samples in a petri dish, and keep them covered to prevent their drying out.

 In subsequent steps, treat each sample individually. Work quickly. To provide consistency, each person should do one task to all cylinders (one person wipe, another measure, another record data).

6. Remove a cylinder from the petri dish, and place it between the folds of a paper towel to blot sides and ends.

7. Using the caliper, measure the length and diameter of the cylinder to the nearest 0.1 mm, and record these measurements in Table 4.5 in the Results section. To measure, both arms of the caliper should touch but not compress the cylinder.

8. Transfer the cylinder to the 0 M (water) beaker.

9. Note the time the cylinder is placed in the 0 M beaker. Time: _____.

10. Repeat steps 6 to 8 with each cylinder, placing the cylinders in the appropriate incubating solution from 0.1 to 0.6 M.

 Be sure that the initial length and diameter of the cylinder placed in each test solution are accurately recorded.

11. Incubate from 1.5 to 2 hours. (During this time period, you will be performing other lab activities.)

12. Swirl each beaker every 10 to 15 minutes as the cylinders incubate.

13. At the end of the incubation period, record the time each cylinder is removed from a solution. Time: _____.

    Calculate the approximate incubation time in Table 4.5.

14. Remove the cylinders in the chronological order in which they were initially placed in the test solutions.

15. Blot each cylinder as it is removed (sides and ends), and use the vernier caliper to measure the length and diameter to the nearest 0.1 mm.

16. Finish recording your data in the Results section, and answer the questions in the Discussion section.

Results

1. Complete Table 4.5. To calculate the volume of a cylinder, use this formula:

$$\text{Volume of a cylinder (mm}^3) = \pi(\text{diameter}/2)^2 \times \text{length}$$
$$(\pi = 3.14)$$

To calculate percentage change in volume, use this formula:

$$\text{Percentage change in volume} = \frac{\text{change in volume}}{\text{initial volume}} \times 100$$

If the sample increases in volume, the value will be positive. If it decreases in volume, the value will be negative.

Table 4.5
Data for Experiment Estimating Osmolarity by Change in Volume

Approximate time in solutions: _____							
Sucrose Molarity							
	0.0	0.1	0.2	0.3	0.4	0.5	0.6
Final diameter (mm)							
Final length (mm)							
Final volume (mm³)							
Initial diameter (mm)							
Initial length (mm)							
Initial volume (mm³)							
Change in volume (mm³)							
% change in volume							

2. Plot percentage change in volume as a function of the sucrose molarity in Figure 4.8.

   a. Place a 0 in the middle of the y axis. Choose appropriate scales.

   b. Label the axes of the graph: Determine dependent and independent variables, and place each on the appropriate axis (see Lab Topic 1).

   c. Graph your results. Volume increase should be above the zero change line on the "percentage change in volume" axis. Volume decrease should be below the zero change line.

Figure 4.8.

_____

_____

_____

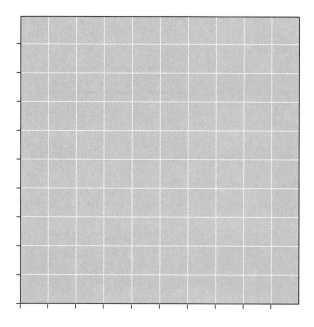

   d. Construct a curve that best fits the data points. Use this curve to estimate the osmolarity of the potato tuber.

   e. Compose an appropriate figure title.

Discussion

1. At what sucrose molarity does the curve cross the zero change line on the graph?

2. Explain how this information can be used to determine the osmolarity of the potato tuber tissue.

3. Estimate the osmolarity of the potato tuber tissue.

Questions for Review

Once you complete this lab topic, you should be able to define and use the following terms. Provide examples if appropriate.

selectively permeable, solvent, solute, diffusion, osmosis, osmotically active substance, hypotonic, hypertonic, isotonic, turgor pressure, osmotic pressure, osmolarity, Brownian movement, lysis, crenate, plasmolysis, plasmolyzed, turgid

Applying Your Knowledge

1. Describe plant wilting in terms of turgor pressure.

2. One traditional method for preserving pork has been to cover the meat with salt and spices. The resulting "country ham" can be stored for months without refrigeration. How do you think this process works? Consider the organisms responsible for food spoilage and how curing ham with salt might prevent spoilage.

3. The emergency room intern treated a patient by administering fluids intravenously. The patient died as a result of her error. What kind of osmotic solution would have resulted in the patient's death? Why?

4. A student read that plants require several essential elements for healthy growth and decided to fertilize his yellowing begonia. When he mixed the plant food, he made the solution three times as concentrated as the directions suggested. The next day his plant was not only yellow but also badly wilted. Can you help the student understand his error and suggest a remedy?

5. Constipation in infants can be a problem to treat because the common adult remedies, such as additional fiber in the diet or mild laxatives, are not options for small babies. One home remedy sometimes suggested is increasing fluids and adding dark Karo syrup to the infant's milk. Can you explain why this remedy might work?

6. Shrimp fishing off the coast of Georgia was closed in 2001 due to a drastic reduction in the shrimp population. Captain Forsyth, a local shrimper, suspects that increased salinity has killed the shrimp larvae. Three years of drought and greatly reduced freshwater flow from underground aquifers resulted in increased salinity in the coastal estuaries. These habitats between open ocean and fresh water are the "nurseries" for many marine animals. Design an experiment to determine the range of salt concentration that can be tolerated by shrimp larvae.

7. Water pollution is one of the most serious environmental problems of our time. Using information learned in this lab, predict one impact of pollutants in lakes, ponds, rivers, and streams on the plant and animal inhabitants.

References

Lang, F., and S. Waldegger. "Regulating Cell Volume." *American Scientist,* 1997, vol 85, pp. 456–463.

Exercise 4.1, Experiment A, was adapted from D. R. Helms and S. B. Miller, *Principles of Biology: A Laboratory Manual for Biology 110.* Apex, NC: Contemporary Publishing, 1978. Used by permission.

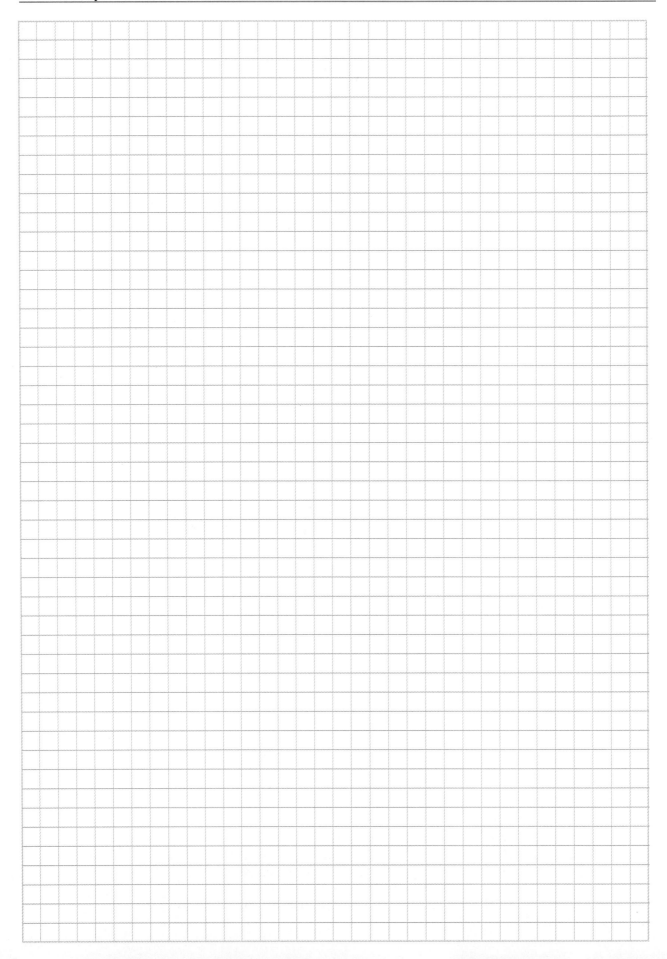

Cellular Respiration and Fermentation

This lab topic gives you another opportunity to practice the scientific process introduced in Lab Topic 1. Before going to lab, review scientific investigation in Lab Topic 1 and carefully read Lab Topic 5. Be prepared to use this information to design an experiment in fermentation or cellular respiration.

Laboratory Objectives

After completing this lab topic, you should be able to:
1. Describe alcoholic fermentation, naming reactants and products.
2. Describe cellular respiration, naming reactants and products.
3. Explain oxidation/reduction reactions in cellular respiration.
4. Name and describe environmental factors that influence enzymatic activity.
5. Explain spectrophotometry and describe how this process can be used to measure aerobic respiration.
6. Propose hypotheses and make predictions based on them.
7. Design and execute an experiment testing factors that influence fermentation or cellular respiration.
8. Practice scientific persuasion and communication by analyzing and interpreting experimental results.

Introduction

You have been investigating cells and their activities in Lab Topics 2–4: enzymatic activities (Lab Topic 2), cellular structure and evolution (Lab Topic 3), and movement across cell membranes (Lab Topic 4). This lab topic and the following one (Photosynthesis, Lab Topic 6) investigate energy transformations in cells. Photosynthesis is the process of transferring the sun's radiant energy to organic molecules, namely, glucose (Figure 5.1). This lab topic investigates **fermentation** and **cellular respiration**, cellular processes that transfer the energy in glucose bonds to bonds in **adenosine triphosphate** (ATP). The energy in ATP can then be used to perform cellular work. Fermentation is an anaerobic (without oxygen) process; cellular respiration is aerobic (utilizing oxygen). *All living organisms, including bacteria, protists, plants, and animals, produce ATP in fermentation or cellular respiration and then use ATP in their metabolism.*

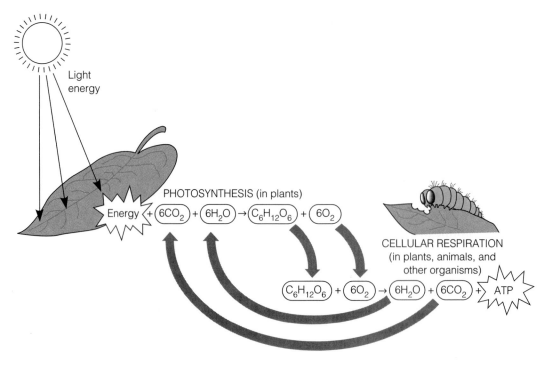

Figure 5.1.
Energy flow through photosynthesis and cellular respiration. Light energy from the sun is transformed to chemical energy in photosynthesis. Carbon dioxide and water are converted to glucose and oxygen. The energy stored in plant organic molecules—glucose, for example—can be utilized by plants or by consumers. The energy in organic molecules is released during cellular respiration in plants, animals, and other organisms.

Fermentation and cellular respiration involve oxidation-reduction reactions (redox reactions). Redox reactions are always defined in terms of electron transfers, oxidation being the *loss* of electrons and reduction the *gain* of electrons. In cellular respiration, two hydrogen atoms are removed from glucose (oxidation) and transferred to a coenzyme called nicotinamide adenine dinucleotide (**NAD$^+$**), reducing this compound to **NADH**. Think of these two hydrogen atoms as 2 electrons and 2 protons. NAD$^+$ is the oxidizing agent that is reduced to NADH by the addition of 2 electrons and one proton. The other proton (H$^+$) is released into the cell solution. NADH transfers electrons to the electron transport chain. The transfer of electrons from one molecule to another releases energy, and this energy can be used to synthesize ATP.

Cellular respiration is a sequence of three metabolic stages: **glycolysis** in the cytoplasm, and the **Krebs cycle** and the **electron transport chain** in mitochondria (Figure 5.2). Fermentation involves glycolysis but does not involve the Krebs cycle and the electron transport chain, which are inhibited at low oxygen levels. Two common types of fermentation are **alcoholic fermentation** and **lactic acid fermentation.** Animals, certain fungi, and some bacteria convert pyruvate produced in glycolysis to lactate. Plants and some fungi, yeast in particular, convert pyruvate to ethanol and carbon dioxide. Cellular respiration is much more efficient than fermentation in producing ATP. Cellular respiration can produce a maximum of 38 ATP molecules; fermentation produces only 2 ATP molecules.

Before you begin today's lab topic, refer to the preceding paragraph and Figure 5.2 as you review major pathways, reactants, and products of fermentation and cellular respiration by answering the following questions:

1. Which processes are anaerobic?

2. Which processes are aerobic?

3. Which processes take place in the cytoplasm of the cell?

4. Which processes take place in mitochondria?

5. What is the initial reactant in cellular respiration?

6. What is (are) the product(s) of the anaerobic processes?

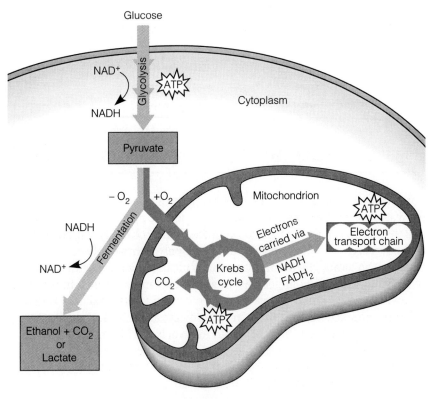

Figure 5.2.
Stages of cellular respiration and fermentation. Cellular respiration consists of glycolysis, the Krebs cycle, and the electron transport chain. Glycolysis is also a stage in fermentation.

7. What is (are) the product(s) of the aerobic processes?

8. Which gives the greater yield of ATP, alcoholic fermentation or cellular respiration?

In this lab topic you will investigate alcoholic fermentation first and then cellular respiration. Working in teams of two to four students, you will first perform two introductory lab studies (Lab Study A of each exercise). Lab Study B in each exercise provides questions and background to help you propose one or more testable hypotheses based on questions from the lab studies or your prior knowledge. Your team will then design and carry out an independent investigation based on your hypotheses, completing your observations and recording your results in this laboratory period. After discussing the results, your team will prepare an oral presentation in which you will persuade the class that your experimental design is sound and that your results support your conclusions. If required to do so by the lab instructor, *each of you* independently will submit Results and Discussion sections describing the results of your experiment (see Appendix A).

 First complete Lab Study A in each exercise. Then discuss possible questions for investigation with your research team. Be certain you can pose an interesting question from which to develop a testable hypothesis. Design and perform the experiment today. Prepare to report your results in oral and/or written form.

EXERCISE 5.1
Alcoholic Fermentation

For centuries, humans have taken advantage of yeast fermentation to produce alcoholic beverages and bread. Consider the products of fermentation and their roles in making these economically and culturally important foods and beverages. Alcoholic fermentation begins with glycolysis, a series of reactions breaking glucose into two molecules of **pyruvate** with a net yield of 2 ATP and 2 NADH molecules. In anaerobic environments, in two steps the pyruvate (a 3-carbon molecule) is converted to ethyl alcohol (ethanol, a 2-carbon molecule) and CO_2. In this process the 2 NADH molecules are oxidized, replenishing the NAD^+ used in glycolysis (Figure 5.2).

Lab Study A. Alcoholic Fermentation in Yeast

Materials

4 respirometers:
   test tubes, 1-mL graduated
   pipettes, aquarium tubing,
   flasks, binder clips
pipette pump
3 5-mL graduated pipettes,
   labeled "DI water," "yeast,"
   and "glucose"

3-inch donut-shaped metal weights
yeast solution
glucose solution
DI water
water bath
wax pencil

Introduction

In this lab study, you will investigate alcoholic fermentation in a yeast (a single-celled fungus), *Saccharomyces cerevisiae,* or "baker's yeast." When oxygen is low, some fungi, including yeast and most plants, switch from cellular respiration to alcoholic fermentation. In bread making, starch in the flour is converted to glucose and fructose, which then serve as the starting compounds for fermentation. The resulting carbon dioxide is trapped in the dough, causing it to rise. Ethanol is also produced in bread making but evaporates during baking.

In this laboratory experiment, the carbon dioxide (CO_2) produced, being a gas, bubbles out of the solution and can be used as an indication of the relative rate of fermentation taking place. Figure 5.3 shows the respirometers you will use to collect CO_2. The rate of fermentation, a series of enzymatic reactions, can be affected by several factors, for example, concentration of yeast, concentration of glucose, or temperature. In this lab study you will

Binder
clip

Aquarium
tubing

Graduated
pipette

Metal weight

Fermentation
solution

Water

Figure 5.3.
Respirometer used for yeast fermentation.

investigate *the effects of yeast concentration.* In your independent study you may choose to investigate other independent variables.

Hypothesis

Hypothesize about the effect of different concentrations of yeast on the rate of fermentation.

Prediction

Predict the results of the experiment based on your hypothesis (if/then).

Procedure

1. Obtain four flasks and add enough tap water to keep them from floating in a water bath (fill to about 5 cm from the top of the flask). Label the flasks 1, 2, 3, and 4. To stabilize the flasks, place a 3-inch donut-shaped metal weight over the neck of the flasks.
2. Obtain four test tubes (fermentation tubes) and label them 1, 2, 3, and 4. Add solutions as in Table 5.1 to the appropriate tubes. Rotate each tube to distribute the yeast evenly in the tube. Place tubes in the corresponding numbered flasks.
3. To each tube, add a 1-mL graduated pipette to which a piece of plastic aquarium tubing has been attached.
4. Place the flasks with the test tubes and graduated pipettes in the water bath at 30°C. Allow them to equilibrate for about 5 minutes.

Table 5.1
Contents of Fermentation Solutions (volumes in mL)

Tube	DI Water	Yeast Suspension	Glucose Solution
1	4	0	3
2	6	1	0
3	3	1	3
4	1	3	3

5. Attach the pipette pump to the free end of the tubing on the first pipette. Use the pipette pump to draw the fermentation solution up into the pipette. Fill it past the calibrated portion of the tube, but do not draw the solution into the tubing. Fold the tubing over and clamp it shut with the binder clip so the solution does not run out. Open the clip slightly, and allow the solution to drain down to the 0-mL calibration line (or slightly below). Quickly do the same for the other three pipettes.

6. In Table 5.2, quickly record your initial readings for each pipette in the "Initial reading" row in each "Actual (A)" column. This will be the *initial* time (I).

7. Two minutes after the initial readings for each pipette, record the actual readings (A) in mL for each pipette in the "Actual (A)" column. Subtract I from A to determine the total amount of CO_2 evolved (A – I). Record this value in the "CO_2 Evolved (A – I)" column. *From now on, you will subtract the initial reading from each actual reading to determine the total amount of CO_2 evolved.*

8. Continue taking readings every 2 minutes for each of the solutions for 20 minutes. Remember, take the actual reading from the pipette and subtract the initial reading to get the total amount of CO_2 evolved in each test tube.

9. Record your results in Table 5.2.

Results

1. Complete Table 5.2.

Table 5.2

Total CO_2 Evolved by Different Concentrations of Yeast. Actual values are the graduated pipette readings. For CO_2 evolved values, subtract the initial reading from the actual reading. This is the amount of CO_2 accumulated over time.

Time (min)	Tube 1		Tube 2		Tube 3		Tube 4	
	Actual (A)	CO_2 Evolved (A – I)	Actual (A)	CO_2 Evolved (A – I)	Actual (A)	CO_2 Evolved (A – I)	Actual (A)	CO_2 Evolved (A – I)
Initial reading (I)								
2								
4								
6								
8								
10								
12								
14								
16								
18								
20								

2. Using Figure 5.4, construct a graph to illustrate your results.

    a. What is (are) the independent variable(s)? Which is the appropriate axis for this variable?

    b. What is the dependent variable? Which is the appropriate axis for this variable?

    c. Choose an appropriate scale and label the *x* and *y* axes.

    d. Should you use a legend? If so, what would this include?

    e. Compose a figure title.

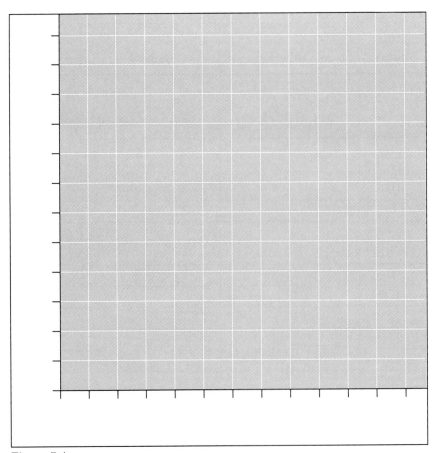

Figure 5.4.

Discussion

1. Explain the experimental design. What is the purpose of each test tube? Which is (are) the control tube(s)?

2. Which test tube had the highest rate of fermentation? Explain why.

3. Which test tube had the lowest rate of fermentation? Explain why.

4. Why were different amounts of water added to each fermentation solution?

Lab Study B. Additional Investigations of Alcoholic Fermentation

Materials

all materials from Lab Study A
beakers
graduated pipettes of various sizes
different substrates: sucrose, saccharin, Nutrasweet™, fructose, starch,
    glycogen, honey, corn syrup, pyruvate
different types of yeast: dry active, quick rise, Pasteur champagne (for
    wine making)
various fermentation inhibitors: sodium fluoride, ethyl alcohol
various salt solutions
various pH buffers
spices: ground cinnamon, cloves, caraway, ginger, cardamom, nutmeg,
    mace, thyme, dry mustard, chili powder
disposable gloves
additional glassware

Introduction

If your team chooses to study alcoholic fermentation for your independent investigation and report, design a simple experiment to investigate some factor that affects alcoholic fermentation. Use the available materials or ask your instructor about the availability of additional materials.

Procedure

1. Collaborating with your research team, read the following potential questions, and choose a question to investigate using this list or an idea from your prior knowledge. You may want to check your text and other sources for supporting information. You should be able to explain the rationale behind your choice of question. For example, if you choose to investigate *starch* as a substrate, you should be able to explain that the yeast must first digest starch before the glucose can be used in alcoholic fermentation and the impact this might have on the experiment.

    a. Would other substrates be as effective as glucose in alcoholic fermentation? Possible substrates:

      sucrose (table sugar—glucose and fructose disaccharide)

      honey (mainly glucose and fructose)

      corn syrup (fructose and sucrose)

      starch (glucose polymer in plants)

      saccharin

      fructose

      pyruvate

    b. Would fermentation rates change with different types of yeasts?

    c. What environmental conditions are optimum for alcoholic fermentation?

      What temperature ranges?

      What pH ranges?

    d. What is the maximum amount of ethyl alcohol that can be tolerated by yeast cells?

 If you select toxins or fermentation inhibitors for your investigation, ask the instructor about safety procedures. Post safety precautions and follow safety protocol, including wearing gloves and protective eyewear. Notify the instructor of any spills.

    e. Sodium fluoride, commonly used to prevent tooth decay, inhibits an enzyme in glycolysis. At what concentration is it most effective?

    f. Would adding $MgSO_4$ enhance glycolysis? $MgSO_4$ provides Mg^{++}, a cofactor necessary to activate some enzymes in glycolysis.

    g. Does a high concentration of sucrose inhibit fermentation?

    h. An old German baker's wisdom says, "A pinch of ginger will make your yeast work better." Some spices enhance yeast activity while others inhibit it (Corriher, 1997). What effect do spices have on yeast activity? Try ginger, ground cardamom, caraway, cinnamon, mace, nutmeg, thyme, dry mustard, or others.

    i. Salt is often used as a food preservative to prevent bacterial and fungal growth (for example, in country ham). But salt is also important to enhance the flavor of bread when added in small amounts. At what concentration does salt begin to inhibit yeast fermentation?

2. Design your experiment, proposing hypotheses, making predictions, and determining procedures as instructed in Exercise 5.3.

EXERCISE 5.2
Cellular Respiration

Most organisms produce ATP using cellular respiration, a process that involves glycolysis, the Krebs cycle, and the electron transport chain. In cellular respiration, many more ATP molecules are produced than were produced in alcoholic fermentation (potentially 38 compared to 2), and water, unlike ethanol, is not toxic to the cells. After the series of reactions in the cytoplasm (glycolysis), pyruvate enters the mitochondria, where enzymes for the Krebs cycle and the electron transport chain are located. The Krebs cycle is a series of eight steps, each catalyzed by a specific enzyme. As one compound is converted to another, CO_2 is given off and hydrogen ions and electrons are removed. The electrons and hydrogen ions are passed to NAD^+ and another electron carrier, FAD (flavin adenine dinucleotide). NADH and $FADH_2$ carry the electrons to the electron transport chain, where the electrons pass along the chain to the final electron acceptor, oxygen. In the process, ATP molecules are produced (Figure 5.2).

Lab Study A. Oxidation-Reduction Reactions in a Mitochondrial Suspension

Materials

mitochondrial suspension
succinate
buffer
DPIP solution
1-mL graduated pipette
pipette pump

4 cuvettes or small test tubes
Parafilm® squares
Kimwipes®
spectrophotometer
wax pencil

Introduction

In this lab study, you will investigate cellular respiration in isolated mitochondria. Your instructor has prepared a mitochondrial suspension from pulverized lima beans. The suspension has been kept on ice to prevent enzyme degradation, and the Krebs cycle will continue in the mitochondria as in intact cells. Sucrose has been added to the mitochondrial suspension as a source of glucose for respiration.

One step in the Krebs cycle is the enzyme-catalyzed conversion of succinate to fumarate in a redox reaction. In intact cells, succinate loses hydrogen ions and electrons to FAD, and, in the process, fumarate is formed (Figure 5.5).

We will utilize this step in the Krebs cycle to study the rate of cellular respiration under different conditions. To perform this study, we will add a substance called DPIP (di-chlorophenol-indophenol), an electron acceptor that

Figure 5.5.
At one point in the Krebs cycle,
succinate is converted to fumarate.
Hydrogens from succinate pass to
FAD, reducing it to $FADH_2$.

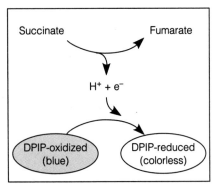

Figure 5.6.
DPIP intercepts the hydrogen
ions and electrons as succinate
is converted to fumarate. DPIP
changes from blue to colorless.

intercepts the hydrogen ions and electrons released from succinate, changing the DPIP from an oxidized to a reduced state. DPIP is *blue* in its oxidized state but changes from blue to *colorless* as it is reduced (Figure 5.6).

We can use this color change to measure the respiration rate. To do this, however, we must have some quantitative means of measuring color change. An instrument called a **spectrophotometer** will allow us to do this. A spectrophotometer measures the amount of light absorbed by a pigment. In the spectrophotometer, a specific wavelength of light (chosen by the operator) passes through the pigment solution being tested—in this case, the blue DPIP. The spectrophotometer then measures the proportion of light *transmitted* or, conversely, *absorbed* by the DPIP and shows a reading on a calibrated scale. As the DPIP changes from blue to clear, it will absorb less light and more light will pass through (be transmitted through) the solution. The change in transmittance will be read by the spectrophotometer. As more light passes through the solution, the transmittance reading goes up. As aerobic respiration takes place, what should happen to the percent transmittance of light through the DPIP?

Our experiment will involve using succinate as the substrate and investigating the effect that *changing the amount of succinate will have on the cellular respiration rate*.

Hypothesis

Hypothesize about the effect of an increased amount of substrate on the rate of cellular respiration.

Prediction

Predict the results of the experiment based on your hypothesis (if/then).

Procedure

1. Prepare the spectrophotometer.

    The instructions that follow are for a Bausch & Lomb Spectronic 20 (Figure 5.7). Turn on the machine (power switch C) at least 5 minutes before beginning.

    a. Using the wavelength control knob (A), select the wavelength: 600 nm. Your instructor has previously determined that this wavelength is absorbed by DPIP.

    b. Zero the instrument by adjusting the control knob (the same as power switch C) so that the meter needle reads 0% transmittance. There should be no cuvette in the instrument, and the sample holder cover must be closed. Once it is set, do not change this setting.

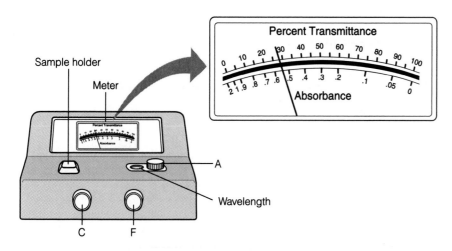

Figure 5.7.
The Bausch & Lomb Spectronic 20.
A spectrophotometer measures the proportion of light of different wavelengths absorbed and transmitted by a pigment solution. Inside the spectrophotometer, light is separated into its component wavelengths and passed through a sample. Transmittance or absorbance can be read on a calibrated scale.

2. Obtain four cuvettes and label them B, 1, 2, and 3. The B will be the blank.

3. Prepare the blank first by measuring 4.6 mL buffer, 0.3 mL mitochondrial suspension, and 0.1 mL succinate into the B cuvette. Cover the cuvette tightly with Parafilm and invert it to mix the reactants thoroughly.

4. Calibrate the spectrophotometer as follows: Wipe cuvette B with a Kimwipe and insert it into the sample holder. Be sure you align the etched mark on the cuvette with the line on the sample holder. Close the cover. Adjust the light control (F) until the meter reads 100% transmittance, or 0 absorption. Remove cuvette B. You are now ready to prepare the experimental cuvettes. The blank corrects for differences in transmittance due to the mitochondrial solution.

5. Measure the buffer, DPIP, and mitochondrial suspension into cuvettes 1, 2, and 3 as specified in Table 5.3.
    Do not add the succinate yet!

Table 5.3
Contents of Experimental Tubes (volumes in mL)

Tube	Buffer	DPIP	Mitochondrial Suspension	Succinate (add last)
1	4.4	0.3	0.3	0
2	4.3	0.3	0.3	0.1
3	4.2	0.3	0.3	0.2

6. Perform the next two steps as *quickly* as possible. First, add the succinate to each cuvette.

7. Cover tube 1 with Parafilm, wipe it with a Kimwipe, insert it into the sample holder, and record the percent transmittance in Table 5.4 in the Results section. Repeat this step for tubes 2 and 3.

 If the initial reading is higher than 30%, tell your instructor immediately. You may need to add another drop of DPIP to each tube and repeat step 7. The reading must be low enough (the solution dark enough) to give readings for 20–30 minutes. If the solution is too light (the transmittance is above 30%), the reactions will go to completion too quickly to detect differences in the tubes.

8. Before each reading, insert the blank, cuvette B, into the sample holder. Adjust to 100% transmittance if necessary.

9. Continue to take readings at 5-minute intervals for 20–30 minutes. *Each time, before you take a reading, cover the tube with Parafilm and invert it to mix the contents.* Record the results in Table 5.4.

Results

1. Complete Table 5.4. Compose a title for the table.

Table 5.4

	Time (min)						
Tube	0	5	10	15	20	25	30
1							
2							
3							

2. Using Figure 5.8, construct a graph to illustrate your results.

   a. What is (are) the independent variable(s)? Which is the appropriate axis for this variable?

   b. What is the dependent variable? Which is the appropriate axis for this variable?

   c. Choose an appropriate scale and label the *x* and *y* axes.

   d. Should you use a legend? If so, what would this include?

   e. Compose a figure title.

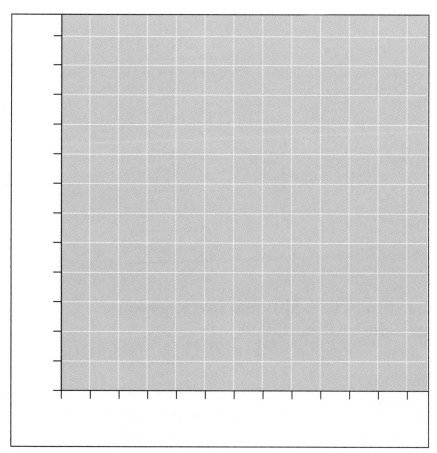

Figure 5.8.

Discussion

1. Explain the experimental design. What is the role of each of the components of the experimental mixtures?

2. Which experimental tube is the control?

3. In which experimental tube did transmittance increase more rapidly? Explain.

4. Why should the succinate be added to the reaction tubes last?

5. Was your hypothesis falsified or supported by the results? Use your data to support your answer.

6. What are some other independent variables that could be investigated using this technique?

Lab Study B. Additional Investigations in Cellular Respiration

Materials

all materials from Lab Study A
additional substrates: glucose, fructose, maltose, artificial sweeteners, starch, glycogen
inhibitors: rotenone, oligomycin, malonate, antimycin A
different pH buffers
ice bath
water bath
disposable gloves

Introduction

If your team chooses to study cellular respiration for your independent investigation and report, design a simple experiment to investigate some factor that affects cellular respiration. Use the available materials, or ask your instructor about the availability of additional materials.

 If you select toxins or respiratory inhibitors for your investigation, ask the instructor about safety procedures. Post safety precautions and follow safety protocol, including wearing gloves and protective eyewear. Notify the instructor of any spills.

Procedure

1. Collaborating with your research team, read the following potential questions, and choose a question to investigate using this list or an idea from your prior knowledge. You may want to check your text and other sources for supporting information.

   a. Would other substrates be as effective as glucose in cellular respiration? Possible substrates:

   sucrose (table sugar—glucose and fructose disaccharide)

   starch (glucose polymer in plants)

   saccharin, Nutrasweet™, or other artificial sweeteners

   fructose

   b. What environmental conditions are optimum for cellular respiration?

   What temperature ranges?

   What pH ranges?

   c. What inhibitors of cellular respiration are most effective? Consider the following list:

   Rotenone, an insecticide, inhibits electron flow in the electron transport chain.

   Oligomycin, an antibiotic, inhibits ATP synthesis.

   Malonate blocks the conversion of succinate to malate. How would you determine if this is competitive or noncompetitive inhibition?

   Antimycin A is an antibiotic that inhibits the transfer of electrons to oxygen.

2. Design your experiment, proposing hypotheses, making predictions, and determining procedures as instructed in Exercise 5.3.

EXERCISE 5.3
Designing and Performing Your Independent Investigation

Materials

See each Lab Study B materials list in Exercises 5.1 and 5.2.

Introduction

Now that you have completed both introductory investigations, your research team should decide if you will investigate fermentation or cellular respiration. Use Lab Topic 1 as a reference for designing and performing a scientific investigation. Be ready to assign tasks to members of your lab team. Be sure that everyone understands the techniques that will be used. Your experiment will be successful only if you plan carefully, cooperate with your team members, perform lab techniques accurately and systematically, and record and report data accurately.

Procedure

1. **Decide on one or more questions to investigate**. (Refer to Lab Topic 1, Exercise 1.1, Lab Study A. Asking Questions.)
   Question:

2. **Formulate a testable hypothesis**. (Refer to Exercise 1.1, Lab Study B. Developing Hypotheses.)
   Hypothesis:

3. **Summarize the experiment**. (Use separate paper.)

4. **Predict the results of your experiment based on your hypothesis**. (Refer to Lab Topic 1, Exercise 1.2, Lab Study C. Making Predictions.)
   Prediction: (If/then)

5. **Outline the procedures used in the experiment**. (Refer to Exercise 1.2, Lab Study B. Choosing or Designing the Procedure.)
   a. On a separate sheet of paper, list each step in your procedure in numerical order.
   b. Remember to include the number of repetitions (usually a minimum of five), levels of treatment, appropriate time intervals, and controls for each procedure.

c. If you have an idea for an experiment that requires materials other than those provided, ask your laboratory instructor about their availability. If possible, additional supplies will be made available.

d. When carrying out an experiment, remember to quantify your measurements when possible.

6. **Perform the experiment**, making observations and collecting data for analysis.

 If your experiment involves the use of toxins or respiration inhibitors, use them only in liquid form as provided by the instructor. Wear protective gloves and eyewear. Ask your instructor about proper disposal procedures. If a spill occurs, notify your instructor immediately for proper cleanup.

7. **Record observations and data** on a separate sheet of paper. Design tables and graphs, at least one of each. Be thorough when collecting data. Do not just write down numbers, but record what they mean as well. Do not rely on your memory for information that you will need when reporting your results.

8. **Prepare your discussion.** Discuss your results in light of your hypothesis.

a. Review your hypothesis. Review your results (tables and graphs). Do your results support or falsify your hypothesis? Explain your answer, using your data for support.

b. Review your prediction. Did your results correspond to the prediction you made? If not, explain how your results are different from your predictions, and why this might have occurred.

c. If you had problems with the procedure or questionable results, explain how they might have influenced your conclusion.

d. If you had an opportunity to repeat and expand this experiment to make your results more convincing, what would you do?

e. Summarize the conclusion you have drawn from your results.

9. **Be prepared to report your results to the class.** Prepare to persuade your fellow scientists that your experimental design is sound and that your results support your conclusions.

10. If your instructor requires it, **submit Results and Discussion sections** of a scientific paper (see Appendix A). Keep in mind that although you have performed the experiments as a team, you must turn in a lab report of *your original writing*. Your tables and figures may be similar to those of your team members, but your Results and Discussion sections must be the product of your own literature search and creative thinking.

Questions for Review

1. Having completed this lab topic, you should be able to define, describe, and use the following terms: *aerobic, anaerobic, substrate, reactants, products, spectrophotometer, respirometer, NAD$^+$, NADH, FAD, FADH$_2$, ATP.*

2. State the beginning reactants and the end products of glycolysis, alcoholic fermentation, the Krebs cycle, and the electron transport chain. Describe where these processes take place in the cell and the conditions under which they operate (aerobic or anaerobic).

glycolysis:

alcoholic fermentation:

Krebs cycle:

electron transport chain:

3. Suppose you do another experiment using DPIP to study cellular respiration in isolated mitochondria, and the results using the spectrophotometer show a final percent transmittance reading of 42% in tube 1 and 78% in tube 2. Both tubes had an initial reading of 30%. In which tube did the greater amount of cellular respiration occur? Explain your answer in terms of the changes that take place in DPIP.

4. How do you know that the electrons causing the change in color of DPIP are involved in the succinate–fumarate step?

Applying Your Knowledge

1. Your mother has been making yeast bread all afternoon, and she has just put two loaves in the oven. You open the oven door to see what is baking. Your mother yells, "Don't slam the door!" Why?

2. Two characteristics of natural wines are that they have a maximum alcohol content of 14% and are "sparkling" wines. Apply your understanding of alcoholic fermentation to explain these characteristics.

3. In the spring of 2001, more than 500 stillbirths and deaths of newborn foals were reported for Kentucky thoroughbred horses. Veterinarians and scientists investigating the cause of these deaths discovered that these foals tested positive for cyanide. Scientists uncovered an ecological web beginning with black cherry trees that concentrate cyanide in their leaves. These were eaten by abundant tent caterpillars, which in turn fell to the ground or defecated, thus contaminating the pastures and water sources. Pregnant mares ingested large quantities of cyanide in grass and water. News reports erroneously claimed that cyanide blocked oxygen delivery. However, cyanide is a respiratory inhibitor that combines with a cytochrome (not oxygen) in the electron transport chain. What would be the result of blocking the terminal cytochrome in the electron transport chain?

4. Skunk cabbage is a plant that is able to generate heat and regulate its body temperature, like a warm-blooded animal. Botanists have suggested that the ability to produce heat is important in these plants because it provides a warm environment for pollinators. The heat may also help to dissipate the carrion-like scent produced by some skunk cabbage flowers. Clearly, these plants must have a high respiratory rate to produce temperatures as high as 37°C. How could you determine if the temperature is the result of cellular respiration? What features of the plant surface and cell structure might be present if respiration is actively occurring in the flowers?

References

Campbell, N. and J. Reece. *Biology,* 6th ed. San Francisco, CA: Benjamin/Cummings, 2002.

Corriher, S. O. *Cookwise: The Hows and Whys of Successful Cooking.* New York: William Morrow, 1997.

Lehninger, A. L., D. L. Nelson, and M. M. Cox. *Principles of Biochemistry,* 3rd ed. New York: Worth Publishers, 2000.

Seymour, R. S. "Plants That Warm Themselves." *Scientific American,* 1997, vol. 276, pp. 104–107.

Some procedures and many ideas in this lab topic were based on an exercise written by Jean Dickey, published in J. Dickey, *Laboratory Investigations for Biology*. Menlo Park, CA: Addison Wesley Longman, 1995.

The procedure used to assay mitochondrial activity was based on a procedure from "Succinic Acid Dehydrogenase Activity of Plant Mitochondria," in F. Witham, D. Blaydes, and R. Devlin, *Exercises in Plant Physiology*. Boston, MA: Prindle, Weber & Schmidt, 1971.

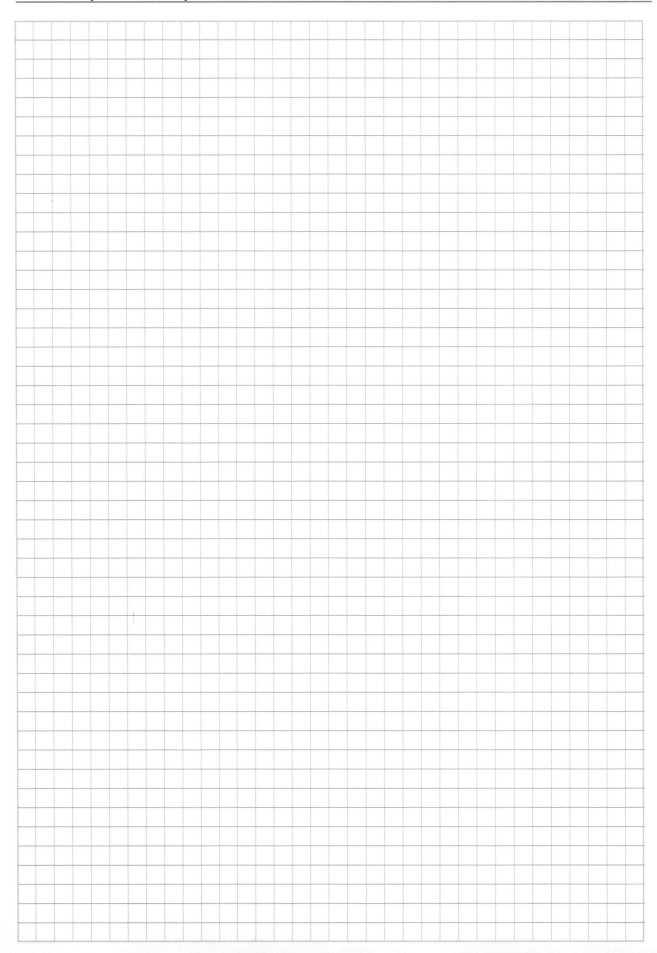

Photosynthesis

Laboratory Objectives

After completing this lab topic, you should be able to:

1. Describe the roles played by light and pigment in photosynthesis.
2. Name and describe pigments found in photosynthesizing tissues.
3. Explain the separation of pigments by paper chromatography, based on their molecular structure.
4. Demonstrate an understanding of the process of spectrophotometry and the procedure for using the spectrophotometer.

Introduction

Without photosynthesis, there could be no life on Earth as we know it. The Earth is an open system constantly requiring an input of energy to drive the processes of life. All energy entering the biosphere is channeled from the sun into organic molecules via the process of photosynthesis. As the sun's hydrogen is converted to helium, energy in the form of photons is produced. These photons pass to Earth's surface and are absorbed by pigments in the chloroplasts of plants, initiating the process of photosynthesis.

Photosynthesis ultimately produces glucose and oxygen from carbon dioxide and water. Glucose, a primary source of energy for all cells, may be converted to sucrose and transported or stored in the polymer starch. These organic molecules are building blocks for plant growth and development. Animals consume plants and convert the plant molecules into their own organic molecules and energy sources—the ultimate in recycling. Oxygen, also produced by photosynthesis, is necessary for aerobic respiration in the cells of plants, animals, and other organisms (Figure 6.1).

In this laboratory, you will investigate cellular and environmental components utilized in the process of photosynthesis. In several experiments, you will determine photosynthetic activity by testing for the production of starch, using iodine potassium iodide (I_2KI), which stains starch purple-black. A change from the yellow-amber color of the iodine solution to a purple-black solution is a positive test for the presence of starch.

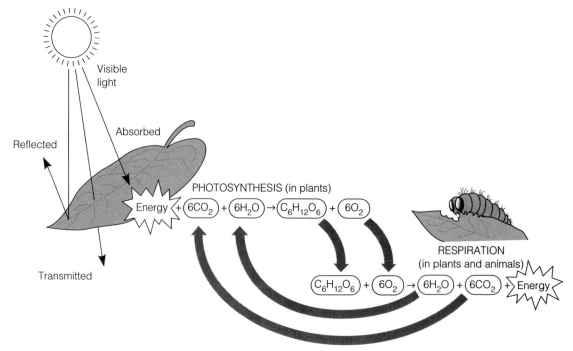

Figure 6.1.
Energy flow through plants and animals. Energy flows from the sun into the biological systems of Earth, and visible light is reflected, transmitted, or absorbed. Plants absorb light energy and convert it to chemical energy during photosynthesis. In this process, carbon dioxide and water are converted to oxygen and glucose and ultimately to other organic molecules. These organic molecules and the energy stored in them can be utilized by animals and other organisms that consume them. The energy in organic molecules is released during cellular respiration in plants and animals.

EXERCISE 6.1
The Wavelengths of Light for Photosynthesis

Materials

black construction paper
green, red, and blue plastic filters
paper clips
forceps
1 geranium plant with at least 4 good leaves per 8 students
1 1,000-mL beaker filled with 300 mL of water
1 400-mL beaker filled with 200 mL of 80% ethyl alcohol
dropper bottle with concentrated I_2KI solution

hot plate
petri dish
squirt bottle of water
scissors

Introduction

In this exercise, you will determine if products of photosynthesis are present in leaf tissue that has been exposed to different wavelengths of light for several days. Working with other students in groups of eight, you will cover small portions of different leaves of a geranium plant with pieces of black paper and green, red, and blue plastic filters. Each pair of students will be responsible for one of the four treatments. Later you will determine photosynthetic activity by testing for the presence of starch under the paper or filters.

What wavelength of light will be reflected and transmitted by the black paper and the colored filters? (Check wavelengths in Color Plate 9, which shows the electromagnetic spectrum.) Note that the same wavelengths of light are reflected and transmitted by the filters.

Hypothesis

Hypothesize about photosynthetic activity in cells treated as described.

Prediction

Predict the results of the experiment based on your hypothesis (if/then).

Procedure

1. Four to five days before the experiment is to be carried out, cut a piece from each color of plastic filter and one from the black construction paper. Each piece should be a rectangle approximately 2.5 cm by 5 cm. Double over the strip and slide the edge of a healthy geranium leaf, still attached to the plant, between the folded edges. Carefully slip a slightly sprung paper clip over the paper, securing the paper to the leaf. The paper should be on both sides of the leaf. Follow this procedure with the other colors and the black construction paper, using a different leaf for each strip. Return the plant with treated leaves to bright light. Your instructor may have already carried out this step for you.

2. On the day of the lab, carry the plant with leaves covered to your desk. You will have to be able to recognize each leaf after the paper is removed and the leaf is boiled. To facilitate this, with your teammates devise a way to distinguish each leaf, and write the distinction in the space provided. Differences in size or shape may distinguish different leaves, but it may be necessary to introduce distinguishing features, such as by cutting the petioles to different lengths or cutting out small notches in a

portion of the leaf not covered by the paper. Record below the distinguishing differences for each treatment.

black paper:

green filter:

red filter:

blue filter:

3. After you have distinguished each leaf, sketch the leaf in the Results section, showing the position of the paper or filter on the leaf.

4. Set up the boiling alcohol bath. Place a 1,000-mL beaker containing 300 mL of water on the hot plate. Carefully place the 400-mL beaker containing 200 mL of 80% ethyl alcohol into the larger beaker of water. Turn on the hot plate and bring the nested beakers to a boil. Adjust the temperature to maintain slow boiling. Do not place the beaker of alcohol directly on the hot plate.

 Ethyl alcohol is highly flammable! Do not place the beaker of alcohol directly on the hot plate. To bring it to a boil, raise the temperature of the hot plate until the alcohol just boils, and then reduce the temperature to maintain slow boiling. Do not leave boiling alcohol unattended.

5. Remove the paper and filters from each leaf; using forceps, carefully drop all the leaves into the boiling alcohol solution to extract the pigments. Save the plastic filters.

6. When the leaves are almost white, use forceps to remove them from the alcohol. Place them in separate petri dishes, rinse with distilled water, and add enough distilled water to each dish to just cover the leaf. Turn off the hot plate if all teams have completed boiling leaves for this exercise (and Exercise 6.2).

7. Add drops of I_2KI solution to the water until a pale amber color is obtained. I_2KI reacts with starch to produce a purple-black color.

8. Wait about 5 minutes and sketch each leaf in the Results section, showing which areas of the leaf tested positive for starch.

Results

1. Sketch and label each leaf before boiling, showing the location of the paper or filter.

2. Sketch and label each leaf after staining to show the location of the stain.

Discussion

1. Which treatment allowed the greatest photosynthetic activity? (Explain your results in terms of your hypothesis.)

2. When the red filter is placed on a leaf, what wavelengths of light pass through and reach the leaf cells below? (Check wavelengths in Color Plate 9, which shows the electromagnetic spectrum.)

   Green filter?

   Blue filter?

3. Was starch present under the black construction paper? Explain this in light of the fact that black absorbs all wavelengths of light.

EXERCISE 6.2
Pigments in Photosynthesis

Materials

Coleus plant with multicolored leaves
forceps
1 1,000-mL beaker filled with 300 mL of water
1 400-mL beaker filled with 200 mL of 80% ethyl alcohol
dropper bottle with concentrated I_2KI solution
hot plate
squirt bottle of water

Introduction

A variety of pigments are found in plants, as anyone who visits a botanical garden in spring or a deciduous forest in autumn well knows. A pigment is a substance that absorbs light. If a pigment absorbs all wavelengths of visible light, it appears black. The black construction paper used in Exercise 6.1 is colored with such a pigment. Other pigments absorb some wavelengths and reflect others. Yellow pigments, for example, reflect light wavelengths in the yellow portion of the visible light spectrum, green reflects in the green portion, and so on.

Some colors are produced by only one pigment, but an even greater diversity of colors can be produced by the cumulative effects of different pigments in cells. Green colors in plants are produced by the presence of chlorophylls *a* and *b* located in the chloroplasts. Yellow, orange, and bright red colors are produced by carotenoids, also in chloroplasts. Blues, violets, purples, pinks, and dark reds are usually produced by a group of water-soluble pigments, the anthocyanins, that are located in cell vacuoles and do not contribute to photosynthesis. Additional colors may be produced by mixtures of these pigments in cells.

Working with one other student, you will use the I_2KI test for starch as in Exercise 6.1 to determine which pigment(s) in a *Coleus* leaf support photosynthesis. Before beginning the experiment, examine your *Coleus* leaf and hypothesize about the location of photosynthesis based on the leaf colors. (See Color Plate 10.)

Hypothesis

Hypothesize about the location of photosynthesis based on the leaf colors.

Prediction

Predict the results of the experiment based on your hypothesis (if/then).

Procedure

1. Remove a multicolored leaf from a *Coleus* plant that has been in strong light for several hours.
2. In Table 6.1, list the colors of your leaf, predict the pigments present to create that color, and predict the results of the I_2KI starch test in each area of the leaf.
3. Sketch the leaf outline in the Results section, mapping the color distribution before the I_2KI test.
4. Extract the pigments as previously described in Exercise 6.1, and test the leaf for photosynthetic activity using I_2KI.

 Ethyl alcohol is highly flammable! Do not place the beaker of alcohol directly on the hot plate. To bring it to a boil, raise the temperature of the hot plate until the alcohol just boils, and then reduce the temperature to maintain slow boiling. Do not leave boiling alcohol unattended.

---

5. Sketch the leaf again in the Results section, outlining the areas showing a positive starch test.

Results

1. Record the results of the I_2KI test in Table 6.1.
2. Compare the sketches of the *Coleus* leaf before and after the I_2KI test.

   Before I₂KI Test: **After I₂KI Test:**

3. Which pigments supported photosynthesis? Record your results in Table 6.1.

Discussion

Describe and explain your results based on your hypothesis.

Table 6.1
Predicted and Observed Results for the Presence of
Starch in Colored Regions of the *Coleus* Leaf

Color	Pigments	Starch Present (predicted) + or −	Starch Present (actual results) + or −
Green			
Purple			
Pink			
White			
Other			

EXERCISE 6.3

Separation and Identification of Plant Pigments by Paper Chromatography

Materials

capillary tube   forceps
beakers   scissors
extractions of leaf pigments   acetone
    in acetone
chromatography paper stapled into a cylinder marked with a pencil line
    about 1 cm from one end
quart jar with lid, containing solvent of petroleum ether and acetone

Introduction

Your instructor has prepared an extract of chloroplast pigments from fresh green grass or fresh spinach. A blender was used to rupture the cells, and the pigments were then extracted with acetone, an organic solvent. Working with one other student, begin this exercise by separating the pigments extracted using paper chromatography. To do this, you will apply the pigment extract to a cylinder of chromatographic paper. You will then place the cylinder in a jar with the organic solvents petroleum ether and acetone. The solvents will move up the paper and carry the pigments along; the pigments will move at different rates, depending on their different solubilities in the solvents used and the degree of attraction to the paper. The leading edge of the solvent is called the **front.** Discrete pigment bands will be formed from the front back to the point where pigments were added to the paper.

The following information will be helpful to you as you make predictions and interpret results:

1. **Polar molecules** or substances dissolve (or are attracted to) polar molecules.
2. **Nonpolar molecules** are attracted to nonpolar molecules to varying degrees.
3. Chromatography paper (cellulose) is a polar (charged) substance.
4. The solvent, made of petroleum ether and acetone, is relatively nonpolar.
5. The *most nonpolar* substance will dissolve in the nonpolar solvent *first*.
6. The *most polar* substance will be attracted to the polar chromatography paper; therefore, it will move *last*.

a. Chlorophyll *a*

b. Chlorophyll *b*

c. Beta carotene

d. Xanthophyll

Figure 6.2.
Molecular structure of major leaf pigments. The molecular structure of chlorophyll *a*, chlorophyll *b*, carotene, and xanthophyll. To determine polarity, count the number of polar oxygens present in each molecule.

Use this information and the molecular structure of major leaf pigments to predict the relative solubilities and separation patterns for the pigments and to identify the pigment bands. Study the molecular structure of the four common plant pigments in Figure 6.2. As you study these diagrams, rank the pigments according to polarity in the space provided.

Most polar:

Least polar:

Hypothesis

State a hypothesis relating polarities and solubilities of pigments.

Prediction

Predict the results of the experiment based on your hypothesis (if/then).

Procedure

1. Using a capillary tube, streak the leaf pigment extract on a pencil line previously drawn 1 cm from the edge of the paper cylinder. Allow the chlorophyll to dry. Repeat this step three or four times, allowing the extract to air-dry each time. You should have a band of green pigments along the pencil line. The darker your band of pigments, the better the results of your experiment will be.

 Perform the next step in a hood or in a well-ventilated room. Do not inhale the fumes of the solvent. *NO SPARKS!* Acetone and petroleum ether are extremely flammable. Avoid contact with all solutions. Wash hands with soap and water. If a spill occurs, notify the instructor. If an instructor is not available, do not attempt to clean up. Leave the room.

- Cylinder of chromatography paper
- Front as solvent moves
- Pigments loaded on pencil line
- Solvent

Figure 6.3.
Paper chromatography of photosynthetic pigments. Add the pigment solution to the paper cylinder along the pencil line. Then carefully place the cylinder into a jar containing a small amount of solvent. Close the lid and watch the pigments separate according to their molecular structures and solubilities.

2. Obtain the jar containing the petroleum ether and acetone solvent. Using forceps, carefully lower the loaded paper cylinder into the solvent, and quickly cover the jar tightly with the lid (Figure 6.3). *Avoid inhaling the solvent.* The jar should now contain a saturated atmosphere of the solvent. Allow the chromatography to proceed until the solvent front has reached to within 3 cm of the top of the cylinder.

3. Remove the cylinder from the jar, allow it to dry, and remove the staples.

4. Save your paper with the separated pigments for the next exercise.

Results

Sketch the chromatography paper. Label the color of the various bands. The front, or leading edge of the paper, should be at the top. The pencil line where pigment was added originally should be at the bottom.

Discussion

Based on your hypothesis and predictions, identify the various pigment bands. *The entire class should come to a consensus about the identifications.* Label your drawing in the Results section above, indicating the correct identification of the pigment bands.

EXERCISE 6.4

Determining the Absorption Spectrum for Leaf Pigments

Materials

spectrophotometer
Kimwipes®
2 cuvettes
20-mL beakers to elute pigments

1 150-mL beaker to hold cuvettes
acetone
cork stoppers for cuvettes

Introduction

In Exercise 6.1, you applied colored plastic filters and black paper to leaves to determine which wavelengths of light would support photosynthesis. Review your conclusions from that exercise and from Exercise 6.2 about pigments used in photosynthesis. Which pigments did you conclude support photosynthesis?

In Exercise 6.4, you will work in teams of four or five students, carrying your investigation a step further by plotting the absorption spectrum of leaf pigments separated by paper chromatography. The **absorption spectrum** is the absorption pattern for a particular pigment, showing relative absorbance at different wavelengths of light. For example, we know that chlorophyll *a* is a green pigment, and we know that it reflects or transmits green wavelengths of light. We do not know, however, the relative proportions of wavelengths of light absorbed by chlorophyll *a*. This information is of interest because it suggests that those wavelengths showing greatest absorbance are important in photosynthesis.

The absorption spectrum can be determined with an instrument called a **spectrophotometer,** or **colorimeter.** A spectrophotometer measures the proportions of light of different wavelengths (colors) absorbed and transmitted by a pigment solution. It does this by passing a beam of light of a particular wavelength (designated by the operator) through the pigment solution being tested. The spectrophotometer then measures the proportion of light transmitted or, conversely, absorbed by that particular pigment and shows the reading on the calibrated scale.

Before measuring the absorption spectrum of the four pigments separated by paper chromatography, consult the diagram of the electromagnetic spectrum (Color Plate 9), and predict the wavelengths of light at which absorption will be greatest for each pigment. Record your predictions in Table 6.2.

Table 6.2
Predicted Wavelengths of Greatest Absorption
for the Photosynthetic Pigments

Pigment	Wavelengths of Greatest Absorption (predicted)
1. Chlorophyll *a*	
2. Chlorophyll *b*	
3. Carotene	
4. Xanthophyll	

Hypothesis

State a hypothesis that describes the general relationship of each of the pigments to the color of light that it absorbs.

Prediction

Predict the results based on your hypothesis (if/then).

Procedure

1. Cut out the pigments you separated by paper chromatography, and distribute the paper strips as follows:

   Team 1: carotene

   Team 2: xanthophyll

   Team 3: chlorophyll *a*

   Team 4: chlorophyll *b*

   Teams 5 and 6: will determine the absorption spectrum of the total pigment solution

---

 Perform the next three steps in a hood or in a well-ventilated room. Do not inhale the fumes of the solvent. *NO SPARKS!* Acetone is extremely flammable. Avoid contact with all solutions. If a spill occurs, notify the instructor. Wash hands with soap and water.

---

2. *Teams 1 to 4.* Dilute the pigments as follows: Cut up the chromatography paper with your assigned pigment into a small (20-mL) beaker. Add 10 mL of acetone to the beaker and swirl. This solution containing a single pigment will be your solution B, to be used to determine the absorption spectrum for that pigment. Your reference material will be acetone with no pigments, solution A.

3. *Teams 5 and 6.* Add drops of the original chlorophyll extract solution (acetone pigment mixture) to 10 mL of acetone until it looks pale green. This will be your pigment solution for cuvette B. Your reference material will be acetone with no pigment. This will be in cuvette A.

4. Each team should fill two cuvettes two-thirds full, one (B) with the pigment solution, the other (A) with the reference material (acetone only). Wipe both cuvettes with a Kimwipe to remove fingerprints, and handle cuvettes only with Kimwipes as you proceed.

   What is the purpose of the cuvette with reference material only?

5. Measure the absorption spectrum. Record your measurements in Table 6.3. The instructions that follow are for a Bausch & Lomb Spectronic 20 (Figure 6.4). Turn on the machine (power switch C) for at least 5 minutes before beginning.

   a. *Select the beginning wavelength* using the wavelength control knob (A). Begin measurements at 400 nanometers (nm).

   b. *Zero the instrument* by adjusting the 0 control knob (same as the power switch C) so that the meter needle reads 0% transmittance. There should be no cuvette in the instrument, and the sample holder cover must be closed.

Figure 6.4.

The Bausch & Lomb Spectronic 20.
A spectrophotometer measures the proportion of light of different wavelengths absorbed and transmitted by a pigment solution. Inside the spectrophotometer, light is separated into its component wavelengths and passed through a sample. The graph of absorption at different wavelengths for a solution is called an *absorption spectrum.*

c. *Calibrate the instrument.* Insert cuvette A into the sample holder and close the lid. (Be sure to align the etched mark on the cuvette with the line on the sample holder.) Adjust the light control (F) until the meter reads 100% transmittance, or 0 absorption. You are now ready to make your first reading.

d. *Begin your readings.* Remove cuvette A and insert cuvette B. (Align the etched mark.) Close the cover. Record the reading on the absorbance scale. Remove cuvette B.

e. *Recalibrate the instrument.* Insert cuvette A into the sample holder, and set the wavelength to 420 nm. Again, calibrate the instrument to 100% transmittance (0 absorption) with cuvette A in place, using the light control (F).

f. *Take the second reading.* Remove cuvette A and insert cuvette B. Record absorbance at 420 nm. Remove cuvette B.

g. *Continue your observations,* increasing the wavelength by 20-nm increments until you reach 720 nm. Be sure to recalibrate each time you change the wavelength.

6. Pool data from all teams to complete Table 6.3.

Results

1. Using the readings recorded in Table 6.3, plot in Figure 6.5 the absorption spectrum for each pigment.

2. Refer to Lab Topic 1 for information about constructing graphs. Choose appropriate scales for the axes, determine dependent and independent variables, and plot data points. Draw smooth curves to fit the values plotted. Label the graph for easy identification of pigments plotted, or prepare a legend and use colored pencils.

Discussion

1. List in the margin or on another page the pigments extracted and the optimum wavelength(s) of light for absorption for each pigment.

Table 6.3

Absorbance of Photosynthetic Pigments Extracted from Fresh _____*

Wavelength	Chlorophyll *a*	Chlorophyll *b*	Xanthophyll	Carotene	Total Pigment
400					
420					
440					
460					
480					
500					
520					
540					
560					
580					
600					
620					
640					
660					
680					
700					
720					

*Complete title with name of plant used for extract, for example, beans.

2. Which pigment is most important in the process of photosynthesis? Support your choice with evidence from your results.

3. Chlorophyll *b* and carotenoids are called *accessory pigments*. Using data from your results, speculate about the roles of these pigments in photosynthesis.

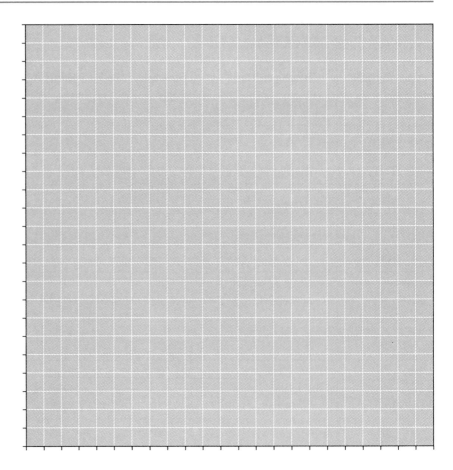

Figure 6.5.
Absorption spectrum for chlorophyll *a*, chlorophyll *b*, carotene, and xanthophyll. Plot your results from Exercise 6.4. Label all axes, and draw smooth curves to fit the data. Label the graph for easy identification of pigments.

Questions for Review

1. Write a summary equation for photosynthesis.

2. Using your previous knowledge of photosynthesis and the results from today's exercises, explain the role, origin, or fate of each factor involved in the process of photosynthesis.

3. A pigment solution contains compound A with 4 polar groups and compound B with 2 polar groups. You plan to separate these compounds using

paper chromatography with a nonpolar solvent. Predict the location of the two bands relative to the solvent front. Explain your answer.

Applying Your Knowledge

1. In what form is carbohydrate transported out of the leaf to other parts of the plant, and when does this occur?

2. Dr. William C. Dooley's students did not get the expected results for their investigation of the effects of different wavelengths of light on photosynthesis in the geranium (Exercise 6.1). Regardless of the treatment, all their geranium leaves tested positive for the presence of starch. Confused by these results, Dr. Dooley began to look for problems in the preparation of the experiment that could be responsible for the presence of starch under even the black paper. Can you suggest one or more problems that might lead to these results?

3. In response to shortened day length and cool temperatures, many trees begin a period of senescence when the breakdown of chlorophyll exceeds chlorophyll production. The leaves of these trees appear to change to yellow and orange. Using your knowledge of photosynthetic pigments, explain the source of these yellow-orange hues.

4. Land plants and many algae appear green, due to the chlorophyll stored in their chloroplasts. However, the deep-ocean-dwelling red algae, as

their name suggests, range in color from pink to red to dark purple, almost black. These red colors are attributed to the photosynthetic pigment phycoerythrin. What color and wavelengths of light do you think phycoerythrin absorbs (see Color Plate 10)? Can you suggest how the environmental conditions of red algae might be related to this different pigment system?

References

Lehninger, A. L., D. L. Nelson, and M. M. Cox. *Principles of Biochemistry,* 2nd ed. New York: Worth Publishers, 1993.

Taiz, L., and E. Zeigler. *Plant Physiology,* 2nd ed. Sunderland, MA: Sinauer, 1998.

Uno, G., R. Storey, and R. Moore. *Principles of Botany.* Boston, MA: McGraw-Hill Co., 2001.

Website

The Photosynthesis Center:
http://photoscience.la.asu.edu/photosyn/default.html

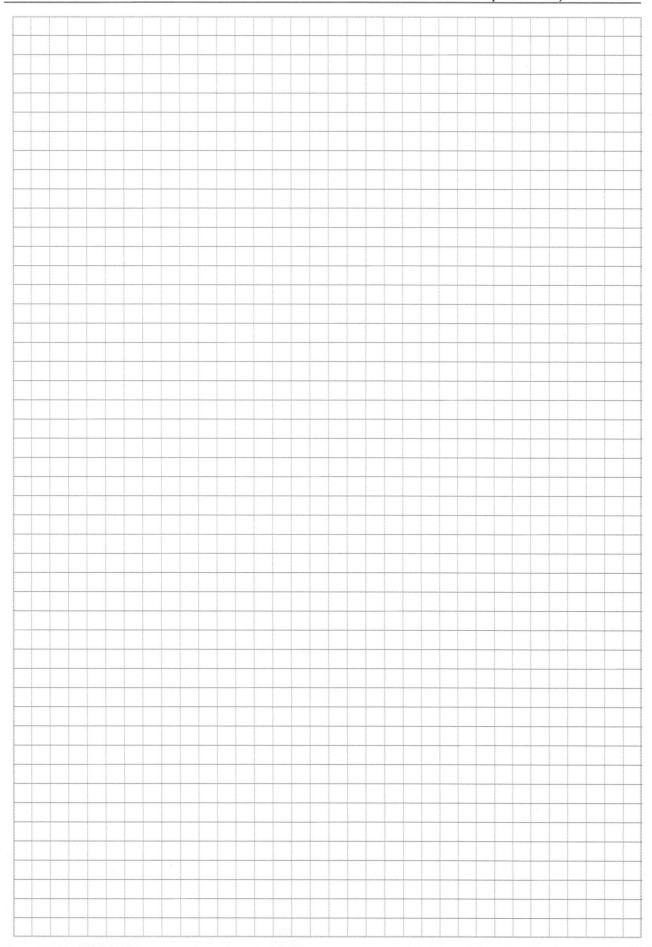

Mitosis and Meiosis

Laboratory Objectives

After completing this lab topic, you should be able to:

1. Describe the activities of chromosomes, centrioles, and microtubules in the cell cycle, including all phases of mitosis and meiosis.
2. Recognize human chromosomes in leukocytes.
3. Identify the phases of mitosis in root tip and whitefish blastula cells.
4. Describe differences in mitosis and cytokinesis in plant and animal cells.
5. Describe differences in mitosis and meiosis.
6. Explain crossing over, and describe how this can bring about particular arrangements of ascospores in the fungus *Sordaria*.

Introduction

The nuclei in cells of eukaryotic organisms contain chromosomes with clusters of **genes,** discrete units of hereditary information consisting of double-stranded deoxyribonucleic acid (DNA). Structural proteins in the chromosomes organize the DNA and participate in DNA folding and condensation. When cells divide, chromosomes and genes are duplicated and passed on to daughter cells. Single-celled organisms divide for reproduction. Multicellular organisms have reproductive cells (eggs or sperm), but they also have somatic (body) cells that divide for growth or replacement.

In somatic cells and single-celled organisms, the nucleus divides by **mitosis** into two daughter nuclei, which have the same number of chromosomes and the same genes as the parent cell. In multicellular organisms, in preparation for sexual reproduction, a type of nuclear division called **meiosis** takes place. In meiosis, nuclei of certain cells in ovaries or testes (or sporangia in plants) divide twice, but the chromosomes replicate only once. This process results in four daughter nuclei with differing alleles on the chromosomes. Eggs or sperm (or spores in plants) are eventually formed. Generally, in both mitosis and meiosis, after nuclear division the cytoplasm divides, a process called **cytokinesis.**

Events from the beginning of one cell division to the beginning of the next are collectively called the **cell cycle.** The cell cycle is divided into two major phases: interphase and mitotic phase (M). The M phase represents the division of the nucleus and cytoplasm (Figure 7.1).

Figure 7.1.
The cell cycle. In interphase (G_1, S, G_2), DNA replication and most of the cell's growth and biochemical activity take place. In the M phase, the nucleus divides in mitosis, and the cytoplasm divides in cytokinesis.

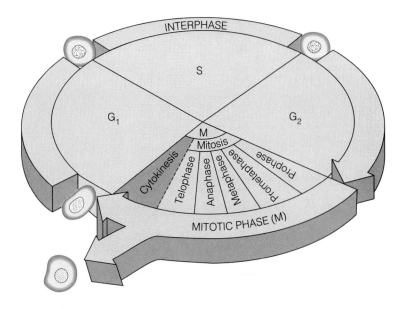

EXERCISE 7.1

Modeling the Cell Cycle and Mitosis in an Animal Cell

Materials

60 pop beads of one color   4 magnetic centromeres
60 pop beads of another color   4 centrioles

Introduction

Scientists use models to represent natural structures and processes that are too small, too large, or too complex to investigate directly. Scientists develop their models from observations and experimental data, usually accumulated from a variety of sources. Building a model can represent the culmination of a body of scientific work, but most models represent a well-developed hypothesis that can then be tested against the natural system and modified.

Linus Pauling's novel and successful technique of building a physical model of hemoglobin was based on available chemical data. This technique was later adopted by Francis Crick and James Watson to elucidate the nature of the hereditary material, DNA. Watson and Crick built a wire model utilizing evidence collected by many scientists. They presented their conclusions about the structure of the DNA helix in the journal *Nature* in April 1953 and were awarded the Nobel Prize for their discovery in 1962.

Today in lab you will work with a partner to build models of cell division: mitosis and meiosis. Using these models will enhance your understanding of the behavior of chromosomes, centrioles, membranes, and microtubules during the cell cycle. After completing your model, you will consider ways in which it is and is not an appropriate model for the cell cycle. You and your partner should discuss activities in each stage of the cell cycle as you build your model. After going through the exercise once together, you will demonstrate the model to each other to reinforce your understanding.

In the model of mitosis that you will build, your cell will be a **diploid** cell ($2n$) with four chromosomes. This means that you will have two homologous pairs of chromosomes. One pair will be long chromosomes, the other pair, short chromosomes. (**Haploid** cells have only one of each homologous pair of chromosomes, denoted n.)

Lab Study A. Interphase

During interphase, a cell performs its specific functions: Liver cells produce bile; intestinal cells absorb nutrients; pancreatic cells secrete enzymes; skin cells produce keratin. Interphase consists of three subphases, G_1, S, and G_2, which begin as a cell division ends. As interphase begins, there is approximately half as much cytoplasm in each cell as there was before division. Each new cell has a nucleus that is surrounded by a **nuclear envelope** and that contains chromosomes in an uncoiled, or decondensed, state. In this uncoiled state, the mass of DNA and protein is called **chromatin.**

Procedure

1. Build a homologous pair of single-stranded chromosomes using 10 beads of one color for one member of the long pair and 10 beads of the other color for the other member of the pair. Place the centromere at any position in the chromosome, but note that it must be in the same position on homologous chromosomes. Build the short pair with the same two different colors, but use fewer beads. You should have enough beads left over to duplicate each chromosome.

2. Model **interphase** of the cell cycle:

    a. Pile all the assembled chromosomes in the center of your work area to represent the decondensed chromosomes as a mass of chromatin in G_1 (**gap 1**).

    b. Position two centrioles as a pair just outside your nucleus. Have the two members of the centriole pair at right angles to each other. (Recall, however, that most plant cells do not have centrioles.)

    In the G_1 phase, the cytoplasmic mass increases and will continue to do so throughout interphase. Proteins are synthesized, new organelles are formed, and some organelles such as mitochondria and chloroplasts grow and divide in two. Throughout interphase one or more dark, round bodies, called **nucleoli** (singular, **nucleolus**), are visible in the nucleus.

    c. Duplicate the centrioles: Add a second pair of centrioles to your model; again, have the two centrioles at right angles to each other.

    Centriole duplication begins in late G_1 or early S phase.

    d. Duplicate the chromosomes in your model cell to represent DNA replication in the **S (synthesis) phase:** Make a second strand that is identical to the first strand of each chromosome. In replicating chromosomes, you will use two magnets to form the new centromere. Recall, however, that the centromere in a cell is a single unit until it splits in metaphase. In your model, consider the pair of magnets to be the single centromere.

Unique activities taking place during the S phase of the cell cycle are the replication of chromosomal DNA and the synthesis of chromosomal proteins. DNA synthesis continues until chromosomes have been duplicated. Each chromosome is now described as **double-stranded,** and each strand is called a **sister chromatid.** Sister chromatids are identical to each other.

e. Do not disturb the chromosomes to represent G_2 **(gap 2).**

During the G_2 phase, in addition to continuing cell activities, cells prepare for mitosis. Enzymes and other proteins necessary for cell division are synthesized during this phase.

f. Separate your centriole pairs, moving them toward opposite poles of the nucleus to represent that the G_2 phase is coming to an end and mitosis is about to begin.

How many pairs of homologous chromosomes are present in your cell during this stage of the cell cycle?

Lab Study B. M Phase (Mitosis and Cytokinesis)

In the M phase, the nucleus and cytoplasm divide. Nuclear division is called *mitosis.* Cytoplasmic division is called *cytokinesis.* Mitosis is divided into five subphases: prophase, prometaphase, metaphase, anaphase, and telophase.

Procedure

1. To represent **prophase,** leave the chromosomes piled in the center of the work area.

Prophase begins when chromosomes begin to coil and condense. At this time they become visible in the light microscope. Centrioles continue to move to opposite poles of the nucleus, and as they do so, a fibrous, rounded structure tapering toward each end, called a **spindle,** begins to form between them. Nucleoli begin to disappear.

What structures make up the fibers of the spindle? (Check text if necessary.)

2. At **prometaphase,** the centrioles are at the poles of the cell. To represent prometaphase, move the centromeres of your chromosomes to lie on an imaginary plane (the equator) midway between the two poles established by the centrioles.

During prometaphase chromosomes continue to condense. The nuclear envelope breaks down as the spindle continues to form. Some spindle fibers become associated with chromosomes, and the push and pull of spindle fibers on the chromosomes ultimately leads to their movement to the equator. When the centromeres lie on the equator, prometaphase ends and the next phase begins.

Describe the association of chromosomes and spindle fibers (check your text).

How many double-stranded chromosomes are present in your prophase/prometaphase nucleus?

 Students often find it confusing to distinguish between chromosome number and chromatid number. To simplify this problem, count the number of centromeres. The number of centromeres represents the number of chromosomes.

3. To represent **metaphase,** a relatively static phase, leave the chromosomes with centromeres lying on the equator.

    In metaphase, double-stranded chromosomes lie on the equator (also called the metaphase plate). The two sister chromatids are held together by the centromere. Metaphase ends as the centromere splits.

    Label Figure 7.2 with *chromosome, sister chromatids, spindle fibers, centromere, centrioles.*

Figure 7.2.
The mitotic spindle at metaphase.

4. Holding on to the centromeres, pull the magnetic centromeres apart and move them toward opposite poles. This action represents **anaphase.**

   After the centromere splits, sister chromatids separate and begin to move toward opposite poles. Chromatids are now called **chromosomes.** Anaphase ends as the chromosomes reach the poles.

   Describe the movement of the chromosome arms as you move the centromeres to the poles.

   Certain biologists are currently investigating the role played by spindle fibers in chromosome movement toward the poles. Check your text for a discussion of one hypothesis, and briefly summarize it here.

5. Pile your chromosomes at the poles to represent **telophase.**

   As chromosomes reach the poles, anaphase ends and telophase begins. The spindle begins to break down. Chromosomes begin to uncoil, and nucleoli reappear. A nuclear envelope forms around each new cluster of chromosomes. Telophase ends when the nuclear envelopes are complete.

   How many chromosomes are in each new nucleus?

   How many chromosomes were present in the nucleus when the process began?

6. To represent cytokinesis, leave the two new chromosome masses at the poles.

   The end of telophase marks the end of nuclear division, or mitosis. Sometime during telophase, the division of the cytoplasm, or cytokinesis, results in the formation of two separate cells. In cytokinesis in animal cells, a **cleavage furrow** forms at the equator and eventually pinches the parent cell cytoplasm in two (Figure 7.3a). In plant cells membrane-bound vesicles migrate to the center of the equatorial plane and fuse to form the **cell plate.** This eventually extends across the cell, dividing the cytoplasm in two. Cell wall materials are secreted into the space between the membranes of the cell plate (Figure 7.3b, c).

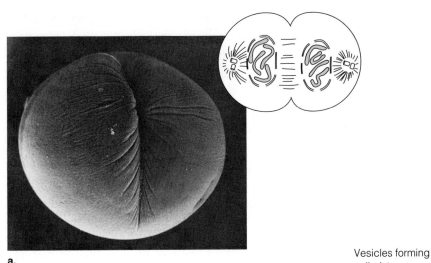

a.

Figure 7.3.
Cytokinesis in animal and plant cells. (a) In animal cells, a cleavage furrow forms at the equator and pinches the cytoplasm in two. (b) In plants, a cell plate forms in the center of the cell and grows until it divides the cytoplasm in two. (c) Photomicrograph of cytokinesis in a plant cell.

Membrane-bound vesicles

Double membrane enclosing cell plate

Secreted material, the new cell wall

b.

Vesicles forming cell plate

Nucleus

Wall of parent cell

Nucleus

c.

EXERCISE 7.2

Observing Mitosis and Cytokinesis in Plant Cells

Materials

prepared slide of onion root tip
compound microscope

Introduction

The behavior of chromosomes during the cell cycle is similar in animal and plant cells. However, differences in cell division do exist. Plant cells have no

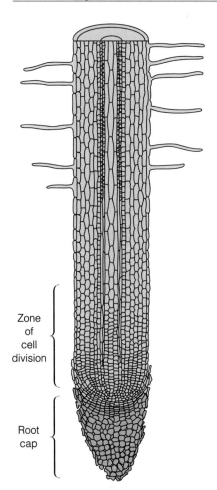

Figure 7.4.
Longitudinal section through a root tip. Cells are dividing in the zone of cell division just behind the root cap.

centrioles, yet they have bundles of microtubules that converge toward the poles at the ends of a spindle. Cell walls in plant cells dictate differences in cytokinesis. In this exercise, you will observe dividing cells in the zone of cell division of a root tip.

Procedure

1. Examine a prepared slide of a longitudinal section through an onion root tip using low power on the compound microscope.

2. Locate the region most likely to have dividing cells, just behind the root cap (Figure 7.4).

   At the tip of the root is a root cap that protects the tender root tip as it grows through the soil. Just behind the root cap is the zone of cell division. Notice that rows of cells extend upward from this zone. As cells divide in the zone of cell division, the root tip is pushed farther into the soil. Cells produced by division begin to mature, elongating and differentiating into specialized cells, such as those that conduct water and nutrients throughout the plant.

3. Focus on the zone of cell division. Then switch to the intermediate power, focus, and switch to high power.

4. Survey the zone of cell division and locate stages of the cell cycle: interphase, prophase, prometaphase, metaphase, anaphase, telophase, and cytokinesis.

5. As you find a dividing cell, speculate about its stage of division, read the following descriptions given of each stage to verify that your guess is correct, and, if necessary, confirm your conclusion with the instructor.

6. Draw the cell in the appropriate boxes provided. Label nucleus, nucleolus, chromosome, chromatin, mitotic spindle, and cell plate when appropriate.

Interphase (G_1, S, G_2)

Nuclear material is surrounded by a nuclear envelope. Dark-staining bodies, nucleoli, are visible. Chromosomes appear only as dark granules within the nucleus. Collectively, the chromosome mass is called *chromatin.* The chromosomes are not individually distinguishable because they are uncoiled into long, thin strands. Chromosomes are replicated during this phase.

Prophase

Chromosomes begin to coil and become distinguishable thin, thread-like structures, widely dispersed in the nucleus during prophase. Although there are no centrioles in plant cells, a spindle begins to form. Nucleoli begin to disappear. The nuclear envelope is still intact.

Prometaphase

By prometaphase, the chromosomes are thick and short. Each chromosome is double-stranded, consisting of two chromatids held together by a centromere. The nuclear membrane breaks down in prometaphase. Chromosomes move toward the equator.

Metaphase

Metaphase begins when the centromeres of the chromosomes lie on the equator of the cell. The arms of the chromatids extend randomly in all directions. A spindle may be apparent. Spindle fibers are attached to centromeres and extend to the poles of the cell. As metaphase ends and anaphase begins, the centromeres split.

Anaphase

The splitting of centromeres marks the beginning of anaphase. Each former chromatid is now a new single-stranded chromosome. These chromosomes are drawn apart toward opposite poles of the cell. Anaphase ends when the migrating chromosomes reach their respective poles.

Telophase and Cytokinesis

Chromosomes have now reached the poles. The nuclear envelope re-forms around each compact mass of chromosomes. Nucleoli reappear. Chromosomes begin to uncoil and become indistinct. Cytokinesis is accomplished by the formation of a cell plate that begins in the center of the equatorial plane and grows outward to the cell wall.

EXERCISE 7.3

Observing Chromosomes, Mitosis, and Cytokinesis in Animal Cells

In this exercise, you will look at the general shape and form of human chromosomes and observe chromosomes and the stages of mitotic division in the whitefish. You will also compare these chromosomes with the plant chromosomes studied in Exercise 7.2. Chromosome structure in animals and plants is basically the same in that both have centromeres and arms. However, plant chromosomes are generally larger than animal chromosomes.

Lab Study A. Human Chromosomes in Dividing Leukocytes

Materials

slides of human leukocytes (white blood cells) on demonstration with compound microscopes

Introduction

Cytogeneticists examining dividing cells of humans can frequently detect chromosome abnormalities that lead to severe mental retardation. To examine human chromosomes, leukocytes are isolated from a small sample of the patient's blood and cultured in a medium that inhibits spindle formation during mitosis. As cells begin mitosis, chromosomes condense and become distinct, but in the absence of a spindle they cannot move to the poles in anaphase. You will observe a slide in which many cells have chromosomes condensed as in prometaphase or metaphase, but they are not aligned on a spindle equator (see Color Plate 11).

Procedure

1. Attempt to count the chromosomes in one cell in the field of view. Normally, humans have 46 chromosomes. Persons with trisomy 21, or Down syndrome, have 47 chromosomes. Are the cells on this slide from a person with a normal chromosome number?

2. Notice that each chromosome is double-stranded, being made up of two sister chromatids held together by a single centromere. In very high magnifications, bands can be seen on the chromosomes. Abnormalities in banding patterns can also be an indication of severe mental retardation.

Lab Study B. Mitosis in Whitefish Blastula Cells

Materials

prepared slide of sections of whitefish blastulas
compound microscope

Introduction

The most convenient source of actively dividing cells in animals is the early embryo, where cells are large and divide rapidly with a short interphase. In blastulas (an early embryonic stage), a large percentage of cells will be dividing at any given time. By examining cross sections of whitefish blastulas, you should be able to locate many dividing cells in various stages of mitosis and cytokinesis.

Procedure

1. Examine a prepared slide of whitefish blastula cross sections. Find a blastula section on the lowest power, focus, switch to intermediate power, focus, and switch to high power.

2. As you locate a dividing cell, identify the stage of mitosis. Be able to recognize all stages of mitosis in these cells.

3. Identify the following in several cells:

   nucleus, nuclear envelope, and **nucleolus**

   chromosomes

   mitotic spindle

   asters—an array of microtubules surrounding each centriole pair at the poles of the spindle

   centrioles—small dots seen at the poles around which the microtubules of the spindle and asters appear to radiate

   cleavage furrow

Results

1. List several major differences you have observed between mitosis in animal cells and mitosis in plant cells:

2. Locate, draw, and label in the space provided a blastula cell in metaphase and a cell in telophase/cytokinesis to illustrate these differences.

Metaphase

Telophase/Cytokinesis

EXERCISE 7.4
Modeling Meiosis

Materials

60 pop beads of one color
60 pop beads of another color
8 magnetic centromeres

4 centrioles
letters *B, D, b,* and *d* printed on
    mailing labels

Introduction

Meiosis takes place in all organisms that reproduce sexually. In animals, meiosis occurs in special cells of the gonads; in plants, in special cells of the sporangia. Meiosis consists of *two* nuclear divisions, **meiosis I** and **II,** with an atypical interphase between the divisions during which cells do not grow and synthesis of DNA does not take place. This means that meiosis I and II result in four cells from each parent cell, each containing half the number of chromosomes, one from each homologous pair. Recall that cells with only one of each homologous pair of chromosomes are haploid (*n*) cells. The parent cells, with pairs of homologous chromosomes, are diploid (2*n*). The haploid cells become sperm (in males), eggs (in females), or spores (in plants). One advantage of meiosis in sexually reproducing organisms is that it prevents the chromosome number from doubling with every generation when fertilization occurs.

What would be the consequences in successive generations of offspring if the chromosome number were not reduced during meiosis?

Lab Study A. Interphase

Working with another student, you will build a model of the nucleus of a cell in interphase before meiosis. Nuclear and chromosome activities are similar to those in mitosis. You and your partner should discuss activities in the nucleus and chromosomes in each stage. Go through the exercise once together, and then demonstrate the model to each other to reinforce your understanding. Compare activities in meiosis with those in mitosis as you build your model.

Procedure

1. Build the premeiotic interphase nucleus much as you did the mitotic interphase nucleus. Have two pairs of chromosomes (2*n* = 4) of distinctly different sizes and different centromere positions. Have one member of each pair of homologues be one color, the other, a different color.

2. To represent G_1 (gap 1), pile your four chromosomes in the center of your work area. The chromosomes are decondensed.

   Cell activities in G_1 are similar to those activities in G_1 of the interphase before mitosis.

   In G_1, are chromosomes single-stranded or double-stranded?

3. Duplicate the chromosomes to represent DNA duplication in the S (synthesis) phase. Recall that in living cells, the centromeres remain single, but in your model you must use two magnets. What color should the sister chromatids be for each pair?

4. Duplicate the centriole pair.

5. Leave the chromosomes piled in the center of the work area to represent G_2 (gap 2).

   As in mitosis, in G_2 the cell prepares for meiosis by synthesizing proteins and enzymes necessary for nuclear division.

Lab Study B. Meiosis I

Meiosis consists of two consecutive nuclear divisions, called *meiosis I* and *meiosis II*. As the first division begins, the chromosomes coil and condense, as in mitosis. Meiosis I is radically different from mitosis, however, and the differences immediately become apparent. In your modeling, as you detect the differences, make notes in the margin of your lab manual.

Procedure

1. Meiosis I begins with the chromosomes piled in the center of your work area.

   As chromosomes begin to coil and condense, prophase I begins. Each chromosome is double-stranded, made up of two sister chromatids. Two pairs of centrioles are located outside the nucleus.

2. Separate the two centriole pairs and move them to opposite poles of the nucleus.

   The nuclear envelope breaks down and the spindle begins to form as in mitosis.

3. Move each homologous chromosome to pair with its partner. You should have four strands together.

   Early in prophase I, each chromosome finds its homologue and pairs in a tight association. The process of pairing is called **synapsis.** Because the chromosomes are double-stranded, this means that each paired doubled chromosome complex is made of four strands. This complex is called a **tetrad.**

   How many tetrad complexes do you have in your cell, which is $2n = 4$?

4. Represent the phenomenon of **crossing over** by detaching and exchanging identical segments of any two nonsister chromatids in a tetrad.

   Crossing over takes place between nonsister chromatids in the tetrad. In this process, a segment from one chromatid will break and exchange with the exact same segment on a nonsister chromatid in the tetrad. The crossover site forms a **chiasma** (plural, **chiasmata**).

5. Return the exchanged segments of chromosome to their original chromosomes before performing the crossing-over activity in the next step.

   Genes (traits) are often expressed in different forms. For example, when the gene for seed color is expressed in pea plants, the seed may be green or yellow. Alternative forms of genes are called **alleles.** Green and yellow are alleles of the seed-color gene. It is significant that crossing over produces new allelic combinations among genes along a chromatid. To see how new allelic combinations are produced, proceed to step 6.

6. Using the letters printed on mailing labels, label one bead (gene locus) on each chromatid of one chromosome *B* for brown hair color. Label the beads in the same position on the two chromatids of the other member of the homologous pair *b* for blond hair color.

   The *B* and *b* represent alleles, or alternate forms of the gene for hair color.

   On the chromatids with the *B* allele, label another gene *D* for dark eye color. On the other member of the homologous pair of chromosomes, label the same gene *d* for pale eyes. In other words, one chromosome will have *BD,* the other chromosome, *bd* (Figure 7.5).

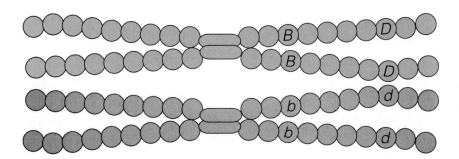

Figure 7.5.
Arrangement of alleles *B*, *b*, *D*, and *d* on chromosome models. One double homologous chromosome has *B* alleles and *D* alleles on each chromatid. The other has *b* and *d* alleles on each chromatid.

7. Have a crossover take place between the loci for hair color and eye color. Remember, the crossover must take place between nonsister chromatids.

   What combinations of alleles are now present on the chromatids?

8. Confirm your results with your laboratory instructor.

If you are having difficulty envisioning the activities of chromosomes in prophase I and understanding their significance, discuss these events with your lab partner and, if needed, ask questions of your lab instructor before proceeding to the next stage of meiosis I.

9. Move your tetrads to the equator, midway between the two poles.

   Late in prophase I, tetrads move to the equator.

10. To represent metaphase I, leave the tetrads lying at the equator.

    During this phase, tetrads lie on the equatorial plane. *Centromeres do not split as they do in mitosis.*

11. To represent anaphase I, separate each double-stranded chromosome from its homologue, and move one homologue toward each pole. In our model, the two magnets in sister chromatids represent one centromere holding together the two sister chromatids of the chromosome.

    How does the structure of chromosomes in anaphase I differ from that in anaphase in mitosis?

12. To represent telophase I, place the chromosomes at the poles. You should have one long and one short chromosome at each pole, representing a homologue from each pair.

    Two nuclei now form, followed by cytokinesis. How many chromosomes are in each nucleus?

The number of chromosomes is equal to the number of centromeres. In this model, two magnets represent one centromere in double-stranded chromosomes.

Would you describe the new nuclei as being diploid (2*n*) or haploid (*n*)?

13. To represent meiotic interphase, leave the chromosomes in the two piles formed at the end of meiosis I.

    The interphase between meiosis I and meiosis II is usually short. There is little cell growth and no synthesis of DNA. All the machinery for a second nuclear division is synthesized, however.

14. Duplicate the centriole pairs.

Lab Study C. Meiosis II

The events that take place in meiosis II are similar to the events of mitosis. Meiosis I results in two nuclei with half the number of chromosomes as the parent cell, but the chromosomes are double-stranded (made of two chromatids), just as they are at the beginning of mitosis. The events in meiosis II must change double-stranded chromosomes into single-stranded chromosomes. As meiosis II begins, two new spindles begin to form, establishing the axes for the dispersal of chromosomes to each new nucleus.

Procedure

1. To represent prophase II, separate the centrioles and set up the axes of the two new spindles. Pile the chromosomes in the center of each spindle.

   The events that take place in each of the nuclei in prophase II are similar to those of a mitosis prophase. In each new cell the centrioles move to the poles, nucleoli break down, the nuclear envelope breaks down, and a new spindle forms. The new spindle forms at a right angle to the axis of the spindle in meiosis I.

2. Align the chromosomes at the equator of their respective spindles.

   As the chromosomes reach the equator, prophase II ends and metaphase II begins.

3. Leave the chromosomes on the equator to represent metaphase II.

4. Pull the two magnets of each double-stranded chromosome apart.

   As metaphase II ends, the centromeres finally split and anaphase II begins.

5. Separate sister chromatids (now chromosomes) and move them to opposite poles.

   In anaphase II, single-stranded chromosomes move to the poles.

6. Pile the chromosomes at the poles.

   As telophase II begins, chromosomes arrive at the poles. Spindles break down. Nucleoli reappear. Nuclear envelopes form around each bunch of chromosomes as the chromosomes uncoil. Cytokinesis follows meiosis II.

   a. What is the total number of nuclei and cells now present?

b. How many chromosomes are in each?

c. How many cells were present when the entire process began?

d. How many chromosomes were present per cell when the entire process began?

e. How many of the cells formed by the meiotic division just modeled are genetically identical? (Assume that alternate forms of genes exist on homologues.)

Results

Summarize the major differences between mitosis and meiosis in Table 7.1.

Table 7.1

Comparing Nuclear and Chromosomal Activities in Mitosis and Meiosis

	Mitosis	**Meiosis**
Synapsis		
Crossing over		
When centromeres split		
Chromosome structure and movement during anaphase		
No. of divisions		
No. of cells resulting		
No. of chromosomes in daughter cells		
Genetic similarity of daughter cells to parent cells		

EXERCISE 7.5

Meiosis in *Sordaria fimicola*: A Study of Crossing Over

Materials

petri dish containing mycelia resulting from a cross between *Sordaria* with black and tan spores
slides and coverslips
dropper bottles of water
matches

wire bacterial transfer loop
alcohol lamp

Introduction

In the study of meiosis, you demonstrated that genetic recombination may occur as a result of the exchange of genetic material between homologous chromosomes in the process of crossing over. Crossing over occurs during prophase I, when homologous chromosomes synapse. While they are joined in this complex, nonsister chromatids may break at corresponding points and exchange parts. A point at which they appear temporarily joined as a result of this exchange is called a **chiasma** (Figure 7.6).

Sordaria fimicola is a fungus that spends most of its life as a haploid **mycelium,** a mass of cells arranged in filaments. When conditions are favorable, cells of filaments from two different mating types fuse (see Figures 7.7a and b); ultimately, the nuclei fuse (Figure 7.7c) and 2*n* zygotes are produced, each inside a structure called an **ascus** (plural, **asci**) (Figure 7.7d). Asci are protected within a **perithecium.** Each 2*n* zygote undergoes meiosis, and the resulting cells (ascospores) remain aligned, the position of an ascospore within the ascus depending on the orientation of separating chromosomes on the equatorial plane of meiosis I. After meiosis, each resulting ascospore divides once by mitosis (Figure 7.7e), resulting in eight ascospores per ascus (Figure 7.7f). This unique sequence of events means that it is easy to detect the occurrence of crossing over involving chromatids carrying alleles that encode for color of spores and mycelia.

If two mating types of *Sordaria,* one with black spores and the other with tan spores, are grown on the same petri dish, (Color Plate 12), mycelia from

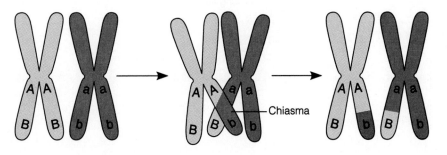

Figure 7.6.
Crossing over. Chromatid arms break and rejoin with a nonsister member of the tetrad, forming a chiasma between nonsister chromatids. This process results in the exchange of genetic material.

Figure 7.7.
Abbreviated diagram of the life cycle of *Sordaria fimicola*.
(a) Cells from filaments of two different mating types fuse.
(b) One cell with two nuclei is formed.
(c) The two nuclei fuse, forming a 2*n* zygote. (d) The zygote nucleus begins meiosis, and an ascus begins to form in a perithecium. (e) Meiosis continues, followed by mitosis.
(f) The mature ascus contains eight ascospores. (g) Micrograph of crushed perithecium with asci containing ascospores.

a. Specialized cells from two 1*n* filaments fuse.

Fungal filaments

b. One cell with two nuclei eventually forms.

c. 2*n* zygote

Meiosis I

d. Two 1*n* nuclei

Meiosis II

Young ascus

e. Four 1*n* nuclei

g.

Perithecium

Ascus

Asci

Ascospore

Mitosis

f.

Perithecium

Eight ascospores in ascus

Fungal filaments

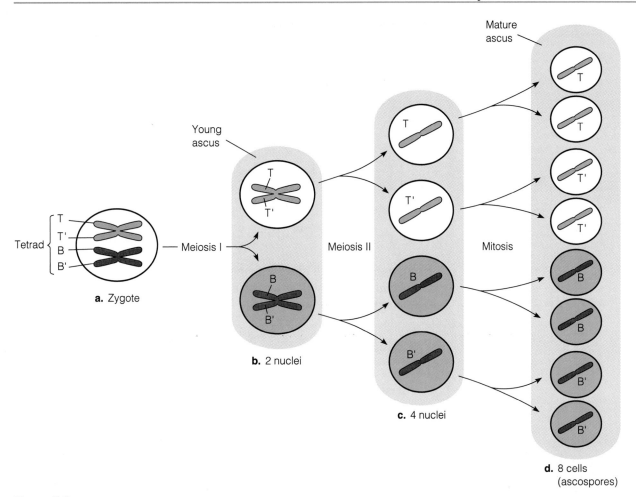

Mature
ascus

Young
ascus

Tetrad

Meiosis I

Meiosis II

Mitosis

a. Zygote

b. 2 nuclei

c. 4 nuclei

d. 8 cells
(ascospores)

Figure 7.8.

**Arrangement of spores in asci resulting from a cross
between fungi with black spores and fungi with tan
spores when no crossing over takes place.** (a) In the
zygote nucleus, the light homologous chromosome has
chromatids labeled T and T′. Each chromatid has identical
tan alleles for spore color. The dark homologous chromosome (chromatids labeled B and B′) has black alleles.
(b) During meiosis I, the two homologous chromosomes
separate into two different nuclei retained in one developing ascus. (c) Meiosis II produces four nuclei, two containing a chromosome with the tan allele and two containing
a chromosome with the black allele, still within the one
ascus. (d) Now each nucleus divides by mitosis, followed
by cytokinesis, resulting in eight cells, called ascospores.
The ascus now contains eight ascospores. Four of the
spores have the tan allele in their nuclei and appear tan-
colored. Four ascospores have the black allele and appear
black.

the two may grow together, and certain cells may fuse. Nuclei from two
fused cells then fuse, and the resulting zygote contains one chromosome
carrying the allele for black spores and another carrying the allele for tan spores.
After meiosis takes place, one mitosis follows, and the result is eight ascospores
in one ascus: four black spores and four tan spores. If no crossing over has
taken place, the arrangement of spores will appear as in Figure 7.8.

If crossing over does take place, the arrangement of spores will differ. In the
spaces provided, using Figure 7.8 as a reference, draw diagrams that illustrate the *predicted* arrangement of spores in the ascus when crossing over

takes place between the following chromatids and the alleles for color are exchanged: (a) T and B, (b) T and B′, (c) T′ and B, and (d) T′ and B′.

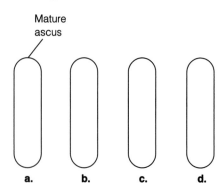

In lab today, you will observe living cultures of crosses between black and tan *Sordaria*. You will look for asci with spores arranged as in your predictions.

Procedure

1. Place a drop of water on a clean slide, and carry it and a coverslip to the demonstration table.
2. Light the alcohol lamp and flame a transfer loop.
3. Open the lid of the *Sordaria* culture slightly, and use the loop or other instrument to remove several perithecia from the region near the edge of the dish where the two strains have grown together (Figure 7.9).
4. Place the perithecia in the drop of water on your slide, and cover it with the coverslip.
5. Return to your work area.
6. Using the eraser end of a pencil, tap lightly on the coverslip to break open and flatten out the perithecia.
7. Systematically scan back and forth across the slide using the intermediate power of the compound microscope. When you locate clusters of asci, focus, switch to high power, count the asci, and determine if crossing over has taken place. Record your numbers in Table 7.2.

Results

In Table 7.2, record the numbers of asci with (a) spores all of one color (indicating that the zygote was formed by fusion of cells of the same strain), (b) black and tan spores with no crossover, and (c) black and tan spores with a crossover.

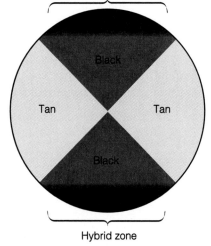

Figure 7.9.
Most likely location for perithecia containing asci with hybrid spores. Following the procedure, collect dark, round perithecia from zones of hybridization along the petri dish perimeter as indicated (Color Plate 12).

Table 7.2
Numbers of Asci in Each Category

Spores all one color	
Crossover absent	
Crossover present	

Discussion

1. What percentage of asci observed resulted from the fusion of cells from different strains?

2. What percentage of those asci resulting from the fusion of different strains demonstrates crossovers?

Questions for Review

1. Define the following terms and use each in a meaningful sentence. Give examples when appropriate.

    mitosis, meiosis, cytokinesis, chromosome, chromatin, centromere, centriole, spindle, aster, homologous chromosome, synaptonemal complex, synapsis, tetrad, chiasma, sister chromatid, nucleolus, mitotic spindle, cell plate, cleavage furrow, diploid, haploid, mycelium, perithecium, ascus

2. Describe the activity of chromosomes in each stage of mitosis.

3. In the photomicrograph of dividing root cells at right, identify interphase and the following phases of mitosis: prophase, metaphase, anaphase, telophase, and cytokinesis.

4. Describe the activity of chromosomes in each stage of meiosis I.

5. Describe the activity of chromosomes in each stage of meiosis II.

6. Provide examples of plant and animal cells that typically undergo mitosis. Provide examples for meiosis.

Applying Your Knowledge

1. Self-fertilization frequently takes place in fungi. Discuss the adaptive advantages of different strains mating.

2. What advantage does the process of crossing over bring to reproduction?

3. Can you think of any way in which new gene combinations resulting from crossovers might be disadvantageous?

4. Explain why models are important to scientific study of biological systems. Provide two examples of models other than those described in the exercises.

5. Why would the method of cytokinesis in animal cells not work in plant cells?

6. Biologists have hypothesized that centrioles in animal cells play a role in the organization of the mitotic spindle. Most plant cells, on the other hand, have no centrioles but are able to form spindles. Use your text or other sources and write a paragraph discussing hypotheses that explain this observation.

7. Identical twins Jan and Fran were very close sisters. So, when Jan died suddenly, Fran moved in to help take care of Jan's daughter (her niece), Millie. Some time later Fran married her brother-in-law and became Millie's stepmother. When Fran announced that she was pregnant, poor Millie became confused and curious. "So," Millie asked, "who is this baby? Will she be my twin? Will she be my sister, my stepsister, my cousin?" Can you answer her questions? What is the genetic relationship between Millie and the baby? What processes are involved in the formation of gametes and how do they affect genetic variation?

References

Becker, W. M., L. Kleinsmith, and J. Hardin. *The World of the Cell*, 4th ed. Redwood City, CA: Benjamin/Cummings, 2000.

Bold, H. C., C. J. Alexopoulos, and T. Delevoryas. *Morphology of Plants and Fungi*. New York: Harper & Row, 1980.

Websites

The following are websites dealing with the cell cycle and mitosis:

http://www.cellsalive.com/cellcycle.html
http://www.cellsalive.com/mitosis.html
http://www.biology.arizona.edu/cell_bio/tutorials/
    cell_cycle/cells2.html

Animation of meiosis and independent assortment:
http://www.csuchico.edu/~Bio/207/animations/
assortment.html

Mendelian Genetics: Fast Plants

Laboratory Objectives

After completing this lab topic, you should be able to:

1. Describe the mode of inheritance of three traits in *Brassica rapa* (Wisconsin Fast Plants™).
2. Use the Mendelian model to test for patterns of inheritance.
3. Describe and use the chi-square test to compare observed and expected results from genetic crosses.
4. Describe at least one type of non-Mendelian inheritance.
5. Define terminology used in the study of genetics.

Introduction

Gregor Mendel's study of inheritance in garden peas provided evidence that traits were inherited as "particles" rather than by blending, which was the generally accepted model of that time. Although the Mendelian model does not explain every type of inheritance, it remains the cornerstone of genetics because it provides a testable model from which a scientist can generate hypotheses with predictable results.

In this lab topic, you will investigate the inheritance of traits in a small plant, *Brassica rapa,* using the Mendelian model to develop your hypotheses. You will actually follow many of Mendel's procedures as you work with a **monohybrid** (single trait) **cross** and a **dihybrid** (two traits) **cross.** Each cross begins with true-breeding parents, each of which is **homozygous** (has two identical alleles for a given trait). If parents with different traits (for example, yellow and green pea pods) are cross-pollinated, under the Mendelian model the offspring will be **heterozygous** (receiving one allele from each parent). However, the offspring will express only one allele, which Mendel described as **dominant;** that is, only one allele needs to be present to be expressed. The masked trait is **recessive;** two alleles must be present for a **recessive** trait to be expressed. The parents in this cross are referred to as the **P generation,** and the hybrid offspring as the F_1 (first filial or hybrid) **generation.** Two F_1 hybrids are then crossed to produce the next group of offspring, or F_2 **generation.** The predicted Mendelian results for the F_2 generation from a monohybrid cross would be one-fourth of the offspring with the recessive trait and three-fourths with the dominant trait (Figure 8.1). To explain these results, Mendel formulated the **law of segregation,** which states that allele pairs separate during the formation of gametes (during meiosis), with the paired condition being restored during fertilization to form the zygote.

183

Figure 8.1.

Mendel's law of segregation. Mendel proposed that allele pairs separate during the formation of gametes and that the paired condition is restored during fertilization. The expected results for the F_2 generation of a monohybrid cross would be 75% dominant (green) and 25% recessive (yellow).

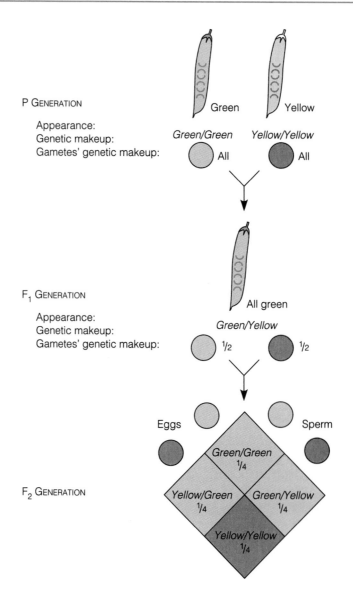

The results of Mendel's dihybrid crosses indicated that traits did segregate and that pairs of alleles assorted themselves independently of other pairs of alleles during meiosis. This is Mendel's **law of independent assortment,** which integrates the processes studied in Lab Topic 7, mitosis and meiosis, with the inheritance of alleles that is carried on chromosomes (Figure 8.2).

Part of the intrigue of genetics comes from the non-Mendelian results of experiments, which require modified hypotheses and novel procedures. Imagine the excitement in Thomas Hunt Morgan's lab when crosses involving white-eyed fruit flies suggested that the inheritance of eye color might somehow be related to the sex of the fly! (This is an example of what is called **sex linkage.**) Mendel could not have investigated sex linkage in peas because peas, like most plants, do not have sex chromosomes but produce both sexes in one flower.

Cytoplasmic inheritance is another example of non-Mendelian inheritance. Not all genetic information is determined by nuclear genes. Both the mitochondria and chloroplasts carry genetic information, which is passed to the next generation in the cytoplasm rather than in the nucleus. These

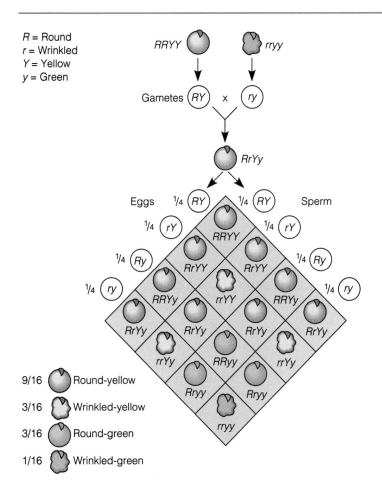

R = Round
r = Wrinkled
Y = Yellow
y = Green

Gametes (RY) x (ry)

RrYy

Eggs ¼ (RY)   ¼ (RY) Sperm
¼ (rY)   ¼ (rY)
¼ (Ry)   ¼ (Ry)
¼ (ry)   ¼ (ry)

9/16 Round-yellow
3/16 Wrinkled-yellow
3/16 Round-green
1/16 Wrinkled-green

Figure 8.2.

Dihybrid cross. If two traits segregate independently, then four kinds of gametes will be produced by the F_1 generation, and the offspring will have a 9:3:3:1 phenotypic ratio.

genes are inherited from the maternal parent because the cytoplasm of the zygote comes entirely from the egg. The sperm contributes only nuclear material. Each person carries the mitochondrial DNA of his or her mother, and, likewise, mitochondrial and chloroplast DNA in plants is maternally inherited.

Genetics has a unique vocabulary that you must master if you are to understand and communicate the concepts. You began developing this vocabulary when you studied mitosis and meiosis. Before you begin today's lab, review definitions of *gene, trait, allele,* and *chromosome* from Lab Topic 7; use your textbook to define any terms you do not recognize in Table 8.1 on the next page.

In this laboratory, you will investigate inheritance of three traits (genes) in Wisconsin Fast Plants. These plants, developed by Dr. Paul Williams and a team of scientists in the Department of Plant Pathology, University of Wisconsin, Madison, are strains of *Brassica rapa* (RCBr, rapid-cycling brassicas) that complete their entire breeding cycle from seed to seed in 35 days (see Color Plate 12 and Figure 8.3). Because of their rapid breeding cycle, plants in the Brassica, or mustard, family are emerging as model plants for teaching and research, much as *Drosophila,* the fruit fly, has historically been the animal of choice for research in eukaryotic genetics. The Wisconsin scientists have developed several strains of plants with strongly contrasting traits. In this lab topic, you will investigate the inheritance of three of these traits: presence or absence of anthocyanin, yielding green or purple plants;

Table 8.1
Genetic Terminology

Term	Definition
Genotype	
Phenotype	
Wild-type trait	
Mutant trait	
F_1	
F_2	
Dominant trait	
Recessive trait	
Hybrid	
Homozygous	
Heterozygous	

color of plant—yellow-green or green; and presence or absence of variegated (green and white) leaves.

The Crucifer Genetics Cooperative for *Brassica* has developed guidelines for designating symbols to represent particular genotypes of *Brassica* that are similar to symbols used in other model systems, such as *Drosophila* (see Lab Topic 9, Mendelian Genetics: *Drosophila*). Students who wish to perform extended investigations using *Brassica* should refer to the *Wisconsin Fast Plants Manual* (Carolina Biological Supply, 1989) for guidelines for allelic and genotypic symbols. However, for the purposes of this lab, you should

Figure 8.3. (☞)

Life cycle of *Brassica rapa*, Fast Plant. The entire life cycle of this Fast Plant is completed from seed to seed in 35 days. Note the stages of development and the day in the life cycle.

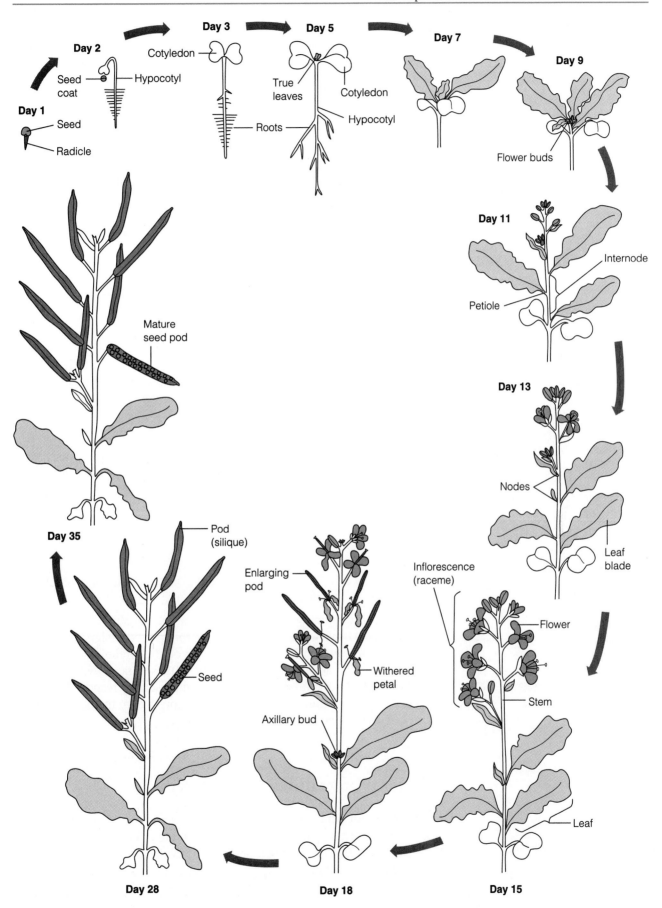

use the commonly used symbols of Mendelian inheritance, in which the dominant allele is designated by the capitalized first letter of the trait name, and the recessive allele by the lowercase letter.

Materials for All Exercises

seeds of designated phenotypes	water and dropper
seed-collecting pan	potting mix
small envelopes	fertilizer pellets
wicks	watering tray
label tape	petri dish with filter paper

Styrofoam "quads" used to germinate seeds (see Figure 8.4)

fluorescent light bank (see Figure 8.5)

water reservoir for petri dish (plastic dish of appropriate size or cut-off base of 2 L bottle)

Overview of Exercises

The crosses for each exercise are briefly outlined below, along with the general procedures that will be used in all exercises. These include planting seeds, pollinating flowers, and harvesting and germinating seeds. Specific instructions are provided within each exercise.

Exercises 8.1 and 8.2

You will begin with F_1 hybrid seeds resulting from a cross previously made between homozygous wild-type plants and homozygous mutant plants. You will germinate these F_1 seeds, cross-pollinate the flowers, allow the flowers to mature and produce F_2 seeds, collect the mature F_2 seeds, germinate the F_2 seeds, and record phenotypic ratios in this generation.

Exercise 8.3

You will grow green plants and variegated plants, cross these parent plants, and then grow the offspring from this cross and record the phenotypes.

You will begin planning for this lab and germinating all seeds (unless otherwise noted) *6 to 8 weeks* before the laboratory period designated for making final observations. Before coming to lab on this preliminary date, plan your schedule of activities carefully. Notice that several activities will take place outside of scheduled lab time. You are personally responsible for the success of this laboratory, and you will be responsible for maintaining plants and carrying out activities.

General Procedures for All Exercises

Complete and detailed procedures are provided with Exercises 8.1–8.3, starting on the next page; procedures common to all exercises are described for planting seeds, pollinating flowers, and harvesting and germinating seeds of the next generation.

Planting Seeds

Plant the appropriate seeds in quads (Figure 8.4).

1. Add one wick to each cell in a quad; wicks should extend from the base.

2. Add potting soil to each cell until half full.

3. Add three fertilizer pellets to each cell.

4. Add more soil and press to make a depression.

5. Add two or three seeds to each cell and barely cover with potting mix.

6. Using a dropper, water each cell until water drips from the wick.

7. Place quad on watering tray under fluorescent light bank (Figure 8.5). Be sure that the wicks in the quad make good contact with the mat on the watering tray.

8. Use tape to label your quad with your name, the date, and the plant type(s).

9. After 4 or 5 days, record phenotypes of plants in the appropriate table and thin plants, leaving only the most vigorous single plant in each cell (Figure 8.4d).

a. Quad and wicks

b. Planting

Figure 8.4.
Planting and thinning Fast Plants.
(a) Place absorbent wicks in the quad, with the tips extending from holes in the bottom. (b) Place potting soil, fertilizer pellets, and more soil in each cell. Make a small depression, and plant two or three seeds in each cell; then cover with soil. (c) Water seeds with a dropper until water drips from the wicks. Place on watering tray. (d) After recording seedling phenotypes, remove all but one large healthy seedling in each cell.

c. Initial watering

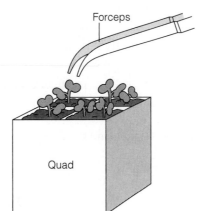

d. Thinning

Figure 8.5.
Growing system for Fast Plants.
Fast Plants require high light to complete their life cycle in 35 days. The light bank should be adjusted to remain 5–8 cm above plants. The light should be on 24 hours a day.

Rack

Light bank

Quad

Watering tray

Mat

Pollinating Flowers

After two or three flowers open on most plants (approximately day 14), pollinate as follows (Figure 8.6):

1. Using a "bee-stick" (Williams, 1980), made by gluing a dry honeybee thorax to the top of a toothpick, transfer pollen from one plant to another. (You can also use a small, soft paintbrush.)
2. Save the stick by inserting it into one cell of the quad. Use it to pollinate again 2 and 4 days later.
3. After the third pollination, pinch off all unopened buds.
4. Remove and discard all new buds and shoots for the next 2 weeks.

Harvesting Seeds

Seeds are ready to harvest approximately 21 days after pollination.

1. Remove quad with plants from the watering tray and dry for 5 days.
2. Remove dry seed pods and roll them between your hands over a collecting pan to free the seeds from the pod.
3. Store seeds in an envelope labeled with your name, the date, and the seed type.

a. Pollen transfer to bee-stick   **b.** Cross-pollination   **c.** Removal of unopened buds

Figure 8.6.
Pollination of Fast Plants. (a, b) Using a bee-stick, transfer pollen from one plant to another. Plants are self-incompatible and must be cross-pollinated. (c) After pollinating on 3 days, remove all remaining flowers and buds.

Germinating Seeds

Seeds in Exercises 8.2 and 8.3 will be germinated in quads by planting as described above for initial seeds (p. 189). Seedlings can be scored as soon as the first leaves are produced, and the phenotype of interest can be observed.

Seeds of offspring in Exercise 8.1 will be germinated in petri dishes as described below (Figure 8.7).

1. Moisten a piece of filter paper in a petri dish, labeling the paper with your name, the date, and the seed type. Pour off excess water.
2. Place 25 of the harvested seeds in neat rows in the upper two-thirds of the filter paper.
3. Place the petri dish tilted on end in a water reservoir. Add about 2 cm water.
4. Place the dish and reservoir under the light bank.
5. In approximately 48–96 hours, observe seedlings and record phenotypes in the appropriate table.
6. Tabulate results, and perform a chi-square test on class results.

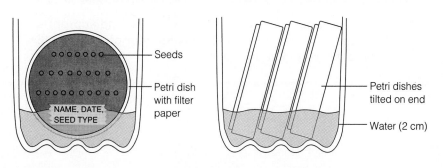

Seeds

Petri dish with filter paper

NAME, DATE, SEED TYPE

Petri dishes tilted on end

Water (2 cm)

Figure 8.7.
Germination of seeds in petri dishes. In Exercise 8.1, seeds are germinated on moist filter paper in petri dishes.

EXERCISE 8.1

Inheritance of Anthocyanin Gene

Materials

12 F_1 seeds resulting from a cross previously made between a homozygous plant that has anthocyanin present and a true-breeding plant that has no anthocyanin

1 quad and related planting supplies (refer to Materials for All Exercises section)

2 mature plants with parental phenotypes

Introduction

Wild-type *Brassica rapa* has a red-purple pigment present, called *anthocyanin*. Plants with even a faint red or purple coloration are considered to show the phenotype for anthocyanin (Color Plate 13). Mutant plants have no anthocyanin and are completely green. In this exercise, you will investigate the inheritance of this trait. Formulate a hypothesis for this trait that describes a mode of inheritance based on the Mendelian model. Will these traits conform to Mendel's laws? Is one trait dominant or recessive? Refer to Figure 8.1 and your text if necessary.

Hypothesis

Hypothesize about the inheritance of these traits.

Prediction

Predict the results based on your hypothesis (if/then). Outline the cross(es) for your predictions in the margin of your lab manual, and provide expected results for each in the form of a Punnett square if appropriate. Refer to Figure 8.1 and Figure 8.2 and your textbook if needed.

Procedure

 Refer to General Procedures (pp. 188–191) and appropriate figures. All days are approximate. Monitor plants for initiation of flowering and seed set.

1. Refer to the checklist of activities in Table 8.2, and record dates, procedures, and any observations as you follow the procedure for this exercise. Initial the final column when you have completed each step.

2. *Day 1.* Plant F_1 hybrid seeds resulting from crosses previously made between homozygous purple plants and homozygous green plants.

3. *Day 4 or 5.* Observe germinating seedlings and compare phenotypes with parental plants on demonstration (Color Plate 13). Record numbers of each phenotype in Table 8.3 in the Results section and on the class data sheet. Thin plants to one per cell. Remember to keep plants watered.

4. *Days 14, 16, 18.* Cross the F_1 plants. Pollinate plants three times, with 1 day between pollinations. Pollinate at least six to eight flowers.

5. *Days 20 to 39.* Remove new buds and shoots. Keep plants watered.

6. *Day 39.* (It should be a minimum of 21 days after the last pollination.) Harvest the F_2 seeds and germinate them in the petri dish as directed in the General Procedures section.

7. *Day 42 (or next lab period).* Count the numbers of each phenotype, and record these data in Table 8.4 in the Results section.

 You and your lab partner are responsible for the care and maintenance of your plants. Remember to check the reservoir for water, and be sure that the wicks make good contact with the watering tray, ensuring moisture flow to quads. A scientist has to remember the organism!

Table 8.2
Checklist of Activities for Exercise 8.1. Record the date and initial the final column indicating that you have completed each step.

Approximate Day	Date	Activity	Initials
Day 1		Plant F_1 hybrid seeds.	
Day 4 or 5		Observe seedlings and record numbers of each phenotype. Thin plants to one per cell.	
Days 14, 16, 18		Pollinate on 3 days; pollinate at least 6–8 flowers.	
Days 20 to 39		Remove buds and shoots.	
Day 39		Harvest F_2 seeds and germinate in petri dishes.	
Day 42		Count and record numbers of each phenotype.	

Results

1. Record the phenotypes of the F_1 seeds in Table 8.3 and the phenotypes of the F_2 offspring in Table 8.4. Compile results from all teams.
2. Note any changes in procedure or problems with the experiment in the margin of your lab manual or on the schedule of activities (Table 8.2).
3. Compare your observed and expected results by calculating the chi-square test in Table 8.5. Refer to your hypothesis and predictions and use the class data from Table 8.4. Refer to Appendix B for an explanation of the chi-square test.

Discussion

1. What do the results suggest is the inheritance pattern of this trait? Which is the dominant trait, anthocyanin present (purple) or anthocyanin absent (green)? Assign symbols and write genotypes and phenotypes of all F_1 and F_2 offspring.

What evidence supports your conclusion?

Table 8.3

Phenotypes of F_1 *B. rapa* Seedlings from Crosses Between Plants with Anthocyanin (Purple) and Without Anthocyanin (Green)

Number of Plants					
Team No.	Purple	Green	Team No.	Purple	Green
1			7		
2			8		
3			9		
4			10		
5			11		
6			12		
Class total Purple:			Green:		

Table 8.4
Phenotypes of F$_2$ Seedlings

Number of Plants					
Team No.	Purple	Green	Team No.	Purple	Green
1			7		
2			8		
3			9		
4			10		
5			11		
6			12		
Class total Purple:			Green:		

Table 8.5
Chi-Square Calculations

	Anthocyanin Present (Purple)	Anthocyanin Absent (Green)
Observed value (o)		
Expected value (e)		
Deviation ($o - e$) or d		
Deviation^2 (d^2)		
d^2/e		
Chi-square, $\chi^2 = \Sigma d^2/e$		

2. Did the results support your hypothesis? Explain, describing the results of the chi-square test.

3. Explain the significance of the *p* value (see Appendix B).

4. If the results do not support expected Mendelian ratios, what are other possible explanations for these results? What other patterns of inheritance could explain the results?

5. What additional experiments can you suggest to further test your original or modified hypothesis? Outline your crosses.

E X E R C I S E   8 . 2

Inheritance of Plant Color: Green, Yellow-Green, and Purple (Anthocyanin Present)

Materials

12 F_1 seeds resulting from a cross previously made between a true-breeding, homozygous normal bright green parent (no purple) and a true-breeding homozygous yellow-green with purple parent

1 quad and related planting supplies (see Materials for All Exercises section)

2 mature plants with the paternal phenotypes

Introduction

The wild-type plant of *Brassica rapa* is green with purple. However, variants exist that are bright green (no purple), yellow-green with purple, and yellow-green (no purple) (Color Plate 14). In this exercise, you will investigate the inheritance of these phenotypes. You will determine if one or two genes are involved. You will determine if the inheritance pattern suggests simple dominance and recessiveness, intermediate inheritance, or other modes of inheritance. Formulate a hypothesis for these traits that describes a mode of inheritance based on the Mendelian model. Will these traits conform to Mendel's laws? Is one trait dominant or recessive?

Hypothesis

Hypothesize about the inheritance of these phenotypes.

Prediction

Predict the results of the experiment based on your hypothesis. Outline the cross(es) for your predictions in the margin of your lab manual. Provide expected offspring for each cross in a Punnett square if appropriate. Refer to Figure 8.1 and Figure 8.2 and your text if necessary.

Procedure

Refer to General Procedures (pp. 188–191) and appropriate figures. All days are approximate. Monitor plants for initiation of flowering and seed set.

1. Refer to the checklist of activities in Table 8.6, and record dates, procedures, and your observations as you follow the procedure for this exercise. Initial the final column when you have completed each step.
2. *Day 1.* Plant F_1 hybrid seeds resulting from previously made crosses between homozygous bright green (no purple) and homozygous yellow-green (with purple) plants.
3. *Day 4 or 5.* Observe germinating seedlings and compare phenotypes with the adult parental plants on demonstration (Color Plate 14). Record the numbers of each phenotype in Table 8.7 and on the class data sheet.

Modify the table to accommodate your results. Write in the headings for the phenotypes and draw in columns. Thin plants to one per cell. Remember to keep plants watered.

4. *Days 14, 16, 18.* Cross the F_1 plants. Pollinate plants three times, with 1 day between pollinations. Pollinate at least six to eight flowers.

5. *Days 20 to 39.* Remove and discard new buds and shoots. Keep plants watered.

6. *Day 39.* (It should be a minimum of 21 days after the last pollination.) Harvest the F_2 seeds and begin the next generation. Germinate seeds in a quad.

7. *Days 47 to 52.* (Plants should be large enough to score phenotypes.) Count the numbers of each phenotype, and record these data in Table 8.8. Modify the table to accommodate your results. Write in the headings for the phenotypes and draw in columns.

 You and your lab partner are responsible for the care and maintenance of your plants. Remember to check the reservoir for water, and be sure that the wicks make good contact with the watering tray, ensuring moisture flow to quads. The organism must survive to reproduce!

Table 8.6
Checklist of Activities for Exercise 8.2. Record the date and initial the final column indicating that you have completed each step.

Approximate Day	Date	Activity	Initials
Day 1		Plant F_1 hybrid seeds.	
Day 4 or 5		Observe seedlings and record numbers of each phenotype. Thin plants to one per cell.	
Days 14, 16, 18		Pollinate on 3 days; pollinate at least 6–8 flowers.	
Days 20 to 39		Remove buds and shoots.	
Day 39		Harvest F_2 seeds and germinate in quads.	
Days 47 to 52		Count and record numbers of each phenotype.	

Results

1. Record the F$_1$ offspring in Table 8.7 and the F$_2$ offspring in Table 8.8. Modify these tables to accommodate observed phenotypes. Compile results from all teams.

2. Note any modifications of procedures or problems in the experiment in the margin of your lab manual or on your schedule of activities (see Table 8.6).

3. Compare your observed and expected results by calculating the chi-square test in Table 8.9. Refer to your hypothesis and predictions and use the class data from Table 8.8. Refer to Appendix B for an explanation of chi-square analysis.

Table 8.7

Phenotypes of F$_1$ *B. rapa* Seedlings from a Cross Between a Homozygous Normal Green Parent and a Yellow-Green with Purple Parent. Write in headings for the phenotypes and draw in columns.

Team No.	Phenotypes
1	
2	
3	
4	
5	
6	
7	
8	
9	
10	
11	
12	
Class total	

Table 8.8

Phenotypes of F_2 Seedlings. Write in headings for the phenotypes and draw in columns.

Team No.	Phenotypes		
1			
2			
3			
4			
5			
6			
7			
8			
9			
10			
11			
12			
Class total			

Discussion

1. What do the results suggest is the inheritance pattern of these traits? Assign symbols and write genotypes and phenotypes of all F_1 and F_2 offspring.

Table 8.9
Chi-Square Calculations. Write in headings for the phenotypes and draw in columns.

	Phenotypes
Observed value (o)	
Expected value (e)	
Deviation ($o - e$) or d	
Deviation^2 (d^2)	
d^2/e	
Chi-square, $\chi^2 = \Sigma d^2/e$	

What evidence supports your conclusion?

2. Did the results support your hypothesis? Explain, describing the results of the chi-square test.

3. Write a statement explaining the significance of the p value (see Appendix B).

4. If the results do not support expected Mendelian ratios, what are other possible explanations for these results? What other patterns of inheritance could explain the results?

5. What additional experiments can you suggest to further test your original or modified hypothesis? Outline your crosses.

EXERCISE 8.3
Inheritance of Variegated and Nonvariegated Leaf Color

Materials

6 seeds from homozygous green plants
6 seeds from homozygous variegated plants
2 quads and related planting supplies (see Materials for All Exercises section)
5-in. by 8-in. index cards
stakes (small wooden applicator sticks)

Introduction

In one strain of *Brassica rapa* plants, wild-type plants are entirely green (nonvariegated). However, other plants have white or yellow blotches or streaks on the green leaves and stems (variegated). In this exercise, you will investigate the inheritance of this trait for leaf color. Which trait is dominant, variegated or nonvariegated? Does the inheritance of this trait follow predicted Mendelian ratios? Formulate a hypothesis for these traits that describes a mode of inheritance based on the Mendelian model.

Hypothesis

Hypothesize about the inheritance of this trait.

Prediction

Predict the results of the experiment based on your hypothesis. Outline the cross(es) for your predictions in the margin of your lab manual. Provide expected offspring for each cross in a Punnett square if appropriate. Refer to Figure 8.1 and Figure 8.2 and your text if necessary.

Procedure

 Refer to the General Procedures section (pp. 188–191) and relevant figures. All days are approximate. Monitor plants for initiation of flowering and seed set.

1. Refer to the checklist of activities in Table 8.10 on the next page and record dates, procedures, and your observations as you follow the procedure for this exercise. Initial the final column when you complete each step.

2. About 3 or 4 days *before* day 1 in the previous exercises, plant three seeds from variegated plants in two cells of the quad. Leave the other two cells empty. (Your instructor may have already done this.) Variegated plants grow more slowly than totally green plants and must be planted earlier.

3. *Day 1.* Plant three seeds from green plants in each of the two empty cells of your quad.

4. *Day 4 or 5.* Thin the green seedlings to one per cell. Thin variegated seedlings, leaving one plant that is definitely variegated in each cell.

5. *Days 10 to 14.* To prevent "like" plants from pollinating each other, place a 5-in. by 8-in. card supported by two stakes across the quad, separating green from green and variegated from variegated plants. One variegated and one green plant should be on each side of the card. Be sure flowers do not extend above the card. If they do, substitute a larger card. Keep plants watered.

6. *Days 16, 18, 20.* Using a bee-stick, transfer pollen from a flower on a white or variegated stem to flowers on the totally green plant. Using a different bee-stick, carry out the **reciprocal pollination;** that is, transfer pollen from a flower of a green plant to a flower of a white or variegated plant. Pollinate plants three times, with three consecutive pollinations, with 1 day between pollinations.

7. *Days 20 to 39.* Remove and discard new buds and shoots. Keep plants watered.

8. *Day 39.* (It should be a minimum of 21 days after the last pollination. This may be performed during the next lab period.) Harvest seeds from green plants. Next, *keeping seeds separate,* harvest seeds from variegated plants.

Table 8.10
Checklist of Activities for Exercise 8.3. Record the date and initial the final column indicating that you have completed each step.

Approximate Day	Date	Activity	Initials
Before day 1		Plant seeds from variegated parents in two cells.	
Day 1		Plant seeds from green parents in remaining two cells.	
Day 4 or 5		Thin seedlings to one per cell. Leave clearly variegated seedlings in two cells.	
Days 10 to 14		Place card in quad so each side has a green and a variegated plant. Prevent pollination between like plants.	
Days 16, 18, 20		Cross-pollinate green and variegated flowers. Use a different bee-stick for reciprocal pollinations. Pollinate on 3 days.	
Days 20 to 39		Remove buds and shoots.	
Day 39		Harvest F_1 seeds and germinate in quads.	
Days 47 to 52		Count and record numbers of each phenotype.	

 Collect and store seeds in separate envelopes labeled with the date and seed type. Throw away any seeds if you are unsure of the parents.

9. Begin the second generation. Germinate seeds in a quad. Plant five seeds from the green plants in each of two cells and five seeds from the variegated plants in each of the other two cells. Label quads to indicate the parents: "green" or "variegated."

10. *Days 47 to 52.* Record phenotypes of plants from green parents and phenotypes of plants from variegated parents in Table 8.11 below. Modify the table to accommodate the phenotypes for each cross.

Table 8.11
Phenotypes of Germinated Seeds Taken from Green Plants Pollinated with Variegated Pollen (**A**) and Variegated Plants Pollinated with Green Pollen (**B**). Write in headings for the phenotypes and draw in columns.

Team No.	Phenotypes A	Phenotypes B
1		
2		
3		
4		
5		
6		
7		
8		
9		
10		
11		
12		
Class total		

You and your lab partner are responsible for the care and maintenance of your plants. Remember to check the reservoir for water, and be sure that the wicks make good contact with the watering tray, ensuring moisture flow to quads.

Results

1. Record the offspring phenotypes in Table 8.11. Record your results separately for the reciprocal crosses: (**A**) seeds from green plants pollinated with pollen from variegated plants and (**B**) seeds from variegated plants pollinated with pollen from green plants. Modify the table to accommodate the observed phenotypes for each cross. Compile results from all teams.

2. Note any modifications of procedures or problems in the experiment in the margin of your lab manual or on your schedule of activities (see Table 8.10).

3. Compare your observed and expected results for cross **A** and cross **B**. Refer to your hypothesis and predictions and use the class data from Table 8.11.

Discussion

1. Did the results support your hypothesis? Explain, comparing your predictions and results.

2. If the results do not support expected Mendelian ratios, what are other possible patterns of inheritance that could explain the results?

3. Why would it be inappropriate to use the chi-square test for these data?

4. What additional experiments can you suggest to further test your original or modified hypothesis? Outline your crosses.

Questions for Review

1. Review all terminology used in this laboratory. Define and provide examples of all terms indicated in bold type.

2. The fruit fly, *Drosophila,* is an extremely useful organism in the study of genetics today. *Brassica rapa,* a Fast Plant, is also becoming a popular organism for study. Based on your knowledge and experience, what are some important characteristics of fruit flies and Fast Plants that make them ideal for genetic experiments?

3. In general terms, explain why a scientist would use the chi-square test as part of his or her data analysis. What important information does it provide?

Applying Your Knowledge

1. If two traits, dwarfism and stem color, were both on the same pair of chromosomes, would you expect an F_2 generation of $9:3:3:1$ for a dihybrid cross? Use Mendel's laws and your understanding of meiosis to explain your answer. Refer to Figure 8.2, if needed.

2. What other examples of inheritance can you find that would not follow Mendel's basic model?

3. Molecular geneticists interested in the evolutionary history of the human race have concentrated their research on samples of DNA from women representing all races and continents. Why might the DNA of women—and not men—be of interest?

References

Williams, Paul H. "Bee-Sticks, an Aid in Pollinating Cruciferae." 1980, *HortScience,* vol. 115 (6) pp. 802–803.

Wisconsin Fast Plants Manual. Burlington, NC: Carolina Biological Supply, 1989. Procedures for exercises adapted by permission of Carolina Biological Supply, Burlington, NC 27215, and Wisconsin Alumni Research Foundation, Madison, WI 53707. © 1989 Wisconsin Alumni Research Foundation.

Websites

Practice genetics problems:
http://biology.clc.uc.edu/courses/bio105/geneprob.html

Wisconsin Fast Plants web site:
http://www.fastplants.org/

Carolina Biological Supply Co. information on Fast Plants:

http://www.carolina.com/fastplants/wfpids.html

Mendelian Genetics: *Drosophila*

Laboratory Objectives

After completing this lab topic, you should be able to:

1. Discuss why *Drosophila* is one of the most important organisms used in eukaryotic genetics.
2. Explain how a biochemical assay can be used as an indication of biochemical phenotypes.
3. Describe the inheritance pattern of the gene for aldehyde oxidase.
4. Name genes using the convention recommended in *Drosophila* genetics.
5. Determine parental genotypes by investigating offspring.
6. Use the chi-square test to evaluate experimental results.
7. Describe gene mapping.

Introduction

The exercises in this lab topic exemplify some of the classic areas of genetic research that led to an understanding of the principles governing the inheritance of specific traits. Initial experiments were concerned with the transmission of hereditary factors from generation to generation and led to the discovery of Mendel's laws, which define the pattern of inheritance of individual genes. Later experiments identified chromosomes as the physical structures wherein the units of heredity reside and provided firm cytological evidence for the theorems of Mendelian genetics. More recent investigations have addressed the biochemical and molecular basis of gene expression.

One of the classic tools of genetic research is the fruit fly, *Drosophila melanogaster.* This organism has been used in genetic studies for nearly 80 years and has played an important role in the development of our knowledge of heredity. *Drosophila melanogaster* has been important in such studies because this organism has a very low chromosome number. The haploid (*n*) number of chromosomes is 4, and the chromosomes are designated X(1), 2, 3, and 4 (Figure 9.1). The 2, 3, and 4 chromosomes are the same in both sexes and are referred to as **autosomes** to distinguish them from the X and Y **sex chromosomes.** *Drosophila* females are characterized by two X chromosomes while *Drosophila* males have an X and a Y chromosome. Chromosome 4 and the Y chromosome contain so few genes that, for all practical purposes, they can be ignored. Thus, almost the entire genetic content of the *Drosophila* genome resides on only three chromosomes: X, 2, and 3.

Figure 9.1.
Metaphase chromosomes from a dividing cell in *Drosophila melanogaster.* The haploid number of chromosomes is 4. Females have two X chromosomes while males have an X and a Y chromosome.

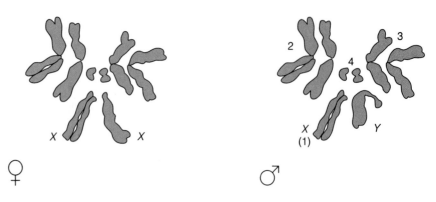

Another characteristic of *Drosophila* that makes it an excellent genetic research tool is its short generation time. At 25°C, a *Drosophila* culture will produce a new generation in 10 days: 1 day in the egg (embryo) stage, 5 days in the larval stage, and 4 days in the pupal stage (Figure 9.2).

You will use *Drosophila melanogaster* in each of the following exercises. You will be asked to investigate the inheritance of a gene called *aldox,* and you will determine the position of this gene on its chromosome; that is, you will map the gene.

E X E R C I S E   9 . 1
Establishing the Enzyme Reaction Controls

Materials

stereoscopic microscope
vials 1a and 1b
ether dropper bottles or FlyNap
re-etherizer
2 spot assay plates
large and small white index cards

toothpicks
pestle
Kimwipes®
assay mixture dropper bottles
water bottle

Introduction

The trait to be studied in each exercise of this lab topic is the presence or absence of the enzyme **aldehyde oxidase (AO),** which catalyzes the oxidation of a number of aldehydes, including acetaldehyde and benzaldehyde. AO activity is controlled by one gene, the **aldox** gene. Although *Drosophila* flies possess AO activity, its physiological importance to the organism is not well understood. Mutant strains that exhibit no AO activity are available, and their viability and fertility are normal. This latter observation indicates that AO activity is not a vital enzyme activity for a fly that is reared in a laboratory setting.

To test for AO activity, you will use an **enzyme spot test,** or **spot assay.** This test works on the following principle: In the presence of AO, the substrate benzaldehyde, when mixed with the color indicator nitroblue-tetrazoliun (NBT)–phenazine methylsulfate (PMS), will oxidize to form ben-

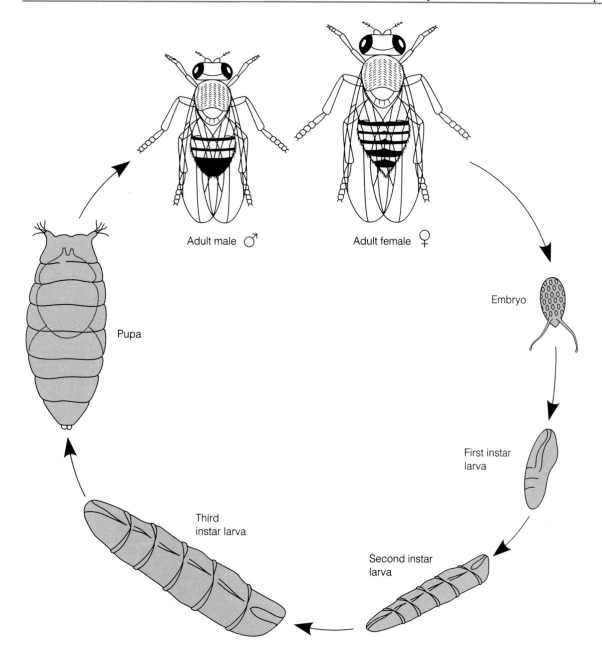

Figure 9.2.
Developmental stages of *Drosophila melanogaster*. An embryo hatches to a
larva, which undergoes two molts and then pupates. The pupae develop into
adult winged flies.

zoic acid and a blue color. The blue color indicates that the enzyme is present and active.

This reaction can be diagrammed as follows:

Substrate	**Enzyme AO**	**Product**
benzaldehyde + NBT + PMS	$\longrightarrow$	benzoic acid + blue products
(assay mixture)		

Without AO, the reaction will not proceed, and no blue color will be produced.

This first exercise will demonstrate the positive and negative enzyme reactions as seen in the spot assay. Vial 1a contains flies that have the enzyme present. What will be the results if flies from this vial are homogenized in the assay mixture? Will they demonstrate AO activity? (Remember that AO activity produces a blue color with the assay.)

Vial 1b contains flies that do not have the enzyme present. What will be the results if these flies are homogenized in the assay mixture? Will they demonstrate AO activity?

Hypothesis

Hypothesize about AO activity in flies from vial 1a and flies from vial 1b.

Prediction

Predict the results of the experiment (test) based on your hypothesis (if/then).

Procedure

1. Anesthetize the flies in vials 1a and 1b as follows:

    a. From your ether dropper bottle, place 2 or 3 drops of ether on the cotton plug of your vial. Be sure to recap the ether bottle tightly.

     Remember that ethyl ether fumes are explosive. Use in a well-ventilated room. No flames or sparks! If a spill occurs, call an instructor.

    b. Invert your vial so that the adult flies will fall asleep on the cotton plug rather than on the culture medium.

    c. When flies have become immobilized on the cotton plug, remove them for examination.

    d. Using the stereoscopic microscope, examine the flies on a white card using a toothpick to turn them.

    e. A fly "re-etherizer" petri dish with a gauze pad taped in the lid is provided in case the adults begin to awaken before phenotype classification is concluded. Place the lid/gauze pad saturated with ether over the flies when needed.

2. From each vial, identify two or three females and two or three males, and return the rest to their appropriate vial. (Vial 1a will be used again in later experiments.) Use the following criteria to distinguish adult males and females (Figure 9.3).

a. *Size.* The female is generally larger than the male.

b. *Shape of abdomen.* The female abdomen is larger and more pointed than the male abdomen.

c. *Abdominal pigmentation.* In dorsal view, the alternating dark and light bands on the entire rear portion of the female abdomen are visible; the last few segments of the male are uniformly pigmented.

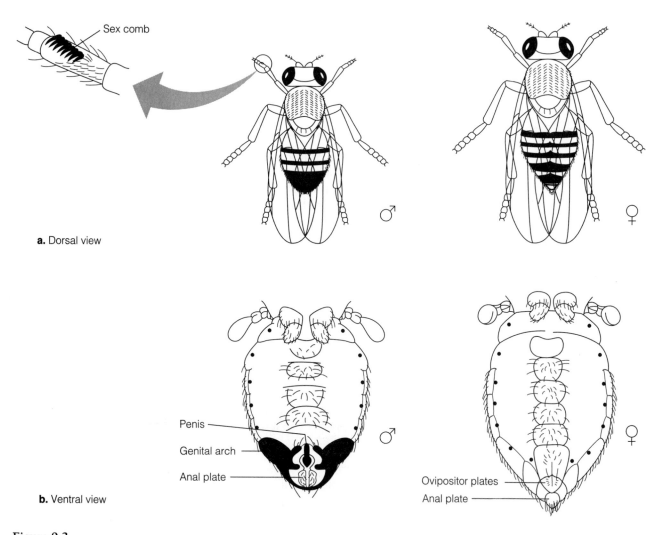

Figure 9.3.
Characteristics of male and female *Drosophila melanogaster*. The female is larger and has alternating dark and light dorsal bands on the abdomen. The dorsal abdomen of the male is uniformly pigmented. Conspicuous sex combs are visible on each foreleg of the male. In ventral view, the male's darkly pigmented genital arch and penis are visible.

d. *Sex comb.* On males, there is a tiny brushlike tuft of hairs on the basal tarsal segment of each foreleg. This is the most reliable characteristic for sexing males accurately.

e. *External genitalia.* On the ventral portion of the abdomen, the female has anal plates and lightly pigmented ovipositor plates. The male has anal plates and a darkly pigmented genital arch and penis.

3. Keeping track of the sexes, place the flies from vial 1a in one row of a spot assay plate, one fly per well.

4. Place the flies from vial 1b in a different row.

The next two steps need to be done quickly, since the assay mixture is light sensitive. Cover the spot plate with an index card if there is any delay between steps.

5. Add 1 drop of assay mixture to each well.

The assay mixture contains carcinogens. Do not allow it to contact skin. Wash hands thoroughly after performing the tests. Disposable gloves may be provided for your use. Notify an instructor if a spill occurs. If an instructor is unavailable, wipe up the spill wearing disposable gloves and using dry paper towels. Follow dry towels with towels soaked in soap and water. Dispose of all towels and gloves in a plastic bag in the trash.

6. Homogenize the flies with a pestle. Wipe off the pestle after each fly to avoid contamination. Why is it necessary to homogenize the flies?

7. Place the spot plate in a place away from light, such as a desk drawer.

8. After 5 minutes, check the reactions, and record your results in Table 9.1 in the Results section.

9. Thoroughly rinse your spot plate, and shake off the excess water.

Results

Complete Table 9.1 on the next page as the results of the assay tests are determined.

Table 9.1

AO Activity in Male and Female Flies from Vials 1a and 1b

Vial 1a (AO Present)			Vial 1b (AO Absent)		
Fly No.	Sex (F, M)	AO Activity (+/–)	Fly No.	Sex (F, M)	AO Activity (+/–)
1			1		
2			2		
3			3		
4			4		
5			5		
6			6		

Discussion

1. Do your results match your predictions?

2. Does the sex of the fly appear to have an impact on the results of the assay test?

3. Which two characteristics are most useful to your group in determining the sex of flies?

EXERCISE 9.2

Determining the Pattern of Inheritance of the Aldox Gene

Materials

vial 1a
vial 2
remaining materials from Exercise 9.1

Introduction

This exercise initiates our study of the pattern of inheritance of the aldox gene, which determines the activity of aldehyde oxidase (AO).

 The gene is called the *aldox gene;* the enzyme produced by this gene is *aldehyde oxidase* and is abbreviated AO.

In this exercise, you will determine which **allele** (form of the gene) is dominant: enzyme-present or enzyme-absent. In addition, you will determine if the gene is **autosomal** or **sex-linked.** A sex-linked gene is located on one sex chromosome but not on the other. An autosomal gene is located on any chromosome *except* a sex chromosome. Finally, you will use this information to name the gene according to conventional naming procedures used by *Drosophila* geneticists.

The organisms you will use are in vial 2, which contains the offspring (called F_1 progeny) from a mating between a female that *lacks the enzyme* and a male that *has the enzyme*. For now, name the enzyme-present allele *AO-present* and the enzyme-absent allele *AO-absent*. The female is from a stock of flies that, when inbred, *consistently* lacks the enzyme from generation to generation. We say that this stock **breeds true** for AO-absent. The male is from a stock that *consistently* has the enzyme from generation to generation; that is, it breeds true for AO-present. This stock, which has the enzyme, is genetically like flies most commonly found in nature and is called the **wild type.**

It is necessary to understand this background information to be able to predict the outcome of this cross. To help you in your predictions, answer the following questions.

1. What is the genotype of the female (maternal parent—lacks the enzyme) in our cross?

2. What would be the genotype of the male (paternal parent—has the enzyme) in our cross if the gene is *not* sex-linked?

3. What would be the genotype of the male if the gene *is* sex-linked?

4. What would be the genotypes of the F_1 progeny if the gene is *not* sex-linked?

5. What would be the genotype if the gene *is* sex-linked?

Hypothesis

Hypothesize about the inheritance of this gene. Is it sex-linked? According to your hypothesis, what will be the genotypes of the parents?

Prediction

Predict the offspring from the hypothesized parents. (*Hint:* Set up a Punnett square.)

Procedure

1. Anesthetize the flies in vial 2.
2. Count out ten males and ten females. Keep track of the sexes of flies as you place them in the spot plate. Record the sex of each fly in Table 9.2.

 It is easier to keep accurate records if you put all males in one row of the spot plate and all females in another row. Do not write on the spot plates!

3. Perform the spot assay as described in Exercise 9.1 with the following addition: From vial 1a, select a single fly and assay it with this and all following experiments. This will provide you with a *positive control* to compare with your unknown assays.

 The assay mixture is light sensitive. Cover the spot plate with an index card between steps.

---

4. When you see that the positive control has turned blue, indicating that the assay is working, record the results in Table 9.2.
5. Rinse out the spot plate carefully.

Results

Record the sex of each fly and the results of the spot assay tests in Table 9.2.

Table 9.2

Data Sheet for Exercise 9.2: Results of Spot Assay Tests on F_1 Progeny from a Female That Lacks AO Activity and a Male That Has AO Activity

Fly No.	Sex (F, M)	AO Activity (+/−)	Fly No.	Sex (F, M)	AO Activity (+/−)
1			11		
2			12		
3			13		
4			14		
5			15		
6			16		
7			17		
8			18		
9			19		
10			20		
Positive control:					

Discussion

1. What allele appears to be dominant?

2. What evidence of your results in Table 9.2 supports your answer?

3. Determine the conventional way to name this gene. The following information will assist you. For any gene with two alleles, there exists the wild type and the mutation. Recall that the wild type is the allele most commonly found in nature. In this case, the wild type is AO-present. AO-absent is considered a **mutation,** a change in the DNA of the gene. In naming genes and alleles, give the gene an appropriate name. (In this case, the gene is named *aldox* because the enzyme that it produces catalyzes the oxidation of aldehydes.) If the mutation is dominant, capitalize the first letter in the name. If the mutation is recessive, do not capitalize. Based on the results of your experiment (see question 1), should the aldox gene be written beginning with a capital or a lower-case letter?

4. Correctly write the names of the wild-type and mutant alleles. By convention, wild-type alleles are designated by a superscript + after the name.

5. Did you hypothesize that the gene was sex-linked (on a sex chromosome) or autosomal (not on a sex chromosome)?

6. Describe how your results either support or falsify your hypothesis.

7. Write a statement describing your conclusions from this experiment.

EXERCISE 9.3

Determining Parental Genotypes Using Evidence from Progeny

Materials

vial 1a
vial 3
remaining materials from Exercise 9.1

Introduction

Once the pattern of inheritance has been determined, this information can be used to predict genotypes and phenotypes of individuals by observing parents, siblings, and offspring. Vial 3 contains the first-generation (F_1) progeny from a mating between unknown parents. The objective of this exercise is to determine the genotypes of the parents. At this stage in the investigation, you have no data from observations on which to base a hypothesis. The following procedure will allow you to collect preliminary data, then, using this data, to propose and test a hypothesis about the genotypes of the parents.

Procedure, Preliminary Observations

1. Anesthetize the flies in vial 3.
2. Count out 24 flies and place them in individual spot plate wells.
3. Perform the spot assay, including a positive control, a fly from vial 1a.
4. Record the results on *two* data sheets, Table 9.3, and the data sheet for the total class (provided by the instructor).

Results, Preliminary Observations

1. Record results of assay tests on progeny of the unknown parents in Table 9.3 on the next page.
2. Total the number of offspring in each phenotype category.

                        Your Totals   Class Totals

   AO-present _____   _____

   AO-absent _____   _____

3. Review observations made in previous experiments.
   a. Is the trait sex-linked?

   b. Which allele is dominant?

Table 9.3
Data Sheet for Exercise 9.3: Results of Assay
Tests on Progeny of Unknown Parents

Fly No.	AO Activity (+/−)	Fly No.	AO Activity (+/−)
1		13	
2		14	
3		15	
4		16	
5		17	
6		18	
7		19	
8		20	
9		21	
10		22	
11		23	
12		24	
Positive control:			

Hypothesis

Using all observations, hypothesize the genotypes of the parent flies, making sure to name the alleles correctly.

Prediction

Predict the results of the experiment (if/then).

Procedure—Testing Your Hypothesis

Using the total class data and Table 9.4, refer to Appendix B and perform the chi-square test to determine if the results of the exercise support or falsify your hypothesis. Calculate the expected values for each trait based on the total number of flies counted in your class. (For a discussion of the chi-square test, see Appendix B.)

Results

Complete the chi-square calculations in Table 9.4.

Table 9.4
Chi-Square Calculations to Evaluate Results of Exercise 9.3
(Observed value represents total class data.)

	AO Activity (+)	AO Activity (−)
Observed value (o)		
Expected value (e)		
Deviation ($o - e$) or d		
Deviation² (d^2)		
d^2/e		
Chi-square (χ^2) $= \Sigma d^2/e$		
Degrees of freedom (df)		
Probability (p) (see a χ^2 table)		

Discussion

1. Do the class results support or falsify your hypothesis?

2. Does this experiment support or contradict your conclusions concerning the pattern of inheritance derived from Experiment 9.2?

EXERCISE 9.4
Mapping Genes

Materials

vial 1a
vial 4
remaining materials from Exercise 9.1

Introduction

In this exercise, you will investigate the inheritance of two genes in *Drosophila*: the aldox gene and a gene that influences eye color named **sepia**. In the wild-type fly (sepia$^+$), eye color is red. In the mutant fly, eye color is dark brown. The wild-type allele is dominant over the mutant. The flies you will be studying are the offspring from a cross in which the parents differ in these two genes: a **dihybrid cross**. You will ask if these two genes are transmitted from parent to offspring *linked* together or if each gene is inherited independently of the other. If genes are transmitted from parent to offspring linked together, this means that they are located on the same chromosome. Then if the location of one gene is known, the pattern of inheritance can provide evidence that will allow you to determine the location of the second gene. With this information, you can construct a map showing gene locations.

Vial 4 contains the F_1 progeny from a mating between parents having the following genotypes:

$$\text{Parent 1} \qquad\qquad \text{Parent 2}$$
$$\frac{\text{sepia}^+ \text{ aldox}^+}{\text{sepia aldox}} \quad\times\quad \frac{\text{sepia aldox}}{\text{sepia aldox}}$$

where sepia$^+$ represents the dominant, wild-type eye color allele that produces red eye color and sepia represents the mutant, recessive allele that produces a dark-brown eye color.

Hypothesis

Hypothesize about the inheritance of these two genes. Are they inherited linked together or independently of each other?

Prediction

Predict the ratios of phenotypic classes of offspring resulting from the mating described above.

Use a Punnett square to illustrate your prediction.

Procedure

1. Anesthetize the flies in vial 4.
2. Count out 50 flies, and classify them on the basis of eye color (red or sepia).
3. Keeping the eye colors separate, perform the spot assay, including a positive control from vial 1a.
4. Record the results in Table 9.5 on the next page.
5. Rinse out the spot plate.

Results

1. Record the results of the eye color classification and the spot test for each fly in Table 9.5. Total your results below. Add your results to the total class data sheet provided by the instructor. Total the class data and record below.

	Your Totals	Class Totals
red eyes, AO-present	_____	_____
red eyes, AO-absent	_____	_____
sepia eyes, AO-present	_____	_____
sepia eyes, AO-absent	_____	_____

2. What phenotypic classes were observed in the total class data, and in what approximate ratio?

3. On separate paper, using class totals, perform the chi-square test to determine if the results support or falsify your hypothesis (see Appendix B).

Table 9.5
Data Sheet for Exercise 9.4: Mapping Genes,
Recording Eye Color and AO Activity for 50 Flies

Fly No.	Eye Color	AO (+/−)	Fly No.	Eye Color	AO (+/−)
1			26		
2			27		
3			28		
4			29		
5			30		
6			31		
7			32		
8			33		
9			34		
10			35		
11			36		
12			37		
13			38		
14			39		
15			40		
16			41		
17			42		
18			43		
19			44		
20			45		
21			46		
22			47		
23			48		
24			49		
25			50		

Discussion

1. Do the data support your predicted results?

2. If the results differ from what was expected, can you suggest an explanation for these differences?

3. Suppose that the aldox gene and the sepia gene are located on the same chromosome. This means that when meiosis takes place, the two genes will *not* assort independently but will be linked together, moving into the same gamete *unless crossing over has taken place* (refer to Lab Topic 7 to review independent assortment in meiosis). Only if crossing over takes place will **recombinant classes** of phenotypes be observed. A **recombinant chromosome** is one emerging from meiosis with a combination of alleles not present on the chromosomes entering meiosis.

   What are the recombinant classes of phenotypes for this cross?

4. The distance between two genes is related to the frequency of recombinants produced during meiosis. The closer two genes are, the fewer recombinants. Geneticists use an arbitrary measure, or map unit, to represent the distance between two genes. The specific relationship between map units and recombinants is

$$\text{Map units} = \frac{\text{number of recombinants}}{\text{total}} \times 100$$

5. In your experiment, did recombinant classes exist? If they did, how frequent were they?

6. Do your data suggest that aldox and sepia are on the same chromosome, and if so, how far is the aldox locus from the sepia locus?

7. What would be the exact map position of the aldox locus if the sepia locus is 26.0? Are you sure?

Questions for Review

1. List the most obvious characteristics used to determine the sex of a fruit fly.

2. In *Drosophila,* crosses between male flies with normal bristles on their bodies (the wild type) and female flies with short, stubby bristles result in an F_1 generation with all flies having short, stubby bristles. Which allele, normal or mutant, is dominant?

    Using *Drosophila* convention, suggest an appropriate name or designation for this gene.

Applying Your Knowledge

1. In a testcross between a heterozygous tomato plant with round fruit shape and smooth fruit skin and a homozygous recessive plant with elongated fruit shape and fuzzy skin, the following numbers of offspring were counted: smooth, round = 246; smooth, long = 24; fuzzy, round = 24; fuzzy, long = 266.

    Do these results deviate from expected results of a testcross? Explain fully.

2. Explain why we cannot use a testcross to detect linkage between two genes located on the same chromosome 50 map units apart.

References

This lab topic was first published as J. G. Morgan and V. Finnerty, "Inheritance of Aldehyde Oxidase in *Drosophila melanogaster*" in *Tested Studies for Laboratory Teaching* (Volume 12), Proceedings of the 12th Workshop/Conference of the Association for Biology Laboratory Education (ABLE), Corey A. Goldman, Editor. Used by permission.

Manning, Gerard. The *Drosophila* Virtual Library. [online] available at http://www.ceolas.org/fly/, 2001.

Website

Interactive fruitfly genetics lab, requires registration: http://biologylab.awlonline.com/Flylab/

Molecular Biology

Laboratory Objectives

After completing this lab topic, you should be able to:

1. Describe the function of restriction enzymes.
2. Discuss the basic principles of electrophoresis in general and for DNA specifically.
3. Construct a tentative map of DNA molecules based on restriction fragments.
4. Explain the use of enzymes to map DNA molecules, and discuss the importance of mapping.
5. Use gel results to estimate DNA fragment sizes.
6. Discuss the universality of the genetic code.
7. Describe ways in which the technology of molecular biology is being used in industry, medicine, criminal justice, agriculture, and basic research.

Introduction

Although a German scientist, Friedrich Miescher, isolated **DNA (deoxyribonucleic acid)** in 1869, it took nearly a century to recognize this chemical as the genetic material for all living cells. In 1953, James Watson and Francis Crick determined that DNA structure is a **double helix,** and in the following decade the essence of the genetic code was solidly established. Scientists developed DNA technology in the 1980s, and the importance and applications of this achievement were soon realized. Scientists are now applying recombinant DNA technology in hopes of curing cancer, Alzheimer's disease, heart disease, and many other hereditary diseases. DNA technology is important in areas other than medical applications. These include the genetic manipulation of corn for high yield and enhanced flavor (Figure 10.1) and the genetic manipulation of tomatoes for slower ripening. What's more, the criminal justice system is now using DNA fingerprinting to identify criminals in cases of rape and murder.

In 2000, DNA research reached another milestone when scientists announced that essentially all the human genome had been sequenced. Deciphering the sequence of chemical "letters" that make up the genome is the next step in knowing how human genes work. Although scientists still must determine even basic information such as how many genes make up the human genome, what proteins they produce in the body, and how these proteins interact, knowing the 3 billion or so letters is a remarkable achievement.

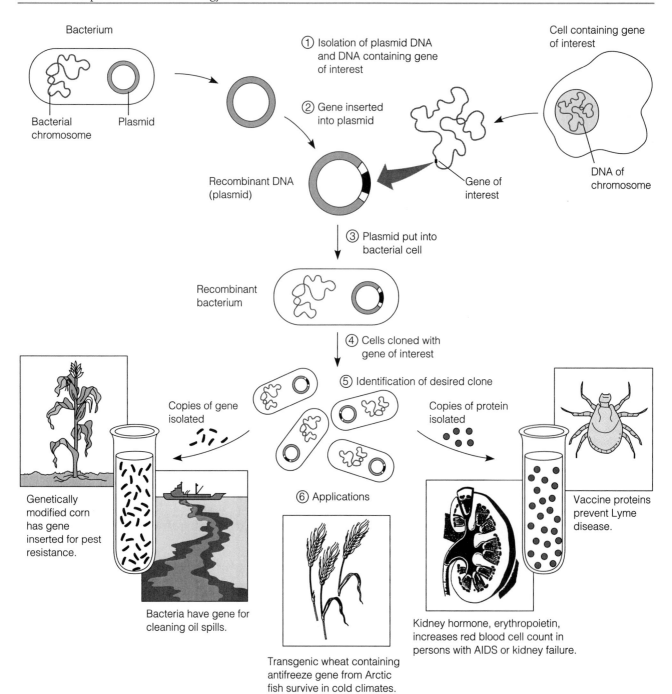

Figure 10.1.

Overview of recombinant DNA technology. 1. The genetic engineer isolates plasmid DNA from bacteria and purifies DNA containing the gene of interest from another cell. **2.** A piece of DNA containing the gene is inserted into the plasmid, producing recombinant DNA. **3.** The plasmid is put back into a bacterial cell. **4.** This genetically engineered bacterium is then grown in culture. The bacterial culture now contains many copies of the gene (one per cell in this example). **5.** The cell clone carrying the gene of interest is isolated. **6.** The bottom of the figure illustrates a few of the current applications of genetically engineered bacteria.

Not only does an understanding of DNA and how it works have medical and agricultural applications, understanding the universality of the genetic code has applications in studies of evolution. The similarity in structure and function of many of the protein products determined by this code in organisms as diverse as viruses, mosses, birds, and human beings provides some of the most convincing evidence supporting the theory of evolution. For example, cytochrome *c*, an important electron carrier in the respiratory pathway, is found in all aerobic eukaryotes. Although mutations have occurred over time, the structure of cytochrome *c* is similar in all members of this diverse group of organisms. This universality has allowed information gleaned from the study of organisms such as yeasts and flies to be applied to human beings. Molecular biology is one powerful tool that has been used successfully to explore the evolutionary relationships among living organisms on Earth.

In the following exercise, you will employ some of the basic molecular techniques used in laboratories worldwide to study everything from the virus that causes AIDS to DNA extracted from mummies. Following the procedures outlined in Exercise 10.1, you will use enzymes to cut the DNA and propose a tentative map of the location of genetic material. Then you will be asked to answer a series of questions that will lead you through a process of analyzing your results and constructing a restriction map.

EXERCISE 10.1

Mapping DNA Using Restriction Enzymes and Electrophoresis

Materials

gel electrophoresis apparatus:
    gel plates
    comb to make wells
    chamber for electrophoresis
    chamber cover
power supply with electrodes
heat-resistant gloves
250-mL Erlenmeyer flask
100-mL graduated cylinders
microwave or hot plate
deionized water
agarose
pUC 19 (plasmid) DNA
TBE (Tris base; boric acid; ethylenediaminetetraacetic acid, or EDTA; NaOH), 10✕ to be diluted in lab to 1✕
microcentrifuge (helpful, not necessary)
micropipettors and tips or microcapillary pipettes and plunger (various sizes from 1 to 100 μL)
37°C incubator or water bath
55°C water bath for agarose
portable freezer box or ice chest
Polaroid camera with Polaroid 667 film

ice
restriction enzymes:
    Ava II, *Pvu* II
restriction buffers
molecular weight markers
gel loading dye (bromophenol blue)
plastic wrap
15 1.5-mL microtubes (various colors)
thermometer
metric rulers

methylene blue stain:
    0.025% methylene blue
    staining trays
    light box
    deionized water

alternative stain: ethidium bromide
    ethidium bromide
    UV-protective goggles
    UV light box
    disposable gloves

Introduction

The first step in any refined DNA analysis, such as DNA sequencing or expressing a gene in another organism, is to construct a map of the molecule. Scientists use naturally occurring enzymes to cut large DNA molecules into smaller pieces. These fragments are sorted and separated by size using a technique called *electrophoresis*. The results are then used to reconstruct the DNA molecule. This initial process of DNA analysis is called **mapping.**

Molecular biologists use some of nature's own tools to do this mapping. In this experiment, you will use **restriction endonucleases** to help manipulate DNA molecules. Restriction endonucleases are enzymes that have been purified from different species of bacteria. Restriction enzymes recognize a specific DNA sequence wherever it occurs in a DNA molecule (Figure 10.2) and cut the DNA at or near that site; thus, the name: *Restriction* refers to cutting, *endo* to inside a molecule (as opposed to *exo*, which refers to the ends of a molecule), and *nuclease* to the digestion of a nucleic acid such as DNA. Each restriction enzyme is named for the species of bacteria from which it is isolated. For example, *Eco* RI was discovered in *Escherichia coli*, strain R, Roman numeral "I."

Cutting (also called **restricting**, or **digesting**) requires energy in the form of adenosine triphosphate (ATP) and involves a physical cleaving of chemical bonds. The specific recognition sites where the cuts occur are often **palindromic;** that is, the sequences of the complementary strands read the same backward and forward (Figure 10.3). (The phrase *race car* is an example of a palindrome. Can you think of others?) In nature, bacteria use restriction enzymes to recognize and metabolize foreign DNA. This constitutes a primitive immune system, since it recognizes and rids the organism of an invader.

In this exercise, you will use restriction endonucleases in conjunction with gel electrophoresis to map the 2,686-**base-pair** (bp) pUC 19 **plasmid.** A plasmid is a relatively small extrachromosomal and circular molecule of DNA found in bacteria and yeasts. pUC 19, a plasmid found in *E. coli*, is one of the most significant cloning tools used in molecular biology labs. Because of its size and DNA sequence, it is an excellent system to study.

Once you have cut pUC 19 into discrete fragments, you will need a method of detecting the digested products. Agarose gel electrophoresis is commonly used to separate these fragments (Figure 10.4). The DNA fragments are placed in the gel, and an electric current runs through the matrix of the gel-like agarose. The fragments will move through the gel at different rates, depending on their charge and size. How does the charge of a DNA molecule vary with its size? How is this different from what you see with proteins?

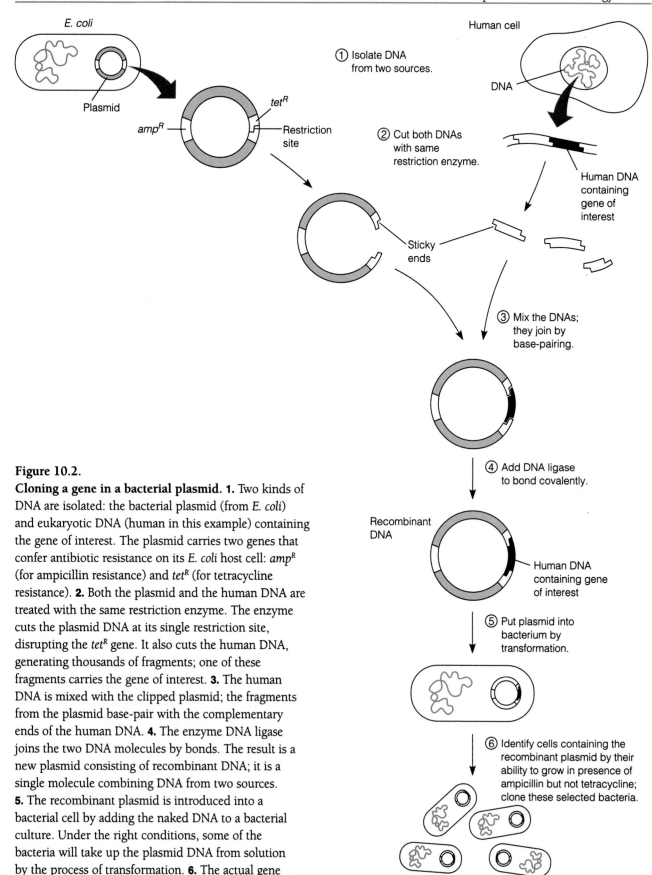

Figure 10.2.
Cloning a gene in a bacterial plasmid. 1. Two kinds of DNA are isolated: the bacterial plasmid (from *E. coli*) and eukaryotic DNA (human in this example) containing the gene of interest. The plasmid carries two genes that confer antibiotic resistance on its *E. coli* host cell: amp^R (for ampicillin resistance) and tet^R (for tetracycline resistance). **2.** Both the plasmid and the human DNA are treated with the same restriction enzyme. The enzyme cuts the plasmid DNA at its single restriction site, disrupting the tet^R gene. It also cuts the human DNA, generating thousands of fragments; one of these fragments carries the gene of interest. **3.** The human DNA is mixed with the clipped plasmid; the fragments from the plasmid base-pair with the complementary ends of the human DNA. **4.** The enzyme DNA ligase joins the two DNA molecules by bonds. The result is a new plasmid consisting of recombinant DNA; it is a single molecule combining DNA from two sources. **5.** The recombinant plasmid is introduced into a bacterial cell by adding the naked DNA to a bacterial culture. Under the right conditions, some of the bacteria will take up the plasmid DNA from solution by the process of transformation. **6.** The actual gene cloning takes place, producing multiple copies of the gene of interest.

Figure 10.3.

Using a restriction enzyme and DNA ligase to make recombinant DNA. The restriction enzyme (*Eco* RI) recognizes a six-base-pair sequence and makes staggered cuts in the sugar-phosphate backbone within this sequence. Notice that the recognition sequence along one DNA strand is the exact reverse of the sequence along the complementary strand (that is, they are palindromic). Complementary ends will stick to each other by hydrogen bonding, rejoining fragments in their original combinations or in new recombinant combinations. The enzyme DNA ligase can then catalyze the formation of bonds joining the fragment ends. If the fragments are from two different sources, the result is recombinant DNA.

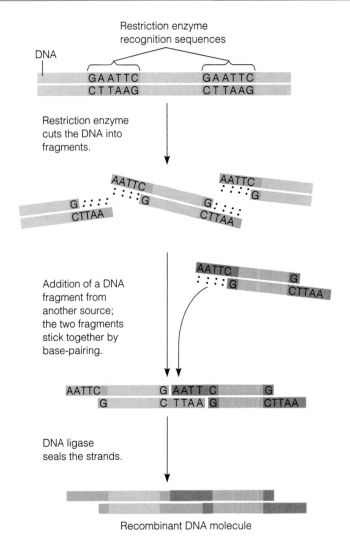

(For another application of electrophoresis, refer to Lab Topic 12, Population Genetics II: Determining Genetic Variation.) After running the DNA samples in a gel, the gel is stained with methylene blue and viewed on a light box, allowing the visualization of discrete DNA bands on the gel. Alternatively, the gel is stained with ethidium bromide, which binds the DNA and fluoresces under ultraviolet (UV) light.

Preliminary Questions

Based on your knowledge of the structure and function of DNA and the technique of gel electrophoresis, answer the following questions before beginning your investigation.

1. DNA will move through the gel along the electric current, its direction depending in part on the molecule's charge. In which direction, positive to negative or vice versa, will DNA move in the electric field? Why?

Figure 10.4.
Electrophoresis apparatus. The apparatus should include the gel tray, comb, agarose, running chamber with electrodes, and power supply.

2. Given that all DNA molecules have similar charge-to-mass ratios, what property do you think is most important in determining migration within the gel? Why?

3. To map the plasmid, you will need to know the size of the fragments on the gel. Can you suggest a way to determine the size of these fragments?

4. Given that the distance a fragment of DNA moves into the gel is inversely proportional to the log of the size of the fragment in base pairs, what will a graph of fragments 0.5, 1, 5, 10, and 20 kilobases look like? (The

size of DNA fragments is measured in nucleotide bases, and 1,000 bp equals 1 kilobase, Kb.) What do the axes represent?

Hypothesis

Based on your understanding of restriction enzymes and electrophoresis, state a hypothesis concerning the migration of DNA fragments.

Prediction

Predict the banding patterns you will observe in the gel based on your hypothesis.

Procedure

1. Practice pipetting and loading a gel

If you have not used a micropipettor or microcapillary pipette before, practice the technique. You may want to have your instructor check your technique because errors as small as one-half microliter can result in inappropriate digests. Although a microliter (µL) seems very small, it can be an amazing amount in molecular biology. For example, 1 µL might contain the amount of DNA in all the genes in a human cell!

a. Set the micropipettor to 20 µL.

b. Attach the pipette tip.

c. Using the practice mixture of water, glycerin, and a blue dye, practice drawing the liquid into the pipette tip. Micropipettors usually have two stop positions. Depressing the pipette to the *first position* and then releasing it while keeping the tip in the liquid withdraws the correct amount into the pipette. To expel the liquid, the pipette should be depressed to the *second position,* which ensures that no liquid remains in the pipette. Do not withdraw liquids by fully depressing the pipette. You would withdraw an unknown volume.

d. Practice loading a gel. Your instructor has prepared practice gels in a petri dish. The gel should be covered with water. Draw 20 μL into the pipette tip and hold the micropipettor with two hands—one hand to deliver the sample and the other to stabilize the end. Be sure that the sample is all the way down in the tip of the pipette and that there is no air between the sample and the tip. Carefully place the tip just inside the well but not piercing the side or bottom of the well. Slowly release the liquid into the well. All students should practice this procedure several times.

In all cases, a fresh, unused pipette tip or microcapillary pipette should be used every time a pipetting task is performed. This is true even if you are pipetting repeatedly from the same solution, especially in the case of enzymes, which are easily contaminated.

2. Prepare the digestions

a. Your instructor has already prepared three color-coded microtubes containing deionized (DI) water and an appropriate buffer. Obtain these three microtubes and label them **A** (for *Ava* II), **P** (for *Pvu* II), and **AP** (for both). Be sure that your labels correspond to the color key provided by the instructor. Write that color in the appropriate cell in the first column of Table 10.1. When prompted, you will add the amounts of each substance indicated in Table 10.1 to these microtubes. Read and understand steps b–d before you prepare your microtubes. *Do not begin to prepare your microtubes until step e.*

b. The buffers added by your instructor are endonuclease buffers for the respective restriction enzymes. They contain a Tris buffer to maintain the pH and salts such as NaCl to maintain optimal ionic strength and $MgCl_2$ required by the enzymes for catalytic activity.

c. The concentration of pUC 19 DNA solution in Table 10.1 has been prepared by your instructor to contain 1 μg/2 μL of DNA (or 0.5 μg/μL). This DNA will be cut into smaller pieces by the restriction enzymes.

d. You will use restriction enzymes *Ava* II (found in *Anabena variabilis*) and *Pvu* II (found in *Proteus vulgaris*). Enzymes are assigned units based on the amount required to digest 1 μg of DNA in 1 hour. Thus, 5 μg of DNA requires 5 units of enzyme to completely digest the DNA in 1 hour. Given that we will be digesting 1 μg of DNA, at the appropriate time, you will add 1 μL of the appropriate enzyme to each microtube.

Table 10.1
Contents of the Three Tubes

Write the appropriate color for each tube, A, P, and AP. These tubes will be incubated in a 37°C water bath for at least 30 minutes. Some items in the tube have already been added by the instructor. Students will add the DNA and enzyme. Note that each tube should have a total of 20 μL of solution.

Tube Label/Color	Instructor Adds	Student Adds Before Incubating Tube
A/ _____	15 μL DI water 2 μL *Ava* II buffer	2 μL pUC 19 DNA 1 μL *Ava* II enzyme
P/ _____	15 μL DI water 2 μL *Pvu* II buffer	2 μL pUC 19 DNA 1 μL *Pvu* II enzyme
AP/ _____	14 μL DI water 2 μL *Ava* II* buffer	2 μL pUC 19 DNA 1 μL *Ava* II enzyme 1 μL *Pvu* II enzyme

*Use the *Ava II* buffer only.

 The restriction endonucleases must be added last to the mixture. Adding the enzyme early will result in immediate and inappropriate digestion of the DNA!

Once you understand each component added to the microtubes, proceed with step e.

  e. Add 2 μL of pUC 19 DNA to each tube. Tap the bottom of the tube on the lab bench to move the DNA to the bottom of the tube. Return the stock supply of DNA to the cold box.

  f. Add the appropriate enzyme(s) to each tube. Tap the bottom of the tube on the lab bench. Be sure all 20 μL of the reaction mix is together at the bottom of the tube. If it is not, gently tap the bottom of the tube on the lab bench until all the liquid accumulates at the bottom. Return stock supplies of enzymes to the cold box.

  g. Place the tubes at 37°C in a water bath or incubator for at least 30 minutes.

3. Prepare and pour the agarose gel

While the DNA digestions are incubating, your instructor will demonstrate how to make a gel, or you will make your own gel. Refer to Figure 10.5 as you make and pour your gel. Your instructor may have already performed steps a–c. If so, skip to step d.

  a. Put 0.8 g of agarose in a 250-mL Erlenmeyer flask and add 100 mL of 1✕ Tris-borate-EDTA, or TBE (if the TBE is 10✕, be sure to dilute tenfold with deionized water).

(+) red   (−) black

a. Pour gel with comb in position   **b.** Gel covers half of comb teeth   **c.** Load samples

Figure 10.5.
Preparing, loading, and running the gel. (a) Pouring the gel into the gel tray. Note position of comb. (b) The gel is poured so that it covers approximately half the height of the comb teeth. The comb will be removed before the samples are loaded. (c) Loading samples and dye using a micropipettor. (d) Gel running with electrodes attached. Note that the dye bands are moving through the gel.

b. Cover the flask loosely with plastic wrap, and place it in a microwave oven for 2–3 minutes or on a hot plate until the solution boils. In either case, swirl the solution intermittently while wearing a protective glove. Continue until the solution is clear, indicating that all of the agarose is in solution.

 Watch closely to ensure that the solution does not boil over!

d. Gel running—note loading dye moving on gels

c. Allow the gel solution to cool to about 50°C. This process can be expedited by carefully swirling the flask under cool water from the sink. Be careful not to let the gel solidify in the flask.

d. Set the comb over the gel plate so that the teeth rest just above the plate (Figure 10.5a).

e. Slowly pour the gel onto the plate until the solution covers about one-half the height of the comb's teeth (Figure 10.5a, b). Avoid creating bubbles. If any form, quickly and carefully pop them with a sharp object, such as a micropipette tip. (Why would bubbles be a problem?) If the gel is too thin, it will fall apart; if it is too thick, it will take too long to run.

f. If you will be using ethidium bromide, your instructor will add 5 μL of a 10 mg/mL solution to your molten gel and mix so as to have a homogeneous solution. Once the ethidium bromide is added to the gel, you must wear gloves for all work.

Ethidium bromide is carcinogenic and should be handled with gloves that are thrown away immediately after use. Ethidium bromide should be used only in a confined area, and all lab equipment that comes in contact with the ethidium should be treated with bleach. Once ethidium bromide is added to the gel, you must wear gloves and avoid handling the gel.

g. Allow the gel to solidify. It will become opaque.

h. When the gel has hardened, squirt some water around the comb and then pull the comb teeth from the gel slowly, carefully, and evenly. If you pull too fast, the suction will break out the bottom of the wells created by the comb.

4. Load the gel and do electrophoresis of samples

a. Place your gel in the running chamber with the wells nearest the negative (black) electrode, and completely cover the gel with 1X TBE. Orient the running chamber so you can see in the wells. *Do not move the running chamber from this point on.*

b. Before you load the gel, you must assemble three additional samples. Obtain these tubes from the instructor. One sample (labeled 1) is for loading dye only. A second sample (labeled 2) contains **molecular weight markers,** and the third (labeled 6) is for uncut pUC 19 DNA. Your instructor will give you the key for tube colors. Write the color for each of these tubes below. These tubes contain the following, already added by your instructor:

1 (color _____): 20 μL of DI water

2 (color _____): 2 μL of λ DNA, 18 μL of DI water (the molecular weight markers)*

6 (color _____): 18 μL of DI water

*The molecular weight markers (tube 2) are used to determine the size of a DNA fragment. These markers, purchased commercially, are of known sizes with which you can compare your results. You will analyze these markers simultaneously in the same gel with your fragments of unknown size.

c. Assemble the six microtubes with respective solutions that you will load on your gel and arrange in this order in a microtube rack:

(1) Tube 1 from step b (DI water)

(2) Tube 2 from step b (molecular weight markers)

(3) Digestion sample A (*Ava* II digest)

(4) Digestion sample P (*Pvu* II digest)

(5) Digestion sample AP (*Ava* II and *Pvu* II digest)

(6) Tube 6 from step b (DI water)

d. Add 2 μL of loading dye to each of the six tubes. Tap the end of each tube on the table to mix.

e. Add 2 μL of pUC 19 DNA that has not been digested (uncut DNA) to tube 6. Tap the tube on the table. What is the purpose of the uncut or undigested DNA in tube 6?

		(−)			
1	2	3	4	5	6
Loading dye	Mol. weight markers	*Ava* II digest	*Pvu* II digest	*Ava* II / *Pvu* II digest	Uncut DNA
▭	▭	▭	▭	▭	▭

(+)

Figure 10.6.
Wells for loading the gel. Well 1 is used only to practice loading dye. Refer to this figure to ensure that the correct sample is loaded into the appropriate well. Write the appropriate microtube color above each well.

f. Carefully load each of the six samples into their corresponding wells in your gel, as shown in Figure 10.6. Tube 1 will be in well 1, tube 2 in well 2, the *Ava* II digest in well 3, the *Pvu* II digest in well 4, the *Ava* II/*Pvu* II digest in well 5, and the uncut DNA in well 6. *Set your micropipettor to 20 μL.* Load 20 μL of each sample.

Hold the micropipettor with two hands, one hand to deliver the sample and the other to stabilize the end. Be sure that the sample is all the way down in the tip of the pipette and that no air is between the sample and the tip. Place the tip of the pipette below the surface of the buffer and just into the well. Be careful not to puncture the well bottom. Slowly release the sample into the well. The density of the dye will help it sink into the well (Figure 10.5c).

g. Carefully attach positive (red) and negative (black) electrodes to the corresponding terminals (red into red, black into black) on the power supply and on the gel box (Figure 10.5d).

h. Turn the power on to about 100–120 volts, and make sure that small bubbles arise from the electrodes in the gel buffer, verifying current flow. Check the loading dye to make sure that the samples are running in the correct direction, toward the positive electrode (see Figure 10.5d).

Turn off the power to the gel before making any adjustments to the electrophoresis setup.

   i. Run the gel until the loading dye (bromophenol blue) moves down the gel 10 cm (this will take 60–75 minutes). Watch the gel carefully. After 10 minutes, first turn off the power; then check to make sure that the gel is not hot. Accidentally making the gel or gel buffers from the wrong concentration of TBE can result in gel and buffer overheating. If this occurs, your experiment will fail.

5. Practice mapping

While the gel is running, work the practice mapping problem (Exercise 10.2) at the end of the lab topic.

6. Visualize the DNA in the gel

The dye you see on the gel does not stain the DNA but is added so that the movement of the current can be verified. The DNA must be stained by another means, by adding either methylene blue or ethidium bromide. To visualize the DNA, proceed as follows.

Methylene Blue Staining Procedure

1. Turn off the power. Remove the gel tray from the running chamber.
2. Slide the gel out of the tray into a 0.025% solution of methylene blue in a staining tray for 30 minutes.
3. Transfer the gel to a destaining tray and destain for several hours or overnight in enough water to just cover the gel. DNA bands will become visible when the gel is viewed over a visible light box.
4. Photograph the gel using a Polaroid camera.
5. If you do not photograph the gel, measure the distance traveled for each band on the gel, sketch the bands in Figure 10.7, and record your measurements next to the corresponding bands.

Alternative Staining Procedure—Ethidium Bromide

1. Turn off the power. Wear disposable gloves.
2. Remove the gel tray from the running chamber and slide the gel out of the tray onto a UV light source in a darkroom, with lights off to observe the DNA bands. Wear UV-protective goggles! The DNA is stained by the ethidium bromide already present in the gel.

 UV-safe goggles must be worn at all times when viewing gels on the UV box.

3. Photograph the gel using a camera with shields for UV photography. This will minimize exposure to the UV light and provide a permanent record of your gel.

Figure 10.7.
Results of gel electrophoresis.
Sketch the bands seen on your gel.
Record next to each band the distance
traveled, as measured on the photograph, and the size of each fragment,
determined from the molecular weight
marker standards.

4. Using the photograph, measure the distance traveled for each band on
    the gel, sketch the bands in Figure 10.7, and record your measurements
    next to the corresponding bands.

Results

1. What are the "controls" in the gel you ran?

2. In the wells where uncut DNA is run, you will see more than one band.
    Hypothesize: What types of DNA molecules might be represented in
    the different bands? How could you test your ideas? (*Hint:* Remember

that the agarose gel is a matrix and consider if your uncut pUC 19 is linear or circular.)

3. On the photo of your gel, measure the distance traveled for each band on the gel. Sketch the bands in Figure 10.7. Write the distance beside each band. (If you did not photograph the gel, you will already have made these measurements and sketches.)

4. Obtain the known sizes of the DNA molecular weight marker fragments from your instructor. Write these sizes (in bp or Kb) beside the molecular weight marker bands in Figure 10.7. In Figure 10.8, graph the distance traveled by the marker fragments (bands) on your gel (in cm on the x axis) versus the log of the size of the corresponding fragments (in bp or Kb on the y axis). Draw a best-fit line through these points on the graph.

5. Using the graph you constructed in Figure 10.8, determine the size of every other band on the gel. To do this, on the line drawn in Figure 10.8, locate the distance traveled by each restriction fragment (measured and recorded in step 3). Follow this point over to the y axis to determine the number of base pairs in the restriction fragment. Record your results next to the corresponding band in Figure 10.7.

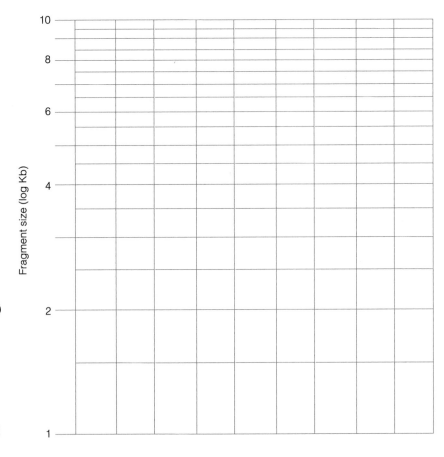

Figure 10.8.
Relationship of distance traveled (cm) and the size of the restriction fragment (log Kb) for known DNA molecular weight markers. Note the distances traveled for each marker, and choose and add an appropriate scale for the x axis. Obtain the known marker sizes from your instructor, and graph them with the corresponding distances from your gel.

Use the following Discussion section as a guide to analyzing your data. If you have not already worked the practice problem, Exercise 10.2, do it now, before continuing to the Discussion section. Your final analysis should include a complete restriction map of the pUC 19 plasmid.

Discussion

Do not begin the discussion questions until you understand the practice problem. Then refer to your results as you answer the following questions about the map of pUC 19.

1. How many Kb is pUC 19?

2. How many DNA fragments were produced by the enzyme digestions?
   By *Ava* II?

   By *Pvu* II?

   By the double digest with *Ava* II and *Pvu* II?

3. Note that both the small fragments generated in the single digest are still present in the double digest. What does this mean?

4. Draw the two restriction fragments for *Ava* II in the space provided. Label the two ends "*Ava* II." Indicate the size of the fragments that were produced in the double digest, and place the *Pvu* II sites on the large *Ava* II fragment. Refer to the practice problem for assistance.

5. Join the fragments you have drawn above to re-create the original plasmid.

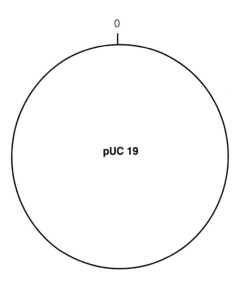

6. Now that you have mapped some DNA fragments, what could you do to further characterize the DNA you have isolated? Refer back to the introduction to this lab topic.

EXERCISE 10.2

Practice Problem for Mapping DNA

The construction of a DNA map is really a logic puzzle. You must compare results for the single digests with those of the double digests (those cut with two enzymes) to correctly orient the sites on the DNA molecule. As with anything else, the process becomes easier with practice. The experience you will gain as you solve the following problem will help prepare you to analyze your exercise results.

You are investigating the pathogenic organism *Bacillus anthrax,* which has recently been isolated from infected individuals. It is known that this organism contains a plasmid, and because these genetic elements often contain antibiotic resistance genes, you decide to begin your investigation with the plasmid. Initial studies indicate that the DNA molecule is 4,000 bp (4 Kb) long.

Figure 10.9.
Restriction pattern generated by restriction digest of the *Bacillus anthrax* plasmid. Note the position of the origin and the molecular weight markers.

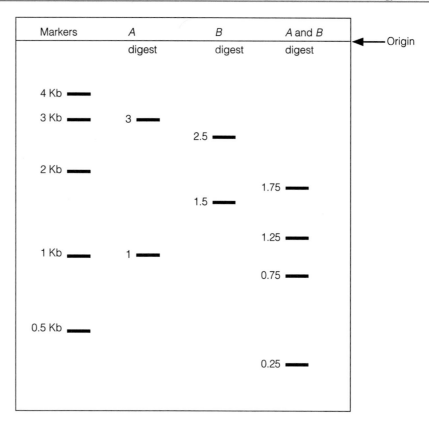

Procedure

1. Inspect the gel diagrammed in Figure 10.9. The restriction pattern shown in the gel diagram was produced by digestion of the bacterial plasmid with two restriction enzymes, *A* and *B*.

2. Determine the number of fragments produced by each enzyme, and determine the number of fragments produced by the double digest.

    How does the number of fragments correlate with the number of restriction sites in the DNA molecule? Remember that plasmids are circular.

3. Note that the size of the fragments has to be determined by comparison to the molecular weight markers. In this problem, the size of the fragments has already been determined and is recorded next to each band.

4. Make a restriction map of the isolated plasmid by determining the relative positions of the restriction sites. The best approach is to realize that the double digest is really an extension of the single digests. For example, the double digest is analogous to taking the bands you see in the *A*

restriction digest and digesting these bands with the *B* enzyme. The smaller bands you see in the double digest should add up to the bands seen in the *A* digest alone.

a. Determine which bands of the double digest come together to form the small *A* restriction fragment.

b. Determine which bands of the double digest make up the large *A* fragment.

c. Draw the two *A* restriction fragments in the space provided, and indicate where the *B* restriction sites fall on the fragments. Indicate the size of the fragments that are produced in the double digest.

d. Do the same analysis on the *B* fragments. Compare the double digest with the single *B* digest.

e. Draw the *B* restriction fragments in the space provided, and indicate where the *A* restriction sites fall on the fragments. Indicate the size of the fragments that are produced in the double digest.

Figure 10.10.
Alignment of the large fragments from single digests. The large fragments from both single digests can be aligned so that one longer fragment is drawn.

f. Align the fragments from the preceding analysis. You will notice from your drawings that there are double digest fragments of the same size. These fragments are the key to solving our puzzle because they represent overlap. If we align the large *B* fragment and the large *A* fragment, we find that we can match up restriction sites (Figure 10.10).

g. Continue to align fragments. As shown in Figure 10.10, the alignment is used to draw out one longer fragment. By continuing to align fragments, it is possible to re-create the entire restriction map. Which fragments would you try to line up next?

Since we are working with a circular DNA molecule, would you expect to eventually repeat yourself?

h. Continue to align fragments until you have finished your complete map.

   i. Draw the map in the space provided. *Hint:* Arbitrarily place one of the *A* sites at position 0 (the very top of your circle) and use that as your reference site.

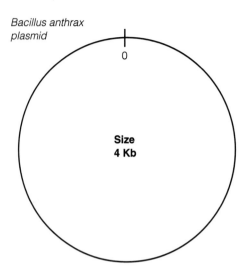

After completing the practice problem, resume your work to complete Exercise 10.1.

Questions for Review

1. Hypothesize about why restriction enzyme digestions are performed at 37°C.

2. Restriction endonucleases are enzymes. What type of macromolecule are endonucleases? Think of a general way that these enzymes might go about the business of cutting DNA.

Applying Your Knowledge

1. Scientists are developing genetically engineered foods that are insect-resistant, are more nutritious than traditional foods, and can grow in poorer soils. Many scientists believe that genetically modified (GM) foods will become essential as human populations continue to grow. Other scientists fear, however, that GM foods can pose serious threats to humans, wildlife, and the environment. Using resources from the Web, the library, and your text, write a short essay answering the following about GM foods.

a. How are they produced?

b. Give specific examples of benefits derived from GM foods.

c. Give examples of concerns that these foods may be harmful; for example, why do some fear that insects such as monarch butterflies may be harmed?

2. More and more, in cases of rape or murder, forensic scientists are using DNA fingerprinting as evidence for the guilt or innocence of a suspect. In this process, a few selected portions of DNA from small amounts of blood or semen from the crime scene can be analyzed and compared with DNA from a suspect. If gel electrophoresis shows that two samples match, the probability that the two samples are *not* from the same person can be anywhere from one chance in 100,000 to one in 1 billion, depending on how the test was performed. And yet, even with compelling DNA evidence to the contrary, suspects are sometimes found "not guilty." What problems with this type of evidence can arise to create doubt about the guilt of the person?

3. The Carlos Museum of Emory University recently acquired a mummy believed possibly to be Rameses I. You can imagine the excitement this acquisition created because if it is so, this would be the only former pharaoh residing outside of Egypt! Now it is up to university researchers to develop a protocol to test this hypothesis. You have been hired by the university to develop this protocol and perform these tests. How might you set about to investigate the lineage of this pharaoh?

References

Arri Eisen and Walter Escobar, Biology Department, Emory University, contributed significantly to the writing of this lab topic.

Bloom, M. V., G. A. Freyer, and D. A. Micklos. *Laboratory DNA Science.* Menlo Park, CA: Benjamin/Cummings, 1996.

Brown, K. "Seeds of Concern." *Scientific American,* 2001, vol. 284, (4), pp. 52–57.

Hopkin, K. "The Risks on the Table." *Scientific American,* 2001, vol. 284, (4), pp. 60–61.

Websites

An introduction to the concepts of molecular genetics: http://www.bis.med.jhmi.edu/Dan/DOE/intro.html

Describes the technology of cloning the insulin gene including the action of restriction enzyme EcoRI: http://esg-www.mit.edu:8001/esgbio/rdna/cloning.html

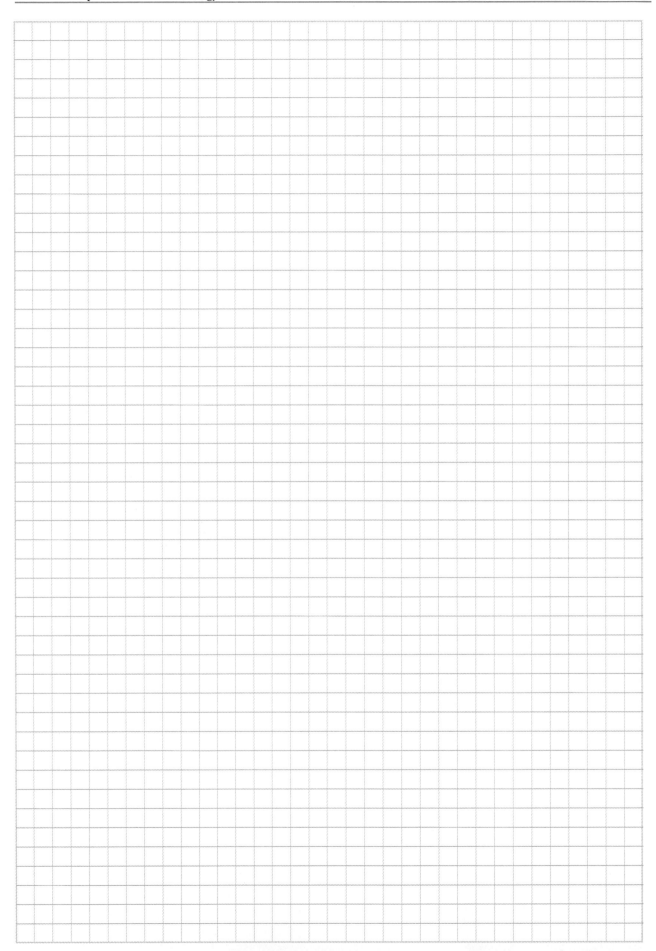

Population Genetics I:
The Hardy-Weinberg Theorem

Laboratory Objectives

After completing this lab topic, you should be able to:

1. Explain Hardy-Weinberg equilibrium in terms of allelic and genotypic frequencies and relate these to the expression $(p + q)^2 = p^2 + 2pq + q^2 = 1$.

2. Describe the conditions necessary to maintain Hardy-Weinberg equilibrium.

3. Use the bead model to demonstrate conditions for evolution.

4. Test hypotheses concerning the effects of evolutionary change (migration, mutation, genetic drift by either bottleneck or founder effect, and natural selection) using a computer model.

Introduction

Charles Darwin's unique contribution to biology was not that he "discovered evolution" but, rather, that he proposed a mechanism for evolutionary change—**natural selection,** the differential survival and reproduction of individuals in a population. In *On the Origin of Species,* published in 1859, Darwin described natural selection and provided abundant and convincing evidence in support of **evolution,** the change in populations over time. Evolution was accepted as a theory with great explanatory power supported by a large and diverse body of evidence. However, at the turn of the century, geneticists and naturalists still disagreed about the role of natural selection and the importance of small variations in natural populations. How could these variations provide a selective advantage that would result in evolutionary change? It was not until evolution and genetics became reconciled with the advent of population genetics that natural selection became widely accepted.

Ayala (1982) defines evolution as "changes in the genetic constitution of populations." A **population** is defined as a group of organisms of the same species that occur in the same area and interbreed or share a common **gene pool,** all the alleles at all gene loci of all individuals in the population. The population is considered the basic unit of evolution. *Populations evolve, not individuals.* Can you explain this statement in terms of the process of natural selection?

In 1908, English mathematician G. H. Hardy and German physician W. Weinberg independently developed models of population genetics that showed that the process of heredity by itself did not affect the genetic structure of a population. The **Hardy-Weinberg theorem** states that the frequency of alleles in the population will remain the same regardless of the starting frequencies. Furthermore, the equilibrium genotypic frequencies will be established after one generation of random mating. This theorem is valid only if certain conditions are met:

1. The population is very large.
2. Matings are random.
3. There are no net changes in the gene pool due to mutation; that is, mutation from *A* to *a* must be equal to mutation from *a* to *A*.
4. There is no migration of individuals into and out of the population.
5. There is no selection; all genotypes are equal in reproductive success.

It is estimated, for example, that before the Industrial Revolution in Great Britain, more than 90% of the peppered moths were light colored, while less than 10% were dark. Under Hardy-Weinberg equilibrium, these proportions would be maintained in each generation for large, random-breeding populations with no change in the mutation rate and migration rate, as long as the environment was relatively stable. The process of heredity would not change the frequency of the two forms of the moth. Later in this laboratory, you will investigate what happened to these moths as the environment changed following the Industrial Revolution.

Basically, the Hardy-Weinberg theorem provides a baseline model in which gene frequencies do not change and *evolution does not occur.* By testing the fundamental hypothesis of the Hardy-Weinberg theorem, evolutionists have investigated the roles of mutation, migration, population size, nonrandom mating, and natural selection in effecting evolutionary change in natural populations. Although some populations maintain genetic equilibrium, the exceptions are intriguing to scientists.

Use of the Hardy-Weinberg Theorem

The Hardy-Weinberg theorem provides a mathematical formula for calculating the frequencies of alleles and genotypes in populations. If we begin with a population with two alleles at a single gene locus—a dominant allele, *A*, and a recessive allele, *a*—then the frequency of the dominant allele is *p*, and the frequency of the recessive allele is *q*. Therefore, $p + q = 1$. If the frequency of one allele, *p*, is known for a population, the frequency of the other allele, *q*, can be determined by using the formula $q = 1 - p$.

During sexual reproduction, the frequency of each type of gamete produced is equal to the frequency of the alleles in the population. If the gametes combine at random, then the probability of *AA* in the next generation is p^2, and the probability of *aa* is q^2. The heterozygote can be obtained two ways, with either parent providing a dominant allele, so the probability would be $2pq$. These genotypic frequencies can be obtained by multiplying $p + q$ by $p + q$. The general equation then becomes

$$(p + q)^2 = p^2 + 2pq + q^2 = 1$$

To summarize:

$$p^2 = \text{frequency of } AA$$
$$2pq = \text{frequency of } Aa$$
$$q^2 = \text{frequency of } aa$$

Follow the steps in this example.

1. If alternate alleles of a gene, *A* and *a*, occur at equal frequencies, *p* and *q*, then during sexual reproduction, 0.5 of all gametes will carry *A* and 0.5 will carry *a*.

2. Then $p = q = 0.5$.

3. Once allelic frequencies are known for a population, the genotypic makeup of the next generation can be predicted from the general equation. In this case,

$$[0.5(p) + 0.5(q)]^2 = 0.25(p^2) + 0.50(2pq) + 0.25(q^2) = 1$$

This represents the results of random mating as shown in Figure 11.1.

4. The genotypic frequencies in the population are specifically

$$p^2 = \text{frequency of } AA = 0.25$$
$$2pq = \text{frequency of } Aa = 0.50$$
$$q^2 = \text{frequency of } aa = 0.25$$

5. The allelic frequencies remain $p = q = 0.5$.

In actual populations the frequencies of alleles are not usually equal. For example, 4% of a population might be albinos (a recessive trait), and the frequency of the albino allele could be calculated as the square root of 0.04.

1. Albino individuals $= q^2 = 0.04$ (genotypic frequency); therefore, $q = \sqrt{0.04} = 0.2$ (allelic frequency).

2. Since $p + q = 1$, the frequency of *p* is $(1 - q)$, or 0.8. So 4% of the population are albinos, and 20% of the alleles in the gene pool are for albinism and the other 80% are for normal pigmentation. (Note that you could not determine the frequency of *A* by taking the square root of the frequency of all normally pigmented individuals because you cannot distinguish the heterozygote and the homozygote for this trait.)

3. The genotypic frequencies of the next generation now can be predicted from the general Hardy-Weinberg theorem. First determine the results of random mating by completing Figure 11.2.

4. What will be the genotypic frequencies from generation to generation, provided that alleles *p* and *q* remain in genetic equilibrium?

$$AA =$$
$$Aa =$$
$$aa =$$

The genetic equilibrium will continue indefinitely if the conditions of the Hardy-Weinberg theorem are met. How often in nature do you think these conditions are met? Although natural populations may seldom meet all the conditions, Hardy-Weinberg equilibrium serves as a valuable model from which we can predict genetic changes in populations as a result of natural selection or other factors. This allows us to understand quantitatively and in genetic language how evolution operates at the population level.

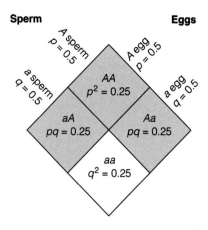

Figure 11.1.
Random mating in a population at Hardy-Weinberg equilibrium. The combination of alleles in randomly mating gametes maintains the allelic and genotypic frequency generation after generation. The gene pool of the population remains constant, and the populations do not evolve.

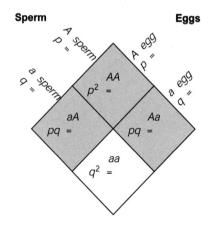

Figure 11.2.
Random mating for a population at Hardy-Weinberg equilibrium. Complete the mating combinations for albinism and normal pigmentation.

EXERCISE 11.1

Testing Hardy-Weinberg Equilibrium Using a Bead Model

Materials

plastic or paper bag containing 100 beads of two colors

Introduction

Working in pairs, you will test Hardy-Weinberg equilibrium by simulating a population using colored beads. The bag of beads represents the gene pool for the population. Each bead should be regarded as a single gamete, the two colors representing different alleles of a single gene. Each bag should contain 100 beads of the two colors in the proportions specified by the instructor. Record in the space provided below the color of the beads and the initial frequencies for your gene pool.

$A =$ _____ color _____ allelic frequency

$a =$ _____ color _____ allelic frequency

1. How many diploid individuals are represented in this population?

2. What would be the color of the beads for a homozygous dominant individual?

3. What would be the color of the beads for a homozygous recessive individual?

4. What would be the color of the beads for a heterozygous individual?

Hypothesis

State the Hardy-Weinberg theorem in the space provided. This will be your hypothesis.

Predictions

Predict the genotypic frequencies of the population in future generations (if/then).

Procedure

1. Without looking, randomly remove two beads from the bag. These two beads represent one diploid individual in the next generation. Record in the margin of your lab manual the diploid genotype (*AA, Aa,* or *aa*) of the individual formed from these two gametes.

2. *Return the beads to the bag* and shake the bag to reinstate the gene pool. By replacing the beads each time, the size of the gene pool remains constant, and the probability of selecting any allele should remain equal to its frequency. This procedure is called **sampling with replacement.**

3. Repeat steps 1 and 2 (select two beads, record the genotype of the new individual, and return the beads to the bag) until you have recorded the genotypes for 50 individuals who will form the next generation of the population.

Results

1. *Before calculating the results of your experiment,* determine the *expected* frequencies of genotypes and alleles for the population. To do this, use the original allelic frequencies for the population provided by the instructor. (Recall that the frequency of $A = p$, and the frequency of $a = q$.) Calculate the expected genotypic frequencies using the Hardy-Weinberg equation $p^2 + 2pq + q^2 = 1$. The number of individuals expected for each genotype can be calculated by multiplying 50 (total population size) by the expected frequencies. Record these results in Table 11.1.

Table 11.1
Expected Genotypic and Allelic Frequencies for the
Next Generation Produced by the Bead Model

Parent Populations		New Populations					
Allelic Frequency		Genotypic Number (and Frequency)			Allelic Frequency		
A	*a*	*AA*	*Aa*	*aa*	*A*	*a*	
		( )	( )	( )			

2. Next, *using the results of your experiment,* calculate the *observed* frequencies in the new population created as you removed beads from the bag. Record the number of diploid individuals for each genotype in Table 11.2, and calculate the frequencies for the three genotypes (*AA, Aa, aa*). Add the numbers of each allele, and calculate the allelic frequencies for *A* and *a*. These values are the observed frequencies in the new population. Genotypic frequencies and allelic frequencies should each equal 1.

Table 11.2
Observed Genotypic and Allelic Frequencies for the
Next Generation Produced by the Bead Model

Parent Populations		New Populations				
Allelic Frequency		Genotypic Number (and Frequency)			Allelic Frequency	
A	a	AA	Aa	aa	A	a
		( )	( )	( )		

3. To compare your observed results with those expected, you can use the statistical test, chi-square. Table 11.3 will assist in the calculation of the chi-square test. See Appendix B for an explanation of this statistical test.

Table 11.3
Chi-Square of Results from the Bead Model

	AA	Aa	aa
Observed value (o)			
Expected value (e)			
Deviation $(o - e) = d$			
d^2			
d^2/e			
Chi-square $(\chi^2) = \Sigma d^2/e$			

Degrees of freedom =

Level of significance, $p < 0.05$

4. Is your calculated χ^2 value greater or smaller than the given χ^2 value (Appendix B, Table B.2) for the degrees of freedom and p value for this problem?

Discussion

1. What proportion of the population was homozygous dominant?

   Homozygous recessive?

   Heterozygous?

2. Were your observed results consistent with the expected results based on your statistical analysis? If not, can you suggest an explanation?

3. Compare your results with those of other students. How variable are the results for each team?

4. Do your results match your predictions for a population at Hardy-Weinberg equilibrium?

What would you expect to happen to the frequencies if you continued this simulation for 25 generations?

Is this population evolving?

Explain your response.

5. Consider each of the conditions for the Hardy-Weinberg model. Does this model meet each of those conditions?

EXERCISE 11.2
Simulation of Evolutionary Change Using the Bead Model

Under the conditions specified by the Hardy-Weinberg model (random mating in a large population, no mutation, no migration, and no selection), the genetic frequencies should not change, and evolution should not occur. In this exercise, the class will modify each of the conditions and determine the effect on genetic frequencies in subsequent generations. You will simulate the evolutionary changes that occur when these conditions are not met.

Working in teams of two or three students, you will simulate two of the experimental scenarios presented and, using the bead model, determine the changes in genetic frequencies over several generations. The scenarios include the migration of individuals between two populations, also called **gene flow;**

the effects of small population size, called **genetic drift**; and examples of **natural selection**. The effects of mutation take longer to simulate with the bead model, so you will use computer simulation to consider these in Exercise 11.3. All teams will begin by simulating the effect of genetic drift, specifically, the bottleneck effect (Experiment A.1). For the second simulation, you can choose to investigate migration, one of two examples of natural selection, or the founder effect—another example of genetic drift.

The procedure for investigating each of the conditions will follow the general procedures described as follows. Before beginning one of the simulation experiments, be sure you understand the procedures to be used.

Procedure

1. Sampling with Replacement

Unless otherwise instructed, the gene pool size will be 100 beads. Each new generation will be formed by randomly choosing 50 diploid individuals represented by pairs of beads. After removing each pair of beads (representing the genotype of one individual) from the bag, replace the pair before removing the next set, *sampling with replacement.* Continue your simulations for several generations. For example, if the starting population has 50 beads each of *A* and *a* (allelic frequency of 0.5), then in the next generation you might produce the following results:

Number of individuals: 14*AA*, 24*Aa*, 12*aa*
Number of alleles (beads): 28*A* + 24*A*, 24*a* + 24*a*
Total number of alleles: 100

$$\text{Frequency of } A: 28 + 24 = \frac{52}{100} = 0.52$$

$$\text{Frequency of } a: 24 + 24 = \frac{48}{100} = 0.48$$

In this example, the frequency should continue to approximate 0.5 for *A* and *a*.

2. Reestablishing a Population with New Allelic Frequencies

In some cases, the number of individuals will decrease as a result of the simulation. In those cases, return the population to 100 but reestablish the population with new allelic frequencies. For example, if you eliminate by selection all homozygous recessive (*aa*) individuals in your simulation, then the resulting frequencies would be:

Number of individuals: 14*AA*, 24*Aa*, 0*aa*
Number of alleles (beads): 28*A* + 24*A*, 24*a*
Total number of alleles: 76

$$\text{Frequency of } A: 28 + 24 = \frac{52}{76} = 0.68$$

$$\text{Frequency of } a: 24 = \frac{24}{76} = 0.32$$

To reestablish a population of 100, then, the number of beads should reflect these new frequencies. *Adjust the number of beads so that A is now* $^{68}/_{100}$ *and a is* $^{32}/_{100}$. Then continue the next round of the simulation.

If this information is not clear to you, ask for assistance before beginning your simulations.

Experiment A. Simulation of Genetic Drift

Materials

plastic or paper bag containing 100 beads, 50 each of two colors
additional beads as needed

Introduction

Genetic drift is the change in allelic frequencies in small populations as a result of chance alone. In a small population, combinations of gametes may not be random, owing to sampling error. (If you toss a coin 500 times, you expect about a 50:50 ratio of heads to tails; but if you toss the coin only 10 times, the ratio may deviate greatly in a small sample owing to chance alone.) **Genetic fixation,** the loss of all but one possible allele at a gene locus in a population, is a common result of genetic drift in small natural populations. Genetic drift is a significant evolutionary force in situations known as the **bottleneck effect** and the **founder effect.**

All teams will investigate the bottleneck effect. You may choose the founder effect (pp. 276–277) for your second simulation.

1. Bottleneck Effect

A **bottleneck** occurs when a population undergoes a drastic reduction in size as a result of chance events (not differential selection), such as a volcanic eruption or hurricane. (Bad luck, not bad genes!) In Figure 11.3, the beads pass through a bottleneck, which results in an unpredictable combination of

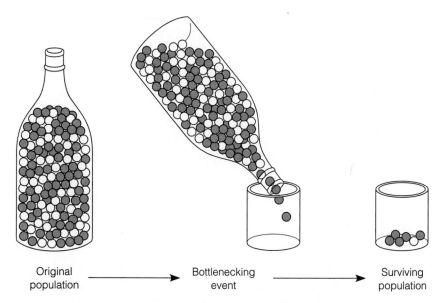

Original population → Bottlenecking event → Surviving population

Figure 11.3.
The bottleneck effect. The gene pool can drift by chance when the population is drastically reduced by factors that act unselectively. Bad luck, not bad genes! The resulting population will have unpredictable combinations of genes. What has happened to the amount of variation?

beads that pass to the other side. These beads would constitute the beginning of the next generation.

Hypothesis

As your hypothesis, either propose a hypothesis that addresses the bottleneck effect specifically or state the Hardy-Weinberg theorem.

Prediction

Either predict equilibrium values as a result of Hardy-Weinberg or predict the type of change that you expect to occur in a small population (if/then).

Procedure

1. To investigate the bottleneck effect, establish a starting population containing 50 individuals (how many beads?) with a frequency of 0.5 for each allele (Generation 0).

2. *Without replacement,* randomly select 5 individuals (10% of the population), two alleles at a time. This represents a drastic reduction in population size. On a separate sheet of paper, record the genotypes and the number of *A* and *a* alleles for the new population.

3. Count the numbers of each genotype and the numbers of each allele. Using these numbers, determine the genotypic frequencies for *AA, Aa,* and *aa* and the new allelic frequencies for *A* (*p*) and *a* (*q*) for the surviving 5 individuals. These are your *observed* frequencies. Enter these frequencies in Table 11.4, Generation 1.

4. Using the new observed allelic frequencies, calculate the *expected* genotypic frequencies (p^2, $2pq$, q^2). Record these frequencies in Table 11.4, Generation 1.

5. Reestablish the population to 50 individuals using the new allelic frequencies (refer to the example in the Procedure on p. 272). Repeat steps 2, 3, and 4. Record your results in the appropriate generation in Table 11.4.

6. Reestablish the gene pool with new frequencies after each generation until one of the alleles becomes fixed in the population for several generations.

7. Summarize your results in the Discussion section.

Results

1. How many generations did you simulate?
2. Using the graph paper at the end of the lab topic, sketch a graph of the change in p and q over time. You should have two lines, one for each allele.
3. Did one allele go to fixation in that time period?

   Which allele?

   Remember, genetic fixation occurs when the gene pool is composed of only one allele. The others have been eliminated. Did the other allele ever appear to be going to fixation?

Table 11.4

Changes in Allelic and Genotypic Frequencies for Simulations of the Bottleneck Effect, an Example of Genetic Drift. First, record frequencies based on the observed numbers in your experiment. Then, using the observed allelic frequencies, calculate the expected genotypic frequencies.

Generation	Genotypic Frequency Observed			Allelic Frequency Observed		Genotypic Frequency Expected		
	AA	*Aa*	*aa*	*A (p)*	*a (q)*	p^2	$2pq$	q^2
0	—	—	—	0.5	0.5	0.25	0.50	0.25
1								
2								
3								
4								
5								
6								
7								
8								
9								
10								

4. Did any of the expected genotypic frequencies go to fixation? If none did, why not?

5. Compare results with other teams. Did the same allele go to fixation for all teams? If not, how many became fixed for *A* and how many for *a*?

Discussion

1. Compare the pattern of change for *p* and *q*. Is there a consistent trend or do the changes suggest chance events? Look at the graphs of other teams before deciding.

2. Explain your observations of genetic fixation for the replicate simulations completed by the class. What would you expect if you simulated the bottleneck effect 100 times?

3. How might your results have differed if you had started with different allelic frequencies, for example, *p* = 0.2 and *q* = 0.8?

4. Since only chance events—that is, the effect of small population size—are responsible for the change in gene frequencies, would you say that evolution has occurred? Explain.

 On completion of this simulation, choose one or two of the remaining scenarios to investigate. All scenarios should be completed by at least one team in the laboratory.

2. Founder Effect

When a small group of individuals becomes separated from the larger parent population, the allelic frequencies in this small gene pool may be different from those of the original population as a result of chance alone. This occurs when a group of migrants becomes established in a new area—for instance, the colonization of an island—and is therefore referred to as the **founder effect.**

Hypothesis

As your hypothesis, either propose a hypothesis that addresses founder effect specifically or state the Hardy-Weinberg theorem.

Prediction

Either predict equilibrium values as a result of Hardy-Weinberg or predict the type of change that you expect to occur in a small population (if/then).

Procedure

1. To investigate the founder effect, establish a starting population with 50 individuals with starting allelic frequencies of your choice. Record the frequencies you have selected for Generation 0 in Table 11.5 in the Results section at the end of this exercise.

2. *Without replacement,* randomly select 5 individuals, two alleles at a time, to establish a new founder population. On a separate sheet of paper, record the genotypes and the number of A and a alleles for the new population.

3. Calculate the new frequencies for A (p) and a (q) and the genotypic frequencies for AA (p^2), Aa ($2pq$), and aa (q^2) for the *founder population,* and record this information as Generation 1 in Table 11.5.

4. Reestablish the population to 50 diploid individuals using the new allelic frequencies. (Refer to the example in the Procedure on p. 272.)

5. Follow the founder population through several generations in the new population. From this point forward, each new generation will be produced by *sampling 50 individuals with replacement.* After each generation, reestablish the new population based on the new allelic frequencies. Continue until you have sufficient evidence to discuss your results with the class.

6. Summarize your results in the Discussion section at the end of this exercise. You will want to compare the founder population with the original population and compare equilibrium frequencies if appropriate. Each group will present its results to the class at the end of the laboratory.

Experiment B. Simulation of Migration: Gene Flow

Materials

2 plastic or paper bags, each containing 100 beads of two colors
additional beads as needed

Introduction

The migration of individuals between populations results in gene flow. In a natural population, gene flow can be the result of the immigration and emigration of individuals or gametes (for example, pollen movement). The rate and direction of migration and the starting allelic frequencies for the two populations can affect the rate of genetic change. In this example, the migration rate is equal in the two populations, and the starting allelic frequencies differ for the two. Work in teams of four students.

Hypothesis

As your hypothesis, either propose a hypothesis that addresses migration specifically or state the Hardy-Weinberg theorem.

Prediction

Either predict equilibrium values as a result of Hardy-Weinberg or predict the type of change that you expect to observe as a result of migration (if/then).

Procedure

1. To investigate the effects of gene flow on population genetics, establish two populations of 100 beads each. Choose different starting allelic frequencies for *A* and *a* for each population. For example, in Figure 11.4, population 1 might start with 90*A* and 10*a* while population 2 might have 50 of each allele initially. For comparison, you might choose one population with the same starting frequencies as your population in Exercise 11.1. Record the allelic frequencies for each starting population, Generation 0, in Table 11.5 in the Results section at the end of this exercise.

2. Select 10 individuals (how many alleles?) from each population, and allow them to migrate to the other population by exchanging beads. Do not sample with replacement in this step.

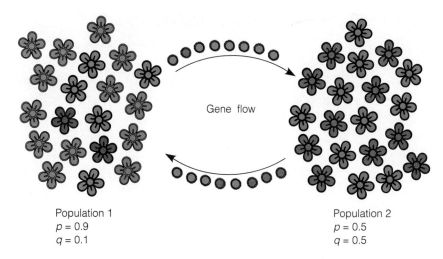

Figure 11.4.
Migration. Migration rates are constant between two populations that differ for starting allelic frequencies.

Population 1
$p = 0.9$
$q = 0.1$

Gene flow

Population 2
$p = 0.5$
$q = 0.5$

3. Select 50 individuals from each of these new populations, *sampling with replacement*. On a separate sheet of paper, record the genotypes and the number of *A* and *a* alleles for population 1 and population 2.

4. Calculate the new allelic and genotypic frequencies in the two populations following migration. Record your results in Table 11.5 in the Results section. Reestablish each bag based on the new allelic frequencies.

5. Repeat this procedure (steps 2 to 4) for several generations. In doing this, you are allowing migration to take place with each generation. Continue until you have a sufficient number to allow you to discuss your results in class successfully.

6. Summarize your results in the Discussion section at the end of this exercise. Each group will present its results to the class at the end of the laboratory.

Experiment C. Simulation of Natural Selection

Materials

plastic or paper bag containing 100 beads of two colors
additional beads as needed

Introduction

Natural selection, the differential survival and reproduction of individuals, was first proposed by Darwin as the mechanism for evolution. Although other factors have since been found to be involved in evolution, selection is still considered an important mechanism. Natural selection is based on the observation that individuals with certain heritable traits are more likely to survive and reproduce than those lacking these advantageous traits. Therefore, the proportion of offspring with advantageous traits will increase in the next generation. The genotypic frequencies will change in the population. Whether traits are advantageous in a population depends on the environment and the selective agents (which can include physical and biological factors). Choose one of the following evolutionary scenarios to model natural selection in population genetics.

a.   b.

Figure 11.5.
Two color forms of the peppered moth. The dark and light forms of the moth are present in both photographs. Lichens are absent in (a) but present in (b). In which situation would the dark moth have a selective advantage?

1. Industrial Melanism

The peppered moth, *Biston betularia,* is a speckled moth that rests on tree trunks during the day, where it avoids predation by blending with the bark of trees (an example of cryptic coloration). At the turn of the century, moth collectors in Great Britain collected primarily light forms of this moth (light with dark speckles) and only occasionally recorded rare dark forms (Figure 11.5). With the advent of the Industrial Revolution and increased pollution, light-colored lichens on the trees died, resulting in strong positive selection for dark moths resting on the now dark bark. The dark moth increased in frequency. However, in unpolluted regions, the light moth continued to occur in high frequencies. (This is an example of the relative nature of selective advantage, depending on the environment.)

Color is controlled by a single gene with two allelic forms, dark and light. Pigment production is dominant (*A*), and the lack of pigment is recessive (*a*). The light moth would be *aa,* but the dark form could be either *AA* or *Aa.*

Hypothesis

As your hypothesis, either propose a hypothesis that addresses natural selection occurring in polluted environments specifically or state the Hardy-Weinberg theorem.

Prediction

Either predict equilibrium values as a result of the Hardy-Weinberg theorem or predict the type of change that you expect to observe as a result of natural selection in the polluted environment (if/then).

Procedure

1. To investigate the effect of natural selection on the frequency of light and dark moths, establish a population of 50 individuals with allelic frequencies of light (a) = 0.9 and dark (A) = 0.1. Record the frequencies of the starting population, Generation 0, in Table 11.5 in the Results section at the end of this exercise.

2. Determine the genotypes and phenotypes of the population by selecting 50 individuals, two alleles at a time, by sampling with replacement (see Procedure, p. 272). On a separate sheet of paper, record the genotypes and phenotypes of each individual.

   Now, assume that pollution has become a significant factor and that in this new population 50% of the light moths but only 10% of the dark moths are eaten. How many light moths must you eliminate from your starting population of 50 individuals? How many dark moths? Can selection distinguish dark moths with AA and Aa genotypes? How will you decide which dark moths to remove? Remove the appropriate number of individuals of each phenotype.

3. Calculate new allelic frequencies for the remaining population. Reestablish the population with these new allelic frequencies for the 100 alleles. (Refer to the Procedure on p. 272.) Record the new frequencies in Table 11.5 in the Results section.

4. Continue the selection procedure, recording the frequencies, for several generations until you have sufficient evidence to discuss your results with the class.

5. Summarize your results in the Discussion section at the end of this exercise. Each group will present its results to the class at the end of the laboratory.

2. Sickle-Cell Disease

Sickle-cell disease is caused by a mutant allele (Hb^-), which, in the homozygous condition, in the past was often fatal to people at quite young ages. The mutation causes the formation of abnormal, sickle-shaped red blood cells that clog vessels, cause organ damage, and are inefficient transporters of oxygen (Figure 11.6). Individuals who are heterozygous (Hb^+Hb^-) have the sickle-cell trait (a mild form of the disease), which is not fatal. Scientists were surprised to find a high frequency of the Hb^- allele in populations in

Figure 11.6.

Effects of the sickle-cell allele.

(a) Normal red blood cells are disk-shaped. (b) The jagged shape of sickled cells causes them to pile up and clog small blood vessels.

(c) The results include damage to a large number of organs. In the homozygous condition, sickle-cell disease can be fatal.

a.

b.

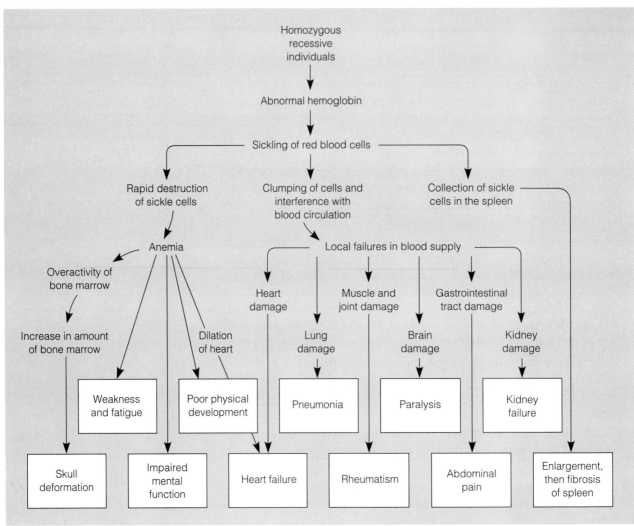

c.

Africa until they determined that heterozygous individuals have a *selective advantage* in resisting malaria. Although the homozygous condition may be lethal, the heterozygotes are under both a positive and a negative selection force. In malarial countries in tropical Africa, the heterozygotes are at an advantage compared to either homozygote.

Hypothesis

As your hypothesis, either propose a hypothesis that addresses natural selection in tropical Africa specifically or state the Hardy-Weinberg theorem.

Prediction

Either predict equilibrium values as a result of the Hardy-Weinberg theorem or predict the type of change that you expect to observe as a result of natural selection in tropical Africa (if/then).

Procedure

1. To investigate the role of selection under conditions of heterozygote advantage, establish a population of 50 individuals with allelic frequencies of 0.5 for both alleles. Record the frequencies of the starting population, Generation 0, in Table 11.5 in the Results section at the end of this exercise.

   For our model, assume that the selection force on each genotype is

   Hb^+Hb^+: 30% die of malaria
   Hb^+Hb^-: 10% die of malaria
   Hb^-Hb^-: 100% die of sickle-cell disease

2. Determine the genotypes and phenotypes of the population by selecting 50 individuals, two alleles at a time, by *sampling with replacement* (see Procedure, p. 272). On a separate sheet of paper, record the 50 individuals. Select against each genotype by eliminating individuals according to the percent mortality shown above. How many Hb^+Hb^+ must be removed? How many Hb^+Hb^-? How many Hb^-Hb^-? Remove the appropriate number of beads for each color.

3. Calculate new allelic and genotypic frequencies based on the survivors, and reestablish the population using these new frequencies. (Refer to the procedure on p. 272 if necessary.) Record your new frequencies in Table 11.5 in the Results section.

4. Continue the selection procedure, recording frequencies, for several generations, until you have sufficient evidence for your discussion in class.

5. Summarize your results in the Discussion section. Each group will present its results to the class at the end of the laboratory.

Results and Discussion for Selected Simulation

Results

Each team will record the results of its chosen experiment in Table 11.5. Modify the table to match the information you need to record for your simulation. Use the margins to expand the table or make additional notes.

Discussion

In preparation for presenting your results to the class, answer the following questions about your chosen simulation. Choose one team member to make the presentation, which should be organized in the format of a scientific paper.

1. Which of the conditions that are necessary for Hardy-Weinberg equilibrium were met?

2. Which condition was changed?

3. Briefly describe the scenario that your team simulated.

4. What were your predicted results?

5. How many generations did you simulate?

Table 11.5

Changes in Allelic and Genotypic Frequencies for Simulations Selected in Exercise 11.2.
Calculate expected frequencies based on the actual observed numbers in your experiment.

Experiment _____ Simulation of _____					
	Allelic Frequency		**Genotypic Frequency**		
Generation	p	q	p^2	$2pq$	q^2
0					
1					
2					
3					
4					
5					
6					
7					
8					
9					
10					

6. Sketch a graph of the change in p and q over time. You should have two lines, one for each frequency.

7. Describe the changes in allelic frequencies p and q over time. Did your results match your predictions? Explain.

8. Describe the changes in the genotypic frequencies.

9. Compare your final allelic and genotypic frequencies with those of the starting population.

10. If you can, formulate a general summary statement or conclusion.

11. Would you expect your results to be the same if you had chosen different starting allelic frequencies? Explain.

12. Critique your experimental design and outline your next simulation.

Be prepared to take notes, sketch graphs, and ask questions during the student presentations. You are responsible for understanding and answering questions for all conditions simulated in the laboratory.

EXERCISE 11.3

Investigating the Evolution of Populations Using Computer Simulations

Simulations involving only a few generations are fairly easy with the bead model, but this model is too cumbersome to obtain information about long-term changes or to combine two or more factors. Computer simulations will allow you to model 50 or 100 generations quickly or to do a series of simulations changing one factor and comparing the results. As with any scientific investigation, design your experiment to test a hypothesis and make predictions before you begin.

Several computer simulation programs are available; the instructor will demonstrate the software. From the following suggestions or your own ideas, pursue one of the factors in more detail or several in combination. Consult with your instructor before beginning your simulations. Be prepared to present your results in the next lab period in either oral or written form. Follow the procedures provided with the simulation program.

Mutation

Evolution can occur only when there is variation in a population, and the ultimate source for that variation is mutation. The mutation rate at most gene loci is actually very small (1×10^{-5} per gamete per generation), and the forward and backward rates of mutation are seldom at equilibrium. Evolutionary change as a result of mutation alone would occur very slowly, thus requiring many generations of simulation. Changes in this condition are best considered using a computer simulation that easily handles the lengthy process. *Do not simulate this condition using the bead model.*

Other Suggestions for Computer Simulations

1. The migration between natural populations seldom occurs at the same rate in both directions. Devise a model to simulate different migration rates between two populations. Compare your results with the bead model.

2. How does the probability of genetic fixation differ for populations that have different starting allelic frequencies? Simulate genetic drift using a variety of allelic frequencies.

3. How large must a population be to avoid genetic drift?

4. Devise a model to simulate selection for recessive lethals. Then, using the same starting allelic frequencies, select against the dominant lethals. Compare rate of change of allelic frequency as a result of lethality for dominant and recessive traits.

5. Mutation alone has only small effects on evolution over long periods of time. Using realistic rates of mutation, compare the evolutionary change for mutation alone with simulations that combine mutation and natural selection.

6. Combine factors (usually two at a time). For example, combine mutation and natural selection, using realistic estimates of mutation rates. Combine genetic drift and migration. Compare your results to simulations of each condition alone.

Questions for Review

1. Define and provide examples of the following terms: *evolution, population, gene pool, gene flow, genetic drift, bottleneck effect, founder effect, natural selection, genetic fixation, genotypic frequency, allelic frequency,* and *model.*

2. State the five conditions necessary for Hardy-Weinberg equilibrium.

3. Describe how gene flow, genetic drift, and natural selection bring about evolution.

4. In a population of 100 rock pink plants, 84 individuals have red flowers while 16 have white flowers. Assume that white petals are inherited as a recessive trait (a) and red petals as a dominant trait (A). What are the frequencies p and q? In the next generation, what will be the equilibrium genotypic frequencies?

5. Explain the difference between evolution and natural selection. Use an example to illustrate your answer.

Applying Your Knowledge

1. Can evolution occur without natural selection? Provide an example to support your answer.

2. A population of snail darters is drastically reduced by the introduction of a large predator fish into an isolated stream. The predators eat almost all darters less than 5 cm long. Is this an example of a bottleneck or natural selection? Defend your answer.

3. Migration occurs at a constant rate between two populations of field mice. In one population, 65% of the population are white; in the other population, only 15% are white. What would you expect to happen to the allelic frequencies of these two populations over time?

4. Cystic fibrosis (CF) is caused by a genetic mutation resulting in defective proteins in secretory cells, mainly in the epithelial lining of the respiratory tract. The one in every 2,000 Caucasian babies who has the disease is homozygous for the recessive mutant. Although medical treatment is becoming more effective, in the past most children with CF died before their teens. About 20 Caucasians in 2,000 are carriers of the trait, having one mutant and one normal allele, but they do not develop the disease. According to rules of population genetics, the frequency of the homozygous recessive genotype should be rarer than it is. What is one possible explanation for the unusually high frequency of this allele in Caucasian populations?

5. The northern right whale that has its calving ground off the coast of Georgia is the most endangered large whale in the world. Although now protected from hunting, at one time this whale was widely sought by

harpooners, and the present population is estimated to be fewer than 400 individuals. This drastic population reduction is an example of which evolutionary force studied in this lab topic?

What might you predict has happened to frequencies of many alleles as a result of this event?

References

Some parts of this lab topic were modified from J. C. Glase, 1993, "A Laboratory on Population Genetics and Evolution: A Physical Model and Computer Simulation," pages 29–41, in *Tested Studies for Laboratory Teaching*, Volume 7/8 (C. A. Goldman and P. L. Hauta, Editors). Proceedings of the 7th and 8th Workshop/Conference of the Association for Biology Laboratory Education (ABLE), 187 pages. Used by permission.

Ayala, F. J. *Population and Evolutionary Genetics: A Primer.* Menlo Park, CA: Benjamin/Cummings, 1982.

Freeman, S., and J. C. Herron. *Evolutionary Analysis,* 2nd ed. Upper Saddle River, NJ: Prentice Hall, 2001.

Hardy, G. H. "Mendelian Proportions in a Mixed Population," *Science* (July 10, 1908) pp. 49–50. In this interesting early application of the "Hardy-Weinberg Theorem," this letter written by Hardy to the editor of *Science* refutes a report that dominant characters increase in frequency over time.

Website

Detailed information about sickle-cell anemia:
http://www.emory.edu/PEDS/SICKLE/

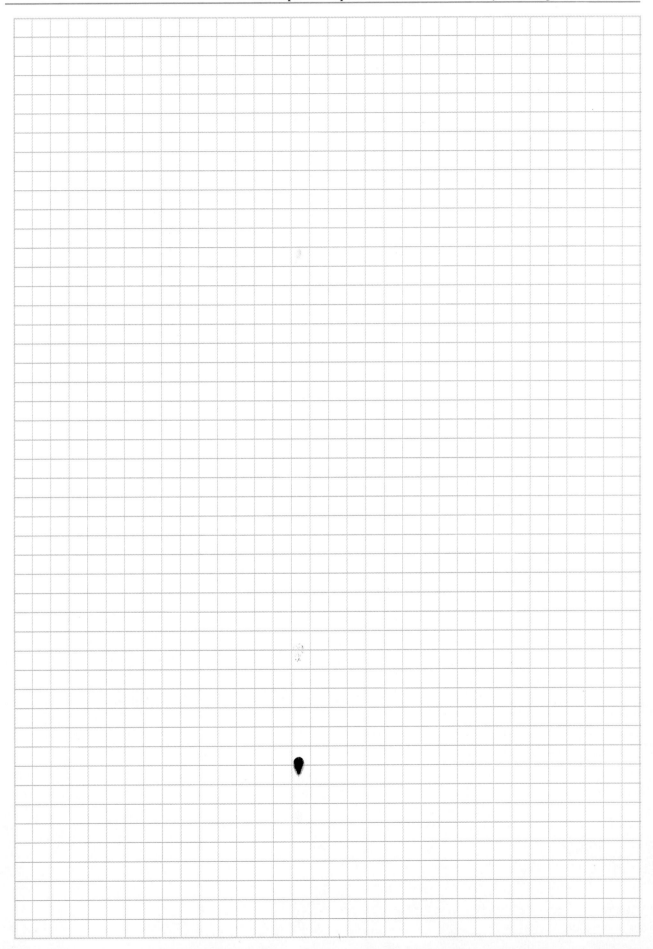

Population Genetics II: Determining Genetic Variation

Laboratory Objectives

After completing this lab topic, you should be able to:

1. Use gels to determine the extent of variation in the gene pool of a natural population.
2. Calculate genotypic and allelic frequencies and expected and observed heterozygosity.
3. Use the statistical tool chi-square to analyze results.
4. Describe how enzymes in a tissue extract can be separated by gel electrophoresis.
5. Discuss the relationship between genetic variation and evolution.

Introduction

Following the Industrial Revolution in England, populations of the peppered moth (*Biston betularia*) changed in response to the changing environmental conditions. The frequency of the dark moths increased as the light-colored lichens covering the trees died. The light moths were no longer camouflaged while at rest on the tree bark and therefore died at a greater rate than the dark moths, which were now hidden while at rest. The case of the peppered moth is probably one of the best-known examples of evolution in action. But what would have happened to the peppered moth if only the light form had existed in these populations? Without the presence of genetic variation, selection might have eliminated the light moths, and local populations could have become extinct. *Heritable variation* is a requirement for evolutionary change.

Variation in populations is easily observed in almost any species; just look around your laboratory and campus. The variation in human populations seems almost limitless. Some variation in populations is the result of environmental differences, while other variation is genetically determined. Although height in humans has a genetic component, evidence suggests that the increase in the average height in humans over the past 50–100 years is primarily due to improvements in diet. Evolutionary biologists are interested in documenting the amount of genetic variation in populations, but separating environmental effects from genetic effects poses a difficult problem. Our earliest estimates of genetic variation came from artificial selection in plant and animal breeding. However, it is not feasible to conduct genetic crosses and analyses for every species of interest. The problem also is compounded by our inability to determine the genotype of individuals with a dominant phenotype; they could be heterozygous or homozygous.

In the 1960s, molecular biologists developed the technique of gel electrophoresis, which allowed scientists to detect differences in proteins based on their size and charge. These protein differences were the result of changes in the amino acid sequences of the proteins, which in turn were the result of **mutations,** or changes in the DNA sequence. Determining variation in proteins is simply one step from detecting changes in the genes themselves, and gel electrophoresis is much simpler and cheaper than DNA sequencing (determining the nucleotide sequences). In addition, proteins are basically inherited as codominant traits, allowing scientists to distinguish the heterozygous phenotype from the homozygous phenotype on gels. Using gel electrophoresis, population geneticists and evolutionary biologists have been able to survey populations of plants and animals, including humans, to determine the genetic variation present at a large number of genes.

The extent of genetic variation in populations is much greater than expected. One way to estimate genetic variation is to determine the proportion of the population that is heterozygous (having different alleles at a gene locus). On average, invertebrates are heterozygous at 11% of their genes; estimates for vertebrates are 4%, and plants, 16% (Hamrick, Linhart, and Mitton, 1979). Humans are heterozygous at approximately 7% of their genes. Assuming that humans have 100,000 genes in their chromosomes, you would have, on average, two different alleles at 7,000 of your genes. In contrast, the cheetah is heterozygous at only a small percentage (0.07%) of its genes. Understanding genetic variation and the factors that affect variation is essential to the management of this endangered species, which has little potential for evolutionary change because of its enormously reduced genetic variation.

As you begin your study of genetic variation, review the concepts and terminology for population genetics. You will be expected to use and understand the Hardy-Weinberg theorem as you investigate genetic variation in a natural population. Before continuing in this lab topic, complete Table 12.1, providing definitions and examples. Refer to your textbook and Lab Topic 11, Population Genetics I: The Hardy-Weinberg Theorem.

EXERCISE 12.1
Interpreting Banding Patterns in a Gel

In this exercise, you will investigate polymorphism in a population of rock pink plants (*Talinum mengesii*) (Color Plate 15), a succulent commonly found growing in shallow soils on rock outcrops in the southeast. You will determine the frequency of (1) different genotypes (genotypic frequency), (2) different alleles (allelic frequency), and (3) heterozygotes (heterozygosity) in the population (see Lab Topic 11). These frequencies will allow you to estimate the extent of genetic variation in the rock pink population.

To perform this investigation, you will study diagrammatic reproductions of starch gels that have been stained for selected enzymes found in these plants. (Although starch gels were used for this exercise, acrylamide, cellulose acetate, and agarose gels can also be used.) Starch gels are made by boiling purified potato starch in a buffer solution with known pH and ionic strength and then allowing it to solidify in a tray. Paper wicks are soaked in

Table 12.1
Population Genetics Terminology

Gene locus
Allele
Allelic frequency
Genotypic frequency
Heterozygote
Hardy-Weinberg theorem
Natural selection
Genetic drift
Migration
Mutation
Random mating

a crude extract made by homogenizing individual flower buds from the various rock pink plants, each wick being soaked in a different plant bud homogenate. The wicks are then inserted in a slot cut along the width of the gel; this slot is referred to as the **origin** (Figure 12.1a). The gel is linked to two buffer tanks by contact wicks and connected to an electric current, creating a charged field through which the proteins migrate based on their charge and size (Figure 12.1b and c). Once the enzymes are sufficiently separated to allow the investigator to detect differences in the distances migrated by the enzymes, the gels are removed from the electric field and sliced into three or more thin slabs. Each gel contains all the enzymes present in the original tissue spread throughout the gel, but the investigator stains for only one enzyme in each gel or slice of gel. Since enzymes have specific substrates, each gel can be treated with the substrate for the enzyme of interest plus a salt that reacts with the product of the enzyme reaction to produce a colored band. The result will be one or more colored bands for each individual surveyed in a population. The number of bands and the distance migrated can be used to determine the genotype of individual organisms.

Figure 12.1.
Preparation of starch gels and techniques of gel electrophoresis.
(a) Wicks containing the enzymes are placed in a slot cut in the starch gel. This slot is called the *origin*. (b) The gel is linked to two buffer tanks by contact wicks and connected to an electric current. (c) Enzymes migrate to characteristic positions in the gel.

Remember that each protein in the gel migrates in a direction and at a rate that depend on two factors: net electrical charge and molecular size. For example, an enzyme with a greater negative charge will move more quickly toward the anode (the positive pole) than an enzyme with a lesser negative charge. Similarly, a smaller molecule will move more rapidly than a larger molecule. The number and type of amino acids that make up an enzyme determine its size and charge, and the differences in number and type of amino acids depend on mutations in genes, producing alternate forms, or alleles. The enzymes you will study in the rock pink population all migrate toward the anode.

The exercise will be carried out using reproductions of photographs of three slabs sliced from a gel. One slab was stained for alcohol dehydrogenase (ADH), another for phosphoglucoisomerase (PGI), and another for phosphoglucomutase (PGM) (Figure 12.2). This gel contained enzymes from 25 individual plants.

a. ADH

b. PGI

c. PGM

Figure 12.2.
The gels to be interpreted in Exercise 12.1. Each gel has been stained to reveal a different enzyme: (a) alcohol dehydrogenase (ADH), (b) phosphoglucoisomerase (PGI), and (c) phosphoglucomutase (PGM).

Lab Study A. Terminology Associated with Enzymes and Gel Electrophoresis

In this lab study, you will become familiar with the terminology used to describe enzymes and the bands that are visible after separating and staining the enzymes.

Materials

No materials are needed for this lab study.

Procedure

1. Observe the enzyme banding patterns in the three gels in Figure 12.2.
2. Identify two **zones of activity.** A zone of activity is a row of colored bands in the gel, representing the products of one gene. The number of zones of activity represents the number of isozymes for the enzyme present in the gel. **Isozymes** are enzymes with the same function specified by two different genes, so two zones of activity would indicate two different genes coding for the same enzyme.

   a. How many zones of activity are present for each enzyme?

   b. Label the zones of activity on each gel in Figure 12.2. Where two or more isozymes are present, the enzyme that migrates the greater distance from the origin is considered to be in the first zone of activity, the lesser distance, in the second zone of activity. To understand the naming of genes, refer to the top of Figure 12.2, stained for ADH. The gene that codes for the faster-migrating isozyme (has moved the greater distance from the origin) is called ADH-1; the gene for the slower-migrating isozyme is ADH-2. If additional isozymes were present, they would be numbered sequentially.

   c. Name each gene by its enzyme and the distance that the isozyme has traveled (isozyme 1 has traveled the greater distance).

   d. Record the number of zones of activity for each enzyme in Table 12.2 in the Results section.

3. Determine whether each gene is monomorphic or polymorphic and identify allozymes. If all individuals in one activity zone have enzymes that migrate the same distance from the origin, the gene is **monomorphic** (for example, PGI-1). All the bands in this activity zone are at the exact same level in the gel. This means that there are no alternate forms of this gene, at least in this population. If the number of bands for individuals of a population varies and there are two or more enzyme bands within an activity zone, the gene is **polymorphic** (for example, PGI-2), and the variant enzymes are called **allozymes** because they are enzymes coded by alleles of a single gene locus.

   a. Designate which genes are monomorphic and which are polymorphic in Table 12.2.

   b. Label allozymes on at least one gel in Figure 12.2.

4. Determine for your study gels (Figure 12.2) whether each enzyme is monomeric, dimeric, or trimeric. Record your answers in Table 12.2 in the Results section. Use Figure 12.3 and the following discussion to help you make your determinations.

When proteins are synthesized from DNA, one polypeptide is made at a time. For some enzymes, this polypeptide is all that is necessary to have a functioning enzyme, and the enzyme is described as being **monomeric.**

Other enzymes may need two or more polypeptides to bind together before the enzyme is active. An enzyme that needs two polypeptides in order to become active is called a **dimeric enzyme,** or **dimer.** If an enzyme requires three polypeptides in order to function, it is called a **trimeric enzyme,** or **trimer;** four polypeptides, a **tetrameric enzyme,** or **tetramer;** and so on.

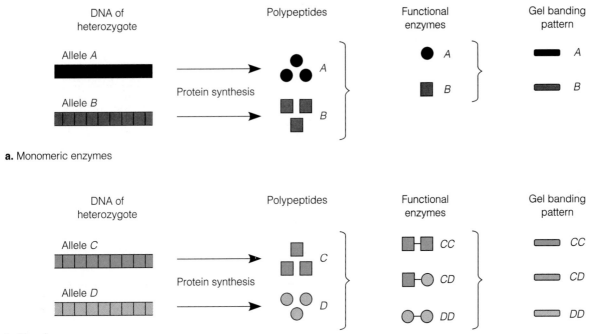

a. Monomeric enzymes

b. Dimeric enzymes

Figure 12.3.
The interpretation of banding patterns for a heterozygote when the enzyme is monomeric or dimeric.
(a) For monomeric enzymes, two different polypeptides are produced in a heterozygote, but either is a functioning enzyme. Therefore, only two bands will form in the heterozygote: A and B. (b) For dimeric enzymes, the enzyme can function only if two polypeptides are linked. In a heterozygous individual, the alleles produce two different polypeptides that may link in three configurations. Two like polypeptides can link (C to C or D to D), or the two unlike polypeptides can link (C to D). Each of these three linkages will migrate at different rates on a gel.

Since our staining procedure requires that the enzymes be functioning in order to be seen, we see only enzymes in their active form (whether that form is monomer, dimer, or some other form). Therefore, if some of the individuals on the gel have two different alleles coding for the polypeptides (that is, if the individuals are heterozygous), you can determine if the enzyme is dimeric, trimeric, or tetrameric.

Distinguishing Monomeric and Dimeric Enzymes

If an enzyme is monomeric, in the homozygous individual only one band will appear on the gel, but in the heterozygote two bands will appear on the gel, indicating functional polypeptides, one for each of the codominant alleles (Figure 12.3a).

If the enzyme is dimeric, it requires two polypeptides bound together to function. An individual that is homozygous for the gene will produce only one kind of polypeptide, which can only bind to the same kind of polypeptide to give one kind of dimer. This will produce only one band on the gel. Heterozygous individuals, however, produce two polypeptides that can bind together in three different ways. Consider a dimeric enzyme with two different polypeptides, one coded for by allele C, the other by allele D. If C polypeptides run faster than D polypeptides on the gel (because of charge), then *CC* dimers will run faster than *CD* dimers, which will run faster than *DD* dimers. This gives a three-band pattern (Figure 12.3b) and is seen in the dimeric enzyme ADH-2.

In summary, homozygotes for both monomeric and dimeric enzymes produce only one band. Heterozygotes for dimeric enzymes produce three bands. Heterozygotes for monomeric enzymes produce two bands. The third band seen in dimeric enzymes (the hybrid band) will be absent, since each polypeptide is functional and hybrid molecules do not form.

Results

Record your observations and conclusions in Table 12.2.

Table 12.2
Observation of Banding Patterns in Figure 12.2. Indicate your answer for each gene locus if there is more than one zone of activity per enzyme.

Enzyme	Number of Zones of Activity (Genes)	Monomorphic or Polymorphic	Monomeric or Dimeric
ADH (Fig 12.2a)			
PGI (Fig 12.2b)			
PGM (Fig 12.2c)			

Discussion

1. What evidence do you have that the zones of activity for PGI represent isozymes rather than allozymes? (Note that the only way to be certain that bands are allozymes of the same gene is to perform genetic crosses and analyses.)

2. Do any of the genes have a rare allele, that is, an allele that appears only occasionally?

3. You see three bands in an individual in the ADH-2 zone of activity. Explain why you conclude that these three bands indicate that this

enzyme is dimeric, that the individual is heterozygous, and that these bands do *not* represent fast, slow, and very slow alleles.

Lab Study B. Scoring the Gel

Materials

calculator

Introduction

Scoring a gel involves examining the banding pattern for each individual represented in the gel and determining the genotype and phenotype of that individual. In this lab study, you will summarize these data for all polymorphic genes represented by the enzymes in the gels (see Figure 12.2).

Procedure

1. Within each zone of activity, identify allozymes according to their rate of migration from the origin (f = fast, or the enzyme band farthest from the origin; s = slow; vs = very slow). Label Figure 12.2 with your results.

2. Determine the genotype and phenotype of each polymorphic individual in the population. Note that at the protein level of expression, alleles are codominant and therefore genotype and phenotype correspond. A heterozygote is immediately known because both alleles are expressed in the form of two bands if the enzyme is monomeric or in the form of three bands if dimeric.

Results

Summarize and record your results in Table 12.3.

Table 12.3
Number of Individuals of Each Genotype for Each Polymorphic Gene
(f = fast allele, s = slow allele, vs = very slow allele)

Polymorphic Gene Locus	Phenotype:	f	s	f/s	vs	f/vs	s/vs	Total Number of Individuals
	Genotype:	f/f	s/s	f/s	vs/vs	f/vs	s/vs	
ADH-1								
ADH-2								
PGI-2								
PGM-2								

Discussion

How many bands would be present in a heterozygote if the enzyme was a tetramer? Draw the heterozygote for a tetramer.

Lab Study C. Determining Genotypic and Allelic Frequencies

In this lab study, you will use the data from Table 12.3 to determine the frequencies of genotypes (genotypic frequencies) and frequencies of alleles (allelic frequencies) in the rock pink population.

Materials

calculator

Procedure

1. Determine genotypic frequencies for ADH-1, ADH-2, PGI-2, and PGM-2. To do this, divide the number of individuals of each genotype by the total number of individuals.

2. Determine allelic frequencies for the same enzymes. Count the number of times the allele appears in the population and divide by the total number of alleles in the population. Record your results in Table 12.4.

   An individual with only a single slow band has two "slow" alleles while a heterozygous fast/slow individual has one "fast" allele and one "slow" allele. The total number of alleles in the sample is twice the number of individuals because each individual carries two alleles.

Results

Record your conclusions in Table 12.4.

Discussion

Explain how this population of the diploid rock pink can have three alleles present.

Table 12.4
Genotypic and Allelic Frequencies for ADH-1, ADH-2, PGI-2, and PGM-2

Polymorphic Gene Locus	Genotypic Frequency						Allelic Frequency		
	f/f	*s/s*	*f/s*	*vs/vs*	*f/vs*	*s/vs*	*f*	*s*	*vs*
ADH-1									
ADH-2									
PGI-2									
PGM-2									

Lab Study D. Determining Heterozygosity

Materials

calculator

Introduction

One way to measure the extent of genetic variation in a population is to determine the percentage of genes that are polymorphic—that is, having more than one allele at a gene locus. This estimate of genetic variation can be problematic because a gene with two alleles is counted in the same way as a gene with five alleles. Also, a rare allele (appearing only occasionally in the population) will be included in the same way as an allele that occurs in 50% of the population. Another measure, heterozygosity, appears to provide a better estimate of genetic variation. **Heterozygosity** (*H*) is the average frequency of heterozygous individuals per gene locus.

To calculate *observed* heterozygosity, first determine the frequency of heterozygotes at each gene locus (divide the number of heterozygotes by the total number of individuals in the population). Then total the frequency of heterozygous individuals for all gene loci and divide by the total number of loci. (This final average is calculated by including both monomorphic and polymorphic loci in your total number.)

Table 12.5
Sample Calculation of Heterozygosity in a Mouse Population

Gene Locus	Number of Heterozygotes	Frequency of Observed Heterozygotes
A-1	9	0.45 (9/20)
A-2	2	0.10
B-1	8	0.40
C-1	0	0
C-2	4	0.20
		Σ 1.15

For example, in a population sample of 20 mice, you might study five gene loci and get the results shown in Table 12.5. Then the average heterozygosity for this population would be

$$H = \frac{1.15}{5} = 0.23$$

The *observed heterozygosity* in this population of mice is 0.23.

Procedure

1. Using data from Table 12.3, record the number of heterozygotes for ADH-1, ADH-2, PGI-2, and PGM-2 in Table 12.6.
2. Divide the number of heterozygotes for each gene locus by the number of individuals in the population. This is the frequency of heterozygotes for that gene locus. Record this information in Table 12.6.
3. Determine the population average heterozygosity. Divide the sum of heterozygosity for all loci by the total number of loci (including both polymorphic and monomorphic gene loci).

Results

Record all results in Table 12.6.

Table 12.6
Heterozygosity for Each Locus and Average Heterozygosity for Population

| Polymorphic Gene Locus | Number of Individuals | | |
	Heterozygotes	Total	Frequency of Observed Heterozygotes
ADH-1			
ADH-2			
PGI-2			
PGM-2			
Population average heterozygosity:			

Discussion

List all the heterozygous genotypes for the PGM-2 locus. Did you record the correct number in Table 12.6?

Lab Study E. Comparing Observed and Expected Heterozygosity

In natural populations, the amount of genetic variation might be affected by the reproductive behavior of the organisms. For example, populations that are highly inbred, from either mating between close relatives in animals or self-pollination in plants, might have a lower heterozygosity than expected for a population with the same allelic frequencies with random mating. (Return to Lab Topic 11 to review the guidelines for a population at Hardy-Weinberg equilibrium.)

You can determine the *expected* heterozygosity (expected in a large, randomly mating population) from the allelic frequencies.

To calculate expected heterozygosity for a gene locus with three alleles, the frequency of the alleles would be $f1$, $f2$, and $f3$. The frequency of the homozygotes (from Hardy-Weinberg) would be $(f1)^2$, $(f2)^2$, and $(f3)^2$. Therefore, the expected frequency of heterozygotes would be

$$H_{exp} = 1 - [(f1)^2 + (f2)^2 + (f3)^2 + \cdots]$$

For the mouse example, if two alleles, *a* and *b*, exist for the A-1 gene locus, and the frequency for each of these alleles is known, then the expected heterozygosity for the A-1 gene locus can be calculated. Suppose that the frequency of *a* is 0.6 and the frequency of *b* is 0.4. Then the expected heterozygosity would be

$$H_{exp} = 1 - [(0.6)^2 + (0.4)^2] = 0.48$$

To calculate the expected *number of heterozygotes,* simply multiply the total number of individuals in the population by the expected heterozygosity. For gene locus A-1 in the mouse example, the expected number of heterozygotes in the sample of 20 individuals would be $(20 \times 0.48) = 10$ (rounded off). Using chi-square analysis, you can then determine whether the observed numbers of heterozygotes are significantly different from those expected in a large, randomly mating population.

In this lab study, you will calculate the expected number of heterozygotes for the enzymes in the gels in Figure 12.2 and then use chi-square analysis to determine whether observed and expected numbers of heterozygotes are significantly different in the rock pink population.

Materials

calculator

Procedure

1. Calculate the expected heterozygosity for ADH-1, ADH-2, PGI-2, and PGM-2. Record your results below. (Refer to Table 12.4 for allelic frequencies.)

	Expected Heterozygosity
ADH-1	
ADH-2	
PGI-2	
PGM-2	

2. Calculate the expected number of heterozygotes for ADH-1, ADH-2, PGI-2, and PGM-2, rounding to the nearest whole number. Record these data in Table 12.7.

3. Using data from Table 12.6, record the observed number of heterozygotes for these gene loci in Table 12.7.

4. Record the number of homozygous individuals observed for these genes in Table 12.7.

5. Calculate the expected number of homozygous individuals. To do this, subtract the number of expected heterozygotes from the total number of individuals in the population.

6. On a separate paper, use the chi-square test to determine whether the observed and expected numbers are significantly different. (Refer to Appendix B to review the chi-square test.) Record your conclusions in Table 12.7.

Results

Record data and significance of the chi-square test results in Table 12.7.

Table 12.7
Observed Heterozygotes and Homozygotes for ADH-1, ADH-2, PGI-2, and PGM-2 and Significance of Chi-Square Test

Polymorphic Gene Locus	Number of Heterozygotes		Number of Homozygotes		Significant Difference	
	Observed	Expected	Observed	Expected	Yes	No
ADH-1						
ADH-2						
PGI-2						
PGM-2						

Discussion

1. What factors, other than nonrandom mating, could account for a significant difference between observed and expected numbers of heterozygotes in living populations?

2. Why do electrophoretic estimates of heterozygosity underestimate genetic variation at the protein level?

EXERCISE 12.2
Interpreting Results of Gels of a Hypothetical Population

In this exercise, you will apply your knowledge and understanding of genetic variation and gel electrophoresis to a hypothetical problem.

Problem

Another species of *Talinum*, called *rock red*, has been found on sandstone outcrops in south Georgia. This rare plant is a succulent that inhabits the shallow soils found on rock outcrops. These rock outcroppings are isolated islands of rock found within a sea of forests, fields, and suburban developments. Although the rock red is insect-pollinated, the position of the reproductive structures in the flowers of some populations promotes self-pollination when the flower closes.

In this exercise, you will evaluate gels for the enzymes aconitase (ACN), glyceraldehyde phosphate dehydrogenase (GDH), and PGI. You will pose hypotheses and make predictions, interpret the gels, score the isozymes and allozymes, determine the genotypic and allelic frequencies, and calculate heterozygosity.

Hypothesis

For this newly discovered species, state a hypothesis concerning the amount of genetic variation present in the population based on the species characteristics (as previously stated) and the factors that affect genetic variation.

Prediction

Predict whether the observed heterozygosity will differ significantly from the expected heterozygosity.

Procedure

1. Interpret the bands and score the gel in Figure 12.4. Determine isozymes, allozymes, and monomorphic and polymorphic loci, and whether the enzymes are monomeric, dimeric, and so on. (If you need assistance, refer to Exercise 12.1.)

a. ACN

b. GDH

c. PGI

Figure 12.4.
Gels representing the hypothetical population. (a) Gel stained for aconitase (ACN).
(b) Gel stained for glyceraldehyde phosphate dehydrogenase (GDH). (c) Gel
stained for phosphoglucoisomerase (PGI).

2. In the Results section, design appropriate tables to record your data.
    (Use Tables 12.3 and 12.4 as examples.) You should have one row for
    each gene locus (include monomorphic and polymorphic genes) and one
    column for each genotype.

3. Count and record the number of individuals of each genotype for the
    gene products stained in the gels.

4. Be prepared to present your results in a class discussion.

Results

1. Determine genotypic and allelic frequencies for the genes, recording your data in tables that you have designed.

2. Calculate the frequency of heterozygotes for each locus and the average heterozygosity for the population. Record your data in an appropriate table.

3. Calculate the expected heterozygosity for each gene locus. Record your data in the margin of your lab manual. Use the formula

$$H_{exp} = 1 - [(f1)^2 + (f2)^2 + \cdots]$$

4. Calculate the expected number of heterozygotes for each gene locus. Multiply heterozygosity by the number of individuals in the population. Record your data in an appropriate table.

5. On separate paper, use the chi-square test to determine if observed and expected numbers are significantly different.

Discussion

1. What was the observed average heterozygosity for this population?

2. Discuss the significance of the chi-square test results.

3. Was your hypothesis supported? Describe the factors that may affect the genetic variation in this population.

4. What is the average heterozygosity for this population?

5. Based on your results, what is the evolutionary potential for this species?

Questions for Review

1. Define the following terms, giving examples when appropriate: *heterozygosity, isozymes, allozymes, monomorphic, polymorphic, monomeric, dimeric, trimeric.*

2. Using a separate paper, practice calculating genotypic frequencies, allelic frequencies, and heterozygosity by solving the following problems (from Ayala, 1982).

   a. Three genotypes were observed at the PGM-1 locus in a human population. In a sample of 1,110 individuals, the three genotypes occurred in the following numbers (1 and 2 represent two different alleles):

Genotypes:	1/1	1/2	2/2
Numbers:	634	391	85

   Calculate the genotypic and allelic frequencies.

b. Two human serum haptoglobins are determined by two alleles at a single locus. In a sample of 219 Egyptians, the three genotypes occurred in the following numbers (1 and 3 represent the two alleles):

Genotypes:	1/1	1/3	3/3
Numbers:	9	135	75

What are the frequencies of the two alleles?

c. Calculate the expected frequency of heterozygotes, assuming random mating, from the data given in problems 2a and 2b. Use the chi-square test to determine whether the observed and expected numbers of heterozygous individuals are significantly different.

3. Observe the two gels below (from Hebert and Beaton, 1989). Gel A is stained for the enzyme leucine aminopeptidase (LAP); gel B, for the enzyme phosphoglucose isomerase (PGI). For each gel:

   a. Identify and label zones of activity.

   b. Indicate isozymes and allozymes.

   c. Tell if the gene is monomorphic or polymorphic.

   d. Determine if the enzyme is monomeric, dimeric, or trimeric.

   e. Calculate allelic and genotypic frequencies.

a. Leucine aminopeptidase (LAP)   **b.** Phosphoglucoisomerase (PGI)

(After Hebert and Beaton, 1989)

Applying Your Knowledge

1. Table 12.8 (from Ayala, 1982) gives the number of individuals in each of the MN blood groups in samples from various human populations. Using a separate paper, calculate the genotypic and allelic frequencies,

Table 12.8
Number of Individuals in Each of the MN Blood Groups

Population	M	MN	N	Total
Belgians	896	1,559	645	3,100
English	121	200	101	422
Egyptians	140	245	117	502
Ainu	90	253	161	504
Fijians	22	89	89	200
Papuans	14	48	138	200

as well as the expected number of heterozygous individuals, for each population. Test whether the observed and expected numbers of heterozygotes agree.

Table 12.9
Frequencies of the Slow (s), Fast (f), and Very Fast (vf) Alleles of Alcohol Dehydrogenase (ADH) in Populations of Adult *Drosophila mojavensis*

Locality	Number of Individuals	s	f	vf	H
Agua Caliente	124	0.448	0.552	0.0	0.363
Grand Canyon	41	0.659	0.341	0.0	0.195
Guaymas	49	0.755	0.163	0.082	0.326
Mulege	50	0.130	0.870	0.0	0.060

H = heterozygosity determined by direct count

2. Table 12.9 (from Cleland et al., 1996) gives the results of starch gel electrophoresis of fruit fly enzymes from four localities in Arizona.

Complete the following table describing populations of *D. mojavensis* studied:

a. Using the heterozygosity data, determine the number of heterozygotes and homozygotes in the population.

b. Calculate the number of homozygous *ss* or *ff* individuals in the population. Remember that each individual in the population has two alleles and that heterozygotes will have one *f* and one *s*. (*Hint:* This population is *not* in Hardy-Weinberg equilibrium.)

Locality	Number of Individuals				Number of *vf* Alleles in Population
	Heterozygotes	Homozygotes	*ss*	*ff*	
Agua Caliente					
Grand Canyon					
Guaymas					
Mulege					

How would you describe the *vf* allele?

Can you determine if *vf* alleles are in heterozygous or homozygous individuals?

References

Ayala, F. J. *Population and Evolutionary Genetics: A Primer.* Menlo Park, CA: Benjamin/Cummings, 1982.

Cleland, S., G. D. Hocutt, C. M. Breitmeyer, T. A. Markow, and E. Pfeiler. "Alcohol Dehydrogenase Polymorphism in Barrel Cactus Populations of *Drosophila mojavensis.*" *Genetica* 1996, vol. 98, pp. 115–117.

Hamrick, J. L., Y. B. Linhart, and J. B. Mitton. "Relationships between Life History Characteristics and Electrophoretically Detectable Genetic Variation in Plants." *Annual Review of Ecology and Systematics* 1979, pp. 173–200.

Hebert, D. N., and M. J. Beaton. *Methodologies for Allozyme Analysis Using Cellulose Acetate Electrophoresis.* Helena Laboratories, 1989.

Kephart, S. R. "Starch Gel Electrophoresis of Plant Isozymes: A Comparative Analysis of Techniques." *American Journal of Botany,* May 1990, vol. 77, pp. 316–368.

May, B. "Starch Gel Electrophoresis of Allozymes." in *Molecular Genetic Analysis of Populations—A Practical Approach,* A. R. Hoelzel, editor. 1992, pp. 1–27.

Soltis, D. E., and P. S. Soltis, eds. *Isozymes in Plant Biology. Advances in Plant Sciences Series,* vol. 4. Portland, OR: Dioscorides Press, 1989.

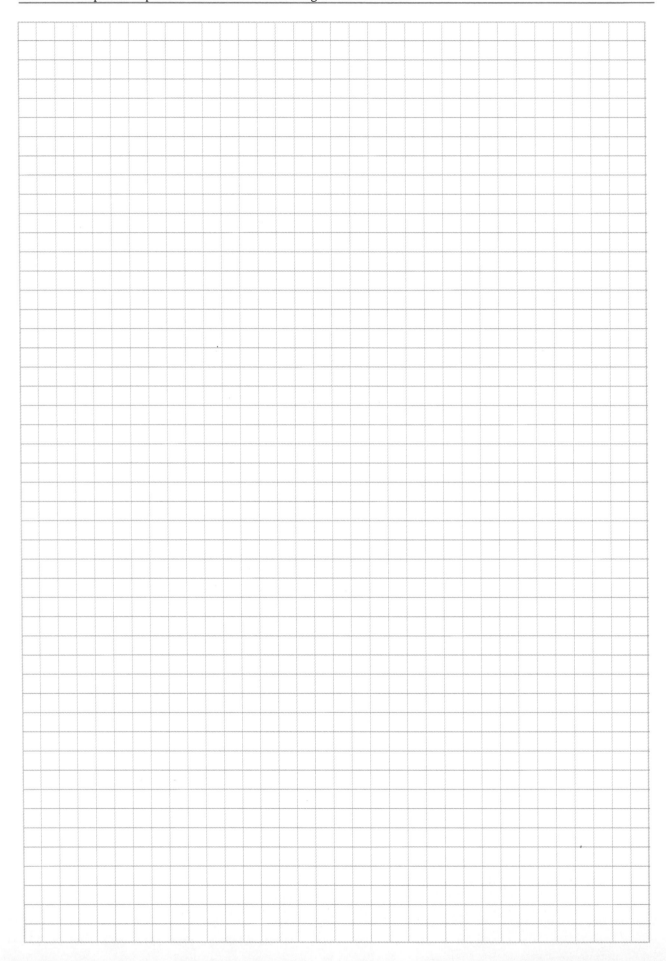

Bacteriology

Laboratory Objectives

After completing this lab topic, you should be able to:

1. Describe bacterial structure: colony morphology, cell shape, growth patterns.
2. Describe the results of Gram staining and discuss the implications to cell wall chemistry.
3. Describe a scenario for succession of bacterial and fungal communities in aging milk, relating this to changes in environmental conditions such as pH and nutrient availability.
4. Practice aseptic techniques producing bacterial streaks, smears, and lawns.
5. Describe the ecology and control of bacteria, applying these concepts to life situations.

Introduction

Humans have named and categorized organisms for hundreds—perhaps even thousands—of years. Taxonomy is an important branch of biology that deals with naming and classifying organisms into distinct groups or categories. Much of the work of early taxonomists included recording characteristics of organisms and grouping them based on appearance, habitat, or perhaps medicinal value. As scientists began to understand the processes of genetics and evolution by natural selection, they realized the value of classifying organisms based on phylogeny, or evolutionary history. Information about phylogeny was obtained from studies of development or homologous features—common features resulting from common genes. In recent years, scientists have begun using biochemical evidence—studies of nucleic acids and proteins—to investigate relationships among organisms, leading to revisions in the taxonomic scheme.

Systematists continue to grapple with the complex challenge of organizing the diversity of life into categories. A three-domain system proposed in the late 1970s is becoming widely accepted, replacing Robert Whittaker's five-kingdom system used since 1969. The five-kingdom system places all prokaryotic organisms in the kingdom Monera, and eukaryotic organisms are in kingdoms Protista, Fungi, Plantae, and Animalia. In the three-domain system, the three domains—Bacteria, Archaea, and Eukarya—are essentially superkingdoms and include the kingdoms, historically the broadest taxonomic category. Prokaryotes are placed in either Bacteria or Archaea, with all eukaryotes categorized in the domain Eukarya. Researchers continue to debate the number of kingdoms to include in the domains. Some have suggested eight kingdoms with Bacteria and Archaea corresponding to their respective domains and six kingdoms in Eukarya—three protistan kingdoms and Plantae, Fungi, and Animalia. Other researchers propose even more kingdoms. (See Figure 26.16 in Campbell and Reece, 2002.)

Although many argue that biological categories are subjective in nature and the criteria for designating the kingdoms of life have been modified by scientists historically, it is nonetheless true that scientists have set definite criteria or guidelines that form the basis of taxonomic classification. Most organisms may be placed into these designated categories.

In this lab topic, you will study organisms commonly called **bacteria.** In the five-kingdom scheme, bacteria were placed in the kingdom **Monera.** In the three-domain, eight-kingdom system, the common bacteria are classified in the **domain Bacteria, kingdom Bacteria.**

Bacteria are small, relatively simple, **prokaryotic,** single-celled organisms. **Prokaryotes,** from the Greek for "prenucleus," have existed on Earth longer and are more widely distributed than any other organismal group. They are found in almost every imaginable habitat: air, soil, and water, in extreme temperatures and harsh chemical environments. They can be photosynthetic, using light, or chemosynthetic, using inorganic chemicals as the source of energy, but most are heterotrophic, absorbing nutrients from the surrounding environment.

Most bacteria have a cell wall, a complex layer outside the cell membrane. The most common component found in the cell wall is peptidoglycan, a complex protein-carbohydrate polymer. There are no membrane-bound organelles in bacteria and the genetic material is not bound by a nuclear envelope. Bacteria do not have chromosomes as described in Lab Topic 6; their genetic material is a single circular molecule of DNA. In addition, bacteria may have smaller rings of DNA called **plasmids** (see page 242), consisting of only a few genes. They reproduce by a process called **binary fission,** in which the cell duplicates its components and divides into two cells. These cells usually become independent, but they may remain attached in linear chains or grapelike clusters. In favorable environments, individual bacterial cells rapidly proliferate, forming colonies consisting of millions of cells.

Differences in colony morphology and the shape of individual bacterial cells are important distinguishing characteristics of bacterial species. In Exercise 13.1, working independently, you will observe and describe the morphology of colonies and individual cells of several bacterial species. You will examine and describe characteristics of bacteria growing in plaque on your teeth. You and your lab partner will compare results of all lab studies.

E X E R C I S E   1 3 . 1

Investigating Characteristics of Bacteria

Because of the small size and similarity of cell structure in bacteria, techniques used to identify bacteria are different from those used to identify macroscopic organisms. Staining reactions and properties of growth, nutrition, and physiology are usually used to make final identification of species. The structure and arrangement of cells and the morphology of colonies contribute preliminary information that can help us determine the appropriate test necessary to make final identification. In this exercise, you will use the tools at hand, microscopes and unaided visual observations, to learn some characteristics of bacterial cells and colonies.

When you are working with bacteria, it is very important to practice certain **aseptic techniques** to make sure that the cultures being studied are not contaminated by organisms from the environment and that organisms are not released into the environment.

1. Wipe the lab bench with disinfectant before and after the lab activities.
2. Wash your hands before and after performing an experiment.
3. Using the alcohol lamp or Bunsen burner, flame all non-flammable instruments used to manipulate bacteria or fungi before and after use.
4. Place swabs and toothpicks in the disposal container immediately after use. *Never place one of these items on the lab bench after use!*
5. Wear a lab coat, a lab apron, or a clean old shirt over your clothes to lessen chances of staining or contamination accidents.

The bacteria used in these exercises are not pathogenic (disease-producing); nevertheless, use appropriate aseptic techniques and work with care! If a spill occurs, notify the instructor. If no instructor is available, wear disposable gloves, and wipe up the spill with paper towels. Follow this by washing the affected area with soap and water and a disinfectant. Dispose of the gloves and soiled towels in the autoclavable plastic bag provided.

Lab Study A. Colony Morphology

Materials

disinfectant
stereoscopic microscope
metric ruler
agar plate cultures with bacterial colonies

Introduction

A **bacterial colony** grows from a single bacterium and is composed of millions of cells. Each colony has a characteristic size, shape, consistency, texture, and color (colony morphology), all of which may be useful in preliminary species identification. Bacteriologists use specific terms to describe colony characteristics. Use Figure 13.1 to become familiar with this terminology and describe the bacterial species provided. Occasionally, one or more **fungal colonies** will contaminate the bacterial plates. Fungi may

Figure 13.1.
Terminology used in describing bacterial colonies. (a) Common shapes, (b) margins, and (c) surface characteristics are illustrated.

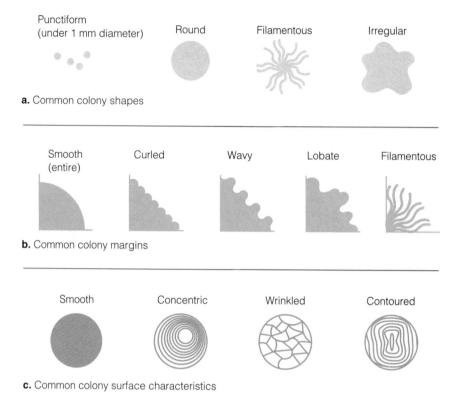

a. Common colony shapes

Punctiform (under 1 mm diameter) · Round · Filamentous · Irregular

b. Common colony margins

Smooth (entire) · Curled · Wavy · Lobate · Filamentous

c. Common colony surface characteristics

Smooth · Concentric · Wrinkled · Contoured

be distinguished from bacteria by the *fuzzy* appearance of the colony (Figure 13.2). The body of a fungus is a mass of filaments called **hyphae** in a network called a **mycelium.** Learn to distinguish fungi from bacteria.

Procedure

1. Wipe the work area with disinfectant and wash your hands.
2. Set up your stereoscopic microscope.
3. Obtain one of the bacterial plates provided. Leaving the plate closed (unless otherwise instructed), place it on the stage of the microscope.
4. Examine a typical individual, separate colony. Measure the size and note the color of the colony, and record this information in Table 13.1, in the Results section.

Figure 13.2.
(a) Bacteria and (b) fungi growing on nutrient agar plates. The body of most fungi consists of filaments called *hyphae* in a network called a *mycelium*. The hyphae give fungal colonies a fuzzy appearance. (See Color Plates 16–19.)

a.   **b.**

5. Using the diagrams in Figure 13.1, select appropriate terms that describe the colony.

6. Record your observations in Table 13.1.

7. Sketch one colony in the margin of your lab manual, illustrating the characteristics observed.

8. Repeat steps 2 to 6 with two additional species. Your lab partner should examine three different species.

9. Observe Color Plates 16, 18, and 19. Describe the shape, margin, surface, and color of these bacterial species.

Results

1. Complete Table 13.1 at the bottom of the page using terms from Figure 13.1 to describe the three bacterial cultures you observed.

2. Compare your observations with those of your lab partner.

Discussion

1. What are the most common colony shapes, colony margins, and colony surface characteristics found in the species observed by you and your lab partner?

2. Based on your observations, comment on the reliability of colony morphology in the identification of a given bacterial species.

Table 13.1
Characteristics of Bacterial Colonies

Name of Bacteria	Size	Shape	Margin	Surface	Color
1.					
2.					
3.					

Lab Study B. Morphology of Individual Cells

Materials

compound microscope
prepared slides of bacillus, coccus,
   and spirillum bacteria
blank slide
clean toothpick
clothespin

dropper bottle of deionized (DI)
   water
dropper bottle of crystal violet stain
squirt bottle of DI water
alcohol lamp or Bunsen burner
staining pan

Introduction

Microscopic examination of bacterial cells reveals that most bacteria can be classified according to three basic shapes: **bacilli** (rods), **cocci** (spheres), and **spirilla** (spirals, or corkscrews). In many species, cells tend to adhere to each other and form aggregates, with each cell maintaining its independence. In this lab study, you will examine prepared slides of bacteria that illustrate the three basic cell shapes, and then you will examine and describe bacteria growing in your mouth.

Procedure

1. To become familiar with the basic shapes of bacterial cells, using the compound microscope, examine prepared slides of the three types of bacteria, and make a sketch of each shape in the space provided.

2. Protein and carbohydrate materials from food particles accumulate at the gum line in your mouth and create an ideal environment for bacteria to grow. This mixture of materials and bacteria is called **plaque.** To investigate the forms of bacteria found on your teeth, prepare a stained slide of plaque.

    a. Set out a clean slide.

    b. Place a drop of water on the slide. This must air-dry, so make the drop of water *small.*

    c. Using a fresh toothpick, scrape your teeth near the gum line and mix the scraping in the drop of water.

    d. Spread this plaque-water mixture into a thin film and allow it to air-dry.

    e. When the smear is dry, hold the slide with a clothespin and pass it quickly over the flame of an alcohol lamp or Bunsen burner several times at a 45° angle. This should warm the slide but not cook the bacteria. Briefly touch the warm slide to the back of your hand. If it is too hot to touch, you are allowing it to get too warm.

Keep long hair and loose clothing away from the flame.
Extinguish the flame immediately after use.

f. Place the slide on the support of a staining pan or tray and apply
three or four drops of crystal violet stain to the smear (Figure 13.3).

Figure 13.3.
Apply several drops of crystal violet
stain to the slide supported in a
staining pan or tray.

 Crystal violet will permanently stain your clothes, and it may
last several days on your hands as well. Work carefully!

g. Leave the stain on the smear for 1 minute.

h. Wash the stain off with a gentle stream of water from a squirt bottle
so that the stain goes into the staining pan (Figure 13.4).

i. Blot the stained slide gently with a paper towel. Do not rub hard or
you will remove the bacteria.

3. Examine the bacteria growing in the plaque on your teeth and determine
bacterial forms. Use the highest magnification on your compound microscope. If you have an oil immersion lens, after focusing on the high-
dry power, without changing the focus knobs, rotate the high-dry objective to the side, add a drop of immersion oil directly to the bacterial
smear, and carefully rotate the oil immersion objective into place. Focus
with the fine adjustment only. After observing the slide, rotate the oil
immersion objective away from the slide and wipe the objective carefully, using lens paper to remove all traces of oil.

Figure 13.4.
Gently rinse the stain into the
staining pan.

Results

1. Record the individual cell shapes of bacteria present in plaque.

2. What shapes are absent?

3. Estimate the relative abundance of each shape.

Discussion

1. Discuss with your lab partner information you have learned from your dentist or health class about the relationship among plaque, dental caries (cavities), and gum disease.

2. Suggest an explanation for differences in the proportion of each type of bacteria in the bacterial community of plaque.

Lab Study C. Identifying Bacteria by the Gram Stain Procedure

Materials

compound microscope
blank slides
alcohol lamp or Bunsen burner
clean toothpicks
staining pan
cultures of *Micrococcus*,
   Bacillus, *Serratia*, and *E. coli*

dropper bottles of Gram
   iodine, crystal violet,
   safranin, DI water, 95% ethyl
   alcohol/acetone mixture
squirt bottle of DI water

Introduction

Gram stain is commonly used to assist in bacterial identification. This stain, first developed in 1884, separates bacteria into groups, depending on their reaction to this stain. Bacteria react by testing either **gram-positive, gram-negative,** or **gram-variable,** with the first two groups being the most common. Although the exact mechanisms are not completely understood, scientists know that the response of cells to the stain is due to differences in the complexity and chemistry of the bacterial cell wall. Recall that bacterial cell walls contain a complex polymer, **peptidoglycan.** The cell walls of gram-negative bacteria contain less peptidoglycan than gram-positive bacteria. In addition, cell walls of gram-negative bacteria are more complex, containing various polysaccharides, proteins, and lipids not found in gram-positive bacteria. Studies of bacterial taxonomy have shown that these differences define major taxonomic groups.

Gram stain relies on the use of three stains: crystal violet (purple), Gram iodine, and safranin (pink/red). *Gram-positive* bacteria (with the thicker peptidoglycan layer) retain the crystal violet/iodine stain and appear blue/purple. *Gram-negative* bacteria lose the blue/purple stain but retain the safranin and appear pink/red (Color Plate 20).

In summary:

Gram-Negative Bacteria	Gram-Positive Bacteria
more complex cell wall	simple cell wall
thin peptidoglycan cell wall layer	thick peptidoglycan cell wall layer
outer lipopolysaccharide wall layer	no outer lipopolysaccharide wall layer
retain safranin	retain crystal violet/iodine
appear pink/red	appear blue/purple

In this lab study, you will prepare and stain slides of two different bacterial species. One member of the lab team should stain *Micrococcus* and *Bacillus*. The other member should stain *Serratia* and *E. coli*.

Procedure

1. Prepare smears as directed for the plaque slide (Lab Study B, steps 2a to 2e), substituting the bacterial species for the plaque. If you are using a liquid bacterial culture, do *not* add water to your slide (step 2b). Label the slide with your initials and the name of the bacterial species being investigated.

2. Support the slide on the staining tray and cover the smear with three or four drops of crystal violet. Wait 1 minute.

3. Rinse the stain gently into the staining pan with water from the squirt bottle.

4. Cover the smear with Gram iodine for 1 minute, setting the stain.

5. Rinse it again with water.

6. Destain (remove the stain) by dropping the 95% alcohol/acetone mixture down the slanted slide one drop at a time. At first a lot of violet color will rinse away. Continue adding drops until only a faint violet color is seen in the alcohol rinse. Do not overdo this step (Figure 13.5). You should be able to see some color in the smear on the slide. If not, you have destained too much. The alcohol/acetone removes the crystal violet stain from the gram-negative bacteria. The gram-positive bacteria will not be destained.

7. Using the water squirt bottle, rinse immediately to prevent further destaining.

Figure 13.5.
Destain by dropping 95% ethyl alcohol/acetone down the slanted slide until only a faint violet color is seen in the solution.

8. Cover the smear with safranin for 30 to 60 seconds. This will stain the destained gram-negative bacteria a pink/red color. The gram-positive bacteria will be unaffected by the safranin (Figure 13.6).

9. Briefly rinse the smear with water as above. Blot it lightly with a paper towel and let it dry at room temperature.

10. Examine each slide using the highest magnification on your microscope.

 If you use oil immersion, remove all traces of oil from the objective after observing the slide.

Figure 13.6.
The Gram stain. Crystal violet and Gram iodine stain all cells blue/purple. Alcohol/acetone destains gram-negative cells. Safranin stains gram-negative cells pink/red.

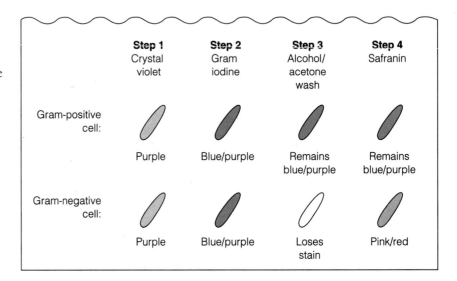

Results

Record your observations of the results of the Gram stain in Table 13.2.

Table 13.2
Bacteria Observed and Results of Gram Stain

Name of Bacteria	Results of Gram Stain
1.	
2.	

Discussion

1. Which of the bacteria observed are probably more closely related taxonomically?

2. What factors can modify the expected results of this staining procedure?

EXERCISE 13.2
Ecological Succession of Bacteria in Milk

Materials

pH paper
flasks of plain and chocolate whole milk aged 1, 4, and 8 days
TGY agar plates of each of the milk types
supplies from Exercise 13.1 for Gram stains

Introduction

Milk is a highly nutritious food containing carbohydrates (lactose, or milk sugar), proteins (casein, or curd), and lipids (butterfat). This high level of nutrition makes milk an excellent medium for the growth of bacteria. Pasteurizing milk does not sterilize it (sterilizing kills *all* bacteria) but merely destroys pathogenic bacteria, leaving many bacteria that will multiply very slowly at refrigerated temperatures; but at room temperature, these bacteria will begin to grow and bring about milk spoilage. Biologists have discovered that as milk ages, changing conditions in the milk bring about a predictable, orderly succession of microorganism communities (associations of species).

Community succession is a phenomenon observed in the organizational hierarchy of all living organisms, from bacterial communities in milk to animal and plant communities in a maturing deciduous forest. In each example, as one community grows, it modifies the environment, and a different community develops as a result.

In this laboratory exercise, you will work in pairs and observe successional patterns in two types of milk, plain whole milk and milk with sucrose and chocolate added. You will record changes in the environmental conditions of the two types of milk as they age. Note certain observations scientists have made about milk bacteria and their environment.

1. *Lactobacillus* (gram-positive rod) and *Streptococcus* (gram-positive coccus) survive pasteurization.

2. *Lactobacillus* and *Streptococcus* ferment lactose to lactate and acetic acid.

3. An acidic environment causes casein to solidify, or curd.

4. Two bacteria commonly found in soil and water, *Pseudomonas* and *Achromobacter* (both gram-negative rods), digest butterfats and give milk a putrid smell.

5. Yeasts and molds (both fungi) grow well in acidic environments.

Scenario

Propose a scenario (the hypothesis) for bacterial succession in each type of milk.

On each lab bench are four flasks of plain whole milk and four flasks of chocolate milk. One flask of each has been kept under refrigeration. One flask of each has been at room temperature for 24 hours, one for 4 days, and one for 8 days. On each bench there are also TGY (tryptone, glucose, yeast) agar plate cultures of each of the types of milk.

One team of two students should work with plain milk, another with chocolate milk. Teams will then exchange observations and results.

Procedure

1. Using the pH paper provided, take the pH of each flask. Record your results in Table 13.3, in the Results section.
2. Record the odor (sour, putrid), color, and consistency (coagulation slight, moderate, chunky) for the milk in each flask.
3. Using the TGY agar plates, observe and describe bacterial/fungal colonies in each age and type of milk. Use the vocabulary you developed while doing Exercise 13.1.
4. Prepare Gram stains of each different bacterial type on each plate using the staining instructions in Exercise 13.1, Lab Study C.
5. Record the results of the Gram stains in Table 13.3, in the Results section.

Results

Complete Table 13.3, in the Results section, describing the characteristics of each milk culture and the bacteria present in each.

Table 13.3
Physical Features and Bacterial/Fungal Communities of
Aged Plain and Chocolate Milk

Age/Type Milk	Environmental Characteristics (pH, Consistency, Odor, Color)	Organisms Present (Bacteria: Gram +/−, Shapes; Yeasts or Fungi)
Refrigerated plain		
24-hr plain		
4-day plain		
8-day plain		
Refrigerated chocolate		
24-hr chocolate		
4-day chocolate		
8-day chocolate		

Discussion

1. Describe the changing sequence of organisms and corresponding environmental changes during succession in plain milk. Do the results of your investigation match your hypothesis?

2. Describe the changing sequence of organisms and corresponding environmental changes during succession in chocolate milk. Do the results of your investigation match your hypothesis?

3. Compare succession in plain and chocolate milk. Propose reasons for differences.

4. Propose an experiment to test the environmental factors and/or organisms changing in your proposed scenario for milk succession.

EXERCISE 13.3
Bacteria in the Environment

In these experiments, you will sample different environments, testing for the presence of bacteria and fungi. In Experiment A, pairs of students will investigate one of five different environments. Each pair will report results to the entire class. In Experiment B, your team will investigate an environment of your choice.

Experiment A. Investigating Specific Environments

Materials

sterile agar plates	soil samples
wax pencil	samples of stream water
2 cotton-tipped sterile swabs	hand soap
bacterial inoculating loop	Parafilm strips
alcohol lamp or Bunsen burner	discard receptacle
piece of raw chicken in a petri dish	

Introduction

The instructor will assign team numbers to each pair of students. Each pair (team) of students will sample bacteria and fungi from one of five environments: food supply, soil, air, stream water, and hands. Read the instructions for all investigations. Think about the following questions, and before you begin your investigation, hypothesize about the relative growth of bacteria and fungi in the different environments.

Where in the environment would bacteria be more common, and where would fungi be more common? Would any of these environments be free of bacteria or fungi?

Seal all plates with Parafilm after preparation! Discard all used swabs in the designated receptacle!

Hypothesis

Hypothesize about the presence of bacteria and fungi in the different environments.

Prediction

Predict the results of the experiment based on your hypothesis (if/then).

Procedure

Team 1

1. Holding the lid in place, invert an agar plate and label the bottom "chicken."

2. Open the dish containing the piece of chicken, and swab the chicken surface using a sterile cotton swab.

 Avoid touching the chicken. Use the swab. Always wash your hands thoroughly after touching raw chicken, owing to the potential presence of *Salmonella,* bacteria that cause diarrhea.

---

3. Isolate bacteria by the **streak plate** method.

    a. Carefully lift the lid of the agar plate to 45° and lightly streak the swab back and forth across the top quarter of the agar (Figure 13.7a). Close the lid and *discard the swab in the receptacle provided.* Minimize exposing the agar plate to the air.

    b. Flame the bacterial inoculating loop using the alcohol lamp or Bunsen burner. Allow the loop to cool; starting at one end of the swab streak, lightly streak the microorganism in the pattern shown in Figure 13.7b. Do not gouge the medium.

    c. Reflame the loop and continue to streak as shown in Figure 13.7c and described in the figure legend.

        By the end of the last streak, the bacteria should be separated and reduced in density so that only isolated bacteria remain. These should grow into isolated, characteristic colonies.

4. Write the initials of your team members, the lab room, and the date on the petri dish.

5. Seal the dish with Parafilm and place it in the area indicated by the instructor.

6. Incubate the culture 1 week and observe results during the next laboratory period.

Figure 13.7.
Isolating bacterial colonies using the streak technique. (a) Streak the swab over the top quarter of the agar plate, region 1. (b) Using the newly flamed loop, pick up organisms from region 1 and streak them into region 2. (c) Reflame the loop and pick up organisms from region 2 and streak them into region 3.

The following week, to avoid exposure to potentially pathogenic bacteria, do not open the petri dish containing the chicken bacteria. Wash hands after handling cultures.

Team 2

1. Holding the lid in place, invert an agar plate and label the bottom "soil."
2. Using a cotton swab, pick up a small amount of soil from the sample.
3. Prepare a streak culture by following step 3 in the procedure for Team 1.
4. Write the initials of your team members, the lab room, and the date on the petri dish.
5. Seal the dish with Parafilm and place it in the area indicated by the instructor.
6. Incubate the culture 1 week and observe results during the next laboratory period.

Team 3

1. Holding the lid in place, invert an agar plate and label the bottom "air."
2. Collect a sample of bacteria by leaving the agar plate exposed (lid removed) to the air in some interesting area of the room for 10 to 15 minutes. Possible areas might be near a heat duct or an animal storage bin.
3. If additional agar plates are available, you may choose to sample several sites.
4. Write the initials of your team members, the lab room, and the date on each petri dish.
5. Seal the dish with Parafilm and place it in the area indicated by the instructor.
6. Incubate the culture(s) 1 week and observe results during the next laboratory period.

Team 4

1. Holding the lid in place, invert an agar plate and label the bottom "stream water."
2. Using a sterile cotton swab, take a sample from the stream water.
3. Prepare a streak culture by following step 3 in the procedure for Team 1.
4. Write the initials of your team members, the lab room, and the date on the petri dish.
5. Seal the dish with Parafilm and place it in the area indicated by the instructor.
6. Incubate the culture 1 week and observe results during the next laboratory period.

Team 5

1. Draw a line across the center of the bottom of an agar plate. Write "unwashed" on the dish bottom on one side of the line and "washed" on the other side of the line.

2. Select one person who has not recently washed his or her hands to be the test subject. The subject should open the petri dish and *lightly* press three fingers on the agar surface in the half of the dish marked "unwashed." Do not break the agar. Close the petri dish.

3. The subject should wash his or her hands for 1 minute and repeat the procedure, touching the agar with the same three fingers on the side of the dish marked "washed."

4. Write the initials of your team members, the lab room, and the date on the petri dish.

5. Seal the dish with Parafilm and place it in the area indicated by the instructor.

6. Incubate the culture 1 week and observe results during the next laboratory period.

Results

Include results from the entire class.

1. During the following laboratory period, observe your agar cultures of bacteria and fungi from the environment and record your observations in Table 13.4.

2. Place your agar culture on the demonstration table and make a label of the environment being investigated. All students should observe every culture.

3. Observe the agar plates prepared by your classmates. Record observations in Table 13.4.

Table 13.4

Abundance and Types of Colonies Associated with
Food (Raw Chicken), Soil, Air, Water, and Hands

Environment	Colony Type(s) and Abundance
Chicken	
Soil	
Air	
Stream water	
Hands before washing	
Hands after washing	
Other	

Discussion

1. How did the plates differ in the number and diversity of bacterial and fungal colonies?

2. Did your predictions match your observations? Describe any discrepancies.

3. What factors might be responsible for your results?

4. Based on the results of your experiments, suggest health guidelines for workers in the food industry, as well as for schoolchildren or others who might be concerned with sanitary conditions.

Experiment B. Investigating the Environment of Your Choice

Materials

agar plates

sterile swab

capped test tube of sterile water

Parafilm strips

discard receptacle

Introduction

In the previous experiment, you tested specific environments for the presence of bacteria and fungi. In this lab study, you will study an environment of your choice. If extra agar plates are available, you may choose to investigate bacteria in an environment before and after some treatment, such as bacteria on the water fountain before and after cleaning.

Seal all plates with Parafilm after preparation!

Hypothesis

Hypothesize about the growth of bacteria in an environment of your choice.

Prediction

Predict the results of the experiment based on your hypothesis.

Procedure

1. Decide what environment you will investigate. It might be some environment in the lab room or somewhere in the biology building. Carry the sterile cotton swab and agar plate to the environment, and use the swab to collect the sample. If you are collecting from a dry surface, you should first dip the cotton swab in the sterile water and then swab the surface. If you apply any treatment to the surface, describe the treatment in the margin of your lab manual.

 Do not do throat or ear swabs! Pathogenic bacteria may be present.

2. Open the agar plate and lightly streak the swab back and forth across the agar. Discard the swab in the receptacle provided.
3. Label the bottom of the agar plate to indicate the environment tested. Record the environment tested in the Results section.
4. Write the initials of your team members, the lab room, and the date on the petri dish.
5. Seal the dish with Parafilm and place it in the area indicated by the instructor.
6. Incubate the culture 1 week and then observe and describe results during the next laboratory period.

Results

1. What environment did you investigate? Indicate any treatment you applied.

2. Characterize the bacterial and fungal colonies from your experiment.

Discussion

1. Do your results match your predictions for the presence of bacteria and fungi in this environment?
2. What factors might be responsible for your results?

EXERCISE 13.4
Controlling the Growth of Bacteria

Bacteria are found almost everywhere on Earth, and most species are directly or indirectly beneficial to other organisms. Bacteria are necessary to maintain optimum environments in animal and plant bodies and in environmental systems. However, even beneficial species, if they are reproducing at an uncontrolled rate, are potentially harmful or destructive to their environment. In addition, several species of bacteria and fungi are known to be pathogenic, that is, to cause disease in animals and plants. Their growth must be controlled. Agents have been developed that control bacterial and fungal growth. In this exercise, you will investigate the efficacy of three of these growth-controlling agents: antibiotics, antiseptics, and disinfectants.

Lab Study A. Using Antibiotics to Control Bacterial Growth

Materials

agar plate
metric ruler
sterile swab
wax pencil
Parafilm strips

broth cultures of *Micrococcus, Bacillus, Serratia,* and *E. coli*
antibiotic dispenser with antibiotic disks

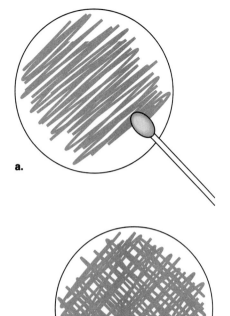

a.

b.

Figure 13.8.
Preparation of a bacterial lawn.
(a) Apply the bacteria evenly over the
entire agar surface. (b) Rotate the
plate and swab at right angles to the
first application.

Antibiotic
disk

Petri
dish

Figure 13.9.
The antibiotic dispenser. Press down
the dispenser handle to dispense the disks.

Introduction

An **antibiotic** is a chemical produced by a bacterium or fungus that has the potential to control the growth of another bacterium or fungus. Many antibiotics are selective, however, having their inhibiting effect on only certain species of bacteria or fungi. In this lab study, you will apply an assortment of antibiotics to a lawn culture of a bacterial species. Working in pairs, you will determine which antibiotics are able to control the growth of the bacteria. Each pair of students in a group of eight should culture a different bacterium. All four species should be cultured.

A lawn of bacteria is like a lawn of grass—a uniform, even layer of organisms covering an entire surface. Prepare the lawn of bacteria carefully. The success of this experiment will largely depend on the quality of your lawn.

Hypothesis

Hypothesize about the effect of different antibiotics on the growth of bacteria.

Prediction

Predict the results of the experiment based on your hypothesis.

Procedure

1. Label the bottom of an agar plate with your initials, the lab room, the date, and a word to indicate the experiment (such as "antibiotic").

2. Prepare a bacterial lawn.

   a. Insert a sterile swab into the bacterial culture in liquid nutrient broth.

   b. Allow the swab to drip for a moment before taking it out of the culture tube, but do *not* squeeze out the tip. The swab should be soaked but not dripping.

   c. Carefully lift the lid of the agar plate to about 45° and swab the *entire* surface of the agar, taking care to swab the bacteria to the edges of the dish (Figure 13.8a).

   d. Rotate the plate 45° and swab the agar again at right angles to the first swab (Figure 13.8b). Close the lid.

3. Carry the agar plate swabbed with bacteria to the demonstration table.

4. Remove the plate lid, place the antibiotic disk dispenser over the plate, and push down on the handle to dispense the disks (Figure 13.9). (Each disk has been saturated with a particular antibiotic. The symbol on the disk indicates the antibiotic name. Your instructor will provide a key to the symbols.)

5. Replace the lid, seal the plate with Parafilm, and place the plate in the area indicated by the instructor. Incubate the dishes at 37°C for 24–48 hours and then refrigerate them.

6. Next week, examine cultures to determine bacterial sensitivity to antibiotics. Measure the diameter of the **zone of inhibition** (area around disk where bacteria growth has been inhibited) for each antibiotic.

7. Record the measurement for your bacterial species and each antibiotic in Table 13.5. If the antibiotic had no effect on bacterial growth, record the size of the zone as 0.

Results

1. Using your results and the results from other teams, complete Table 13.5. Record the sizes of the zone of inhibition for all species of bacteria and all antibiotics.

Table 13.5
Results of Antibiotic Sensitivity Tests (Size of inhibition zone for each antibiotic is given in centimeters.)

Bacteria (Name, Gram + or −)	Antibiotic							
1.								
2.								
3.								
4.								

2. Use the following arbitrary criteria to rank relative bacterial sensitivity to antibiotics:

   NS = not sensitive = no zone of inhibition

   S = sensitive = zone size above 0 but less than 1 cm

   VS = very sensitive = zone size greater than 1 cm

   Write the designation in each blank in the table.

Discussion

1. Did your results support your hypothesis? Was the zone of inhibition the same for all bacteria?

2. Were any bacteria very sensitive (greater than 1 cm) to all antibiotics? If so, which bacteria?

3. Based on your results, which antibiotic would you prescribe for each micro-organism?

4. Were the results different for gram-positive and gram-negative bacteria?

5. Can you think of alternative explanations for the differential effectiveness of some antibiotics?

Lab Study B. Using Antiseptics and Disinfectants to Control Bacterial Growth

Materials

agar plate
forceps
metric ruler
sterile swab
wax pencil
Parafilm strips

broth cultures of *Micrococcus, Bacillus, Serratia,* and *E. coli*
paper disks soaking in disinfectants
paper disks soaking in antiseptics
paper disks soaking in sterile water

Introduction

Other agents besides antibiotics are often used to control bacterial growth. Those used to control bacteria on living tissues such as skin are called **antiseptics.** Those used on inanimate objects are called **disinfectants.** Antiseptics and disinfectants do not kill all bacteria, as would occur in sterilization, but they reduce the *number* of bacteria on surfaces.

Hypothesis

Hypothesize about the effect of antiseptics and disinfectants on the growth of bacteria.

Prediction

Predict the results of the experiment based on your hypothesis.

Procedure

1. Holding the lid in place, invert a sterile agar plate and label the bottom with your initials, the lab room, and the date. Draw four circles on the bottom. Number the circles.

2. Using the same bacterial culture as you used in Lab Study A, prepare a lawn culture as instructed in Lab Study A.

3. Carry the closed agar plate swabbed with bacteria to the demonstration table.

4. Open the agar plate; using forceps soaking in alcohol, pick up a disk soaked in one of the antiseptics or disinfectants, shake off the excess liquid, and place the disk on the agar above one of the circles. Repeat this procedure with two more antiseptics and/or disinfectants. Place a disk soaked in sterile water above the fourth circle to serve as a control.

5. Record the name of the agent placed above each numbered circle in Table 13.6 below. (Example: 1 = Lysol, 2 = Listerine, and so on.) Seal the plate with Parafilm.

6. Place the agar plate in the area indicated by the instructor. Incubate the agar plates at 37°C for 24–48 hours and then refrigerate them.

7. Next week, examine the cultures to determine the bacterial sensitivity to disinfectants and antiseptics. Measure the diameter of the zone of inhibition for each agent.

8. Record the measurement for your bacterial species and each inhibiting agent in Table 13.6. If the agent had no effect on bacterial growth, record the size of the zone as 0.

Table 13.6
Results of Sensitivity Tests of Antiseptics and Disinfectants (Size of inhibition zones given in centimeters.)

Bacteria	Antiseptic/Disinfectant/Control			
	1.	2.	3.	4. Control
1.				
2.				
3.				
4.				

Results

1. Using your results and the results from other teams, complete Table 13.6. Record sizes of the zone of inhibition for all species of bacteria and all antiseptics and disinfectants.

2. Use the following arbitrary criteria to rank relative bacterial sensitivity to antiseptics and disinfectants:

   NS = not sensitive = no zone of inhibition

   S = sensitive = zone size above 0 but less than 1 cm

   VS = very sensitive = zone size greater than 1 cm

   Write the designation in each blank in the table.

Discussion

1. Did your results support your hypothesis? Explain.

2. Based on your results, which disinfectant is most effective in controlling the growth of bacteria?

3. Which antiseptic is most effective?

4. In which situations is it appropriate to use a disinfectant?

   An antiseptic?

Questions for Review

1. Once you have completed this lab topic, you should be able to define and use the following terms, providing examples if appropriate: *sterilize, pasteurize, nutrient broth* and *agar, coccus, bacillus, spirillum, antibiotic, antiseptic, disinfectant, peptidoglycan, aseptic technique*.

2. Compare the techniques used to prepare a lawn culture and a streak culture.

Applying Your Knowledge

1. Would you expect the community of bacteria in plaque sampled 1 week *after* you have your teeth cleaned to differ from the community of bacteria found 1 week *before* you have your teeth cleaned? Explain. In your answer, consider the results of the milk succession experiment.

2. Bacterial species that are harmful, as well as others that are beneficial, are found living in the human body. How can the information learned by antibiotic sensitivity testing be used by physicians who must choose antibiotics that inhibit the growth of bacteria causing disease but that do not interfere with beneficial bacteria?

3. Scientists measure the effectiveness of antiseptics and disinfectants in controlling bacterial growth by a standard called the **phenol coefficient** (PC). PC compares a germicidal agent (antiseptic or disinfectant) with phenol, a disinfectant used since the 1860s. A PC of "1" means that the germicide is as effective as phenol in controlling the growth of germs. A substance with a PC greater than "1" is *more* effective than phenol, and a substance with a PC less than "1" is *less* effective than phenol.

    Salmonellosis (caused by ingesting *Salmonella* sp.) is one of the most serious foodborne diseases of our time. *Salmonella* bacteria may be found in any food substance but are particularly common on poultry and eggs. Using Table 13.7 for reference, which germicide would you recommend to control the growth of *Salmonella* in egg- and poultry-processing plants?

4. Search the Web for information about milk seen in boxes on grocery store shelves. How is this milk prepared? How would you expect bacterial succession in milk prepared in this fashion to differ from succession in milk as investigated in Exercise 13.2?

5. In 1998 physicians discovered that the deadly bacterium *Staphylococcus aureus* had become resistant to the antibiotic vancomycin, once very effective in controlling this bacterium. Using information from your text or the Web, discuss how this unfortunate situation could have come about.

Table 13.7
Phenol Coefficients of Some Common Antiseptics and Disinfectants
Used to Control *Staphylococcus* and *Salmonella* Growth*

Germicide	*Staphylococcus*	*Salmonella*
Phenol	1.0	1.0
Iodine	6.3	5.8
Lysol	5.0	3.2
Clorox	133.0	100.0
Ethyl alcohol	6.3	6.3
Hydrogen peroxide	–	0.01
Formalin	0.3	0.7

*Modified from Table 22.1 in Alcamo (1997).

Investigative Extensions

1. Design experiments to test diffusion rates and dilution factors of antiseptics and disinfectants.
2. Investigate the efficacy of hand washing by varying the type of soap (liquid, bar, antibacterial, deodorant) or the manner of washing (scrubbing time, use of a brush).
3. Investigate the efficacy of waterless hand sanitizers in killing bacteria after various activities—for example, using the rest room, touching raw chicken, shaking hands, or cracking a raw egg. Wear disposable gloves when performing this experiment.
4. The chicken industry and the FDA have recently been criticized for having low health and safety standards. Pursue this topic by a survey of brands or handling techniques. Health officials now recommend that all eggs be cooked before eating to avoid *Salmonella*. Determine the extent of contamination in store-bought eggs and in eggs from local sources.
5. Design an experiment to test bacterial succession in plaque.
6. Onions, garlic, green tea, and grapefruit seeds have all been suggested as having antibiotic properties. Design an experiment to test this.

References

Alcamo, E. I. *Fundamentals of Microbiology,* 5th ed. Menlo Park, CA: Benjamin/Cummings, 1997. Excellent coverage of microbiology. Good discussion of the role of bacteria in dental diseases.

Campbell, N., and J. Reece. *Biology,* 6th ed. San Francisco: Benjamin/Cummings, 2002.

Dill, B., and H. Merilles. "Microbial Ecology of the Oral Cavity," in *Tested Studies for Laboratory Teaching (Volume 10). Proceedings of the 10th Workshop/Conference of the Association for Biology Laboratory Education (ABLE),* Corey Goldman, editor, 1989.

Doolittle, W. F. "Uprooting the Tree of Life" *Scientific American* 2000, vol. 282, pp. 90–95.

Gillen, A. L., and R. P. Williams. "Pasteurized Milk as an Ecological System for Bacteria" *The American Biology Teacher* 1988, vol. 50, pp. 279–282.

Jarrell, K. F., D. P. Bayley, J. D. Correia, and N. A. Thomas. "Recent Excitement about the Archaea" *Bioscience* 1999, vol. 49, pp. 530–541.

Levy, S. B. "The Challenge of Antibiotic Resistance." *Scientific American* 1998, vol. 278, pp. 46–53.

Nester, E. W., C. E. Roberts, N. N. Pearsall, and B. J. McCarthy. *Microbiology,* 2nd ed. Dubuque, IA: WCB/McGraw-Hill, 1998. Good discussion of ecological succession of microbes.

"The Race Against Lethal Microbes." A Report from the Howard Hughes Medical Institute, 1996.

Website

Resource for learning about the Domain Bacteria:
http://www.ucmp.berkeley.edu/bacteria/bacteria.html

Protists and Fungi

 This lab topic gives you another opportunity to practice the scientific process introduced in Lab Topic 1. Before going to lab, review scientific investigation in Lab Topic 1 and carefully read Lab Topic 14. Be prepared to use this information to design an experiment with protists or fungi.

Laboratory Objectives

After completing this lab topic, you should be able to:

1. Discuss the diversity of protists and fungi, and the current interest in their phylogenetic relationships.
2. Describe the diversity of protists, explaining the means of obtaining nutrition and method of locomotion for each group.
3. Identify representative organisms in several major protistan phyla.
4. Discuss the ecological role and economic importance of protists.
5. Describe the characteristics and representative organisms of the green algae and their relationship to land plants.
6. Describe the divisions of the kingdom Fungi, recognizing and identifying representative organisms in each.
7. Describe differences in reproduction in fungal phyla.
8. Discuss the ecological role and economic importance of fungi.
9. Design and perform an independent investigation of a protist or an organism in the kingdom Fungi.

Introduction

Unicellular eukaryotic organisms originated over 2 billion years ago, and today they are found in every habitable region of Earth. The enormous diversity of organisms, their numerous adaptations, and their cellular complexity reflect the long evolutionary history of eukaryotes. For almost 30 years, scientists placed these diverse groups of unicellular organisms into the kingdom Protista. The Protista usually included all organisms not placed in the other eukaryotic kingdoms of Plants, Animals, and Fungi. This catchall kingdom included not only the unicellular eukaryotes, but also their multicellular relatives, like the giant kelps and seaweeds. However, most scientists now agree that the kingdom Protista should be divided into several kingdoms within the domain Eukarya, each reflecting a single evolutionary origin. Some propose six eukaryotic kingdoms, others propose more. (Recall from Lab Topic 13 that prokaryotes are placed in domains Bacteria or Archaea.) In this lab topic we will refer to this diverse group as **protists** (a general term, not a taxonomic category), leaving open the final designation of kingdoms.

The most familiar protists, algae and protozoans, have been well studied since the earliest development of the microscope. Therefore, one might assume that the taxonomic relationships among the various protistans are well understood. However, the phylogeny (evolutionary history) of these groups has been difficult to determine from comparisons of cell structure and function, nutrition, and reproduction. Evolutionary biology and taxonomy are branches of science in which many of the interesting "experiments" occurred millions or even billions of years ago. Scientists cannot repeat these evolutionary "experiments," but they can use multiple sources of evidence to determine which groups of organisms have features in common and therefore represent a single phylogenetic group. Recent molecular and biochemical research, particularly the ability to sequence ribosomal and transfer RNA genes, has provided strong new evidence for reconstructing the relationships of the protists. The results of this work have challenged not only the five-kingdom classification scheme, but also our definition of a kingdom. Some of the evidence is contradictory, requiring further testing. These investigations into the nature of eukaryotic diversity demonstrate the process of scientific inquiry. New technologies, new ideas, and novel experiments are used to test hypotheses, and the resulting evidence must be consistent with the existing body of knowledge and our classification scheme. The results lead to modification of our hypotheses and further research.

Some students may find the changing classification within the protists frustrating, but you should try to view this as the hallmark of science. Even the concept of the kingdom can be challenged and changed in response to new evidence. No matter how many kingdoms are proposed, remember that this is a reflection of the evolution of eukaryotes over the rich history of the earth. It is not surprising that the diversity of life does not easily fit into our constructed categories.

If you complete all of the lab topics in this laboratory manual, you will have studied examples of all the major groups of organisms with the exception of those in domain Archaea. Bacteria are investigated in Lab Topic 13, and several protists are introduced in Lab Topic 3. You will investigate plant evolution and animal evolution in subsequent lab topics. In this lab topic, you will survey the diversity of protists in several phyla, with particular attention to nutrition, locomotion, and cellular complexity. (The designations *phylum* and *division* are equivalent taxonomic groupings and we will use phylum when referring to protists and fungi. Zoologists traditionally used *phylum,* while botanists used *division.* However, both terms now are accepted by the Botanical Code for Nomenclature.) You will continue your investigation of diversity with the Fungi, a kingdom composed of multicellular, heterotrophic eukaryotes that absorb their food.

At the end of this lab topic you will be asked to design a simple experiment to further your investigation of the behavior, ecology, or physiology of one of the organisms studied. As you proceed through the exercises, ask questions about your observations and consider an experiment that you might design to answer one question.

EXERCISE 14.1
The Protists

In this exercise you will investigate the diversity of organisms traditionally considered protists. To organize your study, protists can be divided into three categories (not taxonomic groups) according to their mode of nutrition. The *protozoa* are **heterotrophic** protists that ingest their food by **phagocytosis** (the uptake of large particles or whole organisms by the pinching inward of the plasma membrane). Some protozoa, euglenoids for example, are **mixotrophic**, capable of photosynthesis and ingestion. The *algae* include all photosynthetic (**autotrophic**) unicellular organisms and their multicellular relatives. Traditionally, dinoflagellates have been considered algae, but recent evidence suggests that they are closely related to the protozoa, specifically ciliates. The green algae are included in the protists, although, as you will see, evidence indicates that land plants originated from ancestral green algae, and some classifications place green algae (or at least those known as charophytes) in the kingdom Plantae. The third category includes the *funguslike slime molds* that are heterotrophic, obtaining their nutrition by absorbing nutrients from decomposing organic material. Some scientists propose placing the slime molds in a separate kingdom, Mycetozoa, a name that reflects their close relationship with fungi (*myco*) and animals (*zoa*).

These three general categories—protozoa, algae, and slime molds—provide a framework for the study of the diverse organisms referred to as protists. For each organism that you investigate, you will find a brief statement about protistan classification that incorporates molecular and cytological evidence. (For further discussion of protistan classification, see Campbell and Reece, 2002.)

Lab Study A. Heterotrophic Protists—Protozoa

Materials

compound microscope
slides and coverslips
prepared slides of foraminiferans
prepared slides of radiolarians
    skeletons (demonstration only)
prepared slides of
    Trypanosoma levisi
cultures of living
    Paramecium caudata
Protoslo® or other quieting agent

solution of yeast stained with
    Congo red
cultures of *Paramecium caudata*
    that have been fed yeast stained
    with Congo red (optional)
dropper bottle of 1% acetic acid
transfer pipettes
freshwater and marine
    plankton tows

Introduction

Traditionally, single-celled heterotrophic protists are called *protozoa*. There are three categories of protozoa based on their mode of locomotion. In one group, organisms move and feed using cellular extensions called **pseudopodia**. Included in this group are amoebas, foraminiferans, and actinopods. Other protozoa move using **flagella**, motile structures supported by microtubules. The third means of locomotion in protozoa is by **cilia**, short cellular extensions supported by microtubules.

Protozoa That Move Using Pseudopodia

Although some taxonomists group all protists that move using pseudopodia into one phylum, others divide the group into several phyla. Given the present uncertainty of the protistan classification, we have selected three protozoans with pseudopodia that were traditionally in different phyla.

Rhizopods (Amoebas)

In Lab Topic 3, you studied the rhizopod *Amoeba proteus,* a protozoan species of organisms that move using **pseudopodia** (Color Plate 1). Rhizopod is derived from *rhizo* or root and *pod* or foot; thus, rootlike foot. In this group, organisms have no fixed body shape, and they are naked; that is, they do not have a shell. Different species may be found in a variety of habitats, including freshwater and marine habitats. Recall that pseudopodia are cellular extensions. As the pseudopod extends, endoplasm flows into the extension. By extending several pseudopods in sequence and flowing into first one and then the next, the amoeba proceeds along in an irregular, slow fashion. Pseudopods are also used to capture and ingest food. When a suitable food particle such as a bacterium, another protist, or a piece of detritus (fragmented remains of dead organisms) contacts an amoeba, a pseudopod will flow completely around the particle and take it into the cell by phagocytosis.

If you did not observe *Amoeba proteus* or some other naked amoeba in Lab Topic 3, turn to that section of the laboratory manual (see page 71) and, following the procedure, observe these organisms.

Foraminiferans (Forams)

Foraminiferans, commonly called **forams,** are another example of organisms that move and feed using pseudopodia. Forams are marine planktonic (freely floating) or benthic (bottom-dwelling) organisms that secrete a shell-like *test* (a hard outer covering) made up of chambers. In many species, the test consists of chambers secreted in a spiral pattern, and the organism resembles a microscopic snail. Although most forams are microscopic, some species, called *living sands,* may grow to the size of several centimeters, an astounding size for a single-celled protist. Pseudopodia extend through special pores in the calcium carbonate test. The test can persist after the organism dies, becoming part of marine sand. Remains of tests can form vast limestone deposits.

Procedure

1. Obtain a prepared slide of representative forams (Figure 14.1a).
2. Observe the organisms first on the lowest power of the compound microscope and then on intermediate and high powers.
3. Note the arrangement and attempt to count the number of chambers in the test. In most species, the number of chambers indicates the relative ages of the organisms, with older organisms having more chambers. Which are more abundant on your slide, older or younger organisms?

    Chambers can be arranged in a single row, in multiple rows, or wound into a spiral. Protozoologists determine the foram species based on the appearance of the test. Are different species present?

Results

Sketch several different forams in the margin of your lab manual. Note differences in the organisms on your slide and those depicted in Figure 14.1a.

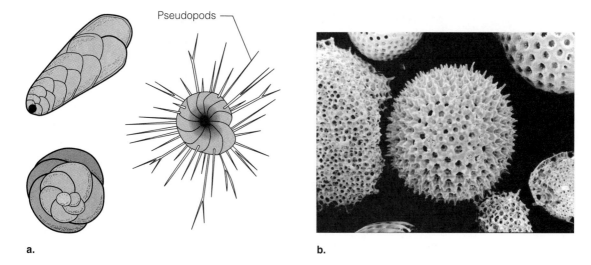

Pseudopods

a.

b.

Figure 14.1.
Heterotrophic organisms (protozoa) that move using pseudopodia. (a)
Forams have a shell-like test made of calcium carbonate. Slender pseudopods
extend through pores in the test. (b) Radiolarians are supported by a skeleton of
silicon dioxide.

Actinopods (Radiolarians)

Actinopods have pseudopodia that are supported by a bundle of microtubules forming very slender **axopodia.** The **radiolarians** studied here are
common in marine plankton. They secrete skeletons of silicon dioxide that
can, as with the forams, collect in vast deposits on the ocean floor. The
axopodia extend outward through pores in the skeleton in all directions
from the central spherical cell body.

Procedure

1. Observe slides of radiolarians on demonstration.
2. Observe the size and shape of the skeletons and compare your observations with Figure 14.1b and Color Plate 21.

Results

Sketch several different radiolarians skeletons in the margin of your lab
manual, noting any differences between the organisms on demonstration
and those in the figure.

Protozoa That Move Using Flagella

Flagellates are generally single-celled, heterotrophic protists. They may be
free-living and parasitic, or they may live in symbiotic relationships with
other organisms. The many diverse single-celled and colonial flagellates
have been a particular challenge to taxonomists. Under the old two-king-
dom system of classification, the heterotrophic flagellates were classified as
animals, and the autotrophic flagellates (with chloroplasts) were classified
as plants. However, the well-defined taxonomic group of flagellates, the
euglenoids, has members of each type, and some members are mixotrophic,
depending on their environment. Recent classification changes proposed

for flagellates would place euglenoids together with symbiotic flagellates, like *Trypanosoma*, in a new category, the **Euglenozoa.**

The heterotrophic organisms that you investigate in this exercise move using one or more flagella, long cytoplasmic extensions supported by a nine-doublet of microtubules surrounding a single central doublet of microtubules. In this exercise, you will observe a flagellate, *Trypanosoma levisi.* Organisms in the genus *Trypanosoma* are parasites that alternate between a vertebrate and an invertebrate host. *Trypanosoma levisi* lives in the blood of rats and is transmitted by fleas. Its flagellum originates near the posterior end but passes to the front end as a marginal thread of a long undulating membrane. Another organism in this same genus, *T. gambiense,* causes African sleeping sickness in humans. Its invertebrate host is the tsetse fly.

If you did not observe several other examples of flagellates in Lab Topic 3 when you studied the organisms living in a termite's gut, turn to that section of the laboratory manual (pp. 71–72) and, following the procedure, observe these organisms. You may see *Trichonympha* and other flagellates, including *Pyrsonympha* with four to eight flagella, *Trichomonas,* and *Calonympha* with numerous flagella originating from the anterior end of the cell.

Procedure

1. Obtain a prepared slide of *T. levisi* (Figure 14.2) and observe it, using low, intermediate, and high powers in the compound microscope.
2. Locate the organisms among the blood cells of the parasite's host.
3. Identify the **flagellum,** the **undulating membrane,** and the **nucleus** in several organisms.

Figure 14.2.

Protozoa that move using flagella.

Trypanosoma is a parasite that lives in the blood of its mammalian host. The flagellum originates near the posterior end but passes along an undulating membrane to the anterior end.

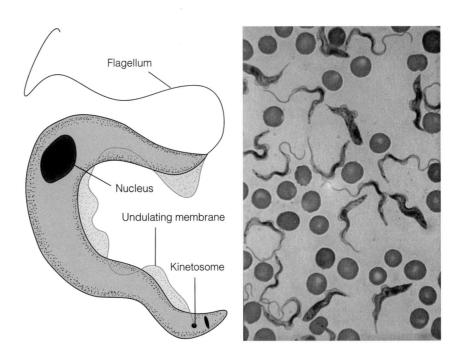

Results

In the margin of your lab manual, draw several representative examples of *T. levisi* and several blood cells to show relative cell sizes.

Protozoa That Move Using Cilia

Protozoans in this category move using cilia, short projections from the cell surface. Cilia are generally shorter and more numerous than flagella. Internally, both structures are similar in their core of a nine-doublet of microtubules surrounding a single central doublet of microtubules. Proposed groupings of protistans place ciliates and dinoflagellates (Lab Study B) into a new taxonomic category, the **Alveolata.** Members of the Alveolata have small subsurface membrane-bound cavities called **alveoli.** Until there is a consensus, we have included ciliates with the protozoans and the dinoflagellates with the algae. In this activity, you will observe the ciliate *Paramecium caudatum.*

Procedure

1. Using the compound microscope, examine a living *Paramecium.* Place a drop of water from the bottom of the culture on a clean microscope slide. Add a *small* drop of Protoslo or some other quieting solution to the water drop; then add the coverslip.

2. Observe paramecia on the compound microscope using low and then intermediate powers.

3. Describe the movement of a single paramecium. Does movement appear to be directional or is it random? Does the organism reverse direction only when it encounters an object, or does it appear to reverse direction even with no obstruction?

4. Locate a large, slowly moving organism, switch to high power, and identify the following organelles:

   Oral groove: depression in the side of the cell that runs obliquely back to the mouth that opens into a **gullet.**

   Food vacuole: forms at the end of the gullet. Food vacuoles may appear as dark vesicles throughout the cell.

   Macronucleus: large, grayish body in the center of the cell. The macronucleus has many copies of the genome and controls most cellular activities, including asexual reproduction.

   Micronucleus: often difficult to see in living organisms, this small round body may be lying close to the macronucleus. Micronuclei are involved in sexual reproduction. Many species of paramecia have more than one micronucleus.

   Contractile vacuole: used for water balance, two of these form, one at each end of the cell. Each contractile vacuole is made up of a ring of radiating tubules and a central spherical vacuole. Your organism may be under osmotic stress because of the Protoslo, and the contractile vacuoles may be filling and collapsing as they expel water from the cell.

5. Observe feeding in a paramecium. Add a drop of yeast stained with Congo red to the edge of the coverslip and watch as it diffuses around the paramecium.

   Study the movement of food particles from the oral groove to the gullet to the formation of a food vacuole that will subsequently move through the cell as the food is digested in the vacuole. You may be able to observe the discharge of undigested food from the food vacuole at a specific site on the cell surface.

6. Observe the discharge of **trichocysts,** structures that lie just under the outer surface of the paramecium. When irritated by a chemical or attacked by a predator, the paramecium discharges these long thin threads that may serve as a defense mechanism, as an anchoring device, or to capture prey. Make a new slide of paramecia. Add a drop of 1% acetic acid to the edge of the coverslip and carefully watch a paramecium. Describe the appearance of trichocysts in this species.

Results

Complete the drawing of a paramecium below, labeling all the organelles and structures shown in bold in the text.

Discussion

1. Describe the mechanism for feeding in amoeboid, flagellated, and ciliated protozoans.

2. How do you think amoeboid organisms with skeletons, such as the radiolarians, move food to their cell bodies?

3. Compare the appearance and rate of locomotion in amoeboid, flagellated, and ciliated organisms observed in this exercise.

4. Describe mechanisms for defense in the organisms studied.

5. Give examples of modifications in cell shape or distribution of cilia or flagella allowing the organism to adapt to its environment.

6. Complete Table 14.1, summarizing characteristics of organisms in the heterotrophic protistan phyla.

Table 14.1

Characteristics of Heterotrophic Protists—Protozoa

Group	Nutritional Mode	Means of Locomotion	Protective Adaptations	Habitat or Lifestyle	Other Unusual Characteristics
Rhizopods					
Foraminiferans					
Actinopods					
Flagellates					
Ciliates					

Lab Study B. Autotrophic Protists—Algae

Materials

compound microscope
slides and coverslips
living cultures or prepared slides
  of dinoflagellates
living cultures of diatoms
prepared slides of diatomaceous
  earth, demonstration only

marine plankton samples
transfer pipettes for all cultures
demonstration materials of
  brown algae and red algae

Introduction

In this lab study you will investigate representatives of four phyla of algae. Body form, flagella, and photosynthetic pigments can distinguish the algae. In **unicellular** organisms, the body is only one cell, and daughter cells separate from each other after division. In **filamentous** organisms, cell division takes place in the same plane, and the daughter cells remain attached, resulting in a long line of cells—a filament. Whereas **aggregates** are random, temporary clusters of cells, **simple** and **complex colonies** are predictable organizations of cells either without physiological connections (a simple colony) or with them (a complex colony). In aggregates, simple colonies, and complex colonies, cell divisions take place in many planes. The complex bodies of **multicellular** algae are differentiated into specialized structures for photosynthesis, flotation, and anchorage.

The phyla of algae are characterized by differences in cellular structure and pigmentation. The exclusively microscopic algae demonstrate differences in cell walls (diatoms) and flagella (dinoflagellates). All the algae have chlorophyll *a* as their primary photosynthetic pigment, but brown and red algae have additional accessory pigments. Green algae, like land plants, have chlorophyll *b* as an accessory pigment. Recall from Lab Topic 6 that accessory pigments increase the spectrum of light available for photosynthesis. This is particularly important for aquatic organisms because many wavelengths of light, including those absorbed by chlorophyll *a*, are absorbed as they pass through ocean waters. Finally, the red algae lack flagella at any stage in their life cycle. In this lab study, you will examine some of the most common and ecologically important protistan algae, learning the characteristics, ecological roles, and economic importance of each.

Dinoflagellates (Dinoflagellata)

Swirl your hand through tropical ocean waters at night, and you may notice a burst of tiny lights. Visit a warm, stagnant inlet and you might notice that the water appears reddish and dead fish are floating on the surface. Both of these phenomena may be due to activities of dinoflagellates, single-celled organisms that are generally photosynthetic. Some are able to bioluminesce, or produce light. They sometimes can *bloom* (reproduce very rapidly) and cause the water to appear red from pigments in their bodies. If the organisms in this "red tide" are a species of dinoflagellate that releases toxins, fish and other marine animals can be poisoned. Red tides in the Chesapeake Bay are thought to be caused by *Pfiesteria*, a dinoflagellate that produces deadly toxins resulting in invertebrate and fish kills, and that also may be implicated in human illness and death. Dinoflagellates have a cellulose cell wall that is often in the form of an armor of numerous plates with two perpendicular

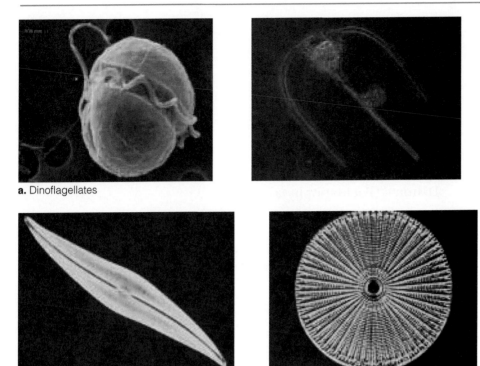

a. Dinoflagellates

b. Diatoms

Figure 14.3.
Autotrophic protists (algae). (a) Dinoflagellates have a cellulose cell wall in the form of plates with two grooves that house flagella. (b) Diatoms have a cell wall made of silica consisting of two valves. Species can be pennate forms or centric forms. (See Color Plate 22.)

grooves, each containing a flagellum. These organisms play an important role in **primary productivity** in oceans, photosynthesis that ultimately provides food for all marine organisms.

Dinoflagellates have traditionally been considered algae, but as previously mentioned, they are now thought to share a common ancestor with ciliates, as evidenced by the presence of subsurface cavities called alveoli. In the future, dinoflagellates and ciliates may be placed in a single group, the Alveolata.

Procedure

1. Obtain a prepared slide or make a wet mount of dinoflagellates (Figure 14.3a).
2. Focus the slide on low power and attempt to locate the cells. You may have to switch to intermediate power to see them.
3. Switch to high power.
4. Identify the perpendicular **grooves** and the **cellulose plates** making up the cell wall. Are the plates in your species elongated into spines? **Flagella** may be visible in living specimens.

Results

1. Draw several examples of cell shapes in the margin of your lab manual. Note differences between the species on your slide and those in Figure 14.3a.

2. Summarize distinguishing characteristics of dinoflagellates.

3. Describe the ecological role and economic importance of these organisms.

Diatoms (Bacillariophyta)

Diatoms also play an important role in primary productivity in oceans. In fact, they are the most important photosynthesizers in cold marine waters. They can be unicellular, or they can aggregate into chains or starlike groups. Protoplasts of these organisms are enclosed by a cell wall made of silica that persists after the death of the cell. These cell wall deposits are mined as **diatomaceous earth** and have numerous economic uses, for example, in swimming pool filters and as an abrasive in toothpaste and silver polish. Perhaps the greatest value of diatoms, however, is the excess carbohydrate and oxygen they produce that can be utilized by other organisms. Ecologists are concerned about the effects of acid rain and changing climatic conditions on populations of diatoms and their rate of primary productivity.

Diatom cells are either elongated, boat-shaped, bilaterally symmetrical **pennate** forms or radially symmetrical **centric** forms (Color Plate 22). The cell wall consists of two valves, one fitting inside the other, in the manner of the lid and bottom of a petri dish. As scientists continue to utilize new information in classifying the protists, the diatoms, brown algae (in the next section), and golden algae (not included in this lab topic) are placed in a single group, **Stramenopila**, based on unique flagella structure usually observed in sex cells.

Procedure

1. Prepare a wet mount of diatoms (Figure 14.3b) from marine plankton samples or other living cultures.
2. Observe the organisms on low, intermediate, and high powers.
3. Describe the form of the diatoms in your sample. Are they centric, pennate, or both?

4. If you are studying living cells, you may be able to detect locomotion. The method of movement is uncertain, but it is thought that contractile fibers just inside the cell membrane produce waves of motion on the cytoplasmic surface that extends through a groove in the cell wall. What is the body form of motile diatoms?

5. Observe a single centric form on high power and note the intricate geometric pattern of the cell wall. Can you detect the two valves?
6. Look for chloroplasts in living forms.

7. Observe diatomaceous earth on demonstration and identify pennate and centric forms.

Results

1. Sketch several different shapes of diatoms in the margin of your lab manual.
2. Summarize distinguishing characteristics of diatoms.

3. Describe the ecological role and economic importance of these organisms.

Discussion

1. Compare dinoflagellates and diatoms. What important ecological role is shared by these two groups?

2. What is one characteristic that you could observe under the microscope to distinguish diatoms and dinoflagellates?

Brown Algae (Phaeophyta)

Some of the largest algae, the **kelps,** are brown algae. The Sargasso Sea is named after the large, free-floating brown algae *Sargassum*. These algae appear brown because of the presence of the brown pigment **fucoxanthin** in addition to chlorophyll *a*. Brown algae are perhaps best known for their commercial value. Have you ever wondered why commercial ice cream is smoother in texture than homemade ice cream? Extracts of **algin,** a polysaccharide in the cell wall of some brown algae, are used commercially as thickening or emulsifying agents in paint, toothpaste, ice cream, pudding, and in many other commercial food products. *Laminaria*, known as *kombu* in Japan, is added to soups, used to brew a beverage, and covered with icing as a dessert. As previously noted, the brown algae and diatoms may share a common ancestor and therefore be placed together in the Stramenopila.

Procedure

Observe the examples of brown algae that are on demonstration.

Results

In Table 14.2 on the next page, list the names and distinguishing characteristics of each brown algal species on demonstration. Compare the examples with those illustrated in Figure 14.4 and Color Plate 23.

Table 14.2

Representative Brown Algae

Name	Body Form (single-celled, filamentous, colonial, leaflike; broad or linear blades)	Characteristics (pigments, reproductive structures, structures for attachment and flotation)

Red Algae (Rhodophyta)

The simplest red algae are single-celled, but most species have a macroscopic, multicellular body form. The red algae, unlike all the other algae, do not have flagella at any stage in their life cycle. Some scientists suggest that the red algae represent a monophyletic (having a single origin) group and should be placed in their own kingdom. Red algae contain chlorophyll *a* and the accessory pigments **phycocyanin** and **phycoerythrin** that often mask the chlorophyll, making the algae appear red. These pigments absorb

Figure 14.4.

Examples of multicellular brown algae (phylum Phaeophyta). The body of a brown alga consists of a broad **blade**, a stemlike **stipe**, and a **holdfast** for attachment. These body parts are found in the kelps (a) *Laminaria* and (b) *Nereocystis*. Rounded air bladders for flotation are seen in (c) *Sargassum* and other species of brown algae. (Color Plate 23.)

a.   b.   c.

green and blue wavelengths of light that penetrate deep into ocean waters. Many red algae also appear green or black or even blue, depending on the depth at which they are growing. Because of this, color is not always a good characteristic to use when determining the classification of algae. Recall that in Lab Topic 13 you grew bacteria and fungi on plates of agar. This substance, **agar,** is a polysaccharide extracted from the cell wall of red algae. Another extract of red algae cell walls, **carrageenan,** is used to give the texture of thickness and richness to foods such as dairy drinks and soups. In Asia and elsewhere, the red algae *Porphyra* (known as *nori*) are used as seaweed wrappers for sushi. The cultivation and production of *Porphyra* constitute a billion-dollar industry.

Procedure

Observe the examples of red algae that are on demonstration.

Results

In Table 14.3, list the names and characteristics of the red algae on demonstration. Compare the demonstration examples with those illustrated in Figure 14.5 and Color Plate 24.

Table 14.3
Representative Red Algae

Name	Body Form (single-celled, filamentous, colonial, leaflike)	Characteristics (reproductive structures, structures for attachment or flotation, pigments)

Discussion

1. What important ecological role is shared by the macroscopic algae (green, red, and brown)?

2. Based on your observations in the laboratory, what two characteristics might you use to distinguish brown and red algae?

a.   b.   c.

Figure 14.5.
Examples of multicellular red algae (phylum Rhodophyta). (a) Some red algae have deposits of carbonates of calcium and magnesium in their cell walls and are important components of coral reefs. (b) Most red algae have delicate, finely dissected blades. (c) *Porphyra* (or *nori*) is used to make sushi. (See Color Plate 24.)

Lab Study C. The Green Algae (Chlorophyta)— The Protist-Plant Connection

Materials

cultures or prepared slides of *Spirogyra* sp.
preserved *Ulva lactuca*
preserved *Chara* sp.

Introduction

The green algae include unicellular motile and nonmotile, colonial, filamentous, and multicellular species that inhabit primarily freshwater environments. Because green algae share many characteristics with land plants, including storage of starch and the presence of chlorophylls *a* and *b*, photosynthetic pathways, and organic compounds called flavonoids, most botanists support the hypothesis that plants evolved from green algae. Results of recent work in sequencing ribosomal and transfer RNA genes confirm the close relationship between green algae and land plants, and have led some scientists to propose that green algae, or at least those known as charophytes, be included in the Plant kingdom. In this exercise you will view several body forms of green algae on demonstration: single-celled, filamentous, colonial, and multicellular. Finally, you will observe the multicellular, branched green algae *Chara* (the stonewort), believed to be most similar to the green algae that gave rise to land plants over 460 million years ago.

If you completed Lab Topic 3 (Microscopes and Cells), you may remember observing aggregates of single-celled algae, *Protococcus*, and the colonial green algae *Volvox*. Your instructor may ask you to review your notes and drawings from Lab Topic 3. In this lab study you will observe the filamentous alga *Spirogyra* sp. and the multicellular algae *Ulva* sp. and *Chara* sp.

Procedure

1. Using your compound microscope, observe living materials or pre-pared slides of the filamentous alga *Spirogyra* sp. (Figure 14.6a). This organism is common in small, freshwater ponds. The most obvious structure in the cells of the filament is a long chloroplast. Can you determine how the alga got its name? Describe the appearance of the chloroplast.

   Can you see a nucleus in each cell of the filament?

2. Observe the preserved specimen of *Ulva* sp., commonly called sea lettuce (see Color Plate 25). This multicellular alga is commonly found on rocks or docks in marine and brackish water.

   a. Describe the body form of Ulva.

   b. Are structures present that would serve to attach *Ulva* to its substrate (dock or rock)? If so, describe them.

   c. Compare your specimen of *Ulva* with that shown in Figure 14.6b and Color Plate 25.

3. Examine the preserved specimen of the multicellular green alga *Chara*. This alga grows in muddy or sandy bottoms of clear lakes or ponds. Its body form is so complex that it is often mistaken for a plant, but careful study of its structure and reproduction confirms its classification as a green alga.

   Note the cylindrical branches attached to nodes. Compare your specimen to Figure 14.6c and Color Plate 26. Sketch the appearance of your specimen in the margin of your lab manual.

a.

b.

c.

Figure 14.6.
Examples of multicellular green algae (phylum Chlorophyta). (a) A filamentous green alga, *Spirogyra*. (b) Some green algae are multicellular as in *Ulva*, sea lettuce. (Color Plate 25.) (c) A multicellular, branched green alga, *Chara*. (Color Plate 26.)

Results

In Table 14.4, list the names and characteristics of each green algal species studied. Compare these examples with those illustrated in Figure 14.6 and color plates 25 and 26.

Table 14.4
Representative Green Algae

Name	Body Form (single-celled, filamentous, colonial, leaflike)	Characteristics (pigments, specialized structures, flagella, structures for attachment)
Spirogyra		
Ulva		
Chara		

Lab Study D. Funguslike Protists—Slime Molds (Mycetozoa)

Materials

stereoscopic microscopes
Physarum growing on agar plates

Introduction

The organisms you will investigate in this lab study have been called plants, fungi, animals, fungus animals, protozoa, Protoctista, Protista, Mycetozoa, and probably many more names. William Crowder, in a classic *National Geographic* article (April 1926), describes his search for these creatures in a swamp on the north shore of Long Island. This is what he says: "Behold! Seldom ever before had such a gorgeous sight startled my unexpectant gaze. Spreading out over the bark [of a dead tree] was a rich red coverlet . . . consisting of thousands of small, closely crowded, funguslike growths. . . . A colony of these tiny organisms extended in an irregular patch . . . covering an area nearly a yard in length and slightly less in breadth. . . . Each unit, although actually less than a quarter of an inch in height, resembled . . . a small mushroom, though more marvelous than any I have ever seen."

The creatures Crowder was describing are commonly called **slime molds.** Many place them in the kingdom Fungi, but this classification causes difficulties because, whereas slime molds are phagocytic like protozoa, fungi are never phagocytic but obtain their nutrition by absorption. Characteristics other than feeding mode, including cellular ultrastructure, cell wall chemistry, and molecular studies, indicate that slime molds fit better with amoeboid protists than with fungi. However, the general consensus among taxonomists is that slime molds represent a separate kingdom, the **Mycetozoa** or "fungus-animals."

There are two types of slime molds, plasmodial slime molds and cellular slime molds. In this lab study, you will observe the plasmodial slime mold *Physarum.* The vegetative stage is called a **plasmodium,** and it consists of a multinucleate mass of protoplasm totally devoid of cell walls. This mass feeds on bacteria as it creeps along the surface of moist logs or dead leaves. When conditions are right, it is converted into one or more reproductive structures, called **fruiting bodies,** that produce spores (see Color Plate 28). You may choose to investigate slime molds further in Exercise 14.3.

Procedure

1. Obtain a petri dish containing *Physarum* and return to your lab bench to study the organism. Keep the dish closed.

2. With the aid of your stereoscopic microscope, examine the plasmodium (Figure 14.7). Describe characteristics such as color, size, and shape. Look for a system of branching veins. Do you see any movement? Speculate about the source of the movement. Is the movement unidirectional or bidirectional—that is, flows first in one direction and then in the other? Your instructor may have placed oat flakes or another food source on the agar. How does the appearance of the plasmodium change as it contacts a food source?

Figure 14.7.
Slime mold. Slime molds are protists that share some characteristics with both protozoa and fungi. The vegetative stage of a plasmodial slime mold includes an amoeboid phase consisting of a multinucleate mass known as a plasmodium. (Color Plate 27.)

3. Examine the entire culture for evidence of forming or mature fruiting bodies. Are the fruiting bodies stalked or are they sessile, that is, without a stalk? If a stalk is present, describe it.

Results

Sketch the plasmodium and fruiting bodies in the margin of your lab manual. Label structures where appropriate.

Discussion

Slime molds were once placed in the kingdom Fungi. What characteristics suggest that these organisms are protistan?

EXERCISE 14.2

The Kingdom Fungi

Introduction

The kingdom Fungi includes a diverse group of organisms that play important economic and ecological roles. These organisms are unicellular (yeasts) or multicellular, heterotrophic organisms that obtain their nutrients by absorption, digesting their food outside their bodies and absorbing the digestion products into their cells. They often have complex life cycles with alternating sexual and asexual (vegetative) reproduction. They may produce spores either asexually by mitosis or sexually by meiosis.

Fungi are beneficial to humans in many ways. We have long used fungi to make wine and bake leavened bread. Yeast, a single-celled fungus, is used in the production of wine, beer, and bread; and other fungi are used to produce other foods. *Penicillium* is a fungus that is used to produce antibiotics. In ecosystems, fungi share with bacteria the essential role of decomposition, returning to the ecosystem the matter trapped in dead organisms.

Although many fungi are beneficial, others play destructive roles in nature. Some species parasitize animals and plants. Athlete's foot and ringworm are diseases commonly known to humans, and potato late blight and wheat rust are common plant diseases caused by fungi. The ergot fungus that parasitizes rye causes convulsive ergotism in humans who eat bread made with infested grains. The bizarre behavior of young women who were later convicted of witchcraft in Salem Village, Massachusetts, in 1692 has been attributed to convulsive ergotism. Fungi are also a source of food in many cultures, with truffles being the most expensive. Truffles are dark, edible subterranean fungi that sell for $200 per pound, with an annual harvest of 30 tons. Truffles cannot be grown in a lab or greenhouse, and are located by specially trained truffle-sniffing pigs or dogs.

In this exercise, you will learn about the structure of typical fungi and the characteristics of four important phyla of fungi: Zygomycota, Ascomycota, Basidiomycota, and Deuteromycota. You will see examples of lichens that are associations between fungi and algae. As you observe these examples, consider interesting questions that might be asked about fungi diversity or ecology. You can choose one of these questions to design a simple experiment in Exercise 14.3.

Lab Study A. Zygote Fungi—Zygomycota

Materials

compound microscope
stereoscopic microscope
cultures of *Rhizopus stolonifer*
   with sporangia
cultures of *Pilobolus crystallinus*
   on demonstration

forceps, ethyl alcohol, alcohol lamp
slides and coverslips
dropper bottles of water

Introduction

One common organism in the phylum Zygomycota is probably growing in your refrigerator right now. The common bread mold, *Rhizopus stolonifer,* grows on many foods as well as bread. In this lab study, you will observe the structure of this species to see many general fungi characteristics. Fungi are made up of threadlike individual filaments, called **hyphae,** which are organized into the body of the fungus, called the **mycelium.** This filamentous mass secretes enzymes into the substrate and digests food that will then be absorbed into its cells. Cells of fungi have cell walls made of **chitin** combined with other complex carbohydrates, including cellulose. You may recall that chitin is the main component of insect exoskeletons.

Rhizopus stolonifer

Rhizopus reproduces both sexually and asexually. In the Zygomycota, cells of the hyphae are haploid. Hyphae grow over a substrate, for example, a slice of bread, giving the bread a fuzzy appearance. In asexual reproduction, certain hyphae grow upright and develop **sporangia,** round structures, on their tips. Haploid spores develop in the sporangia following mitosis, and when they are mature, they are dispersed through the air. If they fall on a suitable medium, they will absorb water and germinate, growing a new mycelium.

Rhizopus also reproduces sexually when compatible mating types designated as (+) and (–) grow side by side. In this case, (+) and (–) hyphae fuse, and, ultimately, nuclei from opposite strains fuse to form $2n$ zygote nuclei that develop in a thick-walled **zygospore.** Following meiosis, haploid spores are produced in sporangia borne on filaments that emerge from the zygospore.

Pilobolus crystallinus

Pilobolus crystallinus (also called the *fungus gun,* or *shotgun fungus*) is another member of the phylum Zygomycota. This fungus is called a **coprophilous** fungus because it grows on dung. It displays many unusual behaviors, one of which is that it is positively phototropic. Perhaps you can investigate this behavior in Exercise 14.3. Bold et al. (1980) describe asexual reproduction in *Pilobolus.* This species has sporangia as does *Rhizopus,* but rather than similarly dispersing single spores, in *Pilobolus* the sporangium is forcibly discharged as a unit; the dispersion is tied to moisture and diurnal cycles. In nature, in the early evening the sporangia form; shortly after midnight, a swelling appears below the sporangium. Late the following morning, turgor pressure causes the swelling to explode, propelling the sporangium as far as 2 meters. The sticky sporangium will adhere to grass leaves and subsequently may be eaten by an animal—horse, cow, or rabbit. The intact sporangia pass through the animal's digestive tract and are excreted, and the spores germinate in the fresh dung.

In this lab study you will investigate *Rhizopus* and observe *Pilobolus* on demonstration.

Procedure

1. Obtain a culture of *Rhizopus* and carry it to your lab station.
2. Examine it using the stereoscopic microscope.
3. Identify the **mycelia, hyphae,** and **sporangia.**

4. Review the life cycle of *Rhizopus* (Figure 14.8). Locate the structures in this figure that are visible in your culture. Circle the structures involved in asexual reproduction.

5. Using forceps and aseptic technique, remove a small portion of the mycelium with several sporangia and make a wet mount.

6. Examine the hyphae and sporangia using the compound microscope. Are spores visible? How have the spores been produced?

How do the spores compare with the hyphal cells genetically?

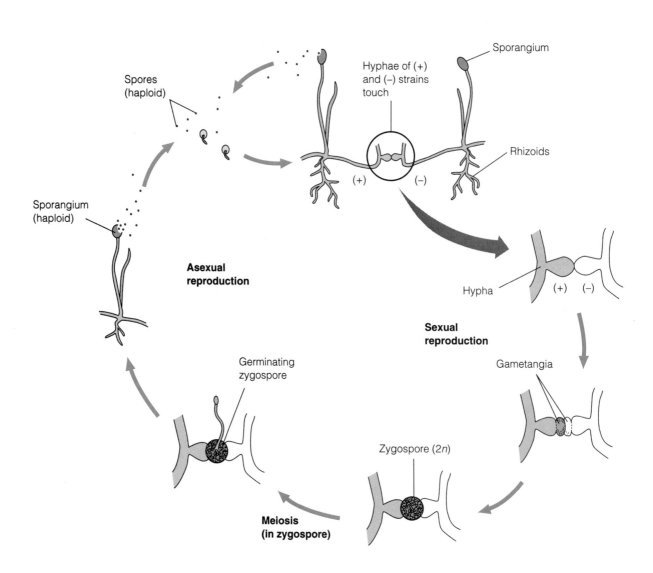

Figure 14.8.
Rhizopus stolonifer. *Rhizopus* reproduces both sexually by zygospores and asexually by sporangia producing asexual spores. In sexual reproduction, (+) and (−) mating types fuse and a $2n$ zygospore results.

How would spores produced by sexual reproduction differ from spores produced asexually?

7. Observe the cultures of *Pilobolus* (Figure 14.9) growing on rabbit dung agar that are on demonstration.
8. Identify the **sporangia, mycelia,** and **hyphae.** What color are the sporangia and spores?

Results

1. Review the life cycle of *Rhizopus* and the structures observed in the living culture and compare with Figure 14.8.
2. Review the structures observed in *Pilobolus* and compare with Figure 14.9.

Discussion

1. The body form of most fungi, including *Rhizopus,* is a mycelium composed of filamentous hyphae. Using your observations as a basis for your thinking, state why this body form is well adapted to the fungus mode of nutrition.

2. Refer back to the description of *Pilobolus.* Speculate about the adaptive advantage of having a system to propel sporangia, as seen in *Pilobolus.*

Figure 14.9.
Pilobolus crystallinus.

Lab Study B. Sac Fungi—Ascomycota

Materials

compound microscope
stereoscopic microscope
dried or preserved *Peziza* specimen

prepared slide of *Peziza* ascocarp
preserved or fresh morels
plastic mounts of ergot in rye
    or wheat

Introduction

Fungi in the phylum Ascomycota are called *sac fungi,* or ascopore-producing fungi. This division includes edible fungi, morels, and truffles, but it also includes several deadly plant and animal parasites. For example, chestnut blight and the Dutch elm disease have devastated native populations of chestnut and

American elm trees. The fungi causing these diseases were introduced into the United States from Asia and Europe. You have already examined one example of the phylum Ascomycota in Lab Topic 7 when you studied meiosis and crossing over in *Sordaria fimicola*.

Sexual reproduction in the ascomycota fungi produces either four or eight haploid **ascospores** after meiosis in an **ascus**. Recall that spores in *Sordaria* form after meiosis within asci (Figure 7.7). Asci form within a structure called an **ascocarp**. In *Sordaria* the ascocarp, called a *perithecium*, is a closed, spherical structure that develops a pore at the top for spore dispersal. In some species of sac fungi, the asci are borne on open cup-shaped ascocarps called *apothecia* (sing., *apothecium*). In asexual reproduction, spores are produced, but rather than being enclosed within a sporangium as in zygote fungi, the spores, called **conidia,** are produced on the surface of special reproductive hyphae.

Other features of sac fungi also vary. For example, yeasts are ascomycetes, yet they are single-celled organisms. Yeasts most frequently reproduce asexually by **budding,** a process in which small cells form by pinching off the parent cell. When they reproduce sexually, however, they produce asci, each of which produces four or eight spores.

In this lab study, you will examine a slide of the sac fungi *Peziza* and will observe demonstrations of additional examples of Ascomycota (see Color Plate 29).

Procedure

1. Obtain a dried or preserved specimen of *Peziza* (Figure 14.10a). Notice the open, cup-shaped apothecium, the **ascocarp,** that bears asci within the cup (not visible with the naked eye). Fungi with ascocarps shaped in this fashion are called **cup fungi.** The cup may be supported by a stalk.

2. Examine a prepared slide of *Peziza* using low and intermediate magnifications on the compound microscope. This slide is a section through the ascocarp. Identify **asci.** How many spores are present per ascus? Are they diploid or haploid?

Figure 14.10.
Examples of sac fungi, phylum Ascomycota. (a) *Peziza* has a cup-shaped ascocarp with asci within the cup. (b) Morels are cup fungi that resemble mushrooms.

a.

b.

3. Complete the sketch of the ascocarp section below, labeling **asci, spores, hyphae**, and **mycelium**.

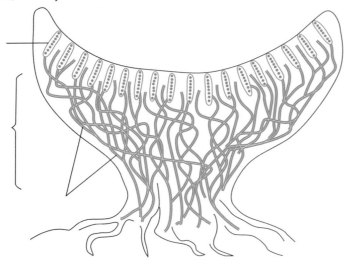

4. Observe the preserved **morels** that are on demonstration (Figure 14.10b). These fungi resemble mushrooms, but the "cap" is convoluted. Asci are located inside the ridges.

5. Observe demonstrations of the mature inflorescence of wheat or rye grass infected with the ascomycete *Claviceps purpurea*, the **ergot** fungus. The large black structures seen among the grains are the ergot.

Results

Review the structures observed in *Peziza*, morels, and ergot. Modify Figures 14.10a and 14.10b to reflect features of your examples not included in these figures. Sketch ergot examples in the margin of your lab manual.

Discussion

What characteristics are common to all sac fungi?

Lab Study C. Club Fungi—Basidiomycota

Materials

compound microscope
stereoscopic microscope
fresh, ripe mushroom basidiocarps
prepared slides of *Coprinus* pileus sections

Introduction

The Basidiomycota phylum (club fungi, or basidiospore-producing fungi) includes the fungi that cause the plant diseases wheat rust and corn smut as well as the more familiar puffballs, shelf fungi, and edible and nonedible mushrooms (the latter often called *toadstools*). A mushroom is actually a reproductive structure that grows upward from an underground mycelial mass and produces spores by meiosis. In asexual reproduction, conidia form by mitosis. In this lab study, you will study mushrooms and learn some features of their life cycle.

Procedure

1. Obtain a fresh mushroom, a **basidiocarp,** and identify its parts: The stalk is the **stipe;** the cap is the **pileus.** Look under the cap and identify **gills.** Spores form on the surface of the gills. Examine the gills with the stereoscopic microscope. Do you see spores? Children often make spore prints in scouts or in elementary school by placing a ripe mushroom pileus with the gill side down on a piece of white paper for several hours, allowing the spores to drop to the paper. Scientists use similar spore prints to accurately identify mushrooms.

2. Label the parts of the mushrooms in Figure 14.11a.

3. Obtain a prepared slide of a section through the pileus of *Coprinus* or another mushroom. Observe it on the compound microscope using low

a.   **b.**

Figure 14.11.
Club fungi, phylum Basidiomycota. (a) Mushrooms, or basidiocarps, each consisting of a cap, the pileus; and a stalk, the stipe. (b) A section through the gills on a whole basidiocarp reveals basidia and basidiospores.

and then intermediate powers. Is your slide a cross section or a longitudinal section through the pileus? Make a sketch in the lab manual margin indicating the plane of your section through the basidiocarp. Compare your section with the fresh mushroom you have just studied and with Figure 14.11b.

4. Using the prepared slide, observe the surface of several gills using high power. Spores are produced at the tips of small club-shaped structures called **basidia.** Locate a basidium and focus carefully on its end. Here you may see four knoblike protuberances. Each protuberance has a haploid nucleus that formed following meiosis, and each becomes a **basidiospore.** When the spores are mature, they are discharged from the basidium and are dispersed by the wind.

Results

Review the structures observed and label Figure 14.11a. Modify the figure to include features observed in your materials that differ from the figure.

Discussion

State the characteristics shared by all Basidiomycota.

Lab Study D. Imperfect Fungi—Deuteromycota

Materials

cultures of *Penicillium* on demonstration
Roquefort cheese on demonstration

Introduction

Most fungi are classified based on their sexual reproductive structures; however, many fungi (as far as is known) reproduce only vegetatively. Because the sexual reproductive stages of these fungi do not exist or have not been found, they are called **asexual,** or **imperfect fungi** (following the botanical use of "imperfect" to indicate a flower lacking one reproductive part). This group is of interest because several human diseases—athlete's foot, ringworm, and candida "yeast" infections—are caused by species of imperfect fungi. Also in this group are several beneficial species—for example, one species of *Penicillium* that produces the antibiotic penicillin and another that is used to make Roquefort and blue cheeses.

Procedure

1. Observe the *Penicillium* on demonstration. You may have observed something similar growing on oranges or other foods in your refrigerator.
2. Describe the texture and the color of the mycelium.

Results

Sketch your observations of *Penicillium* in the margin of your lab manual. Note any features that may be important in distinguishing this organism.

Discussion

Compare the appearance of *Penicillium* with that of *Rhizopus*.

Lab Study E. Lichens

Materials

examples of foliose, crustose, and fruticose lichens on demonstration

Introduction

Lichens are symbiotic associations between fungi and usually algae or cyanobacteria forming a body that can be consistently recognized. The fungal component is usually a sac fungus or a club fungus. The lichen body, called a **thallus**, varies in shape and colors, depending on the species of the components. Reproductive structures can be bright red or pink or green. Photosynthesis in the algae provides nutrients for the fungus, and the fungus provides a moist environment for the algae or cyanobacterium. Because lichens can survive extremely harsh environments, they are often the first organisms to colonize a newly exposed environment such as volcanic flow or rock outcrops, and they play a role in soil formation.

Procedure

Observe the demonstrations of different lichen types: those with a leafy thallus (**foliose**), a crustlike thallus (**crustose**), or a branching, cylindrical thallus (**fruticose**) (Figure 14.12). Look for cup-shaped or clublike reproductive structures.

Results

1. Sketch the lichens on demonstration in the margins of your lab manual.
2. Identify and label each according to lichen type.

Discussion

Imagine that you are the first scientist to observe a lichen microscopically. What observations would lead you to conclude that the lichen is composed of a fungus and an alga?

Figure 14.12.
Lichen types. Lichens may have (a) a leafy thallus (foliose), (b) a crust-like thallus (crustose), or (c) a cylindrical thallus (fruticose).

EXERCISE 14.3
Designing Your Independent Investigation

Introduction

In this exercise, you will choose one of the organisms observed in this lab topic and design a simple experiment answering a question about its behavior, growth patterns, or interactions with other species.

Use Lab Topic 1 as a reference for designing and performing a scientific investigation. Be ready to assign tasks to members of your lab team. Be sure that everyone understands the techniques that will be used. Your experiment will be successful only if you plan carefully, cooperate with your team members, perform lab techniques accurately and systematically, and record and report data accurately.

Materials

protozoa and algae cultures
cultures of slime molds *Physarum,
 Didymium, Dictyostelium*
cultures of *Pilobolus crystallinus,
 Rhizopus, Penicillium*
sterile agar plates to grow
 each species
sterile agar with oat flakes
sterile agar with sugar

sterile agar with albumin
sterile agar with pH 6, 7, or 8
aluminum foil
various breads from the health
 food store—wheat, rye, corn,
 potato, rice
bread with preservatives
sterilized dung from various
 animals

Procedure

1. Choose a question from this list to investigate or choose a question from your own observations. *Write your question in the margin of your lab manual.*

   a. Will varying the molarity of the culture medium change the rate of contractile vacuole formation in paramecia?

   b. Do plasmodia of the same species of slime mold unite when growing on the same agar plate? How about different species of slime mold?

   c. Do slime mold plasmodia demonstrate chemotaxis (response to chemical stimuli such as food molecules) or phototaxis (response to light)?

   d. What happens to slime molds if grown in different temperatures?

   e. Do the same fungi grow on different varieties of bread?

   f. How effective are preservatives in preventing fungal growth on foods?

   g. Is *Pilobolus* phototaxic? What about other fungi?

   h. Does succession take place in dung cultures of fungi? Refer to the milk bacteria succession study in Lab Topic 13 and design a similar experiment to investigate this phenomenon in fungi growing on dung.

2. Formulate a testable hypothesis. (Refer to Exercise 1.1, Lab Study B, Developing Hypotheses.)

   Hypothesis:

3. Summarize the experiment. (Use separate paper.)

4. Predict the results of your experiment based on your hypothesis. (Refer to Lab Topic 1, Exercise 1.2, Lab Study C, Making Predictions.)

   Prediction: (If/then)

5. Outline the procedures used in the experiment. (Refer to Exercise 1.2, Lab Study B, Choosing or Designing a Procedure.)

a. On a separate sheet of paper, list in numerical order each exact step of your procedure.

b. Remember to include the number of replicates (usually a minimum of five), levels of treatment, appropriate time intervals, and controls for each procedure.

c. If you have an idea for an experiment that requires materials other than those provided, ask your laboratory instructor about availability. If possible, additional supplies will be provided.

d. When carrying out an experiment, remember to quantify your measurements when possible.

6. Perform the experiment, making observations and collecting data for analysis.

7. **Record observations and data** on a separate sheet of paper. Design tables and graphs, at least one of each. Be thorough when collecting data. Do not just write down numbers, but record what they mean as well. Do not rely on your memory for information that you will need when reporting your results.

8. **Prepare your discussion.** Discuss your results in light of your hypothesis.

a. Review your hypothesis. Review your results (tables and graphs). Do your results support of falsify your hypothesis? Explain your answer, using data for support.

b. Review your prediction. Did your results correspond to the prediction you made? If not, explain how your results are different from your predictions, and why this might have occurred.

c. If you had problems with the procedure or questionable results, explain how they might have influenced your conclusion.

d. If you had an opportunity to repeat and expand this experiment to make your results more convincing, what would you do?

e. Summarize the conclusion you have drawn from your results.

9. **Be prepared to report your results to the class.** Prepare to persuade your fellow scientists that your experimental design is sound and that your results support your conclusions.

10. If your instructor requires it, **submit a written laboratory report** in the form of a scientific paper (see Appendix A). Keep in mind that although you have performed the experiments as a team, you must turn in a lab report of *your original writing*. Your tables and figures may be similar to those of your team members, but your paper must be the product of your own literature search and creative thinking.

Questions for Review

1. Complete Table 14.5 comparing charactistics of algae.
2. Complete Table 14.6 comparing characteristics of fungi.

Table 14.5

Comparison of Algae by Major Features

Phylum	Example(s)	Characteristics	Ecological Role	Economic Importance
Dinoflagellata				
Bacillariophyta				
Phaeophyta (Brown Algae)				
Rhodophyta (Red Algae)				
Chlorophyta (Green Algae)				

3. Compare spore formation in sac fungi and club fungi.

Table 14.6
Comparison of Fungi by Major Features

Phylum	Example(s)	Sexual Reproductive Structures	Asexual Reproductive Structures
Zygomycota (Zygote Fungi)			
Ascomycota (Sac Fungi)			
Basidiomycota (Club Fungi)			
Deuteromycota (Imperfect Fungi)			

4. Using observations of pigments present, body form, and distinguishing characteristics of the three groups of macroscopic green, brown, and red algae, speculate about where they might be most commonly found in ocean waters.

Applying Your Knowledge

1. Scientists are concerned that the depletion of the ozone layer will result in a reduction of populations of marine algae such as diatoms and

dinoflagellates. Recall the ecological role of these organisms and comment on the validity of this concern.

2. Imagine an ecosystem with no fungi. How would it be modified?

3. In 1950 the living world was classified simply into two kingdoms: plants and animals. More recently, scientists developed the five-kingdom system of classification: plants, animals, monerans, protists, and fungi. In 2000 there was a general consensus among scientists that three domains with more than five kingdoms was a better system for classifying the diversity of life on Earth. However, there is still no consensus on the number of kingdoms or the clustering of organisms that best represents their evolutionary relationships. Using the protists studied in this lab topic, explain why the classification of this diverse group in particular is problematic. How is solving the problem of organizing protistan diversity a model for understanding the process of science?

References

Ahmadjian, V. "Lichens Are More Important Than You Think," *BioScience,* 1995, vol. 45, p. 124.

Alexopoulos, C., C. Mims, and M. Blackwell. *Introductory Mycology,* 4th ed. New York, NY: John Wiley and Sons, Inc., 1996.

Anderson, R. "What to Do with Protists?" *Australian Systematic Botany,* 1998, vol. 11, p. 185.

Bold, H., C. J. Alexopoulos, and T. Delevoryas. *Morphology of Plants and Fungi.* New York: Harper & Row, 1980, p. 654.

Campbell, N., and J. Reece. *Biology,* 6th ed. Menlo Park, CA: Benjamin/Cummings, 2002.

Crowder, W. "Marvels of Mycetozoa." *National Geographic Magazine,* 1926, vol. 49, pp. 421–443.

Doolittle, W. F. "Uprooting the Tree of Life," *Scientific American,* 2000, vol. 282, pp. 90–95.

Hickman, C. P., L. S. Roberts, and A. Larson. *Integrated Principles of Zoology,* 11th ed. Boston: McGraw-Hill, 2001.

Litten, W. "The Most Poisonous Mushrooms," *Scientific American,* 1975, vol. 232.

Websites

Excellent site discussing Protistan systematics:
http://www.ucmp.berkeley.edu/alllife/eukaryotasy.html

Protist Image Data. Excellent page links:
http://megasun.bch.umontreal.ca/protists/protists.html

Links to pictures of red, brown, and green algae:
http://www.sonoma.edu/biology/algae/algae.html

Seaweeds:
http://www.botany.uwc.ac.za/Envfacts/seaweeds/

Information about specific algae and other interesting links:
http://www.botany.uwc.ac.za/mirrors/UCG_Seawwwd/Algae/

Mycological Resources on the Internet:
http://muse/bio.cornell.edu/~fungi/

See an amoeba video and find interesting information on amoebas:
http://www.bms.ed.ac.uk/research/smaciver/amoeba.htm

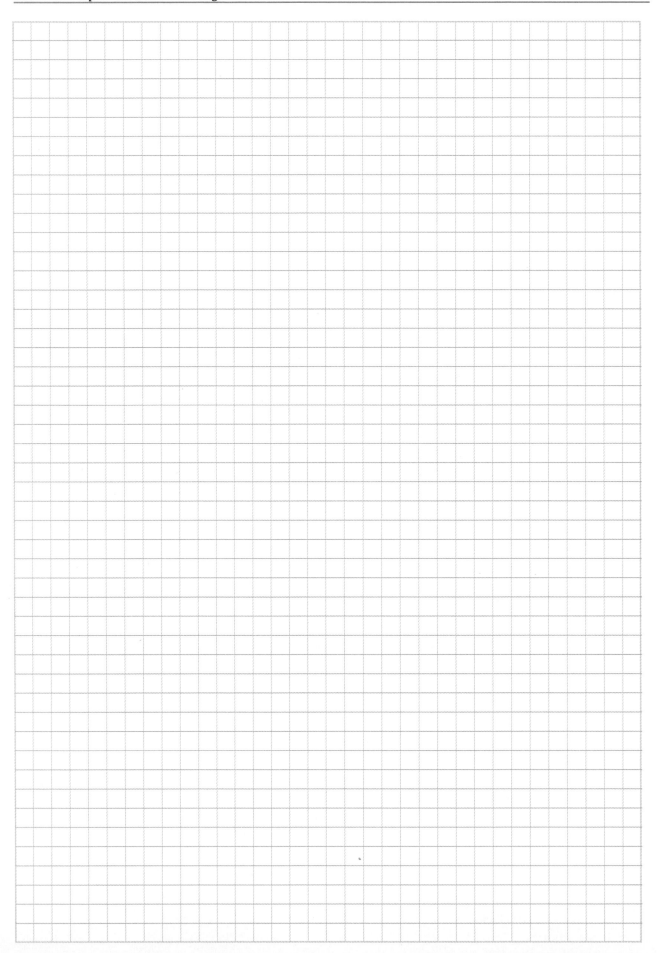

Plant Diversity I: Bryophytes and Seedless Vascular Plants

Laboratory Objectives

After completing this lab topic, you should be able to:

1. Describe the distinguishing characteristics of bryophytes and seedless vascular plants.
2. Discuss the primitive and advanced features of bryophytes and seedless vascular plants relative to their adaptations to the land environment.
3. Recognize and identify representative members of each division of bryophytes and seedless vascular plants.
4. Describe in detail the life cycle of a moss and a fern, including the important structures and processes in each life cycle.
5. Identify fossil members and their extant counterparts in the seedless vascular plants.
6. Describe the general life cycle and alternation of generations in the bryophytes and the seedless vascular plants, and discuss the differences between the life cycles of the two groups of plants using examples.
7. Describe homospory and heterospory, including the differences in spores and gametophytes.
8. Discuss the ecological role and economic importance of these groups of plants.

Introduction

In the history of life on Earth, one of the most revolutionary events was the colonization of land, first by plants, then by animals. Evidence from comparisons of extant land plants and divisions of algae suggests that the first land plants were related to the green algae. These first colonists are thought to be most similar to the living, branched, multicellular green alga *Chara* (studied in Lab Topic 14, Protists and Fungi). Once these primitive plants arrived on land over 500 million years ago, they faced new and extreme challenges in their physical environment. Only individuals that were able to survive the variations in temperature, moisture, gravitational forces, and substrate would thrive. Out of this enormous selective regime would come new and different adaptations and new and different life forms: the land plants.

Land plants generally have complex, multicellular plant bodies that are specialized for a variety of functions. Specialized structures have evolved for protection of the vulnerable stages of sexual reproduction. The plant body is often covered with a waxy cuticle that prevents desiccation. However, the waxy covering also prevents gas exchange, a problem solved by the presence of openings called **stomata** (sing., **stoma**). Some land plants have developed vascular tissue for efficient movement of materials throughout these

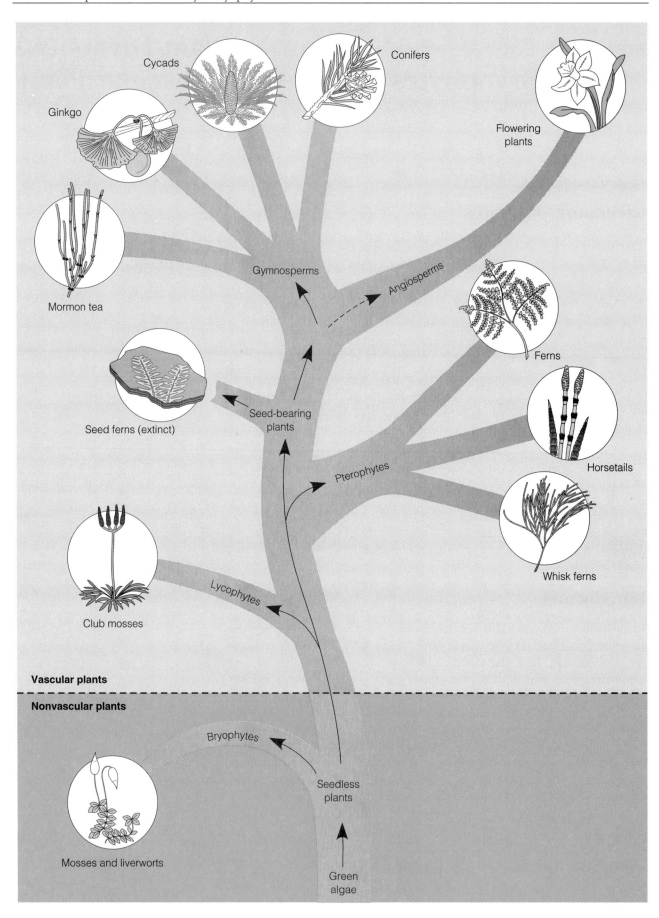

Cycads

Conifers

Ginkgo

Flowering plants

Mormon tea

Gymnosperms

Angiosperms

Ferns

Seed ferns (extinct)

Seed-bearing plants

Horsetails

Pterophytes

Club mosses

Whisk ferns

Lycophytes

Vascular plants

- -

Nonvascular plants

Bryophytes

Mosses and liverworts

Seedless plants

Green algae

Table 15.1
Classification of Land Plants

Classification	Common Name	Illustration
Nonvascular Plants		
Division Bryophyta	Mosses	
Division Hepatophyta	Liverworts	
Division Anthocerophyta	Hornworts	
Vascular Plants		
Seedless Plants		
Division Lycophyta	Club mosses	
Division Pterophyta	Ferns, horsetails, whisk ferns	
Seed Plants		
Gymnosperms		
Division Coniferophyta	Conifers	
Division Cycadophyta	Cycads	
Division Ginkgophyta	Ginkgo	
Division Gnetophyta	Gnetae	
Angiosperms		
Division Anthophyta	Flowering plants	

complex bodies, which are no longer bathed in water. As described in the following section, the reproductive cycles and reproductive structures of these plants are also adapted to the land environment.

In the two plant diversity labs, you will be investigating the diversity of land plants (Table 15.1 and Figure 15.1), some of which will be familiar to you (flowering plants, pine trees, and ferns) and some of which you may never have seen before (whisk ferns, horsetails, and liverworts). Remember as you view the classification that the designations *phylum* and *division* are equivalent taxonomic groupings. Botanists traditionally use division. You will study the bryophytes and seedless vascular plants in this lab topic, Plant Diversity I, and seed plants in Lab Topic 16: Plant Diversity II. *To maintain your perspective in the face of all this diversity—and to remember the major themes of these labs—bear in mind the questions on page 394.*

(🖅) **Figure 15.1.**
Evolution of land plants. The bryophytes and vascular plants probably evolved from green algae over 460 million years ago. Seedless vascular plants dominated Earth 300 million years ago, and representatives of four divisions have survived until the present. Seed plants replaced the seedless plants, and today flowering plants are the most diverse and successful group in an amazing variety of habitats. The representatives studied in Plant Diversity I and II are indicated.

1. What are the special adaptations of these plants to the land environment?
2. How are specialized plant structures related to functions in the land environment?
3. What are the major trends in the plant kingdom as plant life evolved over the past 500 million years?
4. In particular, how has the fundamental reproductive cycle of alternation of generations been modified in successive groups of plants?

Plant Life Cycles

All land plants have a common sexual reproductive life cycle called **alternation of generations,** in which plants alternate between a haploid **gametophyte** generation and a diploid **sporophyte** generation (Figure 15.2). In living land plants, these two generations differ in their morphology. In all land plants except the bryophytes (mosses and liverworts), the diploid sporophyte generation is the dominant (more conspicuous) generation. The sporophyte generation undergoes meiosis to produce haploid **spores** in a protective, nonreproductive jacket of cells called the **sporangium.** The spores germinate to produce the haploid gametophyte, which produces **gametes** inside a jacket of cells forming **gametangia** (sing., **gametangium**). **Eggs** are produced in **archegonia** (sing., **archegonium**), and **sperm** are produced in **antheridia** (sing., **antheridium**). These haploid gametes are formed by mitosis. The gametes fuse, usually by the entrance of the sperm into the archegonium, forming a diploid **zygote,** the first stage of the diploid sporophyte generation.

Note that both gametes and spores are haploid in this life cycle. Unlike the animal life cycle, however, *the plant life cycle produces gametes by mitosis; spores are produced by meiosis.* The difference between these two cells is that

Figure 15.2.
Alternation of generations. In this life cycle, a diploid sporophyte plant alternates with a haploid gametophyte plant. Note that haploid spores are produced on the sporophyte by meiosis, and haploid gametes are produced in the gametophyte by mitosis. *Using a colored pencil, indicate the structures that are haploid, and with another color, note the structures that are diploid.*

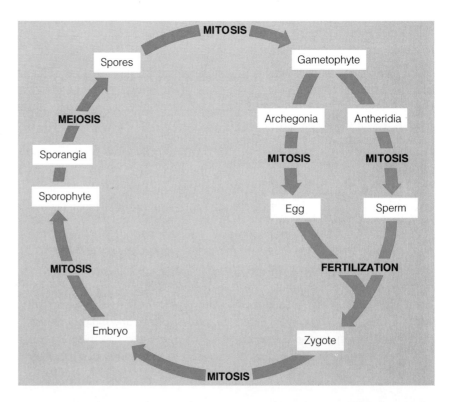

gametes fuse with other gametes to form the zygote and restore the diploid number, while spores germinate to form a new haploid gametophyte plant.

Review the generalized diagram of this life cycle in Figure 15.2. *Using colored pencils, note the structures that are diploid and those that are haploid.* As you become familiar with variations of this life cycle through specific examples, you will want to continue referring to this general model for review.

Major trends in the evolution of this life cycle include the increased importance of the sporophyte as the photosynthetic and persistent plant that dominates the life cycle; the reduction and protection of the gametophyte within the body of the sporophyte; and the evolution of seeds and then flowers.

Bryophytes and Seedless Vascular Plants

In this lab topic, terrestrial plants will be used to illustrate how life has undergone dramatic changes during the past 500 million years. Not long after the transition to land, plants diverged into at least two separate lineages. One gave rise to the bryophytes, a group of mostly nonvascular plants, including the mosses, and the other to the vascular plants (see Figure 15.1). Bryophytes first appear in the fossil record dating over 400 million years ago and remain unchanged, whereas the vascular plants have undergone enormous diversification. As you review the evolution of land plants, refer to the geological time chart for an overview of the history of life on Earth (Figure 15.3, on the next page).

EXERCISE 15.1
Bryophytes

The bryophytes are composed of three divisions of related plants that share some key characteristics and include mosses (Bryophyta) and liverworts (Hepatophyta). The third division, hornworts (Anthocerophyta), will not be seen in lab. (See again Figure 15.1 and Table 15.1.) The term *bryophytes* does not refer to a taxonomic category; rather, bryophytes are an ancient group of plants that appear to have evolved into several different groups independently and did not give rise to any other living groups of plants. They are small plants generally lacking **vascular tissue** (specialized cells for the transport of material), although water-conducting tubes appear to be present in some mosses. (However, these tubes may be unrelated to the vascular tissue in vascular plants.) The life cycle for the bryophytes differs from all other land plants because the gametophyte is the dominant and conspicuous plant. Because bryophytes are nonvascular, they are restricted to moist habitats and have never attained the size and importance of other groups of plants. The gametophyte plants remain close to the ground, enabling the motile sperm to swim from the antheridium to the archegonium and fertilize the egg. They have a cuticle but lack stomata on the surface of the **thallus** (plant body), which is not organized into roots, stems, and leaves.

Years Ago (millions)	Era Period Epoch	Life on Earth
	CENOZOIC Quaternary	
	Recent	• Origin of agriculture and artificial selection; *H. sapiens*
1.8	Pleistocene	
	Tertiary	
5	Pliocene	• Large carnivores; hominoid apes
23	Miocene	• Forests dwindle; grassland spreads
35	Oligocene	• Anthropoid apes
	Eocene	• Diversification of mammals and flowering plants
57		
65	Paleocene	• Specialized flowers; sophisticated pollinators and seed distributors
	MESOZOIC Cretaceous	• Flowering plants established and diversified; many modern families present; extinction of many dinosaurs
145		
	Jurassic	• Origin of birds; reptiles dominant; cycads and ferns abundant; first modern conifers and immediate ancestors of flowering plants
208		
	Triassic	• First dinosaurs and mammals; forests of gymnosperms and ferns; cycads
245		
	PALEOZOIC Permian	• Diversification of gymnosperms; origin of reptiles; amphibians dominant
290		
	Carboniferous	• First treelike plants; giant woody lycopods and sphenopsids form extensive forests in swampy areas; evolution of early seeds (seed ferns) and first stages of leaves
363		
	Devonian	• Diversification of vascular plants; sharks and fishes dominant in the oceans
409		
	Silurian	• First vascular plants
439		
	Ordovician	• Diversification of algae and plants invade land
510		
	Cambrian	• Diversification of major animal phyla
570		
	PRECAMBRIAN Precambrian	• Origin of bacteria, archaea, and eukaryotes

Earth is about 4.6 billion years old

Bryophytes are not important economically, with the exception of sphagnum moss, which in its harvested and dried form is known as *peat moss.* Peat moss is absorbent, has an antibacterial agent, and was reportedly once used as bandages and diapers. Today peat moss is used primarily in the horticultural industry.

Lab Study A. Bryophyta: Mosses

Materials

living examples of mosses
prepared slides of *Mnium* archegonia and antheridia
colored pencils

Introduction

The mosses are the most common group of bryophytes, occurring primarily in moist environments but also found in dry habitats that are periodically wet (Color Plate 30). Refer to Figure 15.4 on the next page as you investigate the moss life cycle, which is representative of the bryophytes.

Procedure

1. Examine living colonies of mosses on demonstration. Usually you will find the two generations, gametophyte and sporophyte, growing together.

2. Identify the leafy **gametophytes** and the dependent **sporophytes,** which appear as elongated structures growing above them. Tug gently at the sporophyte and notice that it is attached to the gametophyte. Recall that the sporophyte develops and matures while attached to the gametophyte and receives its moisture and nutrients from the gametophyte.

3. The gametes are produced by the gametophyte in **gametangia,** which protect the gametes but are not readily visible without a microscope. Observe under the microscope's low-power lens prepared slides containing long sections of heads of the unisex moss *Mnium,* which contain the gametangia. One slide has been selected to show the **antheridia** (male); the other is a rosette of **archegonia** (female). Sperm-forming tissue will be visible inside the antheridia. On the archegonial slide, look for an archegonium. The moss archegonium has a very long neck and rounded base. It will be difficult to find an entire archegonium in any one section. Search for a single-celled **egg** in the base of the archegonium.

4. Refer to Figure 15.4 as you follow the steps of fertilization through formation of the gametophyte in the next generation. The sperm swim

(🖘) **Figure 15.3.**
Geological time chart. The history of life can be organized into time periods that reflect changes in the physical and biological environment. Refer to this table as you review the evolution of land plants in Plant Diversity I and II.

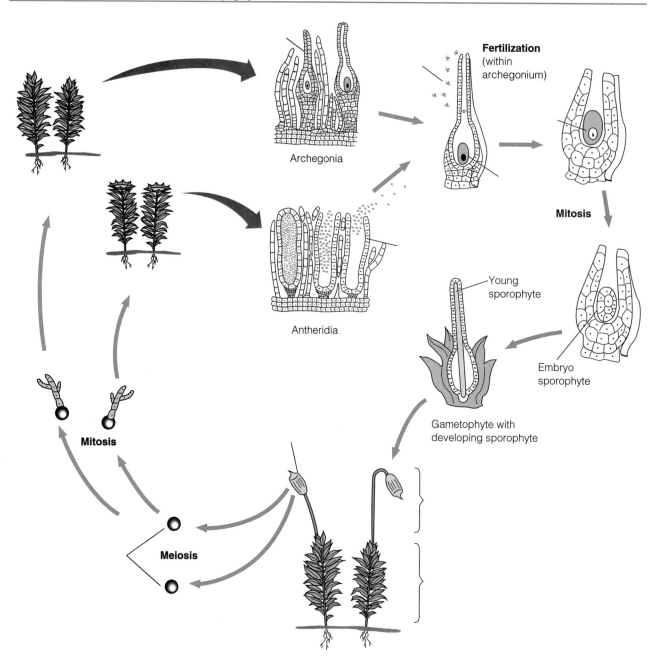

Figure 15.4.
Moss life cycle. The leafy moss plant is the gametophyte, and the sporophyte is dependent on it, deriving its water and nutrients from the body of the gametophyte. Review this variation of alternation of generations and label the structures described in Lab Study A. *Using colored pencils, highlight the haploid and diploid structures in different colors. Circle the processes of mitosis and meiosis.*

through a film of water to the archegonium and swim down the neck to the egg, where fertilization takes place. The diploid zygote divides by mitosis and develops into an embryonic sporophyte within the archegonium. As the sporophyte matures, it grows out of the gametophyte but remains attached, deriving water and nutrients from the gametophyte body. **Spores** develop in the **sporangium** at the end of the sporophyte. The spores are discharged from the sporangium and in a favorable environment develop into new gametophytes.

Results

1. Review the structures and processes observed and then label the moss life cycle diagram in Figure 15.4.
2. Using colored pencils, indicate if structures are haploid or diploid and circle the processes of mitosis and meiosis.

Discussion

Refer to Figure 15.2, the generalized diagram of the plant life cycle.

1. Are the spores produced by the moss sporophyte formed by meiosis or mitosis? Are they haploid or diploid?

2. Do the spores belong to the gametophyte or sporophyte generation?

3. Are the gametes haploid or diploid? Are they produced by meiosis or mitosis?

4. Is the dominant generation for the bryophytes the gametophyte or the sporophyte?

5. Can you suggest any ecological role for bryophytes?

6. What feature of the life cycle differs for bryophytes compared with all other land plants?

Lab Study B. Hepatophyta: Liverworts

Materials

living liverworts

Introduction

Liverworts are so named because their bodies are flattened and lobed (Color Plate 31). Early herbalists believed that these plants were beneficial in the treatment of liver disorders. Although less common than mosses, liverworts can be found along streams on moist rocks, but because of their small size, you must look closely to locate them.

Procedure

Examine examples of liverworts on demonstration. Liverworts have a flat **thallus** (plant body). Note the **rhizoids,** rootlike extensions on the lower surface. Observe the **pores** on the surface of the leaflike thallus. These openings function in gas exchange; however, they are always open since they lack guard cells. On the upper surface of the thallus you should see circular cups called **gemmae cups,** which contain flat disks of green tissue called **gemmae.** The gemmae are washed out of the cups when it rains, and they grow into new, genetically identical liverworts.

Results

Sketch the overall structure of the liverwort in the margin of your laboratory manual. Label structures where appropriate.

Discussion

1. Is the plant you observed the gametophyte or sporophyte?

2. Are the gemmae responsible for asexual or sexual reproduction? Explain.

3. Why are these plants, like most bryophytes, restricted to moist habitats, and why are they always small?

4. In this lab topic, as in Plant Diversity II (Lab Topic 16) and Plant Anatomy (Lab Topic 19), you are asked to complete tables that summarize features advantageous to the adaptation of plant groups to the land environment. You may be asked to compare these derived (advanced) features with others that have changed little (primitive) in the evolution of land plants. For example, for bryophytes, motile sperm might be considered a primitive feature, while the cuticle would be considered advanced.

    Complete Table 15.2, relating the features of bryophytes to their success in the land environment. Refer to the lab topic introduction for assistance.

Table 15.2
Primitive and Advanced Features of Bryophytes as
They Relate to Adaptation to Land

Primitive Features	Advanced Features

EXERCISE 15.2
Seedless Vascular Plants

Seedless, terrestrial plants are analogous to the first terrestrial vertebrate animals, the amphibians, in their dependence on water for external fertilization and development of the unprotected, free-living embryo. Both groups were important in the Paleozoic era but have undergone a steady decline in importance since that time. Seedless plants were well suited for life in the vast swampy areas that covered large areas of the Earth in the Carboniferous period but were not suited for the drier areas of the Earth at that time or for later climatic changes that caused the vast swamps to decline and disappear. The fossilized remains of the swamp forests are the coal deposits of today (Figure 15.3).

Although living representatives of the seedless vascular plants have survived for millions of years, their limited adaptations to the land environment have restricted their range. All seedless vascular plants have vascular tissue, which is specialized for conducting water, nutrients, and photosynthetic products. Their life cycle is a variation of alternation of generations, in which the sporophyte is the dominant plant; the gametophyte is usually independent of the sporophyte. These plants have stomata and structural support tissue. However, since they still retain the primitive feature of motile sperm that require water for fertilization, the gametophyte is small and restricted to moist habitats.

Economically, the only important members of this group are the ferns, a significant horticultural resource.

The divisions included in the seedless vascular plants are Lycophyta and Pterophyta (see again Table 15.1 and Figure 15.1).

Lab Study A. Lycophyta: Club Mosses

Materials

living *Selaginella* and *Lycopodium*
preserved *Selaginella* with microsporangia and megasporangia
prepared slide of *Selaginella* strobilus, l.s.

Introduction

Living members of Lycophyta are usually found in moist habitats, including bogs and streamsides (Color Plates 32 and 33). However, one species of *Selaginella*, the resurrection plant, inhabits deserts. It remains dormant throughout periods of low rainfall, but then comes to life—resurrects—when it rains. During the Carboniferous period, lycophytes were not inconspicuous parts of the flora but rather formed the forest canopy; they were the ecological equivalent of today's oaks, hickories, and pines.

Bryophytes and most seedless vascular plants produce one type of spore (**homospory**), which gives rise to the gametophyte by mitosis. One advanced feature occasionally seen in seedless vascular plants is the production of two kinds of spores (**heterospory**). Large spores called **megaspores** divide by mitosis to produce the female gametophyte. The numerous small spores, **microspores,** produce the male gametophytes by mitosis. Heterospory and separate male and female gametophytes, as seen in *Selaginella,* are unusual in seedless vascular plants, but characteristic of seed-producing vascular plants.

Procedure

1. Examine living club mosses, *Selaginella* and *Lycopodium.* Are they dichotomously branched? (The branches would split in two, appearing to form a Y.) Locate sporangia, which may be present either clustered at the end of the leafy stem tips, forming **strobili,** or **cones,** or dispersed along the leafy stems. Note that these plants have small leaves, or bracts, along the stem.

2. Examine preserved strobili of *Selaginella.* Observe the round sporangia clustered in sporophylls (leaflike structures) at the tip of the stem. These sporangia contain either four megaspores or numerous microspores. Can you observe any differences in the sporangia or spores?

3. Observe the prepared slide of a long section through the strobilus of *Selaginella.* Begin your observations at low power. Are both microspores and megaspores visible on this slide?

    How can you distinguish these spores?

4. Identify the **strobilus, microsporangium, microspores, megasporangium,** and **megaspores** and label Figure 15.5.

a. Mature sporophyte (2*n*)

b.

Figure 15.5.
Selaginella. (a) The leafy plant is the sporophyte. The sporangia are clustered at
the tips in strobili. (b) Photomicrograph of a longitudinal section through the
strobilus of *Selaginella.*

Results

1. Sketch the overall structure of the club mosses in the margin of your lab manual. Label structures where appropriate.

2. Review Figure 15.5 of *Selaginella*. Using a colored pencil, highlight the structures that are haploid and part of the gametophyte generation.

Discussion

1. Are these leafy plants part of the sporophyte or the gametophyte generation? Do you have any evidence to support your answer?

2. What features would you look for to determine if this were a seedless vascular plant?

3. Are microspores and megaspores produced by mitosis or meiosis? (Review the life cycle in Figure 15.2.)

4. Will megaspores divide to form the female gametophyte or the sporophyte?

 Having trouble with life cycles? Return to the introduction and review the generalized life cycle in Figure 15.2. Reread the introduction to the study of seedless vascular plants. The key to success is to determine where meiosis occurs and to remember the ploidal level for the gametophyte and the sporophyte.

Lab Study B. Pterophyta: Ferns, Horsetails, and Whisk Ferns

Materials

living and/or preserved horsetails (*Equisetum*)
living and/or preserved whisk ferns (*Psilotum*)
living ferns

Introduction

If a time machine could take us back 400 million years to the Silurian period, we would find that vertebrate animals were confined to the seas, and early vascular plants had begun to diversify on land (Table 15.3). By the Carboniferous period, ferns, horsetails, and whisk ferns grew alongside the lycophytes. Until recently, these three groups of seedless vascular plants were placed in separate divisions: Pterophyta (ferns), Sphenophyta (horsetails), and Psilophyta (whisk ferns). Strong evidence from molecular biology now reveals a close relationship among these three groups, supporting a common ancestor for the group and their placement in one division, Pterophyta.

Psilophytes (**whisk ferns**) are diminutive, dichotomously branched (repeated Y branches), photosynthetic stems that reproduce sexually by aerial spores. Today, whisk ferns can be found in some areas of Florida and in the tropics (Color Plate 34). Sphenophytes (**horsetails**) have green jointed stems with occasional clusters of leaves or branches. Their cell walls contain silica that give the stem a rough texture. These plants were used by pioneers to scrub dishes—thus their name, scouring rushes. In cooler regions of North America, horsetails grow as weeds along roadsides (Color Plate 35). **Ferns** are the most successful group of seedless vascular plants, occupying habitats from the desert to tropical rain forests. Most ferns are small plants that lack woody tissue (Color Plate 36). An exception is the tree ferns found in tropical regions. Many cultivated ferns are available for home gardeners.

In this lab study you will investigate the diversity of pterophytes, including whisk ferns, horsetails, and a variety of ferns. The plants on demonstration are sporophytes, the dominant generation in seedless vascular plants. You will investigate the life cycle of a fern in Lab Study C, Fern Life Cycle.

Procedure

1. Examine a living **whisk fern** (*Psilotum nudum*) on demonstration. This is one of only two extant genera of psilophytes.

2. Observe the spherical structures on the stem. If possible, cut one open and determine the function of these structures. Note the dichotomous branching, typical of the earliest land plants.

3. Examine the **horsetails** (*Equisetum* sp.) on demonstration. Note the ribs and ridges in the stem. Also examine the nodes or joints along the stem where branches and leaves may occur in some species. Locate the **strobili** in the living or preserved specimens on demonstration. These are clusters of **sporangia,** which produce **spores.**

4. Examine the living **ferns** on demonstration. Note the deeply dissected leaves, which arise from an underground stem called a **rhizome,** which functions like a root to anchor the plant. Roots arise from the rhizome. Observe the dark spots, or **sori** (sing. **sorus**), which are clusters of sporangia, on the underside of some leaves, called **sporophylls** (See Color Plate 37).

Results

1. Sketch the overall structure of the whisk fern, horsetail, and fern in the margin of your lab manual. Label structures where appropriate.

2. Are there any leaves on the whisk fern? On the horsetails?

3. Are sporangia present on the whisk fern? On the horsetails? On the ferns?

Discussion

1. Are the spores in the sporangia produced by mitosis or meiosis?

2. Are the sporangia haploid or diploid? Think about which generation produces them.

3. Once dispersed, will these spores produce the gametophyte or sporophyte generation?

Lab Study C. Fern Life Cycle

Materials

living ferns	stereoscopic microscope
living fern gametophytes with archegonia and antheridia	compound microscope prepared slide of fern gametophytes with archegonia, c.s.
living fern gametophytes with young sporophytes attached	colored pencils Protoslo®

Introduction

In the previous Lab Study you examined the features of the fern sporophyte. In this lab study you will examine the fern life cycle in more detail, beginning with the sporophyte.

Procedure

1. Examine the sporophyte leaf with sori at your lab bench. Make a water mount of a sorus and examine the sporangia using a dissecting microscope. You will find the stalked **sporangia** in various stages of development. Find a sporangium still filled with **spores** and another that has discharged its spores. The sporangia contain cells in different stages of meiosis, leading to spores that are seen in different stages of maturation. These stages will not be distinguishable to you under the microscope.

2. Refer to Figure 15.6 as you observe the events and important structures in the life cycle of the fern. The haploid spores of ferns fall to the ground and grow into heart-shaped, **gametophyte** plants. All seedless terrestrial plants depend on an external source of water for a sperm to swim to an egg to effect fertilization and for growth of the resulting sporophyte plant. The sexual organs, which bear male and female gametes, are borne on the underside of the gametophyte. Egg cells are borne in urn-like structures called **archegonia,** and sperm cells are produced in globular structures called **antheridia.** Archegonia are usually found around the notch of the heart-shaped gametophyte, while antheridia occur over most of the undersurface.

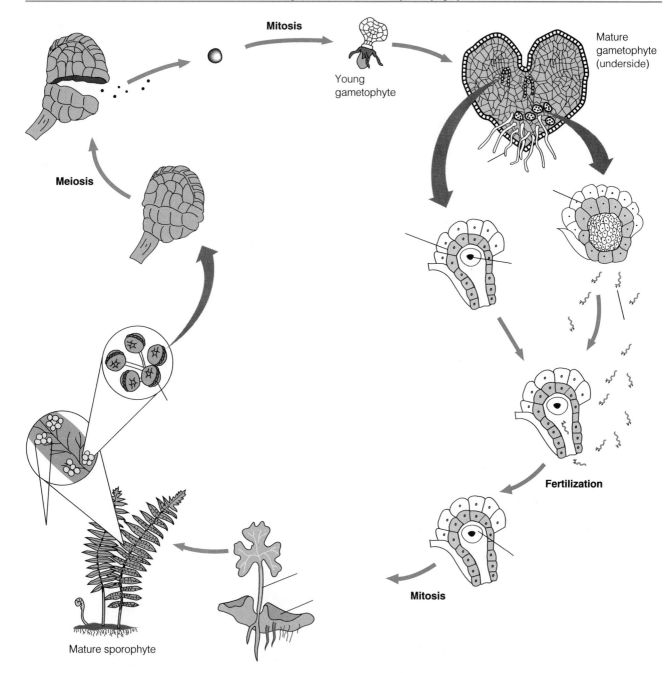

Figure 15.6.
Fern life cycle. The familiar leafy fern plant is the sporophyte, which alternates with a small, heart-shaped gametophyte. Review this life cycle, a variation of alternation of generations, and label the structures and processes described in Lab Study C. *Using colored pencils, highlight the haploid and diploid structures in different colors.*

3. To study whole gametophytes, make a slide of living gametophytes. View them using the stereoscopic microscope or the scanning lens on the compound microscope. Note their shape and color and the presence of **rhizoids,** rootlike multicellular structures. Locate archegonia and antheridia. Which surface will you need to examine? Sketch in the margin of your lab manual any details not included in Figure 15.6.

4. If you have seen antheridia on a gametophyte, remove the slide from the microscope. Gently but firmly press on the coverslip with a pencil eraser. View using the compound microscope first on intermediate and then on high power. Look for motile **sperm** swimming with a spiral motion. Each sperm has two flagella. Add a drop of Protoslo to slow down movement of sperm.

5. Observe the cross section of a fern gametophyte with archegonia. Each archegonium encloses an **egg,** which may be visible on your slide.

6. Make a wet mount of a fern gametophyte with a **young sporophyte** attached. Look for a young **leaf** and **root** on each sporophyte.

   Share slides of living gametophytes with archegonia, antheridia and sperm, and sporophytes until everyone has observed each structure.

Results

1. Review the structures and processes observed, and then label the stages of fern sexual reproduction outlined in Figure 15.6.

2. Using colored pencils, circle those parts of the life cycle that are sporophytic (diploid). Use another color to encircle the gametophytic (haploid) stages of the life cycle. Highlight the processes of meiosis and mitosis.

Discussion

Refer to Figure 15.2, the generalized diagram of the plant life cycle, and Figure 15.6, a representation of the fern life cycle.

1. Are the spores produced by the fern sporophyte formed by meiosis or mitosis?

2. Do the spores belong to the gametophyte or the sporophyte generation?

3. Are the gametes produced by mitosis or meiosis?

4. Are the archegonia and antheridia haploid or diploid? Think about which generation produces them.

5. Is the dominant generation for the fern the gametophyte or the sporophyte?

6. Can you suggest any ecological role for ferns?

Lab Study D. Fossils of Seedless Vascular Plants

Materials

fossils of extinct lycophytes (*Lepidodendron, Sigillaria*)
fossils of extinct sphenophytes (*Calamites*)
fossils of extinct ferns

Introduction

If we went back in time 300 million years to the Carboniferous period, we would encounter a wide variety of vertebrate amphibians moving about vast swamps dominated by spore-bearing forest trees. Imagine a forest of horsetails and lycophytes the size of trees, amphibians as large as alligators, and enormous dragonflies and roaches! Seedless plants were at their peak during this period and were so prolific that their carbonized remains form the bulk of Earth's coal deposits. Among the most spectacular components of the coal-swamp forest were tree ferns, 100-foot-tall trees belonging to the fossil genera *Lepidodendron* and *Sigillaria*, and 60-foot-tall horsetails assigned to the fossil genus *Calamites* (Figures 15.3 and 15.7).

Procedure

Examine flattened fossil stems of *Lepidodendron, Sigillaria, Calamites,* and fossil fern foliage, all of which were recovered from coal mine tailings. Compare these with their living relatives, the lycophytes (club mosses), sphenophytes (horsetails), and ferns, which today are diminutive plants found in restricted habitats.

Results

1. For each division of seedless vascular plants, describe those characteristics that are similar for both living specimens and fossils. For example, do you observe dichotomous branching and similar shape and form of leaves, stems, or sporangia? Refer to the living specimens or your sketches.

    Lycophytes:

    Sphenophytes:

    Ferns:

2. Sketch in the margin of your lab manual the overall structure of the fossils. How would you recognize these fossils at a later date? Label structures where appropriate.

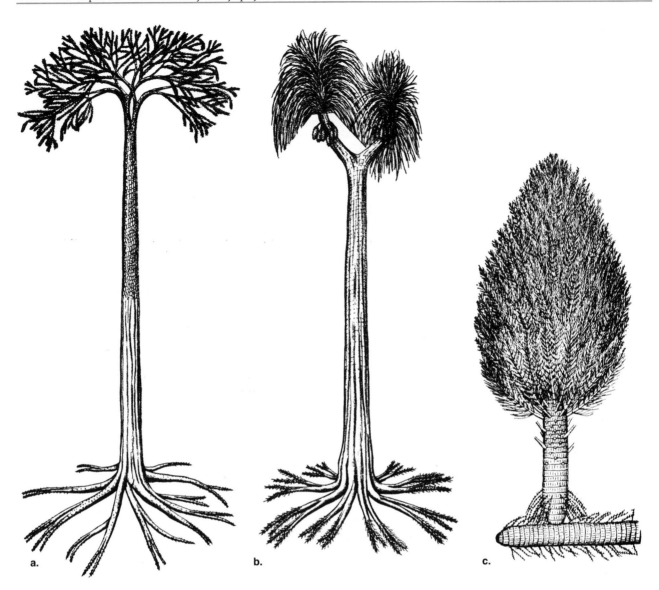

Figure 15.7.
Seedless vascular plants of the Carboniferous period. Reconstruction of
the lycophytes (a) *Lepidodendron* and (b) *Sigillaria.* (c) *Calamites* was a relative
of horsetails.

Discussion

The lycophytes, sphenophytes, and ferns were once the giants of the plant
kingdom and dominated the landscape. Explain why they are presently
restricted to certain habitats and are relatively small in stature.

Questions for Review

1. Complete Table 15.3, indicating the primitive and advanced features of seedless vascular plants relative to success in land environments. Recall that in this context the term *primitive* means an ancestral trait, while the term *advanced* indicates a derived trait, or adaptation, to land. For example, traits shared with the bryophytes (such as sperm requiring water for fertilization) are primitive, while the presence of vascular tissue is advanced.

Table 15.3
Primitive and Advanced Features of Seedless Vascular
Plants as They Relate to Adaptation to Land

Primitive Features	Advanced Features

2. For each of the listed features, describe its contribution, if any, to the success of land plants.

    gametangium

    cuticle

    rhizoid

    motile sperm

    vascular tissue

    gemma

3. Complete Table 15.4. Identify the function of the structures listed. Indicate whether they are part of the gametophyte or sporophyte generation, and provide an example of a plant that has this structure.

Table 15.4
Structures and Functions of the Bryophytes and Seedless Vascular Plants

Structure	Function	Sporophyte/ Gametophyte	Example
Antheridium			
Archegonium			
Spore			
Gamete			
Rhizome			
Gemma			
Sporangium			
Strobilus			
Sorus			

4. What is the major difference between the alternation of generations in the life cycles of bryophytes and seedless vascular plants?

Applying Your Knowledge

1. The fossil record provides little information about ancient mosses. Do you think that bryophytes could ever have been large tree-sized plants? Provide evidence from your investigations to support your answer.

2. On a walk through a botanical garden, you notice a small leafy plant that is growing along the edge of a small stream in a shady nook. You hypothesize that this plant is a lycophyte. What information can you gather to test your hypothesis?

3. German scientists studied air pollution from heavy metals (cadmium, copper, lead, nickel, and zinc) by analyzing the concentration of these metals in moss samples. They compared mosses collected between 1845 and 1974, which were preserved as herbarium specimens, with mosses collected in 1991. In general, the 1991 mosses had lower heavy metal concentrations. These results were attributed to increased air pollution controls. Based on your knowledge of the structure of the moss gametophyte, can you suggest one or more reasons why mosses are particularly useful indicators of air pollution?

4. Heterospory occasionally occurs in lycophytes and ferns, and in all seed plants. Botanists are convinced that heterospory must have originated more than once in the evolution of plants. Can you suggest one or more advantages that heterospory might provide to plants?

References

Herpin, U., B. Markert, V. Wechert, J. Berklekamp, K. Friese, U. Siewers, and H. Lieth. "Retrospective Analysis of Heavy Metal Concentrations at Selected Locations in the Federal Republic of Germany Using Moss Materials from a Herbarium," *Science of the Total Environment*, 1997, vol. 205, pp. 1–12.

Mauseth, J. D. *Botany: An Introduction to Plant Biology*, 2nd ed. Philadelphia, PA: Saunders College Publishing, 1995.

Moore, R., W. D. Clark, and D. Vodopich. *Botany*, 2nd ed. Dubuque, IA: WCB/McGraw-Hill, 1998.

Raven, P. H., R. F. Evert, and S. E. Eichhorn. *Biology of Plants,* 6th ed. New York: W. H. Freeman Publishers, 1999.

Websites

Links to images of horsetails:

http://www.wisc.edu/botit/systematics/Phyla/Sphenophyta/ Sphenophyta.html

Links to images of whisk ferns:

http://www.wisc.edu/botit/systematics/Phyla/Psilophyta/ Psilophyta.html

Links to images of lycophytes:

http://www.wisc.edu/botit/systematics/Phyla/Lycophyta/ Lycophyta.html

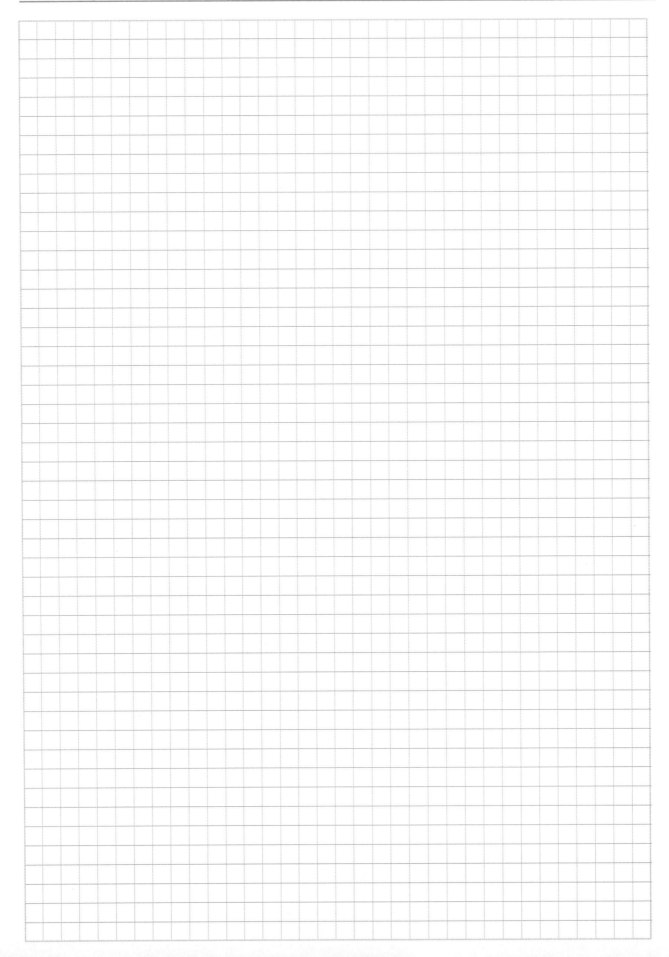

Plant Diversity II: Seed Plants

 Before lab, read the following material on gymnosperms and angiosperms and complete Table 16.1 by listing (and comparing) the traits of each.

Laboratory Objectives

After completing this lab topic, you should be able to:

1. Identify examples of the divisions of seed plants.
2. Describe the life cycle of a gymnosperm (pine tree) and an angiosperm.
3. Describe features of flowers that ensure pollination by insects, birds, bats, and wind.
4. Describe factors influencing pollen germination.
5. Identify types of fruits, recognize examples, and describe dispersal mechanisms.
6. Relate the structures of seed plants to their functions in the land environment.
7. Compare the significant features of life cycles for various land plants and state their evolutionary importance.
8. Summarize major trends in the evolution of land plants and provide evidence from your laboratory investigations.

Gymnosperms

For over 500 million years, plants have been adapting to the rigors of the land environment. The nonvascular bryophytes with their small and simple bodies survived in moist habitats, habitats moist at least for part of their life cycle. During the cool Carboniferous period, vascular seedless plants dominated the landscape of the swamp forests that covered much of the earth. Although these plants were more complex and better adapted to the challenges of the land environment, they still were dependent on water for sperm to swim to the egg. During the Mesozoic era, 150 million years ago, Earth became warmer and drier and the swamp forests declined, presenting another challenge to terrestrial plants and animals. Earth at that time was a world dominated by reptilian vertebrates, including the flying, running, and climbing dinosaurs. The landscape was dominated by a great variety of seed-bearing plants called **gymnosperms** (literally, "naked seeds"), which in the Carboniferous period had been restricted to dry sites. During the Mesozoic, a number of distinct gymnosperm groups diversified, and a few of the spore-bearing plants survived (see Figure 15.1 and Table 15.1 in Lab Topic 15). As you review the evolution of land plants, refer to the geological time chart in Figure 15.3 for an overview of the history of life on Earth.

Vertebrate animals became fully terrestrial during the Mesozoic with the emergence of reptiles, which were free from a dependence on water for sexual reproduction and development. The development of the amniotic egg along with an internal method of fertilization made this major transition possible. The amniotic egg carries its own water supply and nutrients, permitting early embryonic development to occur on dry land, a great distance from external water. In an analogous manner, the gymnosperms became free from dependence on water through the development of a process of internal fertilization via the pollen grain and development of a seed, which contains a dormant embryo with a protective cover and special nutrient tissue.

Several features of the gymnosperms have been responsible for their success. They have reduced (smaller-sized) gametophytes; the male gametophyte is a multinucleated pollen grain, and the female gametophyte is small and retained within the sporangium in the ovule of the sporophyte generation. The pollen grain is desiccation resistant and adapted for wind pollination, removing the necessity for fertilization in a watery medium. The pollen tube conveys the sperm nucleus to an egg cell, and the embryonic sporophyte develops within the gametophyte tissues, which are protected by the previous sporophyte generation. The resulting seed is not only protected from environmental extremes, but also is packed with nutritive materials and can be dispersed away from the parent plant. In addition, gymnosperms have advanced vascular tissues: xylem for transporting water and nutrients and phloem for transporting photosynthetic products. The xylem cells are called *tracheids* and are more efficient for transport than those of the seedless vascular plants.

Angiosperms

A visit to Earth 60 million years ago, during the late Cretaceous period, would reveal a great diversity of mammals and birds and a landscape dominated by **flowering plants,** or **angiosperms** (division **Anthophyta**). Ultimately, these plants would diversify and become the most numerous, widespread, and important plants on Earth. Angiosperms now occupy well over 90% of the vegetated surface of Earth and contribute virtually 100% of our agricultural food plants.

The evolution of the flower resulted in enormous advances in the efficient transfer and reception of pollen. Whereas gymnosperms are all wind-pollinated, producing enormous amounts of pollen that reach the appropriate species by chance, the process of flower pollination is mediated by specific agents—insects, birds, and bats—in addition to water and wind. Pollination agents such as the insect are attracted to the flower with its rewards of nectar and pollen. Animal movements provide precise placement of pollen on the receptive portion of the female structures, increasing the probability of fertilization. The process also enhances the opportunity for cross-fertilization among distant plants and therefore the possibility of increased genetic variation.

Angiosperm reproduction follows the trend for reduction in the size of the gametophyte. The pollen grain is the male gametophyte, and the eight-nucleated **embryo sac** is all that remains of the female gametophyte. This generation continues to be protected and dependent on the adult sporophyte plant. The female gametophyte provides nutrients for the developing sporophyte embryo through a unique triploid **endosperm** tissue. Another unique feature of angiosperms is the **fruit.** The seeds of the angiosperm develop within the flower ovary, which matures into the fruit. This structure provides protection and enhances dispersal of the young sporophyte into new habitats.

In addition to advances in reproductive biology, the angiosperms evolved other advantageous traits. All gymnosperms are trees or shrubs, with a large investment in woody, persistent tissue; and their life cycles are long (5 or more years before they begin to reproduce and 2 to 3 years to produce a seed). Flowering plants, on the other hand, can be woody, but many are herbaceous, with soft tissues that survive from one to a few years. It is possible for angiosperms to go from seed to seed in less than one year. As you perform the exercises in this lab, think about the significance of this fact in terms of the evolution of this group. How might generation length affect the rate of evolution? Angiosperms also have superior conducting tissues. Xylem tissue is composed of *tracheids* (as in gymnosperms), but also contains large-diameter, open-ended *vessels*. The phloem cells, called *sieve-tube members,* provide more efficient transport of the products of photosynthesis. The cell structure and organization of plants will be investigated in Lab Topic 19, Plant Anatomy.

Review the characteristics of gymnosperms and angiosperms described in this introduction, and summarize in Table 16.1 the advantages of these groups relative to their success on land. You should be able to list several characteristics for each. At the end of the lab, you will be asked to modify and complete the table, based on your investigations.

You will want to return to this table after the laboratory to be sure that the table is complete and that you are familiar with all these important features.

EXERCISE 16.1

Gymnosperms

The term *gymnosperms* refers to a diverse group of seed plants that do not produce flowers. Although they share many characteristics, including the production of pollen, they represent four distinct groups, or divisions. In this exercise, you will observe members of these divisions and investigate the life cycle of a pine, one of the most common gymnosperms.

Table 16.1
Traits for Gymnosperms and Angiosperms
Relative to Their Success on Land

	Adaptation to the Land Environment
Gymnosperms	
Angiosperms	

Lab Study A. Divisions of Gymnosperms

Materials

living or pressed examples of conifers, ginkgos, cycads, and Mormon tea

Introduction

Gymnosperms are composed of several divisions (see Figure 15.1 and Table 15.1 in Lab Topic 15). The largest and best known is Coniferophyta, which includes pines and other cone-bearing trees and shrubs (Color Plate 38). Cycads, which have a palmlike appearance, are found primarily in tropical regions scattered around the world (Color Plate 39). Ginkgos, with their flat fan-shaped leaves, are native to Asia and are prized as urban trees. An extract of Ginkgo is used as an herbal medicine purported to improve memory (Color Plates 40 and 41). Gnetophyta is composed of three distinct and unusual groups of plants: gnetums, which are primarily vines of Asia, Africa, and South America; *Welwitschia*, a rare desert plant with two leathery leaves; and Mormon tea (*Ephedra*), desert shrubs of North and Central America (Color Plate 42). Compounds from *Ephedra*, ephedrines, used in diet aids and decongestants, have raised serious concerns due to side effects including cardiac arrest.

Procedure

1. Observe demonstration examples of all divisions of gymnosperms and be able to recognize their representatives. Note any significant ecological and economic role for these plants.
2. Record your observations in Table 16.2.

Table 16.2
Divisions of Gymnosperms

Divisions	Examples	Characteristics/Comments
Coniferophyta		
Ginkgophyta		
Cycadophyta		
Gnetophyta		

Results

1. In the margin of your manual, sketch the overall structure of the plants. Label structures where appropriate.
2. Are there any reproductive structures present for these plants? If so, make notes in the margin of your lab manual.

Discussion

1. What are the key characteristics shared by all gymnosperms?

2. What is the ecological role of conifers in forest systems?

3. What economically important products are provided by conifers?

Lab Study B. Pine Life Cycle

Materials

living or preserved pine branch, male and female cones (1, 2, and 3 years old)

fresh or dried pine pollen or prepared slide of pine pollen

coverslips

prepared slides of male and female pine cones

colored pencils

slides

 Review the pine life cycle (Figure 16.1) before you begin. Follow along as you complete the exercise.

Introduction

All gymnosperms are **wind-pollinated** trees or shrubs, most bearing unisexual, male, and female reproductive structures on different parts of the same plant. Gymnosperms are **heterosporous**, producing two kinds of spores: male **microspores**, which develop into **pollen**, and female **megaspores**. The megaspore develops into the female gametophyte, which is not free-living as with ferns but retained within the **megasporangium** and nourished by the sporophyte parent plant. Numerous pollen grains (the male gametophytes) are produced in each **microsporangium**, and when they are mature they are released into the air and conveyed by wind currents to the female cone. **Pollen tubes** grow through the tissue of the megasporangium, and the **sperm nucleus** is released to fertilize the egg. After fertilization, development results in the formation of an **embryo**. A **seed** is a dormant embryo embedded in nutrient tissue of the female gametophyte and surrounded by the hardened sporangium wall, or **seed coat**.

 Having trouble with life cycles? Return to Lab Topic 15 (Plant Diversity I) and review the generalized life cycle (Figure 15.2). The key to success is to determine where meiosis occurs and to remember the ploidal level for the gametophyte and sporophyte.

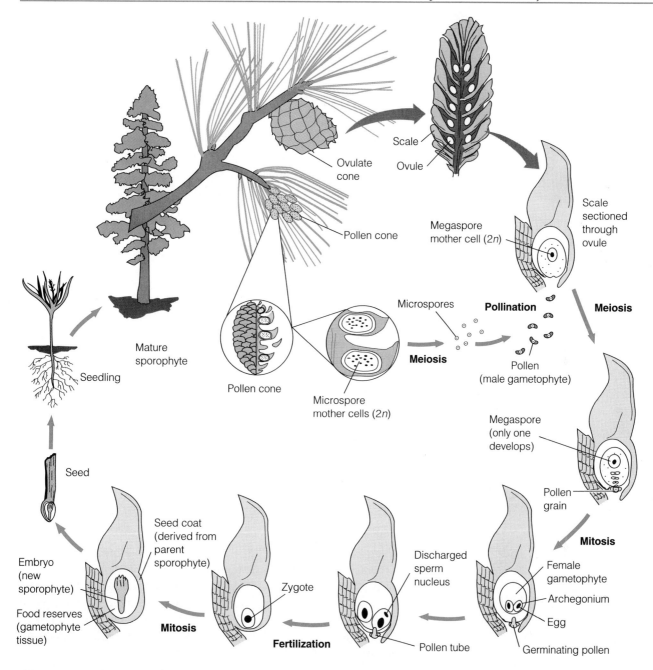

Figure 16.1.
Pine life cycle. Observe the structures and processes as described in Exercise 16.1.
Using colored pencils, indicate the structures that are haploid or diploid. Circle the terms
mitosis, meiosis, *and* fertilization.

Procedure

1. Pine sporophyte.

   a. Examine the pine branch and notice the arrangement of leaves in a
      bundle. A new twig at the end of the branch is in the process of pro-
      ducing new clusters of leaves. Is this plant haploid or diploid?

b. Examine the small **cones** produced at the end of the pine branch on this specimen or others in lab. Recall that cones contain clusters of sporangia. What important process occurs in the sporangia?

c. Locate an ovulate cone and a pollen cone. Elongated male **pollen cones** are present only in the spring, producing pollen within overlapping bracts, or scales. The small, more rounded female cones (which look like miniature pine cones) are produced on stem tips in the spring and are called **ovulate cones.** Female cones persist for several years. Observe the overlapping scales, which contain the sporangia.

d. In the margin of your lab manual, sketch observations for future reference.

2. Male gametophyte—development in pollen cones.

a. Examine a longitudinal section of the pollen cone on a prepared slide and identify its parts. Observe that pollen cones are composed of radiating scales, each of which carries two elongated sacs on its lower surface. The sacs are the **microsporangia. Microspore mother cells** within microsporangia divide by meiosis. Each produces four haploid **microspores,** which develop into **pollen grains.**

b. Observe a slide of pine pollen. If pollen is available, you can make a wet mount. Note the wings on either side of the grain. The pollen grain is the greatly reduced male gametophyte. The outer covering of the pollen is desiccation resistant. Once mature, pollen will be wind dispersed, sifting down into the scales of the female cones.

c. Sketch, in the margin of your lab manual, observations for future reference.

3. Female gametophyte—development in ovulate cones.

a. Examine a longitudinal section of a young ovulate cone on a prepared slide. Note the **ovule** (containing the megasporangium) on the upper surface of the scales. Diploid **megaspore mother cells** contained inside will produce haploid **megaspores,** the first cells of the gametophyte generation. In the first year of ovulate cone development, pollen sifts into the soft bracts (pollination) and the pollen tube begins to grow, digesting the tissues of the ovule.

b. Observe a second-year cone at your lab bench. During the second year, the ovule develops a multicellular female gametophyte with two archegonia in which an egg will form. Fertilization will not occur until the second year, when the pollen tube releases a sperm nucleus into the archegonium, where it unites with the egg to form the **zygote.** In each ovule only one of the archegonia and its zygote develops into a seed.

c. Observe a mature cone at your lab bench. The development of the embryo sporophyte usually takes another year. The female gametophyte will provide nutritive materials stored in the seed for the early stages of growth. The outer tissues of the ovule will harden to form the **seed coat.**

d. In the margin of your lab manual, sketch observations for future reference.

Results

1. Review the structures and processes observed.
2. Using colored pencils, indicate the structures of the pine life cycle in Figure 16.1 that are haploid or diploid, and circle the processes of mitosis, meiosis, and fertilization.

Discussion

1. What is the function of the wings on the pollen grain?

2. Why is wind-dispersed pollen an important phenomenon in the evolution of plants?

3. Are microspores and megaspores produced by mitosis or meiosis?

4. Can you think of at least two ways in which pine seeds are dispersed?

5. One of the major trends in plant evolution is the reduction in size of the gametophytes. Describe the male and female gametophyte in terms of size and location.

EXERCISE 16.2
Angiosperms

A unique characteristic of angiosperms (division Anthophyta) is the **carpel**, a vessel in which ovules are enclosed. After fertilization, the ovule develops into a seed (as in the gymnosperms), while the carpel matures into a fruit (unique to angiosperms). Other important aspects of angiosperm reproduction include additional reduction of the gametophyte, double fertilization, and an increase in the rapidity of the reproduction process.

The **flowers** of angiosperms are composed of male and female reproductive structures, which are frequently surrounded by attractive or protective leaflike structures collectively known as the **perianth** (Color Plate 43). The flower functions both to protect the developing gametes and to ensure pollination and fertilization. Although many angiosperm plants are self-fertile, cross-fertilization is important in maintaining genetic diversity. Plants, rooted and stationary, often require transfer agents to complete fertilization. A variety of insects, birds, and mammals transfer pollen from flower to flower. The pollen then germinates into a pollen tube and grows through the female carpel to deliver the sperm to the egg.

Plants must attract pollinators to the flower. What are some features of flowers that attract pollinators? Color and scent are important, as is the shape of the flower. Nectar and pollen provide nutritive rewards for the pollinators as well. The shape and form of some of the flowers are structured to accommodate pollinators of specific size and structure, providing landing platforms, guidelines, and even special mechanisms for the placement of pollen on body parts. While the flower is encouraging the visitation by one type of pollinator, it also may be excluding visitation by others. The more specific the relationship between flower and pollinator, the more probable that the pollen of that species will be successfully transferred. But many successful flowers have no specific adaptations for particular pollinators and are visited by a wide variety of pollinators.

Some plants do not have colorful, showy flowers and are rather inconspicuous, often dull in color, and lacking a perianth. These plants are usually wind-pollinated, producing enormous quantities of pollen and adapted to catch pollen in the wind (Color Plate 44).

The origin and diversification of angiosperms cannot be understood apart from the coevolutionary role of animals in the reproductive process. Colorful petals, strong scents, nectars, food bodies, and unusual perianth shapes all relate to pollinator visitation. Major trends in the evolution of angiosperms involve the development of mechanisms to exploit a wide variety of pollinators (Color Plates 45, 46, and 47).

In Lab Study A, you will investigate a variety of flowers, observing their shape, structure, and traits that might attract pollinators of various kinds. Following this, in Lab Study B, you will use a key to identify the probable pollinators for some of these flowers. You will follow the life cycle of the lily in Lab Study C and complete the lab by using another key to identify types of fruits and their dispersal mechanisms.

Lab Study A. Flower Morphology

Materials

living flowers provided by the instructor and/or students
stereoscopic microscope

Introduction

Working in teams of two students, you will investigate the structure of the flower (Figure 16.2, Color Plate 43). The instructor will provide a variety of flowers, and you may have brought some with you to lab. You will need to take apart each flower carefully to determine its structure, since it is unlikely that all your flowers will follow the simple diagram used to illustrate the structures. Your observations will be the basis for predicting probable pollinators in Lab Study B.

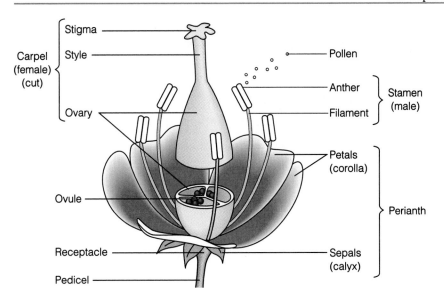

Procedure

1. Examine fresh flowers of four different species, preferably with different floral characteristics.

2. Identify the parts of each flower using Figure 16.2 and the list provided following the heading Floral Parts. You may be able to determine the floral traits for large, open flowers by simply observing. However, most flowers will require that you remove the floral structures from the outside toward the center of the flower. Some flowers or structures may require the use of the stereoscopic microscope. For example, the ovary is positively identified by the presence of tiny crystal-like ovules, and these are best seen with the stereoscopic scope.

3. In the margin of your lab manual, sketch any flower shapes or structures that you might need to refer to in the future.

4. Record the results of your observations in Table 16.3. You will determine pollinators in Lab Study B.

Floral Parts

Pedicel: stalk that supports the flower.

Receptacle: tip of the pedicel where the flower parts attach.

Sepal: outer whorl of bracts, which may be green, brown, or colored like the petals; may appear as small scales or be petal-like.

Calyx: all the sepals, collectively.

Petal: colored, white, or even greenish whorl of bracts located just inside the sepals.

Corolla: all the petals, collectively.

Stamen: pollen-bearing structure, composed of filament and anther.

Filament: thin stalk that supports the anther.

Anther: pollen-producing structure.

Carpel: female reproductive structure, composed of the stigma, style, and ovary, often pear-shaped and located in the center of the flower.

Stigma: receptive tip of the carpel, often sticky or hairy, where pollen is placed; important to pollen germination.

Style: tissue connecting stigma to ovary, often long and narrow, but may be short or absent; pollen must grow through this tissue to fertilize the egg.

Ovary: base of carpel; protects ovules inside, matures to form the fruit.

Results

Summarize your observations of flower structure in Table 16.3.

Discussion

What structures or characteristics did you observe in your (or other teams') investigations that you predict are important to pollination?

Lab Study B. Pollinators

Materials

living flowers provided by the instructor and/or students
stereoscopic microscope

Introduction

Flowers with inconspicuous sepals and petals are usually pollinated by wind (Color Plate 44). Most showy flowers are pollinated by animals. Some pollinators tend to be attracted to particular floral traits, and, in turn, some groups of plants have coevolved with a particular pollination agent that ensures successful reproduction. Other flowers are generalists, pollinated by a variety of organisms, and still others may be visited by only one specific pollinator (Color Plates 45, 46, and 47). Based on the floral traits that attract common pollinators (bees, flies, butterflies, and hummingbirds), you will predict the probable pollinator for some of your flowers using a dichotomous key. (Remember, *dichotomous* refers to the branching pattern and means "divided into two parts.")

In biology, we use a key to systematically separate groups of organisms based on sets of characteristics. Most keys are based on couplets, or pairs of characteristics, from which you must choose one or the other, thus, the term *dichotomous*. For example, the first choice of characteristics in a couplet might be *plants with showy flowers and a scent,* and the other choice in the pair might be *plants with tiny, inconspicuous flowers with no scent.* You must choose one or the other statement. In the next step, you would choose from a second pair of statements listed directly below your first choice. With each choice, you would narrow the group more and more until, as in this case, the pollinator is identified. *Each couplet or pair of statements from which you must choose will be identified by the same letter or number.*

Table 16.3
Flower Morphology and Pollinators

Features	Plant Names			
	1	2	3	4
Number of petals				
Number of sepals				
Parts absent (petals, stamens, etc.)				
Color				
Scent (+/−)				
Nectar (+/−)				
Shape (including corolla shape: tubular, star, etc.)				
Special features (landing platform, guidelines, nectar spur, etc.)				
Predicted pollinator (see Lab Study B)				

Key to Pollination

I. Sepals and petals reduced or inconspicuous; feathery or relatively large stigma; flower with no odor **wind**
I. Sepals and/or petals large, easily identified; stigma not feathery; flower with or without odor
  A. Sepals and petals white or subdued (greenish or burgundy); distinct odor
    1. Odor strong, heavy, sweet **moth**
    1. Odor strong, fermenting or fruitlike; flower parts and pedicel strong **bat**
    1. Odor of sweat, feces, or decaying meat **fly**
  A. Sepals and/or petals colored; odor may or may not be present
    1. Flower shape regular or irregular,* but not tubular
      a. Flower shape irregular; sepals or petals blue, yellow, or orange; petal adapted to serve as a "landing platform"; may have dark lines on petals; sweet, fragrant odor **bee**
      a. Flower shape regular; odor often fruity, spicy, sweet, or carrionlike **beetle**
    1. Flower shape tubular
      a. Strong, sweet odor **butterfly**
      a. Little or no odor; flower usually red **hummingbird**

*A regular flower shape is one that has radial symmetry (like a daisy or carnation), with similar parts (such as petals) having similar size and shape. Irregular flowers have bilateral symmetry.

Procedure

Using the key above, classify the flowers used in Lab Study A based on their floral traits and method of pollination.

Results

1. Record your results in Table 16.3.
2. If you made sketches of any of your flowers, you may want to indicate the pollinator associated with that flower.

Discussion

1. Review the Key to Pollination and describe the characteristics of flowers that are adapted for pollination by each of the following agents:
a. wind

b. hummingbird

c. bat

2. Discuss with your lab partner other ways in which keys are used in biology. Record your answers in the space provided.

Lab Study C. Angiosperm Life Cycle

Materials

pollen tube growth medium in
  dropper bottles
dropper bottle of water
petri dish with filter paper to
  fit inside
prepared slides of lily anthers
  and ovary

dissecting probe
brush bristles
compound microscope
flowers for pollen

Introduction

In this lab study, you will study the life cycle of flowering plants, including the formation of pollen, pollination, fertilization of the egg, and formation of the seed and fruit. You will also investigate the germination of the pollen grain as it grows toward the egg cell.

Refer to Figures 16.2 (flower structures) and 16.3 (angiosperm life cycle) as you complete the exercise.

Procedure

1. Pollen grain—the male gametophyte.

    a. Examine a prepared slide of a cross section through the **stamens** of *Lilium.* The slide shows six anthers and may include a centrally located ovary that contains ovules.

    b. Observe a single **anther,** which is composed of four **anther sacs** (microsporangia). Note the formation of **microspores** (with a single nucleus) from diploid **microspore mother cells.** You may also see mature **pollen grains** with two nuclei.

2. Development of the female gametophyte (Color Plate 48).

    a. Examine a prepared slide of the *Lilium* ovary and locate the developing ovules. Each **ovule,** composed of the megasporangium and other tissues, contains a **megaspore mother cell** (diploid), which produces **megaspores** (haploid), only one of which survives. The megaspore will divide three times by mitosis to produce the eight nuclei in the **embryo sac,** which is the greatly reduced female gametophyte. Note that angiosperms do not even produce an archegonium.

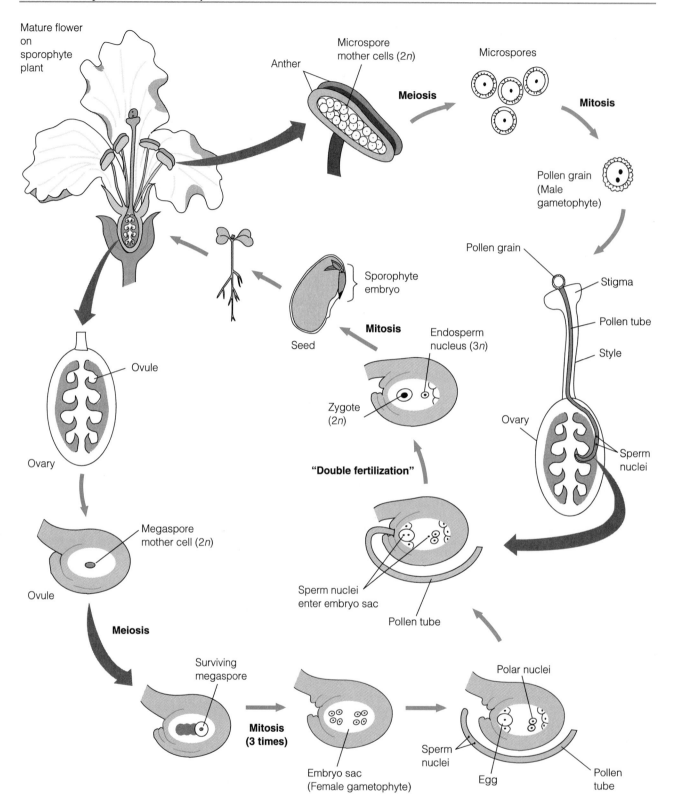

Figure 16.3.
Angiosperm life cycle. Observe the structures and processes as described in Exercise 16.2. *Using colored pencils, indicate the structures that are haploid or diploid. Circle the terms* mitosis, meiosis, *and* double fertilization.

b. Your slide will not contain all stages of development, and it is almost impossible to find a section that includes all eight nuclei. Locate the three nuclei near the opening to the ovule. One of these is called the **egg cell.** The two nuclei in the center are the **polar nuclei.**

3. Pollination and fertilization.

When pollen grains are mature, the anthers split and the pollen is released. When pollen reaches the stigma, it germinates to produce a **pollen tube,** which grows down the style and eventually comes into contact with the opening to the ovule. During this growth, one pollen nucleus divides into two **sperm nuclei.** One sperm nucleus fuses with the egg to form the **zygote,** and the second fuses with the two polar nuclei to form the triploid **endosperm,** which will develop into a rich nutritive material for the support and development of the embryo. The fusion of the two sperm nuclei with nuclei of the embryo sac is referred to as **double fertilization.** Formation of triploid endosperm and double fertilization are unique to angiosperms.

Once the pollen grain is deposited on the stigma of the flower, it must grow through the stylar tissue to reach the ovule. You will examine pollen tube growth by placing pollen in pollen growth medium to stimulate germination. Pollen from some plants germinates easily; for others a very specific chemical environment is required. Work with a partner, following the next steps.

a. Using a dissecting probe, transfer some pollen from the anthers of one of the plants available in the lab to a slide on which there are 2 to 3 drops of pollen tube growth medium and a few brush bristles or grains of sand (to avoid crushing the pollen).

b. Examine the pollen under the compound microscope. Observe the shape and surface features of the pollen.

c. Prepare a humidity chamber by placing moistened filter paper in a petri dish. Place the slide in the petri dish, and place it in a warm environment.

d. Examine the pollen after 30 minutes and again after 60 minutes to observe pollen tube growth. The pollen tubes should appear as long, thin tubes extending from the surface or pores in the pollen grain (Color Plate 49).

e. Record your results in Table 16.4 in the Results section. Indicate the plant name and the times when pollen tube germination was observed.

4. Seed and fruit development.

The zygote formed at fertilization undergoes rapid mitotic divisions, forming the embryo. The endosperm also divides; the mature ovule forms a seed. At the same time, the surrounding ovary and other floral tissues are forming the fruit. In Lab Study D, you will investigate the types of fruits and their function in dispersal.

Results

1. Review the structures and processes observed in the angiosperm life cycle, Figure 16.3. Indicate the haploid and diploid structures in the life cycle, using two different colored pencils.

Having trouble with life cycles? Return to Lab Topic 15, Plant Diversity I, and review the generalized life cycle in Figure 15.2. The key to success is to determine where meiosis occurs and to remember the ploidal level for the gametophyte and sporophyte.

2. Sketch observations of slides in the margin of your lab manual for later reference.
3. Record the results of pollen germination studies in Table 16.4. Compare your results with those of other teams who used different plants. This is particularly important if your pollen did not germinate.

Table 16.4
Results of Pollen Germination Studies

Plant Name	30 min (+/−)	60 min (+/−)

Discussion

1. What part of the life cycle is represented by the mature pollen grain?

2. How does the female gametophyte in angiosperms differ from the female gametophyte in gymnosperms?

3. Do you think that all pollen germinates indiscriminately on all stigmas? How might pollen germination and growth be controlled?

Lab Study D. Fruits and Dispersal

Materials

variety of fruits provided by the instructor and/or students

Introduction

The seed develops from the ovule, and inside is the embryo and its nutritive tissues. The fruit develops from the ovary or from other tissues in the flower. It provides protection for the seeds, and both the seed and the fruit may be involved in dispersal of the sporophyte embryo.

Procedure

1. Examine the fruits and seeds on demonstration.
2. Use the Key to Fruits on the next page to help you complete Table 16.5. Remember to include the dispersal mechanisms for fruits and their seeds in the table.

Results

1. Record in Table 16.5 the fruit type for each of the fruits keyed. Share results with other teams so that you have information for all fruits in the lab.

Table 16.5
Fruit Types and Dispersal Mechanisms

Plant Name	Fruit Type	Dispersal Method

2. For each fruit, indicate the probable method of dispersal—for example, wind, water, gravity, ingestion by birds, mammals, or insects, or adhesion to fur and socks.
3. For some fruits, the seeds rather than the fruit are adapted for dispersal. In the milkweed, for example, the winged seeds are contained in a dry ovary. Indicate in Table 16.5 if the seeds have structures to enhance dispersal. Recall that seeds are inside fruits. The dandelion "seed" is really a fruit with a fused ovary and seed coat.

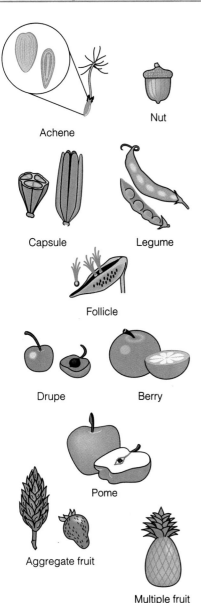

Achene

Nut

Capsule

Legume

Follicle

Drupe

Berry

Pome

Aggregate fruit

Multiple fruit

Key to Fruits

I. Simple fruits (one ovary)
  A. Dry fruits (at maturity)
    1. Fruits with one seed
      a. Ovary wall and seed coat are fused   **achene***
      a. Ovary wall hard or woody but can be separated from the seed   **nut**
    1. Fruits with two to many seeds
      a. Ovary with several cavities (seen when cut in cross section) and several to many seeds   **capsule**
      a. Ovary with one cavity
        b. Mature ovary opens along both sides   **legume**
        b. Mature ovary opens along one side   **follicle**
  A. Fleshy fruits
    1. Ovary with one seed, which is surrounded by a very hard stone (outer covering of the seed is formed from the inner ovary wall)   **drupe**
    1. Ovary with many seeds; does not have a "stone"
      a. All of mature ovary tissue is soft and fleshy; surrounding flower tissue does not develop into fruit   **berry†**
      a. Fleshy fruit develops in part from surrounding tissue of the flower (base of sepals and petals); therefore, ovary wall seen as "core" around seeds   **pome**
I. Compound fruits (more than one ovary)
  A. Fruit formed from ovaries of many flowers   **multiple fruit**
  A. Fruit formed from several ovaries in one flower   **aggregate fruit**

*In the grass family, an achene is called a **grain**.
†Berries of some families have special names: citrus family = **hesperidium**; squash family = **pepo**.

Discussion

1. How might dry fruits be dispersed? Fleshy fruits?

2. Describe the characteristics of an achene, drupe, and berry.

Questions for Review

1. Return to Table 16.1 and modify your entries and complete your comparison of gymnosperms and angiosperms.

2. Identify the function of each of the following structures found in seed plants. Consider their function in the land environment.

pollen grain:

microsporangium:

flower:

carpel:

seed:

fruit:

endosperm:

3. Plants have evolved a number of characteristics that attract animals and ensure pollination, but what are the benefits to animals in this relationship?

4. Why is internal fertilization essential for true terrestrial living?

Applying Your Knowledge

1. Explain how the rise in prominence of one major group (angiosperms, for example) does not necessarily result in the total replacement of a previously dominant group (gymnosperms, for example).

2. Complete Table 16.6. Compare mosses, ferns, conifers, and flowering plants relative to sexual life cycles and adaptations to the land environment.

3. How have gymnosperm ovules evolved to withstand desiccation and herbivorous animals?

Table 16.6
Comparison of Important Characteristics of Land Plants

Features	Moss	Fern	Conifer	Flowering Plant
Gametophyte or sporophyte dominant				
Vascular tissue (+/−)				
Seed (+/−)				
Fruit (+/−)				
Water required for fertilization				
Pollen grain (+/−)				
Homosporous or heterosporous				
Examples				

4. Your neighbor's vegetable garden is being attacked by Japanese beetles, so she dusts her garden with an insecticide. Now, to her dismay, she realizes that the beans and squash are no longer producing. Explain to your neighbor the relationship among flowers, fruits (vegetables, in the gardening language), and insects.

5. In angiosperms, an abundance of pollen is transferred by insects to the stigma. Later, pollen grains germinate to produce pollen tubes that race through the style in their bid to fertilize a limited number of egg cells within the ovules. Explain how this process of gamete competition could be of selective advantage.

6. Review the introduction to Lab Topic 15, Plant Diversity I, and describe the major trends in the evolution of land plants.

Investigative Extensions

Pollen germinates easily in the lab for some species and not at all for others. In some species, a biochemical signal is required from the stigma to initiate germination. If the pollen has not germinated after 30 minutes, you can design an experiment to test the hypothesis that a substance in the stigma is necessary for pollen germination. Mince a small part of the stigma in sucrose and then add it to the slide preparation. The percent sucrose in the growth medium can also be varied. Try 10%, then doubling and halving the sucrose concentration in the growth medium. Some cultivated plants are simply sterile, so do not expect positive results for all species.

References

Mauseth, J. D. *Botany: An Introduction to Plant Biology,* 2nd ed. Philadelphia, PA: Saunders College Publishing, 1995.

Moore, R., W. D. Clark, and D. Vodopich. *Botany,* 2nd ed. Dubuque, IA: WCB/McGraw-Hill, 1998.

Raven, P. H., R. F. Evert, and S. E. Eichhorn. *Biology of Plants,* 6th ed. New York: W. H. Freeman Publishers, 1999.

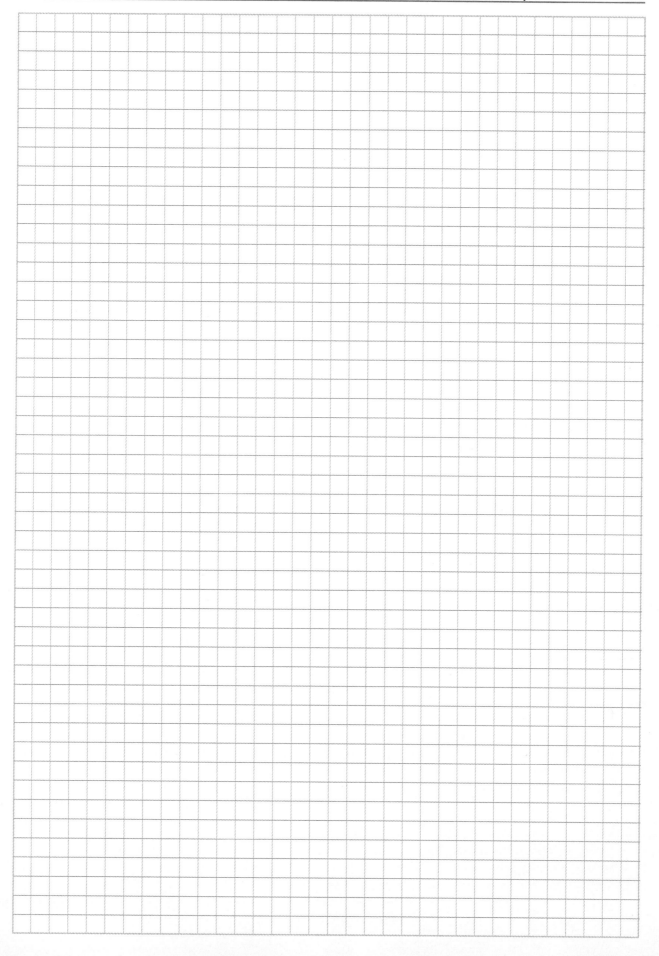

Animal Diversity I

Laboratory Objectives

After completing this lab topic, you should be able to:

1. Compare the anatomy of the representative animals, describing similarities and differences in organs and body form that allow the animal to carry out body functions.
2. Discuss how these similarities and differences may indicate phylogenetic relationships.
3. Discuss the relationship between body form and the lifestyle or niche of the organism.
4. List five characteristics that are criteria for major branching points among less complex animal groups in the phylogenetic tree.

Introduction

Animals are classified in the domain **Eukarya,** kingdom **Animalia.** They are multicellular organisms and are **heterotrophic,** meaning that they obtain food by ingesting other organisms or their by-products. Careful study of comparative anatomy and embryology reveals many similarities in structure and development, implying an ancestral evolutionary relationship among all animals. Animals are thought to have arisen about 565 million years ago, with most body forms appearing by the end of the Cambrian period (see Figure 15.3). Scientists recognize over 35 major groups of present-day animals based on differences in body architecture. In this and the following lab topic, you will investigate body form and function in examples of eight major groups of animals. You will use these investigations to ask and answer questions about the lifestyle of each animal and the **phylogenetic,** or evolutionary, relationships among the animals.

Since the beginning of the scientific study of animals, scientists have attempted to sort and group closely related organisms. Taxonomists have divided the animal kingdom into two **subkingdoms: Parazoa,** which includes the sponges, and **Eumetazoa,** which includes all other animals. This division is made because the body form of sponges is so different from that of other animals that most biologists think that sponges are not closely related to any other animal groups.

Eumetazoa is further divided on the basis of physical characteristics, such as symmetry and the type of body cavity (coelom), and such basic embryological differences as the number of germ layers present in the embryo and the embryonic development of the digestive tract. Some animals have a saclike body form with only one opening into a digestive cavity. Others have two outer openings, a mouth and an anus, and the digestive tract forms essentially a "tube within a tube." Animals with a mouth and an anus are divided into two major groups, depending on the origin of the mouth and the anus. An embryonic structure, the blastopore, develops into a mouth in the **protostomes** and into an anus in the **deuterostomes.**

Zoologists have, somewhat artificially, divided animals into **invertebrates** and **vertebrates,** based on the absence or presence of a backbone. Vertebrates, those animals with a backbone, include only about 5% of total animal species, the remaining 95% being invertebrates. Invertebrates are a heterogeneous group with a diversity of phylogenetic origins. In addition to phylogenetic relationships, many structural and functional adaptive themes related to the size, lifestyle, or environment of the animal appear repeatedly in animal design. Thus, the study of the anatomy of animals can lead both to predictions about their phylogenetic relationships and to conclusions about their lifestyles and environment.

In the next two laboratory periods, you will examine and dissect several invertebrates and observe one vertebrate, relating the morphology of these organisms to their body functions, lifestyles, and phylogenetic relationships.

The animals you will study are the sponge, hydra, planarian, roundworm, clamworm, earthworm, clam (mussel), crayfish, grasshopper, amphioxus (lancelet), and pig. As you study each animal, relate your observations to the unifying themes of this lab: *phylogenetic relationships* and criteria that are the basis for animal classification, the *relationship between form and function,* and the *relationship of the environment and lifestyle to form and function.* The questions at the end of the lab topics will help you do this.

In your comparative study of these organisms, you will investigate 13 characteristics. Before you begin the dissections, become familiar with the following characteristics and their descriptions:

1. *Symmetry.* Is the animal (a) radially symmetrical (parts arranged around a central axis), (b) bilaterally symmetrical (right and left halves are mirror images), or (c) asymmetrical (no apparent symmetry)?

2. *Tissue organization.* Are cells organized into well-defined tissue layers (structural and functional units)? How many distinctive layers are present?

3. *Body cavity.* Is a body cavity present? A body cavity—the space between the gut and body wall—is present only in three-layered organisms, that is, in organisms with the embryonic germ layers ectoderm, mesoderm, and endoderm. There are three types of body forms related to the presence of a body cavity and its type (Figure 17.1).

   a. Acoelomate, three-layered bodies without a body cavity. Tissue from the mesoderm fills the space where a cavity might be; therefore, the tissue layers closely pack on one another.

   b. Pseudocoelomate, three-layered bodies with a cavity between the endoderm (gut) and mesoderm (muscle).

   c. Eucoelomate (coelomate), three-layered bodies with the coelom, or cavity, *within* the mesoderm (completely surrounded by mesoderm). In coelomate organisms, mesodermal membranes suspend the gut within the body cavity.

a. Acoelomate

b. Pseudocoelomate

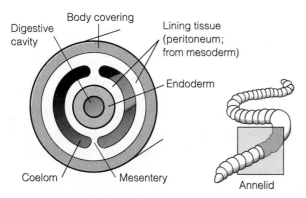

c. Eucoelomate (coelomate)

Figure 17.1.
Three types of body cavities.
(a) In acoelomate animals, the mesoderm fills the space where a cavity might be. (b) In pseudocoelomate animals, the body cavity lies between tissues derived from endoderm and mesoderm.
(c) In eucoelomate (coelomate) animals, the body cavity is lined with mesoderm.

4. *Openings into the digestive tract.* Can you detect where food enters the body and digestive waste exits the body? Some animals have only one opening, which serves as both a mouth and an anus. Others have a body called a "tube within a tube," with an anterior mouth and a posterior anus.

5. *Circulatory system.* Does this animal have open circulation (the blood flows through coelomic spaces in the tissue as well as in blood vessels), or does it have closed circulation (the blood flows entirely through vessels)?

6. *Habitat.* Is the animal terrestrial (lives on land) or aquatic (lives in water)? Aquatic animals may live in marine (sea) or fresh water.

7. *Organs for respiration (gas exchange).* Can you detect the surface where oxygen enters the body and carbon dioxide leaves the body? Many animals use their skin for respiration. Others have special organs, including gills in aquatic organisms and lungs in terrestrial organisms. Insects have a unique system for respiration, using structures called *spiracles* and *tracheae.*

8. *Organs for excretion.* How does the animal rid its body of nitrogenous waste? In many animals, these wastes pass out of the body through the skin by diffusion. In others, there are specialized structures, such as Malpighian tubules, lateral excretory canals, lateral canals with flame cells, structures called *nephridia,* and kidneys.

9. *Type of locomotion.* Does the organism swim, crawl on its belly, walk on legs, burrow in the substrate, or fly? Does it use cellular structures, such as cilia, to glide its body over the substrate?

10. *Support systems.* Is there a skeleton present? Is it an endoskeleton (inside the epidermis or skin of the animal), or is it an exoskeleton (outside the body wall)? Animals with no true skeleton can be supported by water: Fluid within and between cells and in body chambers such as a gastrovascular cavity or coelom provides a "hydrostatic skeleton."

11. *Segmentation.* Can you observe linear repetition of similar body parts? The repetition of similar units, or segments, is called *segmentation.* Segments can be more similar (as in the earthworm) or less similar (as in a lobster). Can you observe any degree of segmentation? Have various segments become modified for different functions?

12. *Appendages.* Are there appendages (organs or parts attached to a trunk or outer body wall)? Are these appendages all along the length of the body, or are they restricted to one area? Are they all similar, or are they modified for different functions?

13. *Type of nervous system.* Do you see a brain and nerve cord? Is there more than one nerve cord? What is the location of the nerve cord(s)? Are sensory organs or structures present? Where and how many? What purpose do such structures serve (for example, eyes for light detection)?

As you carefully study or dissect each organism, refer to these thirteen characteristics, observe the animal, and record your observations in the summary table, Table 18.1, pp. 486–487. You may find it helpful to make sketches of difficult structures or dissections in the margin of your lab manual for future reference.

Before you begin this study, read Appendix C and become thoroughly familiar with dissection techniques, orientation terms, and planes and sections of the body.

 Wear gloves while dissecting preserved animals.

EXERCISE 17.1
Phylum Porifera—Sponges (*Scypha*)

Materials

dissecting needle
compound microscope
stereoscopic microscope
preserved and dry bath sponges

prepared slide of *Scypha* in
   longitudinal section
preserved *Scypha* in watch glass

Introduction

Sponges are classified in a separate subkingdom, Parazoa, because of their unique body form. You will observe the unique sponge structure by observing first a preserved specimen and then a prepared slide of a section taken through the longitudinal axis of the marine sponge *Scypha* (Color Plate 50). You will observe other more complex and diverse sponges on demonstration.

Procedure

1. Obtain the preserved sponge *Scypha* and observe its external characteristics using the stereoscopic microscope, comparing your observations with Figure 17.2a.

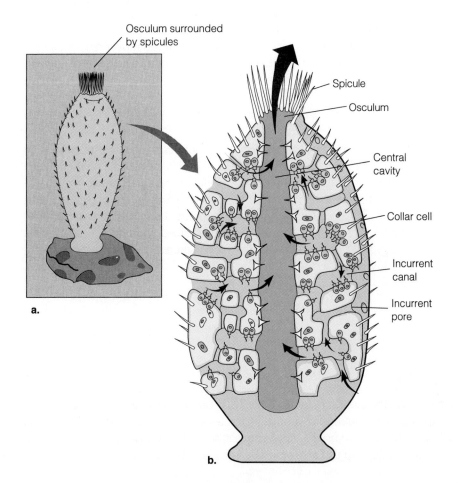

Osculum surrounded
by spicules

Spicule

Osculum

Central
cavity

Collar cell

Incurrent
canal

Incurrent
pore

a.

b.

Figure 17.2.
The sponge *Scypha*. (a) The entire sponge; (b) a longitudinal section through the sponge.

a. Note the vaselike shape of the sponge and the **osculum,** a large opening to the body at one end. The end opposite the osculum attaches the animal to the substrate.

b. Note the invaginations in the body wall, which form numerous folds and channels. You may be able to observe needlelike **spicules** around the osculum and protruding from the surface of the body. These spicules are made of calcium carbonate: They give support and protection to the sponge body and prevent small animals from entering the sponge's internal cavity.

2.   Using the compound microscope, examine a prepared slide of a sponge body in longitudinal section and compare it with Figure 17.2b.

a. Again, locate the osculum. This structure is not a mouth, as its name implies, but an opening used as an outlet for the current of water passing through the body wall and the **central cavity,** or **spongocoel.** The water enters the central cavity from channels and pores in the body. The central cavity is not a digestive tube or body cavity, but is only a channel for water.

b. Note the structure of the body wall. Are cells organized into definite tissue layers, or are they best described as a loose organization of various cell types? Various cells in the body wall carry out the functions of digestion, contractility, secretion of the spicules, and reproduction (some cells develop into sperm and eggs). One cell type unique to sponges is the **choanocyte,** or **collar cell.** These cells line the central cavity and the channels leading into it. Each collar cell has a flagellum extending from its surface. The collective beating of all flagella moves water through the sponge body. Small food particles taken up and digested by collar cells are one major source of nutrition for the sponge. How would you hypothesize about the movement of oxygen and waste throughout the sponge body and into and out of cells?

3.   Observe examples of more complex sponges on demonstration. (See Color Plate 51.) The body of these sponges, sometimes called "bath sponges," contains a complex series of large and small canals and chambers. The same cells that were described in *Scypha* are present in bath sponges, but, in addition to spicules, there is supportive material that consists of a soft proteinaceous substance called **spongin.** These sponges often grow to fit the shape of the space where they live, and observing them gives you a good clue about the symmetry of the sponge body. How would you describe it?

Results

Complete the summary table, Table 18.1, pp. 486–487, in Lab Topic 18, filling in all information for sponge characteristics in the appropriate row. This information will be used to answer questions in the Applying Your Knowledge section at the end of Lab Topic 18, Animal Diversity II.

EXERCISE 17.2
Phylum Cnidaria—Hydras (*Hydra*)

Materials

stereoscopic microscope
compound microscope
living *Hydra* culture
water flea culture
dropper bottles of water, 1% acetic
    acid, and methylene blue

prepared slide of *Hydra* sections
watch glass
depression slide
pipettes and bulbs
microscope slide and coverslip

Introduction

Cnidarians are a diverse group of organisms, all of which have a **tissue grade** of organization, meaning that tissues, but no complex organs, are present. Included in this group are corals, jellies, sea anemones, and Portuguese men-of-war. Most species are marine; however, there are a few freshwater species. Two body forms are present in the life cycle of many of these

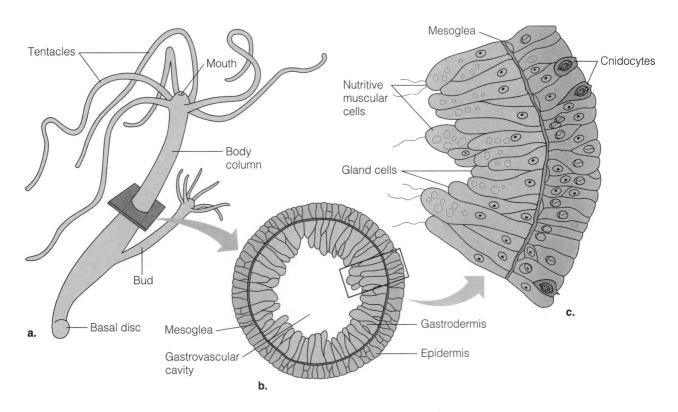

Figure 17.3.
Hydra. (a) A whole mount of *Hydra;* (b) enlargement showing a cross section through the body wall, revealing two tissue layers; and (c) further enlargement showing details of specialized cells in the body wall, including cnidocytes.

animals—an umbrella-like, free-swimming stage, and a cylindrical, attached or stationary form. The stationary forms often grow into colonies of individuals. In this exercise you will observe some of the unique features of this group by observing the solitary, freshwater organism *Hydra* (Color Plate 52).

Procedure

1. Place several drops of freshwater pond or culture water in a watch glass or depression slide. Use a dropper to obtain a living hydra from the class culture, and place the hydra in the drop of water. Using a stereoscopic microscope, observe the hydra structure and compare it with Figure 17.3a. Note any movement, the symmetry, and any body structures present. Note the **tentacles** that surround the "mouth," the only opening into the central cavity. Tentacles are used in capturing food and in performing a certain type of locomotion, much like a "handspring." To accomplish this motion, the hydra attaches its tentacles to the substrate and flips the basal portion of its body completely over, reattaching the base to a new position. If water fleas (*Daphnia*) are available, place one or two near the tentacles of the hydra and note the hydra's behavior. Set aside the hydra in the depression slide and return to it in a few moments.

2. Study a prepared slide of *Hydra* sections using the compound microscope and compare your observations with Figure 17.3b and c.

    Are definite tissue layers present? If so, how many?

    Given what you know of embryology, what embryonic layers would you guess give rise to the tissue layers of this animal's body?

3. Not visible with the microscope is a network of nerve cells in the body wall, which serves as the nervous system. There is no concentration of nerve cells into any kind of brain or nerve cord.

4. Observe the central cavity, called a **gastrovascular cavity.** Digestion begins in this water-filled cavity (**extracellular digestion**), but many food particles are drawn into cells in the **gastrodermis** lining the cavity, where **intracellular digestion** occurs.

5. Do you see signs of a skeleton or supportive system? How do you think the body is supported? Are appendages present?

6. Recalling the whole organism and observing this cross section, are organs for gas exchange present? How is gas exchange accomplished?

7. Do you see any organs for excretion?

8. Are specialized cell types seen in the layers of tissues?

Cnidarians have a unique cell type called **cnidocytes,** which contain a stinging organelle called a **nematocyst.** When stimulated, the nematocyst will evert from the cnidocyte with explosive force, trapping food or stinging predators. Look for these cells.

9. To better observe cnidocytes and nematocysts, turn your attention again to your living hydra and follow this procedure:

   a. Using a pipette, transfer the hydra to a drop of water on a microscope slide and carefully add a coverslip.

   b. Use your microscope to examine the hydra, first on low, then intermediate, and finally on high powers, focusing primarily on the tentacles. The cnidocytes will appear as swellings. If your microscope is equipped with phase contrast, switch to phase. Alternatively, add a drop of methylene blue to the edge of the coverslip. Locate several cnidocytes with nematocysts coiled inside.

   c. Add a drop of 1% acetic acid to the edge of the coverslip and, watching carefully using intermediate power, observe the rapid discharge of the nematocyst from the cnidocyte.

   d. Using high power, study the discharged nematocysts that will appear as long threads, often with large spines, or barbs, at the base of the thread.

Results

Complete the summary table, Table 18.1, recording all information for *Hydra* characteristics in the appropriate row. You will use this information to answer questions in the Applying Your Knowledge section at the end of Lab Topic 18, Animal Diversity II.

Discussion

What major differences have you detected between *Scypha* and *Hydra* body forms? List and describe them.

E X E R C I S E 1 7 . 3
Phylum Platyhelminthes—Planarians (*Dugesia*)

Materials

stereoscopic microscope
compound microscope
living planarian
watch glass

prepared slide of whole mount of
  planarian
prepared slide of planarian cross
  sections

Introduction

Planarians are free-living flatworms; that is, they are not parasitic and their body is dorsoventrally flattened. They are found under rocks, leaves, and debris in freshwater ponds and creeks. They move over these surfaces using a combination of muscles in their body wall and cilia on their ventral sides (Color Plate 53).

Procedure

1. Add a dropperful of pond or culture water to a watch glass. Use a dropper to obtain a living planarian from the class culture. Using your stereoscopic microscope, observe the planarian. Describe its locomotion. Is it directional? What is the position of its head? Does its body appear to contract?

    As you observe the living planarian, you will see two striking new features with regard to symmetry that you did not see in the two phyla previously studied. What are they?

Figure 17.4.

A planarian. The digestive system consists of a mouth, a pharynx, and a branched intestine. A brain and two ventral nerve cords (plus transverse nerves connecting them, not shown) make up the nervous system.

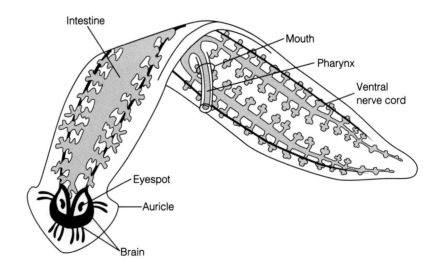

2. Add a *small* piece of fresh liver to the water near the planarian. The planarian may approach the liver and begin to feed by extending a long tubular **pharynx** out of the **mouth,** a circular opening on the ventral side of the body. If the planarian feeds, it will curve its body over the liver and extend the pharynx, which may be visible in the stereoscopic microscope.

    After observing the planarian's feeding behavior, return it to the culture dish, if possible, without the liver.

3. Using the lowest power on the compound microscope, observe the prepared slide of a whole planarian and compare it with Figure 17.4.

 Do not observe these slides using high power! The high power objective may crack the coverslip, resulting in damage to the lens.

Examine the body for possible digestive tract openings. How many openings to the digestive tract are present?

Observe again the pharynx and the mouth. The pharynx lies in a **pharyngeal chamber** inside the mouth. The proximal end of the pharynx opens into a dark-colored, branched intestine. If the intestine has been stained on your slide, you will see the branching more easily.

4. Continue your study of the whole planarian. The anterior blunt end of the animal is the head end. At each side of the head is a projecting **auricle.** It contains a variety of sensory cells, chiefly of touch and chemical sense. Between the two auricles on the dorsal surface are two pigmented **eyespots.** These are pigment cups into which retinal cells extend from the brain, with the photosensitive end of the cells inside the cup. Eyespots are sensitive to light intensities and the direction of a light source but can form no images. Beneath the eyespots are two cerebral ganglia that serve as the **brain.** Two ventral nerve cords extend posteriorly from the brain. These are connected by transverse nerves to form a ladderlike **nervous system.**

5. Study the prepared slide of cross sections of a planarian. You will have several sections on one slide. One section should have been taken at the level of the pharynx and pharyngeal chamber. Do you see a body cavity in any of the sections? (The pharyngeal chamber and spaces in the gut are not a body cavity.) What word describes this body cavity condition (see Figure 17.1a)?

a. How many tissue layers can be detected? Speculate about their embryonic origin.

Flatworms are the first group of animals to have three well-defined embryonic tissue layers, enabling them to have a variety of tissues and organs. Reproductive organs and excretory organs consisting of two lateral excretory canals and "flame cells" that move fluid through the canals are derived from the embryonic mesoderm. Respiratory, circulatory, and skeletal systems are lacking.

b. How do you think the body is supported?

c. How does gas exchange take place?

Results

1. Diagram the flatworm as seen in a cross section at the level of the pharynx. Label the **epidermis, muscle** derived from **mesoderm,** the lining of the digestive tract derived from **endoderm,** the **pharynx,** and the **pharyngeal chamber.**

2. Complete the summary table, Table 18.1, recording all information for planarian characteristics in the appropriate row. You will use this information to answer questions in the Applying Your Knowledge section at the end of Lab Topic 18, Animal Diversity II.

Discussion

One of the major differences between Cnidaria and Platyhelminthes is radial versus bilateral symmetry. Discuss the advantage of radial symmetry for sessile (attached) animals and bilateral symmetry for motile animals.

EXERCISE 17.4

Phylum Nematoda— Roundworms (*Ascaris*)

Materials

dissecting instruments
dissecting pan
dissecting pins
compound microscope
disposable gloves

preserved *Ascaris*
prepared slide of cross section
    of *Ascaris*
hand lens (optional)

Introduction

Ascaris is a **roundworm,** or nematode, that lives as a parasite in the intestines of mammals such as horses, pigs, and humans (Color Plate 54). Most often these parasites are introduced into the mammalian body when food contaminated with nematode eggs is eaten. Keep in mind the problem of adaptation to a parasitic lifestyle as you study the structure of this animal.

 Wear gloves while dissecting preserved animals.

Procedure

1. Wearing disposable gloves, obtain a preserved *Ascaris* and determine its sex. Females are generally larger than males. The posterior end of the male is sharply curved.

2. Use a hand lens or a stereoscopic microscope to look at the ends of the worm. A mouth is present at the anterior end. Three "lips" border this opening. A small slitlike **anus** is located ventrally near the posterior end of the animal.

3. Open the animal by making a middorsal incision along the length of the body with a sharp-pointed probe or sharp scissors. Remember that the anus is slightly to the ventral side (Figure 17.5). Be careful not to go too deep. Once the animal is open, pin the free edges of the body wall

Figure 17.5.
Male and female *Ascaris*.
The digestive tract originates at the mouth and terminates in the anus. Reproductive structures fill the body cavity.

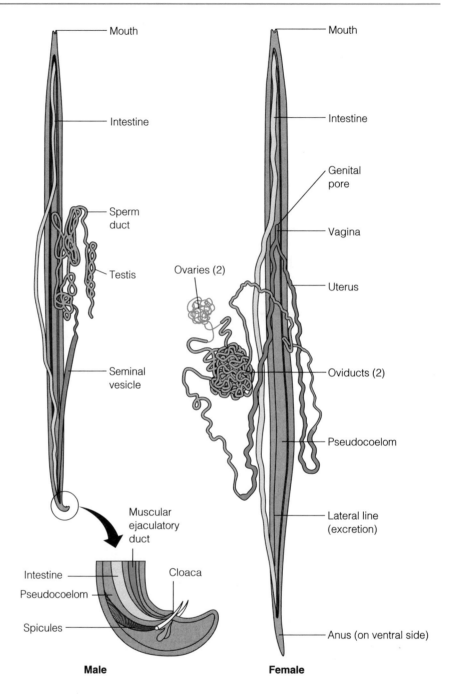

to the dissecting pan, spreading open the body. Pinning the animal near the edge of the pan will allow you to view it using the stereoscopic microscope. As you study the internal organs, you will note that there is a **body cavity.** This is not a true coelom, however, as you will see shortly when you study microscopic sections. From your observations, you should readily identify such characteristics as symmetry, tissue organization, and digestive tract openings.

a. The most obvious organs you will see in the dissected worm are **reproductive organs,** which appear as masses of coiled tubules of varying diameters.

b. Identify the flattened **digestive tract,** or intestine, extending from mouth to anus. This tract has been described as a "tube within a tube," the outer tube being the body wall.

   c. Locate two pale lines running laterally along the length of the body in the body wall. The excretory system consists of two longitudinal tubes lying in these two **lateral lines.**

   d. There are no organs for gas exchange or circulation. Most parasitic roundworms are essentially anaerobic (require no oxygen).

   e. How would nourishment be taken into the body and be circulated?

   f. The nervous system consists of a ring of nervous tissue around the anterior end of the worm, with one dorsal and one ventral nerve cord. These structures will be more easily observed in the prepared slide.

   g. Do you see signs of segmentation in the body wall or in the digestive, reproductive, or excretory systems?

   h. Do you see signs of a support system? What do you think supports the body?

4. Using the compound microscope, observe a prepared slide of a cross section through the body of a female worm. Note that the body wall is made up of (from outside inward) **cuticle** (noncellular), **epidermis** (cellular), and **muscle fibers.** The muscle (derived from mesoderm) lies at the outer boundary of the body cavity. Locate the **intestine** (derived from endoderm). Can you detect muscle tissue adjacent to the endodermal layer?

   What do we call a coelom that is lined by mesoderm (outside) and endoderm (inside) (see Figure 17.1b)?

5. Most of the body cavity is filled with reproductive organs. You should see cross sections of the two large **uteri,** sections of the coiled **oviducts** with small lumens, and many sections of the **ovaries** with no lumen. What do you see inside the uteri?

6. By carefully observing the cross section, you should be able to locate the **lateral lines** for excretion and the dorsal and ventral **nerve cords.**

Results

1. Sketch the cross section of a female *Ascaris*. Label the **cuticle, epidermis, muscle fibers, intestine, body cavity** (give specific name), **reproductive organs, (uterus, oviduct, ovary), lateral lines**, and **dorsal** and **ventral nerve cords.**

2. List some features of *Ascaris* that are possible adaptations to parasitic life.

3. Complete the summary table, Table 18.1, recording all information for roundworm characteristics in the appropriate row. You will use this information to answer questions in the Applying Your Knowledge section at the end of Lab Topic 18, Animal Diversity II.

Discussion

1. Discuss the significance of an animal's having two separate openings to the digestive tract, as seen in *Ascaris*.

2. What are the advantages of a body cavity being present in an animal?

EXERCISE 17.5

Phylum Annelida—Clamworms *(Nereis)* and Earthworms *(Lumbricus terrestris)*

The phylum Annelida includes a diverse group of organisms inhabiting a variety of environments. Examples range in size from microscopic to several meters in length. Most species are marine, living free in the open ocean or burrowing in ocean bottoms. Others live in fresh water or in soils. One group of annelids, the leeches, are parasitic and live on the blood or tissues of their hosts. In this exercise, you will study the clamworm, a marine annelid, and the earthworm, a terrestrial species. Keep in mind features that are adaptations to marine and terrestrial habitats as you study these organisms.

Lab Study A. Clamworms *(Nereis)*

Materials

dissecting tools
dissecting pan
preserved clamworm

disposable gloves
dissecting pins

Introduction

Species of *Nereis* (clamworms) are commonly found in mud flats and on the ocean floor. These animals burrow in sediments during the day and emerge to feed at night. As you observe the clamworm, note features that are characteristic of all annelids, as well as features that are special adaptations to the marine environment (Color Plate 55).

Procedure

1. Observe the preserved, undissected clamworm and compare it with Figure 17.6. How would you describe the symmetry of this organism?

2. Determine the anterior and posterior ends. At the anterior end, the well-differentiated head bears **sensory appendages.** Locate the mouth, which leads into the digestive tract.

Figure 17.6.
The clamworm, *Nereis.* The head has sensory appendages, and each segment of the body bears two parapodia with setae.

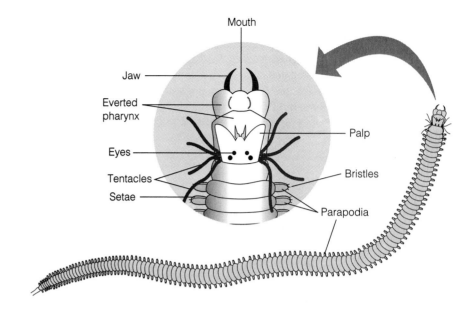

3. A conspicuous new feature of these organisms is the presence of **segmentation,** the division of the body along its length into segments. Posterior to the head region, the segments bear fleshy outgrowths called **parapodia.** Each parapodium contains several terminal bristles called **setae.** In Lab Study B, you will see that the earthworm has setae but does not have parapodia. Suggest functions for parapodia and setae in the marine clamworm.

4. Holding the animal in your hand and using sharp-pointed scissors, make a middorsal incision the full length of the body. Carefully insert the tip of the scissors and lift up with the tips as you cut. Pin the opened body in the dissecting pan but do not put pins through the head region.

5. Locate the **intestine.** Do you see the "tube-within-a-tube" body plan?

6. Two **muscle layers,** one inside the skin and a second lying on the surface of the intestine, may be visible with the stereoscopic microscope. With muscle in these two positions, what kind of coelom does this animal have (see Figure 17.1c)?

7. Continuing your observations with the unaided eye and the stereoscopic microscope, look for **blood vessels,** particularly a large vessel lying on the dorsal wall of the digestive tract. This vessel is contractile and pro-

pels the blood throughout the body. You should be able to observe smaller lateral blood vessels connecting the dorsal blood vessel with another on the ventral side of the intestine. As you will see, in the earthworm these connecting vessels are slightly enlarged as "hearts" around the anterior portion of the digestive tract (around the esophagus). This is not as obvious in *Nereis.* What is this type of circulatory system, with blood circulating through continuous closed vessels?

8. Gas exchange must take place across wet, thin surfaces. Do you see any organs for gas exchange (gills or lungs, for example)? How do you suspect that gas exchange takes place?

9. Do you see any signs of a skeleton? What would serve as support for the body?

10. Clamworms and earthworms have a small bilobed brain (a pair of ganglia) lying on the surface of the digestive tract at the anterior end of the worm. You can see this more easily in an earthworm.

Lab Study B. Earthworms (*Lumbricus terrestris*)

Materials

dissecting instruments
compound microscope
stereoscopic microscope

preserved earthworm
prepared slide of cross section
   of earthworm

Introduction

Lumbricus species, commonly called *earthworms,* burrow through soils rich in organic matter. As you observe these animals, note features that are adaptations to the burrowing, terrestrial lifestyle.

Procedure

1. Obtain a preserved earthworm and identify its anterior end by locating the mouth, which is overhung by a fleshy dorsal protuberance called the **prostomium.** The anus at the posterior end has no such protuberance. Also, a swollen glandular band, the **clitellum** (a structure that secretes a cocoon that holds eggs), is located closer to the mouth than to the anus (Figure 17.7).

   a. Using scissors, make a middorsal incision along the anterior third of the animal, as you did for *Nereis.* You can identify the dorsal surface in a couple of ways. The prostomium is dorsal, and the ventral surface

Figure 17.7.

The earthworm. The small brain leads to a ventral nerve cord. A pair of nephridia lie in each segment.

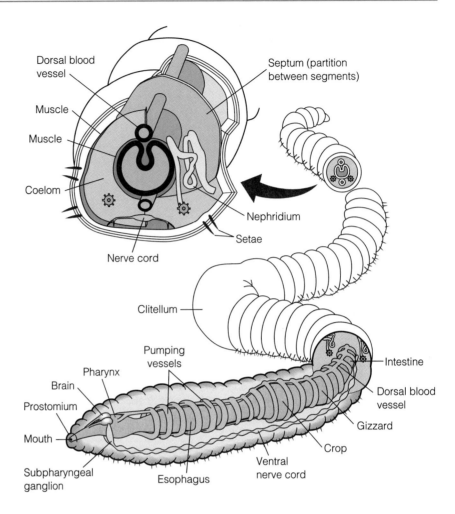

Dorsal blood vessel

Septum (partition between segments)

Muscle

Muscle

Coelom

Nephridium

Setae

Nerve cord

Clitellum

Pumping vessels

Pharynx

Intestine

Brain

Prostomium

Dorsal blood vessel

Mouth

Gizzard

Crop

Subpharyngeal ganglion

Esophagus

Ventral nerve cord

of the worm is usually flattened, especially in the region of the clitellum. Cut to the prostomium. Pin the body open in a dissecting pan near the edge. You may need to cut through the septa that divide the body cavity into segments.

b. Using a stereoscopic microscope or hand lens, look for the small **brain** just behind the prostomium on the surface of the digestive tract. Note the two nerves that pass from the brain around the pharynx and meet ventrally. These nerve tracts continue posteriorly as a **ventral nerve cord** lying in the floor of the coelom.

c. Look for the large **blood vessel** on the dorsal wall of the digestive tract. You may be able to see the enlarged lateral blood vessels (**hearts**) around the anterior portion of the digestive tract.

d. Identify (from anterior to posterior) the **pharynx, esophagus, crop** (a soft, swollen region of the digestive tract), **gizzard** (smaller and more rigid than the crop), and **intestine.**

e. Excretion in the clamworm and earthworm is carried out by organs called **nephridia.** A pair of these minute, white, coiled tubes is located in each segment of the worm body. Nephridia are more easily observed in the earthworm than in *Nereis* and should be studied here. To view these organs, cut out an approximately 2-cm-long piece of the worm posterior to the clitellum and cut it open along its dorsal surface. Cut through the septa and pin the piece to the dissecting pan near the edge to facilitate observation with the stereoscopic microscope. The coiled tubules of the nephridia are located in the coelomic cavity, where waste is collected and discharged to the outside through a small pore.

2. Using the compound microscope, observe the prepared slide of a cross section of the earthworm.

   a. Locate the **thin cuticle** lying outside of and secreted by the **epidermis.** Recall the habitat of this organism and speculate about the function of the cuticle.

   b. Confirm your decision about the type of coelom by locating **muscle layers** inside the epidermis and also lying on the surface of the **intestine** near the body cavity.

   c. Locate the **ventral nerve cord,** lying in the floor of the coelom, just inside the muscle layer.

Results

Complete the summary table, Table 18.1, recording all information for clamworm and earthworm characteristics in the appropriate row. You will use this information to answer questions in the Applying Your Knowledge section at the end of Lab Topic 18, Animal Diversity II.

Discussion

A major new feature observed in the phylum Annelida is the segmented body. Speculate about possible adaptive advantages provided by segmentation.

By the end of today's laboratory period, you should have completed observations of all animals described in Animal Diversity I. The next lab topic, Animal Diversity II, is a continuation of this investigation and will present similar laboratory objectives. In Animal Diversity II, you will continue asking questions and making comparisons as you did in Animal Diversity I. By the end of the two lab topics, you should be able to use what you have learned about the animals to discuss and answer questions about the unifying themes of these laboratory topics.

Applying your Knowledge

A hydra (*Chlorophyra viridissima*) is bright green, and yet it does not synthesize chlorophyll. Think about the structure of the hydra and its feeding and digestive habits. What do you think is the origin of the green pigment in this species?

References

Balavoine, G. "Are Platyhelminthes Coelomates Without a Coelom? An Argument Based on the Evolution of Hox Genes," *American Zoologist,* 1989, vol. 38, pp. 843–858.

Bond, C. "Keeping Up with the Sponges," *Natural History,* 1998, vol. 106, pp. 22–25.

Erwin, D., J. Valentine, and D. Jablonski. "The Origin of Animal Body Plans," *American Scientist,* 1997, vol. 85, pp. 126–137.

Website

Includes descriptions of many invertebrates and vertebrates, links to insect keys, references:

http://animaldiversity.ummz.umich.edu/index.html

Animal Diversity II

 This lab is a continuation of observations of organisms in the animal kingdom as discussed in Animal Diversity I. Return to Lab Topic 17 and review the objectives of the lab on page 445. Review the descriptions of the 13 characteristics you are investigating in the study and dissection of these animals (pp. 446–448).

As you continue your study of representative organisms, continue to record your observations in Table 18.1 at the end of this lab topic. Keep in mind the big themes you are investigating.

1. What clues do similarities and differences among organisms provide about phylogenetic relationships?

2. How is body form related to function?

3. How is body form related to environment and lifestyle?

4. What characteristics can be the criteria for major branching points in producing a phylogenetic tree (representing animal classification)?

EXERCISE 18.1
Phylum Mollusca—Clams

Materials

dissecting instruments
dissecting pan

preserved clam or mussel
disposable gloves

Introduction

Second only to the phylum Arthropoda in numbers of species, the phylum Mollusca includes thousands of species living in many diverse habitats. Most species are marine. Others live in fresh water or on land. Many mollusks are of economic importance, being favorite human foods. Most mollusks share four characteristic features: (1) a hard external **shell** for protection; (2) a thin structure called the **mantle**, which secretes the shell; (3) a **visceral mass** in which most organs are located; and (4) a muscular **foot** used for locomotion.

In this exercise, you will dissect a clam, a molluscan species with a shell made of two parts called **valves.** Most clams are marine, although many genera live in freshwater lakes and ponds (Color Plate 56).

 Wear gloves while dissecting preserved animals.

Procedure

1. Observe the external anatomy of the preserved clam. Certain characteristics will become obvious immediately. Can you determine symmetry, support systems, and the presence or absence of appendages? Are there external signs of segmentation? Record observations in Table 18.1.

2. Before you continue making observations, determine the dorsal, ventral, anterior, posterior, right, and left regions of the animal. Identify the two valves. The valves are held together by a **hinge** near the **umbo,** a hump on the valves. The hinge and the umbo are located **dorsally,** and the valves open **ventrally.** The umbo is displaced **anteriorly.** Hold the clam vertically with the umbo away from your body, and cup one of your hands over each valve. The valve in your right hand is the right valve; the valve in your left hand is the left valve. The two valves are held together by two strong **adductor** muscles inside the shell. Compare your observations with Figure 18.1.

 Be cautious as you open the clam! Hold the clam in the dissecting pan in such a way that the scalpel will be directed toward the bottom of the pan.

Figure 18.1.
Anatomy of a clam. The soft body parts are protected by the shell valves. Two adductor muscles hold the valves closed. Most major organs are located in the visceral mass. In this diagram, the left mantle, left pair of gills, and half of the visceral mass have been removed.

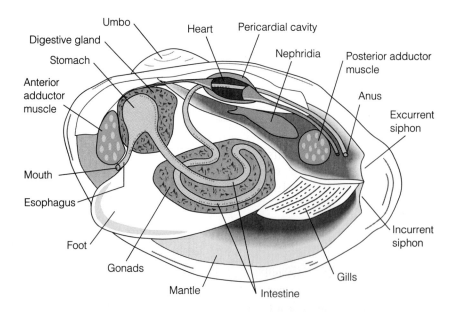

3. To study the internal anatomy of the clam, you must open it by prying open the valves. (A wooden peg may have been inserted between the two valves.) Insert the handle of your forceps or scalpel between the valves and twist it to pry the valves farther open. Carefully insert a scalpel blade, directed toward the dorsal side of the animal, into the space between the left valve and a flap of tissue lining the valve. The blade edge should be just ventral to (that is, below) the anterior adductor muscle (see Figure 18.1). The flap of tissue is the left **mantle.** Keeping the scalpel blade pressed flat against the left valve, carefully loosen the mantle from the valve and press the blade dorsally. You will feel the tough **anterior adductor muscle.** Cut through this muscle near the valve.

4. Repeat the procedure at the posterior end and cut the posterior adductor muscle. Lay the clam on its right valve and carefully lift the left valve. As you do this, use your scalpel to loosen the mantle from the valve. If you have been successful, you should have the body of the clam lying in the right valve. It should be covered by the mantle. Look for pearls between the mantle and the shell. How do you think pearls are formed?

5. Look at the posterior end of the animal where the left and right mantle come together. Hold the two mantle flaps together and note the two gaps formed. These gaps are called **incurrent** (ventral) and **excurrent** (dorsal) **siphons.** Speculate about the function of these siphons.

6. Lift the mantle and identify the **visceral mass** and the **muscular foot.**

7. Locate the **gills,** which have a pleated appearance. One function of these structures is obvious, but they have a second function as well. As water comes into the body (how would it get in?), it passes through the gills, and food particles are trapped on the gill surface. The food is then moved anteriorly (toward the mouth) by coordinated ciliary movements.

8. Locate the **mouth** between two flaps of tissue just ventral to the anterior adductor muscle. Look just above the posterior adductor muscle and locate the **anus.** How is it oriented in relation to the excurrent siphon?

9. Imagine that this is the first time you have seen a clam. From the observations you have made, what evidence would indicate whether this animal is aquatic or terrestrial?

10. The **heart** of the clam is located in a sinus, or cavity, just inside the hinge, dorsal to the visceral mass (see Figure 18.1). This cavity, called the *pericardial cavity,* is a reduced **true coelom.** The single ventricle of

the heart actually surrounds the **intestine** passing through this cavity. Thin auricles, usually torn away during the dissection, empty into the heart via openings called **ostia.** Blood passes from **sinuses** in the body into the auricles. What type of circulatory system is this?

11. Ventral to the heart and embedded in mantle tissue are a pair of greenish brown tissue masses, the **nephridia,** or kidneys. The kidneys remove waste from the pericardial cavity.

12. Open the visceral mass by making an incision with the scalpel, dividing the mass into right and left halves. Begin this incision just above the foot and cut dorsally. You should be able to open the flap produced by this cut and see organs such as the **gonads, digestive gland, intestine,** and **stomach.** Clam chowder is made by chopping up the visceral mass.

13. It is difficult to observe the nervous system in the clam. It consists of three ganglia, one near the mouth, one in the foot, and one below the posterior adductor muscle. These ganglia are connected by nerves.

Now that you have dissected the clam, you should have concluded that there is no sign of true segmentation. Also, appendages (attached to a trunk or body wall) are absent.

Results

Complete Summary Table 18.1, recording all information for clam characteristics in the appropriate row. Use this information to answer questions in the Applying Your Knowledge section at the end of this lab topic.

Discussion

List several features of clam anatomy that enable it to survive in a marine environment.

EXERCISE 18.2
Phylum Arthropoda

Organisms in the phylum Arthropoda have been very successful species. Evidence indicates that arthropods may have lived on Earth half a billion years ago. They can be found in almost every imaginable habitat: marine waters, fresh water, and almost every terrestrial niche. Many species are directly beneficial to humans, serving as a source of food. Others make humans miserable by eating their homes, infesting their domestic animals, eating their food, and biting their bodies. In this exercise, you will observe the morphology of two arthropods: the crayfish (an aquatic arthropod) and the grasshopper (a terrestrial arthropod).

Lab Study A. Crayfish (*Cambarus*)

Materials

dissecting instruments   preserved crayfish
dissecting pan   disposable gloves

Introduction

Crayfish live in streams, ponds, and swamps, usually protected under rocks and vegetation. They may walk slowly over the substrate of their habitat, but they can also swim rapidly using their tails. The segmentation seen in annelids is seen also in crayfish and all arthropods; however, you will see that the segments are grouped into functional units (Color Plate 57).

Procedure

1. Obtain a preserved crayfish, study its external anatomy, and compare your observations with Figure 18.2. Describe the body symmetry, supportive structures, appendages, and segmentation, and state the adaptive advantages of each characteristic.

    a. body symmetry

    b. supportive structures

    c. appendages

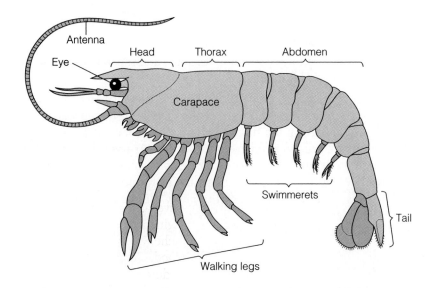

Figure 18.2.
External anatomy of a crayfish.
The body is divided into head, thorax, and abdominal regions. Appendages grouped in a region perform specific functions.

d. segmentation

2. Identify the three regions of the crayfish body: the **head, thorax** (fused with the head), and **abdomen.** Note the appendages associated with each region. Speculate about the functions of each of these groups of appendages.

   a. head appendages

   b. thoracic appendages

   c. abdominal appendages

3. Feathery **gills** lie under the lateral extensions of a large, expanded exoskeletal plate called the **carapace** (see Figure 18.2). To expose the gills, use scissors to cut away a portion of the plate on the left side of the animal. What is the function of the gills? Speculate about how this function is performed.

4. Remove the dorsal portion of the carapace to observe other organs in the head and thorax. Compare your observations with Figure 18.3.

   a. Start on each side of the body at the posterior lateral edge of the carapace and make two lateral cuts extending along each side of the thorax and forward over the head, meeting just behind the eyes. This should create a dorsal flap in the carapace.

   b. Carefully insert a needle under this flap and separate the underlying tissues as you lift the flap.

   c. Observe the **heart,** a small, angular structure located just under the carapace near the posterior portion of the thorax. (If you were not successful in leaving the tissues behind as you removed the carapace, you may have removed the heart with the carapace.) Thin threads leading out from the heart are **arteries.** Look for holes in the heart wall. When blood collects in **sinuses** around the heart, the heart relaxes, and these holes open to allow the heart to fill with blood. The holes then close, and the blood is pumped through the arteries, which distribute it around the body. Blood seeps back to the heart, since no veins are present. What is the name given to this kind of circulation?

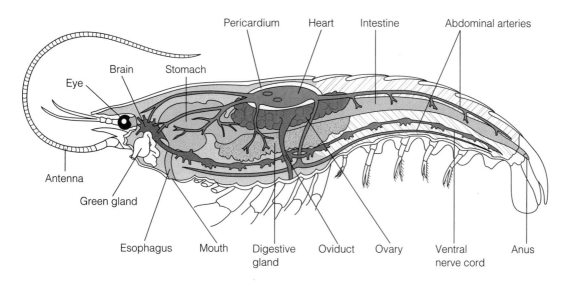

Pericardium   Heart   Intestine   Abdominal arteries

Brain   Stomach

Eye

Antenna

Green gland

Esophagus   Mouth   Digestive gland   Oviduct   Ovary   Ventral nerve cord   Anus

Figure 18.3.
Internal anatomy of the crayfish. Large digestive glands fill much of the body cavity. The intestine extends from the stomach through the tail to the anus. The green glands lie near the brain in the head.

d. Locate the **stomach** in the head region. It is a large, saclike structure. It may be obscured by the large, white **digestive glands** that fill the body cavity inside the body wall. Leading posteriorly from the stomach is the **intestine.** Make longitudinal cuts through the exoskeleton on either side of the dorsal midline of the abdomen. Lift the exoskeleton and trace the intestine to the anus. (When shrimp are "deveined" in preparation for eating, the intestine is removed.) Given all of the organs and tissues around the digestive tract and inside the body wall in the body cavity, what kind of coelom do you think this animal has?

e. Turn your attention to the anterior end of the specimen again. Pull the stomach posteriorly (this will tear the esophagus) and look inside the most anterior portion of the head. Two **green glands** (they do not look green), the animal's excretory organs, are located in this region. These are actually long tubular structures that resemble nephridia but are compacted into a glandular mass. Waste and excess water pass from these glands to the outside of the body through pores at the base of the antennae on the head.

f. Observe the **brain** just anterior to the green glands. It lies in the midline with nerves extending posteriorly, fusing to form a **ventral nerve cord.**

Results

Complete Table 18.1, recording all information for crayfish characteristics in the appropriate row. Use this information to answer questions in the Applying Your Knowledge section at the end of this lab topic.

Discussion

How does the pattern of segmentation differ in the crayfish and the earthworm?

Lab Study B. Grasshoppers (*Romalea*)

Materials

dissecting instruments

dissecting pan

preserved grasshopper

disposable gloves

Introduction

The grasshopper, an insect, is an example of a terrestrial arthropod (Color Plate 58). Insects are the most successful and abundant of all land animals. They are the principal invertebrates in dry environments, and they can survive extreme temperatures. They are the only invertebrates that can fly. As you study the grasshopper, compare the anatomy of this terrestrial animal with that of the aquatic crayfish, just studied. This comparison should suggest ways that terrestrial animals have solved the problems of life out of water.

Procedure

1. Observe the external anatomy of the grasshopper. Compare your observations with Figure 18.4.

    a. Note the symmetry, supportive structures, appendages, and segmentation of the grasshopper.

Figure 18.4.
External anatomy of the grasshopper. The body is divided into head, thorax, and abdominal regions. Wings and large legs are present. Small openings, called *spiracles,* lead to internal tracheae, allowing air to pass into the body.

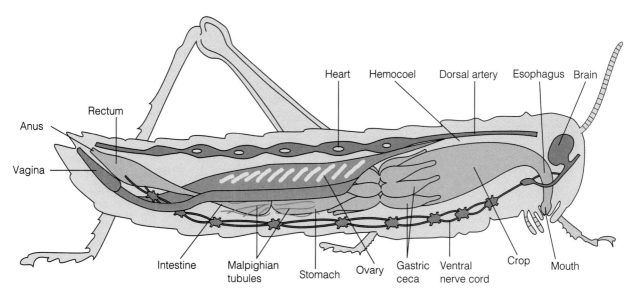

Figure 18.5.
Internal anatomy of the grasshopper. The digestive tract, extending from
mouth to anus, is divided into specialized regions: the esophagus, crop, stomach,
intestine, and rectum. Gastric ceca attach at the junction of the crop and the
stomach. Malpighian tubules empty excretory waste into the anterior end of the
intestine.

   b. Observe the body parts. The body is divided into three regions: the
      head, the **thorax** (to which the legs and wings are attached), and the
      abdomen. Examine the appendages on the head, speculate about
      their functions, and locate the mouth opening into the digestive tract.

   c. Turning your attention to the abdomen, locate small dots along each
      side. These dots are **spiracles,** small openings into elastic air tubes,
      or **tracheae,** that branch to all parts of the body and constitute the
      respiratory system of the grasshopper. This system of tubes brings
      oxygen directly to the cells of the body.

2. Remove the exoskeleton. First take off the wings and, starting at the
   posterior end, use scissors to make two lateral cuts toward the head.
   Remove the dorsal wall of the exoskeleton and note the segmented pattern in the muscles inside the body wall. Compare your observations with
   Figure 18.5 as you work.

   a. A space between the body wall and the digestive tract, the **hemocoel**
      (a true coelom), in life is filled with colorless blood. What type of
      circulation does the grasshopper have?

      The heart of a grasshopper is an elongate, tubular structure lying just
      inside the middorsal body wall. This probably will not be visible.

   b. Locate the digestive tract and again note the mouth. Along the length
      of the tract are regions specialized for specific functions. A narrow **esoph-
      agus** leading from the mouth expands into a large **crop** used for food
      storage. The crop empties into the **stomach,** where digestion takes
      place. Six pairs of fingerlike extensions called **gastric pouches** or
      ceca connect to the digestive tract where the crop and the stomach

meet. These pouches secrete digestive enzymes and aid in food absorption. Food passes from the stomach into the **intestine,** then into the **rectum,** and out the **anus.** Distinguish these regions by observing constrictions and swellings along the tube. There is usually a constriction between the stomach and the intestine where the Malpighian tubules (discussed below) attach. The intestine is shorter and usually smaller in diameter than the stomach. *The intestine expands into an enlarged rectum that absorbs excess water from any undigested food, and relatively dry excrement passes out the anus.*

c. The excretory system is made up of numerous tiny tubules, the **Malpighian tubules,** which empty their products into the anterior end of the intestine. These tubules remove wastes and salts from the blood. Locate these tubules.

d. Push aside the digestive tract and locate the **ventral nerve cord** lying medially inside the ventral body wall. Ganglia are expanded regions of the ventral nerve cord found in each body segment. Following the nerve cord anteriorly, note that branches from the nerve cord pass around the digestive tract and meet, forming a brain in the head.

Results

Complete Table 18.1, recording all information for grasshopper characteristics in the appropriate row. Use this information to answer questions in the Applying Your Knowledge section at the end of this lab topic.

Discussion

1. Describe how each of the following external structures helps the grasshopper live successfully in terrestrial environments.

   a. Exoskeleton

   b. Wings

   c. Large, jointed legs

   d. Spiracles

2. Describe how each of the following internal structures helps the grasshopper live successfully in terrestrial environments.

   a. Tracheae

   b. Malpighian tubules

c. Rectum

EXERCISE 18.3
Phylum Chordata

The phylum Chordata includes another diverse group of organisms. Organisms in two subphyla of chordates are invertebrates, and animals in the largest subphylum have a bony or cartilaginous endoskeleton that includes a vertebral column and are called *vertebrates*. Chordates inhabit terrestrial and aquatic (freshwater and marine) environments. One group has developed the ability to fly. The body plan of chordates is unique in that these animals demonstrate a complex of four important characteristics at some stage in their development. In this exercise, you will discover these characteristics.

You will study two chordate species: the lancelet, an invertebrate in the subphylum Cephalochordata, and the pig, a vertebrate in the subphylum Vertebrata. The third subphylum, Urochordata, will not be studied.

Lab Study A. Lancelets (*Branchiostoma*, formerly *Amphioxus*)

Materials

compound microscope	prepared slide of whole mount of
stereoscopic microscope	lancelet
preserved lancelet in watch glass	prepared slide of cross section of
	lancelet

Introduction

Lancelets are marine animals that burrow in sand in tidal flats. They feed with their head end extended from their burrow. They resemble fish superficially, but their head is poorly developed, and they have unique features not found in fish or other vertebrates. They retain the four unique characteristics of chordates throughout their life cycle and are excellent animals to use to demonstrate these features. In this lab study, you will observe preserved lancelets, prepared slides of whole mounts, and cross sections through the body of a lancelet (Color Plate 59).

Procedure

1. Place a preserved lancelet in water in a watch glass and observe it using the stereoscopic microscope. Handle the specimen with care and *do not dissect it*. Note the fishlike shape of the slender, elongate body. Locate the anterior end by the presence at that end of a noselike **rostrum** extending over the mouth region, surrounded by small tentacles. Notice the lack of a well-defined head. Look for the segmented muscles that surround much of the animal's body. Can you see signs of a tail? If the

animal you are studying is mature, you will be able to see two rows of 20 to 25 white gonads on the ventral surface of the body.

2. Return the specimen to the correct container.

3. Observe the whole mount slide of the lancelet and compare your observations with Figure 18.6.

 Use only the lowest power on the compound microscope to study this slide.

a. Scan the entire length of the body wall. Do you see evidence of segmentation in the muscles?

b. Look at the anterior end of the animal. Do you see evidence of a sensory system? Describe what you see.

c. Locate the mouth of the animal at the anterior end. See if you can follow a tube from just under the rostrum into a large sac with numerous gill slits. This sac is the **pharynx with gill slits,** a uniquely chordate structure. Water and food pass into the pharynx from the mouth. Food passes posteriorly from the pharynx into the intestine, which ends at the anus on the ventral side of the animal, several millimeters before the end. The extension of the body beyond the anus is called a **post-anal tail.** Think of the worms you studied in Lab Topic 17, Animal Diversity I. Where was the anus located in these animals? Was a post-anal region present? Explain.

Figure 18.6.
The lancelet, whole mount. The rostrum extends over the mouth region. The pharynx, including the pharyngeal gill slits, leads to the intestine, which exits the body at the anus. Note that a tail extends beyond the anus. Structures positioned from the dorsal surface of the body inward include a dorsal fin, the nerve cord, and the notochord.

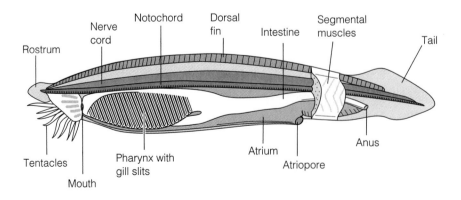

d. Water entering the mouth passes through the gill slits and collects in a chamber, the **atrium,** just inside the body wall. The water ultimately passes out of the body at a ventral pore, the **atripore.** Surprisingly, the gill slits are not the major gas exchange surface in the lancelet body. Because of the great activity of ciliated cells in this region, it is even possible that blood leaving the gill region has less oxygen than that entering the region. The function of gill slits is simply to strain food from the water. The major site for gas exchange is the body surface.

e. Now turn your attention to the dorsal side of the animal. Beginning at the surface of the body and moving inward, identify the listed structures and speculate about the function of each one.

dorsal fin:

nerve cord:

notochord:

The nerve cord is in a dorsal position. Have you seen only a dorsal nerve cord in any of the animals previously studied?

The notochord is a cartilage-like rod that lies ventral to the nerve cord and extends the length of the body. Have you seen a notochord in any of the previous animals?

The lancelet circulatory system is not visible in these preparations, but the animal has **closed circulation** with dorsal and ventral aortae, capillaries, and veins. Excretory organs, or nephridia (not visible here), are located near the true coelom, which surrounds the pharynx.

4. Observe the slide of cross sections taken through the lancelet body. There may be several sections on this slide, taken at several positions along the length of the body. Find the section through the pharynx and compare it with Figure 18.7.

 Study this slide on the lowest power.

Figure 18.7.
Cross section through the
pharyngeal region of the lancelet.

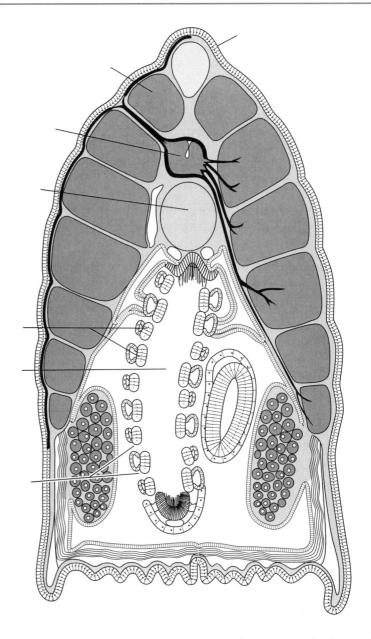

In cross section, it is much easier to see the structural relationships among the various organs of the lancelet. Identify the following structures and label them on Figure 18.7.

a. **Segmental muscles.** They are located on each side of the body, under the skin.

b. **Dorsal fin.** This projects upward from the most dorsal surface of the body.

c. **Nerve cord.** You may be able to see that the nerve cord contains a small central canal, thus making it hollow. The nerve cord is located in the dorsal region of the body, ventral to the dorsal fin between the lateral bundles of muscle.

d. **Notochord.** This is a large oval structure located just ventral to the nerve cord.

e. **Pharynx with gill slits.** This structure appears as a series of dark triangles arranged in an oval. The triangles are cross sections of **gill bars.** The spaces between the triangles are **gill slits,** through which water passes into the surrounding chamber.

Results

1. Complete the diagram of the lancelet cross section in Figure 18.7. Label all the structures listed in step 4 of the Procedure section.
2. Complete Table 18.1, recording all information for lancelet characteristics in the appropriate row. Use this information to answer questions in the Applying Your Knowledge section at the end of this lab topic.

Discussion

Describe the uniquely chordate features that you have detected in the lancelet that were not present in the animals previously studied.

Lab Study B. Fetal Pigs *(Sus scrofa)*

Materials

preserved fetal pig   disposable gloves
dissecting pan

Introduction

The pig is a terrestrial vertebrate. You will study its anatomy in detail in Lab Topics 21, 22, and 23. In this lab study, working with your lab partner, you will observe external features only, observing those characteristics studied in other animals in previous exercises. Compare the organization of the vertebrate body with the animals previously studied. As you dissect the pig in subsequent labs, come back to these questions and answer the ones that cannot be answered in today's lab study.

Procedure

1. Obtain a preserved fetal pig from the class supply and carry it to your desk in a dissecting pan.

 Use disposable gloves to handle preserved animals.

2. With your lab partner, read each of the following questions. Drawing on observations you have made of other animals in the animal diversity lab studies, predict the answer to each question about the fetal pig. Then examine the fetal pig and determine the answer, if possible. Give evidence for your answer based on your observations of the pig, your knowledge of vertebrate anatomy, or your understanding of animal phylogeny.

a. What type of symmetry does the pig body have?
   Prediction:

   Evidence:

b. How many layers of embryonic tissue are present?
   Prediction:

   Evidence:

c. Are cells organized into distinct tissues?
   Prediction:

   Evidence:

d. How many digestive tract openings are present? Would you describe this as a "tube within a tube"?
   Prediction:

   Evidence:

e. Is the circulatory system open or closed?
   Prediction:

   Evidence:

f. What is the habitat of the animal?
   Prediction:

Evidence:

g. What are the organs for respiration?
   Prediction:

   Evidence:

h. What are the organs for excretion?
   Prediction:

   Evidence:

i. What is the method of locomotion?
   Prediction:

   Evidence:

j. Are support systems internal or external?
   Prediction:

   Evidence:

k. Is the body segmented?
   Prediction:

   Evidence:

l. Are appendages present?
    Prediction:

    Evidence:

m. What is the position and complexity of the nervous system?
    Prediction:

    Evidence:

Results

Complete Table 18.1 on pp. 486–487, recording all information for pig characteristics in the appropriate row. Use this information to answer questions in the Applying Your Knowledge section that follows.

Results Summary

Complete the summary table, Table 18.1, recording in the appropriate row information about characteristics of all animals studied. Use this information to answer questions in the Applying Your Knowledge section that follows.

Applying Your Knowledge

1. Using specific examples from the animals you have studied in Lab Topics 17 and 18, describe ways that organisms have adapted to specific environments.
    a. Compare organisms adapted to aquatic environments with those from terrestrial environments.

b. Compare adaptations of parasitic organisms with similar free-living organisms.

2. Using the summary table, Table 18.2, categorize the animals studied based on the 13 basic characteristics discussed in Lab Topic 17.

3. Examine the phylogenetic tree in Figure 18.8 at the end of the topic, which illustrates evolutionary relationships among members of the animal kingdom. Each branching point on the tree represents a major characteristic that separates groups of organisms. For example, tissue organization (presence or absence of distinct tissue layers) separates sponges from all other animals. Based on your observations, select at least seven major criteria to be used for branching points in this phylogenetic tree. Write one criterion in the space provided at each branch point.

4. Upon superficial examination, the body form of certain present-day animals might be described as simple, yet these animals may have developed specialized structures, perhaps unique to their particular phylum. Illustrate this point using examples from some of the simpler organisms you have dissected.

5. From Lab Topics 17 and 18, one might conclude that certain trends can be detected, trends from "primitive" features (those that arose early in the evolution of animals) to more "advanced" traits (those that arose later). However, animals with these alleged primitive characteristics still successfully exist on Earth today. Why is this so? Why have the more advanced animals not completely replaced the more primitive ones? Use examples from the lab to illustrate your answer.

6. A major theme in biology is the relationship between form and function in organisms. Select one of the major characteristics from Table 18.1, and illustrate the relationship of form and function for this characteristic using examples from the organisms studied.

Table 18.1

Summary Table of Animal Characteristics

Animal	Symmetry	Tissue Organization	Type of Body Cavity	Digestive Openings	Circulatory System	Habitat	Respiratory Organs
Sponge							
Hydra							
Planarian							
Roundworm							
Clamworm/ earthworm							
Clam							
Crayfish							
Grasshopper							
Lancelet							
Pig							

Table 18.1
Summary Table of Animal Characteristics *(continued)*

Animal	Excretory System	Locomotion	Support System	Segmentation	Appendages	Nervous System Organization
Sponge						
Hydra						
Planarian						
Roundworm						
Clamworm/ earthworm						
Clam						
Crayfish						
Grasshopper						
Lancelet						
Pig						

Table 18.2
Comparison of Organisms by Major Features

1. Tissue Organization a. distinct tissues absent: b. distinct tissues present:	**5. Circulatory System** a. none: b. open: c. closed:
2. Symmetry a. radial: b. bilateral:	
	6. Habitat a. aquatic: b. terrestrial: c. parasitic:
3. Body Cavity a. acoelomate: b. pseudocoelomate: c. eucoelomate:	
	7. Organs for Gas Exchange a. skin: b. gills: c. lungs: d. spiracles/tracheae:
4. Openings to Digestive Tract a. one: b. two:	

Table 18.2
Comparison of Organisms by Major Features *(continued)*

8. **Organs for Excretion** (list organ and animals)	11. **Segmented Body** a. no: b. yes:
9. **Type of Locomotion** (list type and animals)	12. **Appendages** a. yes: b. no:
10. **Support System** a. external: b. internal: c. hydrostatic:	13. **Nervous System** a. ventral nerve cord: b. dorsal nerve cord: c. other:

References

Hickman, C. P., L. S. Roberts, and A. Larson. *Integrated Principles of Zoology,* 10th ed. Dubuque, IA: Wm. C. Brown, 1997.

Zimmer, C. "An Explosion Defused?" *Discover,* 1996, vol. 17, p. 52.

Zimmer, C. "The Hidden Unity of Hearts," *Natural History,* (2000), vol. 109, pp. 56–60.

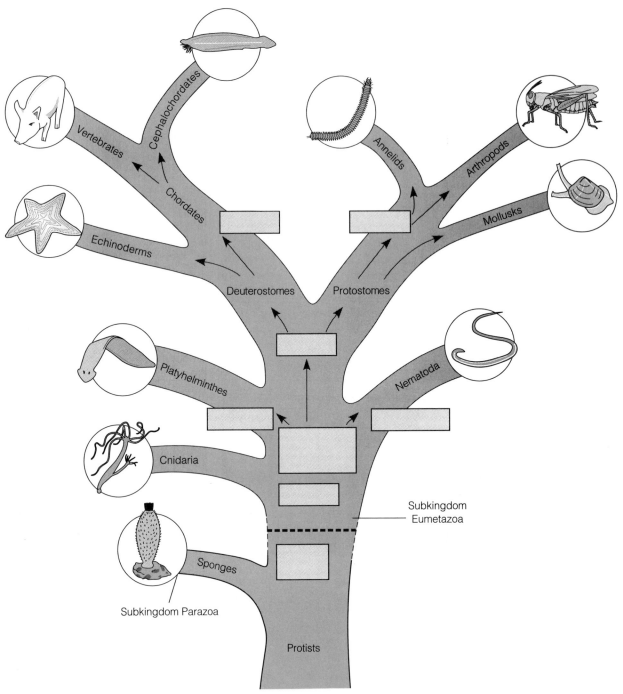

Figure 18.8.
Phylogenetic tree. Complete the figure by writing in the major criteria used to determine branching points.

Website

Includes descriptions of many invertebrates and vertebrates, links to insect keys, references:

http://animaldiversity.ummz.umich.edu/index.html

Plant Anatomy

Laboratory Objectives

After completing this lab topic, you should be able to:

1. Identify and describe the structure and function of each cell type and tissue type.
2. Describe the organization of tissues and cells in each plant organ.
3. Relate the function of an organ to its structure.
4. Describe primary and secondary growth and identify the location of each in the plant.
5. Relate primary and secondary growth to the growth habit (woody or herbaceous).
6. Discuss adaptation of land plants to the terrestrial environment as illustrated by the structure and function of plant anatomy.
7. Apply your knowledge of plants to the kinds of produce you find in the grocery store.

Introduction

Vascular plants have been successful on land for over 400 million years, and their success is related to their adaptations to the land environment. An aquatic alga lives most often in a continuously homogeneous environment: The requirements for life are everywhere around it, so relatively minor structural adaptations have evolved for functions such as reproduction and attachment. In contrast, the terrestrial habitat, with its extreme environmental conditions, presents numerous challenges for the survival of plants. Consequently, land plants have evolved structural adaptations for functions such as the absorption of underground water and nutrients, the anchoring of the plant in the substrate, the support of aerial parts of the plant, and the transportation of materials throughout the relatively large plant body. In angiosperms, the structural adaptations required for these and other functions are divided among three vegetative plant organs: stems, roots, and leaves. Unlike animal organs, which are often composed of unique cell types (for example, cardiac muscle fibers are found only in the heart, osteocytes only in bone), plant organs have many tissues and cell types in common, but they are organized in different ways. The structural organization of basic tissues and cell types in different plant organs is directly related to their different functions. For example, leaves function as the primary photosynthetic organ and generally have thin, flat blades that maximize light absorption and gas exchange. Specialized cells of the root epidermis are long extensions that promote one of the root functions, absorption. The interrelationship of structure and function is a major theme in biology, and you will continue to explore it in this lab topic.

Use the figures in this lab topic for orientation and as a study aid. Be certain that you can identify all items by examining the living specimens and microscope slides. These, and not the diagrams, will be used in the laboratory evaluations.

Summary of Basic Plant Tissues and Cell Types

Following is a review of plant tissues and the most common types of cells seen in plant organs, as well as their functions. Other specialized cells will be described as they are discussed in lab. Refer back to this summary as you work through the exercises.

Dermal Tissue: Epidermis

The **epidermis** forms the outermost layer of cells, usually one cell thick, covering the entire plant body. The epidermal cells are often flattened and rectangular in shape. Specialized epidermal cells include the **guard cells** of the stomata, hairs called **trichomes,** and unicellular **root hairs.** Most epidermal cells on aboveground structures are covered by a waxy **cuticle,** which prevents water loss. The epidermis provides protection and regulates movement of materials.

Ground Tissue: Parenchyma, Collenchyma, and Sclerenchyma

Parenchyma cells are the most common cell in plants and are characteristically thin-walled with large vacuoles. These cells may function in photosynthesis, support, storage of materials, and lateral transport.

Collenchyma cells are usually found near the surface of the stem, leaf petioles, and veins. These living cells are similar to parenchyma cells but are characterized by an uneven thickening of cell walls. They provide flexible support to young plant organs.

Sclerenchyma cells have thickened cell walls that may contain lignin. They provide strength and support to mature plant structures and may be dead at functional maturity. The most common type of sclerenchyma cells are long, thin **fibers.**

Vascular Tissue: Xylem and Phloem

Xylem cells form a complex vascular tissue that functions in the transport of water and minerals throughout the plant and provides support. **Tracheids** and **vessel elements** are the primary water-conducting cells. Tracheids are long, thin cells with perforated tapered ends. Vessel elements are larger in diameter, open-ended, and joined end to end, forming continuous transport systems referred to as **vessels.** Parenchyma cells are present in the xylem and function in storage and lateral transport. Fibers in the xylem provide additional support (Color Plate 60).

Phloem tissue transports the products of photosynthesis throughout the plant as part of the vascular tissue system. This complex tissue is composed of living, conducting cells called **sieve-tube members,** which lack a nucleus and have **sieve plates** for end walls. The cells are joined end to end throughout the plant. Each sieve-tube member is associated with one or more adjacent **companion cells,** which are thought to regulate sieve-tube member function. Phloem parenchyma cells function in storage and lateral transport, and phloem fibers provide additional support.

Meristematic Tissue: Primary Meristem, Cambium, and Pericycle

Primary meristems consist of small, actively dividing cells located in buds of the shoot and in root tips of plants. These cells produce the primary tissues along the plant axis throughout the life of the plant.

Vascular cambium is a lateral meristem also composed of small, actively dividing cells that are located between the xylem and phloem vascular tissue. These cells divide to produce secondary growth, which results in an increase in girth.

Pericycle is a layer of meristematic cells just outside the vascular cylinder in the root. These cells divide to produce lateral branch roots.

EXERCISE 19.1
Plant Morphology

Materials

living bean or geranium plant   paper towel
squirt bottle of water

Introduction

As you begin your investigation of the structure and function of plants, you need an understanding of the general shape and form of the whole plant. In this exercise, you will study a bean or geranium plant, identifying basic features of the three vegetative organs: roots, stems, and leaves. In the following exercises, you will investigate the cellular structure of these organs as viewed in cross sections. Refer to the living plant for orientation before you view your slides.

Procedure

1. Working with another student, examine a living **herbaceous** (non-woody) plant and identify the following structures in the shoot (stems and leaves):

   a. **Nodes** are regions of the stem from which leaves, buds, and branches arise and which contain meristematic tissue (areas of cell division).

   b. **Internodes** are the regions of the stem located between the nodes.

   c. **Terminal buds** are located at the tips of stems and branches. They enclose the shoot apical meristem, which gives rise to leaves, buds, and all primary tissue of the stem. Only stems produce buds.

   d. **Axillary,** or **lateral, buds** are located in the leaf axes at nodes; they may give rise to lateral branches.

   e. Leaves consist of flattened **blades** attached at the node of a stem by a stalk, or **petiole.**

2. Observe the root structures by gently removing the plant from the pot and loosening the soil from the root structure. You may need to rinse a few roots with water to observe the tiny, active roots. Identify the following structures:

    a. **Primary** and **secondary roots.** The primary root is the first root produced by a plant embryo and may become a long taproot. Secondary roots arise from meristematic tissue deep within the primary root.

    b. Root tips consist of a **root apical meristem** that gives rise to a **root cap** (protective layer of cells covering the root tip) and to all the primary tissues of the root. A short distance from the root tip is a zone of **root hairs** (specialized epidermal cells), the principal site of water and mineral absorption.

Results

1. Label Figure 19.1.
2. Sketch in the margin of your lab manual any features not included in this diagram that might be needed for future reference.

Figure 19.1.
A herbaceous plant. The vegetative plant body consists of roots, stems, and leaves. The buds are located in the axils of the leaves and at the shoot tip. The roots also grow from meristem tissues in the root tip. Label the diagram based on your observations of a living plant and the structures named in Exercise 19.1.

Discussion

1. Look at your plant and discuss with your partner the possible functions of each plant organ. Your discussion might include evidence observed in the lab today or prior knowledge. Describe proposed functions (more than one) for each organ.

    Stems:

    Roots:

    Leaves:

2. Imagine that you have cut each organ—roots, stems, and leaves—in cross section. Sketch the overall shape of that cross section in the margin of your lab manual. Remember, you are not predicting the internal structure, just the overall shape.

EXERCISE 19.2
Plant Primary Growth and Development

Materials

prepared slides of *Coleus* stem (long section)
compound microscope

Introduction

Plants produce new cells throughout their lifetime as a result of cell divisions in meristems. Tissues produced from apical meristems are called **primary tissues,** and this growth is called **primary growth.** Primary growth occurs along the plant axis at the shoot and the root tip. Certain meristem cells divide in such a way that one cell product becomes a new body cell and the other remains in the meristem. Beyond the zone of active cell division, new cells become enlarged and specialized for specific functions (resulting, for example, in vessels, parenchyma, and epidermis). The investigation of the genetic and biochemical basis of this cell differentiation continues to be an area of exciting biological research.

In this exercise, you will examine a longitudinal section through the tip of the stem, observing the youngest tissues and meristems at the apex, then moving down the stem, where you will observe more mature cells and tissues.

Procedure

1. Examine a prepared slide of a longitudinal section through a terminal bud of *Coleus.* Use low power to get an overview of the slide; then

increase magnification. Locate the **apical meristem,** a dome of tissue nestled between the **leaf primordia,** young developing leaves. Locate the axillary **bud primordia** between the leaf and the stem.

2. Move the specimen under the microscope so that cells may be viewed at varying distances from the apex. The youngest cells are at the apex of the bud, and cells of increasing maturity and differentiation can be seen as you move away from the apex. Follow the early development of vascular tissue, which differentiates in relation to the development of primordial leaves.

   a. Locate the narrow, dark tracks of **undifferentiated vascular tissue** in the leaf primordia.

   b. Observe changes in cell size and structure of the vascular system as you move away from the apex and end with a distinguishable vessel element of the **xylem,** with its spiral cell wall thickening in the older leaf primordia and stem. You may need to use the highest power on the microscope to locate these spiral cell walls.

Results

1. Label Figure 19.2, indicating the structures visible in the young stem tip.
2. Modify the figure or sketch details in the margin of the lab manual for future reference.

Discussion

1. Describe the changes in cell size and structure in the stem tip. Begin at the youngest cells at the apex and continue to the xylem cells.

2. The meristems of plants continue to grow throughout their lifetime, an example of **indeterminate growth.** Imagine a 200-year-old oak tree, with active meristem producing new buds, leaves, and stems each year. Contrast this with the growth pattern in humans.

EXERCISE 19.3

Cell Structure of Primary Tissues

All **herbaceous** (nonwoody) flowering plants produce a complete plant body composed of primary tissue, derived from apical primary meristem. This plant body consists of *organs*—roots, stems, leaves, flowers, fruits, and seeds—and *tissue systems*—**dermal** (epidermis), **ground** (parenchyma), and **vascular** (xylem and phloem). In this exercise, you will investigate the cellular structure and organization of plant organs and tissues by examining microscopic slides. You will make your own thin cross sections of stems, and view prepared slides of stems, roots, and leaves. Woody stems will be examined in Exercise 19.4.

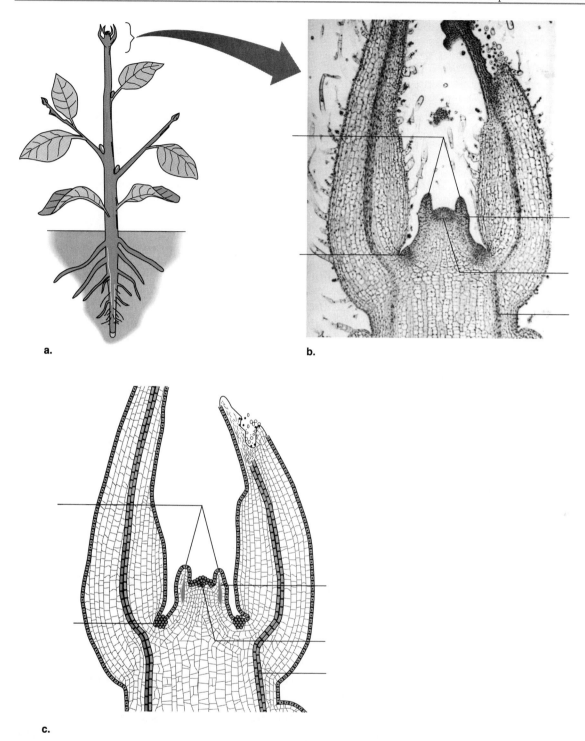

a.

b.

c.

Figure 19.2.
Coleus **stem tip.** (a) Diagram of entire plant body. (b) Photomicrograph of a longitudinal section through the terminal bud. (c) Line diagram of the growing shoot tip with primordial leaves surrounding the actively dividing apical meristem. The most immature cells are at the tip of the shoot and increase in stages of development and differentiation farther down the stem. Label the cells and structures described in Exercise 19.2.

Lab Study A. Stems

Materials

prepared slide of herbaceous dicot
    stem
dropper bottle of distilled water
small petri dish with 50% ethanol
dropper bottle of 50% glycerine
dropper bottle of 0.2% toluidine
    blue stain
nut-and-bolt microtome

warm paraffin
living plant for sections
new single-edged razor blade
forceps
microscope slides
coverslips
compound microscope
dissecting needles

Introduction

A stem is usually the main stalk, or axis, of a plant and is the only organ that produces buds and leaves. Stems support leaves and conduct water and inorganic substances from the root to the leaves and carbohydrate products of photosynthesis from the leaves to the roots. Most herbaceous stems are able to photosynthesize. Stems exhibit several interesting adaptations, including water storage in cacti, carbohydrate storage in some food plants, and thorns that reduce herbivory in a variety of plants.

You will view a prepared slide of a cross section of a stem, and, working with another student, you will use a simple microtome—an instrument used for cutting thin sections for microscopic study—to make your own slides. You will embed the stem tissue in paraffin and cut thin sections. You will stain your sections with toluidine blue, which will help you distinguish different cell types. This simple procedure is analogous to the process used to make prepared slides for subsequent lab studies.

 Read through the procedure and set up the materials before beginning.

Procedure

1. Embed the sections of the stem.
   a. Using a new single-edged razor blade, cut a 0.5 cm section of a young bean stem.
   b. Obtain a nut-and-bolt microtome. The nut should be screwed just into the first threads of the bolt. Using forceps, carefully hold the bean stem upright inside the nut.
   c. Pour the warm paraffin into the nut until full. Continue to hold the top of the stem until the paraffin begins to harden. While the paraffin completely hardens, continue the exercise by examining the prepared slide of the stem.
2. Examine a prepared slide of a cross section through the herbaceous dicot stem (Color Plate 61).
3. Identify the **dermal tissue system,** characterized by a protective cell layer covering the plant. It is composed of the **epidermis** and the

cuticle. Occasionally, you may also observe multicellular **trichomes** on the outer surface of the plants.

4. Locate the **ground tissue system,** background tissue that fills the spaces between epidermis and vascular tissue. Identify the **cortex region** located between the vascular bundles and the epidermis. It is composed mostly of **parenchyma,** but the outer part may contain **collenchyma** as well.

5. Next find the **pith region,** which occupies the center of the stem, inside the ring of vascular bundles; it is composed of parenchyma. In herbaceous stems, these cells provide support through turgor pressure. This region is also important in storage.

6. Now identify the **vascular system,** a continuous system of xylem and phloem providing transport and support. In your stems and in many stems, the **vascular bundles** (clusters of xylem and phloem) occur in rings that surround the pith; however, in some groups of flowering plants, the vascular tissue is arranged in a complex network.

7. Observe that each bundle consists of phloem tissue toward the outside and xylem tissue toward the inside. A narrow layer of vascular cambium, which may become active in herbaceous stems, is situated between the xylem and the phloem. Take note of the following information as you make your observations.

Phloem tissue is composed of three cell types:

a. Dead, fibrous, thick-walled **sclerenchyma cells** that provide support for the phloem tissue and appear in a cluster as a **bundle cap.**

b. **Sieve-tube members,** which are large, living, elongated cells that lack a nucleus at maturity. They become vertically aligned to form sieve tubes, and their cytoplasm is interconnected through sieve plates located at the ends of the cells. Sieve plates are not usually seen in cross sections.

c. **Companion cells,** which are small, nucleated parenchyma cells connected to sieve-tube cells by means of cytoplasmic strands.

Xylem tissue is made up of two cell types:

a. **Tracheids,** which are elongated, thick-walled cells with closed, tapered ends. They are dead at functional maturity, and their lumens are interconnected through pits in the cell walls.

b. **Vessel elements,** which are cylindrical cells that are large in diameter and dead at functional maturity. They become joined end to end, lose their end walls, and form long, vertical vessels.

Vascular cambium is a type of tissue that is located between the xylem and the phloem and which actively divides to give rise to secondary tissues.

8. Complete the Results section below for this slide, then return to step 9 to prepare and observe your own handmade sections of stem preparations.

9. Cut the stem sections in the hardened paraffin.

a. Support the nut-and-bolt microtome with the bolt head down and, using the razor blade, carefully slice off any excess paraffin extending above the nut. Be careful to slice in a direction away from your body and to keep your fingers away from the edge of the razor blade (Figure 19.3).

Figure 19.3.
Using the nut-and-bolt microtome.
A piece of stem is embedded in paraffin in the bolt. As you twist the bolt up, slice thin sections to be stained and viewed. Slide the entire blade through the paraffin to smoothly slice thin sections. Follow the directions in Exercise 19.3, Lab Study A carefully.

Be careful to keep fingers and knuckles away from the razor blade. Follow directions carefully.

  b. Turn the bolt *just a little,* to extend the stem/paraffin above the edge of the nut.

  c. Produce a thin section by slicing off the extension using the full length of the razor blade, beginning at one end of the blade and slicing to the other end of the blade (see Figure 19.3).

  d. Transfer each section to a small petri dish containing 50% ethanol.

  e. Continue to produce thin sections of stem in this manner. The thinnest slices may curl, but this is all right if the stem section remains in the paraffin as you make the transfer. Cell types are easier to identify in very thin sections or in the thin edges of thicker sections.

10. Stain the sections.

  a. Leave the sections in 50% ethanol in the petri dish for 5 minutes. The alcohol *fixes,* or preserves, the tissue. Using dissecting needles and forceps, carefully separate the tissue from the surrounding paraffin.

  b. Using forceps, move the stem sections, free of the paraffin, to a clean slide.

  c. Add several drops of toluidine blue to cover the sections. Allow the sections to stain for 10 to 15 seconds.

  d. Carefully draw off the stain by placing a piece of paper towel at the edge of the stain.

  e. Rinse the sections by adding several drops of distilled water to cover the sections. Draw off the excess water with a paper towel. Repeat this step until the rinse water no longer looks blue.

  f. Add a drop of 50% glycerine to the sections and cover them with a coverslip, being careful not to trap bubbles in the preparation.

  g. Observe your sections using a compound microscope. Survey the sections at low or intermediate power, selecting the specimens with the clearest cell structure. You may have to study more than one specimen to see all structures.

11. Follow steps 3–7 above and identify all structures and cells. Incorporate your observations into the Results section (4, following).

Results

1. Label the stem section in Figure 19.4b and c.

2. Were any epidermal trichomes present in your stem?

3. Note any features not described in the procedure. Sketch these in the margin of your lab manual for future reference. Return to Procedure step 9 in this lab study and complete the preparation of hand sections of the bean stem.

4. Compare your hand sections with the prepared slide. Modify Figure 19.4 or sketch your hand section in the margin. Is there any evidence of vascular cambium and secondary growth (Exercise 19.4)? Compare your results with those of other students.

Figure 19.4.
Stem anatomy. (a) Diagram of whole plant. (b) Photomicrograph of cross section through the stem portion of the plant. (c) Enlargement of one vascular bundle as seen in cross section of the stem.

 The functions of cells were described in the Summary of Basic Plant Tissues and Cell Types, which appeared near the beginning of this lab topic.

Discussion

1. Which are larger and more distinct, xylem cells or phloem cells?

2. What types of cells provide support of the stem? Where are these cells located in the stem?

3. For the cells described in your preceding answer, how does their observed structure relate to their function, which is support?

4. What is the function of xylem? Of phloem?

5. The pith and cortex are made up of parenchyma cells. Describe the many functions of these cells. Relate parenchyma cell functions to their observed structure.

6. What differences did you observe in the prepared stem sections and your hand sections? What factors might be responsible for these differences?

Lab Study B. Roots

Materials

prepared slide of buttercup (*Ranunculus*) root (cross section)
demonstration of fibrous roots and taproots
colored pencils
compound microscope

Introduction

Roots and stems often appear to be similar, except that roots grow in the soil and stems above the ground. However, some stems (rhizomes) grow underground, and some roots (adventitious roots) grow aboveground. Roots and stems may superficially appear similar, but they differ significantly in their functions.

What are the primary functions of stems?

Roots have four primary functions:
1. anchorage of the plant in the soil
2. absorption of water and minerals from the soil
3. conduction of water and minerals from the region of absorption to the base of the stem
4. starch storage to varying degrees, depending on the plant

Hypothesis

Our working hypothesis for this investigation is that the *structure* of the plant body is related to particular *functions*.

Prediction

Based on our hypothesis, make a prediction about the similarity of root and stem structures that you expect to observe (if/then).

You will now test your hypothesis and predictions by observing the external structure of roots and their internal cellular structure and organization in a prepared cross section. This activity is an example of collecting evidence from observations rather than conducting a controlled experiment.

Procedure

1. Examine the external root structure. When a seed germinates, it sends down a **primary root,** or **radicle,** into the soil. This root sends out side branches called lateral roots, and these in turn branch out until a root system is formed.

   If the primary root continues to be the largest and most important part of the root system, the plant is said to have a **taproot** system. If many main roots are formed, the plant has a **fibrous root** system. Most grasses have a fibrous root system, as do trees with roots occurring within 1 m of the soil surface. Carrots, dandelions, and pine trees are examples of plants having taproots.

   a. Observe examples of fibrous roots and taproots on demonstration in the laboratory.

   b. Sketch the two types of roots in the margin of your lab manual.

Figure 19.5.
Cross section of the buttercup root. (a) Whole plant. (b) Photomicrograph of a cross section of a root. (c) Enlargement of the vascular cylinder. Label the root based on your observations of a prepared microscope slide.

2. Examine the internal root structure.

a. Study a slide of a cross section through a buttercup (*Ranunculus*) root. Note that the root lacks a central pith. The vascular tissue is located in the center of the root and is called the **vascular cylinder** (Figure 19.5b).

b. Look for a cortex. The **cortex** is primarily composed of large parenchyma cells filled with numerous purple-stained organelles. Which of the four functions of roots listed in the introduction to this lab study do you think is related to these cortical cells and their organelles?

c. Identify the following tissues and regions and label Figure 19.5b and c accordingly: **epidermis**, parenchyma of **cortex**, **vascular cylinder**, **xylem**, **phloem**, **endodermis**, and **pericycle**. The endodermis and the pericycle are unique to roots. The endodermis is the inner-most cell layer of the cortex. The walls of endodermal cells have a band called the **Casparian strip**—made of **suberin**, a waxy material—that extends completely around each cell, as shown in Figure 19.6. This strip forms a barrier to the passage of anything moving between adjacent cells of the endodermis. All water and dissolved materials absorbed by the epidermal root hairs and transported inward through the cortex must first pass through the living cytoplasm of endodermal cells before entering the vascular tissues. The pericycle is a layer of dividing cells immediately inside the endodermis; it gives rise to lateral roots.

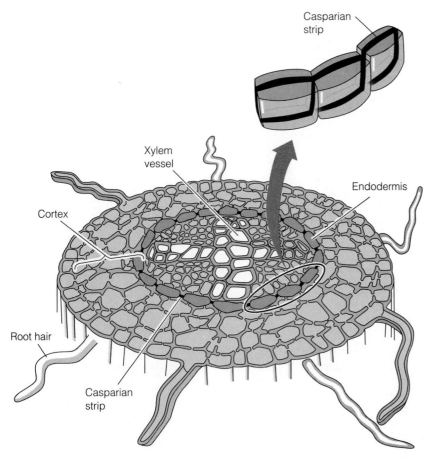

Figure 19.6.
Root endodermis. The endodermis is composed of cells surrounded by a band containing *suberin,* called the *Casparian strip* (seen in enlargement), that prevents the movement of materials along the cells' walls and intercellular spaces into the vascular cylinder. Materials must cross the cell membrane before entering the vascular tissue.

Results

1. Review Figure 19.5 and note comparable structures in Figure 19.6.
2. Using a colored pencil, highlight the representations of structures or cells found in the root but not seen in the stem.

Discussion

1. Suggest the advantage of taproots and of fibrous roots under different environmental conditions.

2. Did your observations support your hypothesis and predictions (page 509)?

3. Compare the structure and organization of roots and stems. How do these two organs differ?

4. Explain the relationship of structure and function for two structures or cells found only in roots.

5. Note that the epidermis of the root lacks a cuticle. Can you explain why this might be advantageous?

6. What is the function of the endodermis? Why is the endodermis important to the success of plants in the land environment?

Lab Study C. Leaves

Materials

prepared slide of lilac (*Syringia*) leaf
slides
compound microscope
coverslips

dropper bottles of water
leaves of purple heart (*Setcreasia*)
   kept in saline and DI water

Introduction

Leaves are organs especially adapted for photosynthesis. The thin blade portion provides a very large surface area for the absorption of light and the uptake of carbon dioxide through stomata. The leaf is basically a layer of parenchyma cells (the **mesophyll**) between two layers of epidermis. The loose arrangement of parenchyma cells within the leaf allows for an extensive surface area for the rapid exchange of gases. Specialized epidermal cells called guard cells allow the exchange of gases and evaporation of water at the leaf surface. Guard cells are photosynthetic (unlike other epidermal cells), and are capable of changing shape in response to complex environmental and physiological factors. Current research indicates that the opening of the stomata is the result of the active uptake of K^+ and subsequent changes in turgor pressure in the guard cells.

In this lab study, you will examine the structure of a leaf in cross section. You will observe stomata on the leaf epidermis and will study the activity of guard cells under different conditions.

Procedure

1. Before beginning your observations of the leaf cross section, compare the shape of the leaf on your slide with Figure 19.7a and b on the next page.

2. Observe the internal leaf structure.

   a. Examine a cross section through a lilac leaf and identify the following cells or structures: **cuticle, epidermis** (upper and lower), parenchyma with chloroplasts (**mesophyll**), **vascular bundle** with **phloem** and **xylem**, and **stomata** with **guard cells** and **substomatal chamber.**

   b. The vascular bundles of the leaf are often called **veins** and can be seen in both cross section and longitudinal sections of the leaf. Observe the structure of cells in the central midvein. Is xylem or phloem on top in the leaf?

a.

b.

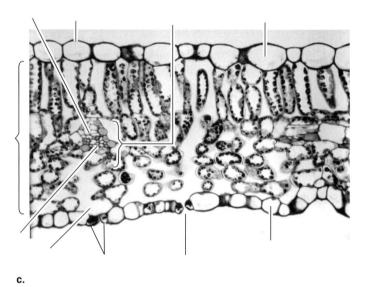

c.

Figure 19.7.
Leaf structure. (a) Whole plant. (b) Photomicrograph of a leaf cross section
through the midvein. (c) Photomicrograph of a leaf cross section adjacent to the
midvein.

c. Observe the distribution of stomata in the upper and lower epidermis. Where are they more abundant?

d. Label the cross section of the leaf in Figure 19.7.

3. Observe the leaf epidermis and stomata.

a. Obtain two *Setcreasia* leaves, one placed in saline for an hour and the other placed in distilled water for an hour.

b. Label two microscope slides, one "saline" and the other "H₂O."

c. To remove a small piece of the lower epidermis, fold the leaf in half, with the lower epidermis to the inside. Tear the leaf, pulling one end toward the other, stripping off the lower epidermis (Figure 19.8). If you do this correctly, you will see a thin purple layer of lower epidermis at the torn edge of the leaf.

d. Remove a small section of the epidermis from the leaf in *DI water* and mount it in water on the appropriate slide, being sure that the outside surface of the leaf is facing up. View the slide at low and high power on your microscope, and observe the structure of the stomata. Sketch your observations in the margin of your lab manual.

e. Remove a section of the epidermis from the leaf in *saline* and mount it on the appropriate slide in a drop of the *saline*. Make sure that the outside surface of the leaf is facing up. View the slide with low power on your microscope, and observe the structure of the stomata. Sketch your observations in the margin of your lab manual.

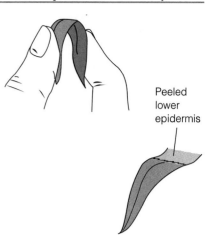

Peeled
lower
epidermis

Figure 19.8.
Preparation of leaf epidermis peel.
Bend the leaf in half and peel away the lower epidermis. Remove a small section of lower epidermis and make a wet mount.

Results

1. Review the leaf cross section in Figure 19.7.
2. Describe the structure of the stomata on leaves kept in DI water.

3. Describe the structure of the stomata on leaves kept in saline.

Discussion

1. Describe the functions of leaves.

2. Provide evidence from your observations of leaf structure to support the hypothesis that structure and function are related. Be specific in your examples.

3. Explain the observation that more stomata are found on the lower surface of the leaf than on the upper.

4. Explain the differences observed, if any, between the stomata from leaves kept in DI water and those kept in saline. Utilize your knowledge of osmosis to explain the changes in the guard cells. (In this activity, you stimulated stomatal closure by changes in turgor pressure due to saline rather than K$^+$ transport.)

EXERCISE 19.4

Cell Structure of Tissues Produced by Secondary Growth

Materials

prepared slides of basswood (*Tilia*) stem
compound microscope

Introduction

Secondary growth arises from meristematic tissue called cambium. Vascular cambium and cork cambium are two types of cambium. The vascular cambium is a single layer of meristematic cells located between the secondary phloem and secondary xylem. Dividing cambium cells produce a new cell at one time toward the xylem, at another time toward the phloem. Thus, each cambial cell produces files of cells, one toward the inside of the stem, another toward the outside, resulting in an increase in stem girth (diameter). The secondary phloem cells become differentiated into sclerenchyma fiber cells, sieve-tube members, and companion cells. Secondary xylem cells become differentiated into tracheids and vessel elements. Certain cambial cells produce parenchyma ray cells that can extend radially through the xylem and phloem of the stem.

The cork cambium is a type of meristematic tissue that divides, producing cork tissue to the outside of the stem and other cells to the inside. The cork cambium and the secondary tissues derived from it are called periderm. The periderm layer replaces the epidermis and cortex in stems and roots with secondary growth. These layers are continually broken and sloughed off as the woody plant grows and expands in diameter.

Procedure

1. Examine a cross section of a woody stem (Color Plate 62).

   a. Observe the cork cambium and periderm in the outer layers of the stem. The outer **cork** cells of the periderm have thick walls impregnated with a waxy material called **suberin.** These cells are dead at maturity. The thin layer of cells that may be visible next to the cork cells is the **cork cambium.** The **periderm** includes the layers of cork and associated cork cambium. The term **bark** is used to describe the periderm and phloem on the outside of woody plants.

   b. Observe the cellular nature of the listed tissues or structures, beginning at the periderm and moving inward to the central pith region. **Sclerenchyma fibers** have thick, dark-stained cell walls and are located in bands in the phloem. **Secondary phloem** cells with thin cell walls alternate with the rows of fibers. The **vascular cambium** appears as a thin line of small, actively dividing cells lying between the outer phloem tissue and the extensive secondary xylem. **Secondary xylem** consists of distinctive open cells that extend in layers to the central **pith** region. Lines of parenchyma cells one or two cells thick form **lateral rays** that radiate from the pith through the xylem and expand to a wedge shape in the phloem, forming a **phloem ray.**

2. Note the **annual rings** of xylem, which make up the **wood** of the stem surrounding the pith. Each annual ring of xylem has several rows of **early wood,** thin-walled, large-diameter cells that grew in the spring and, outside of these, a few rows of **late wood,** thick-walled, smaller-diameter cells that grew in the summer.

3. By counting the annual rings of xylem, determine the age of your stem. Note that the phloem region is not involved with determining the age of the tree.

Results

1. Review Figure 19.9 on the next page and Color Plate 62.
2. Sketch in the margin of your lab manual any details not represented in the figure that you might need for future reference.
3. Indicate on your diagram the region where primary tissues can still be found.

Discussion

1. What has happened to the several years of phloem tissue production?

2. Based on your observations of the woody stem, does xylem or phloem provide structural support for trees?

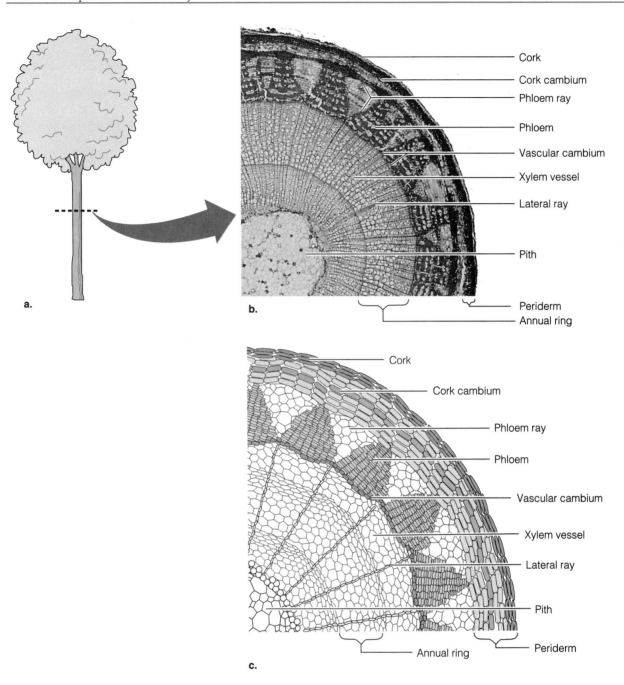

Figure 19.9.
Secondary growth. (a) Whole woody plant. (b) Photomicrograph of a cross section of a woody stem. (c) Compare the corresponding diagram with your observations of a prepared slide. If necessary, modify the diagram to correspond to your specimen.

3. What function might the ray parenchyma cells serve?

4. How might the structure of early wood and late wood be related to seasonal conditions and the function of the cells? Think about environmental conditions during the growing season.

EXERCISE 19.5

Grocery Store Botany: Modifications of Plant Organs

Materials

variety of produce: squash, lettuce, celery, carrot, white potato, sweet potato, asparagus, onion, broccoli, and any other produce you wish to examine

Introduction

Every day you come into contact with the plant world, particularly in the selection, preparation, and enjoyment of food. Most agricultural food plants have undergone extreme selection for specific features. For example, broccoli, cauliflower, cabbage, and brussels sprouts are all members of the same species that have undergone selection for different features. In this exercise, you will apply your botanical knowledge to the laboratory of the grocery store.

Procedure

1. Working with another student, examine the numerous examples of root, stem, and leaf modifications on demonstration. (There may be some reproductive structures as well. Refer to Lab Topic 16, Plant Diversity II, if needed.)

2. For each grocery item, determine the type of plant organ, its modification, and its primary function. How will you decide what is a root, stem, or leaf? Review the characteristics of these plant organs and examine your produce carefully.

Results

Complete Table 19.1 on the next page.

Table 19.1

Grocery Store Botany

Name of Item	Plant Organ (Root, Stem, Leaf, Flower, Fruit)	Function/Features (Storage, Support, Reproduction, Photosynthesis)

Discussion

1. What feature of the white potato provided key evidence in deciding the correct plant organ?

2. Based on your knowledge of the root, why do you think roots have been selected so often as food sources?

Questions for Review

1. Use Table 19.2 to describe the structure and function of the cell types seen in lab today. Indicate the location of these in the various plant organs examined.

2. Some tissues are composed of only one type of cell; others are more complex. List the cell types observed in xylem and in phloem.

   Xylem:

   Phloem:

3. What characteristic of sieve-tube structure provides a clue to the role of companion cells?

4. Compare primary and secondary growth. What cells divide to form primary tissue? To form secondary tissue? Can a plant have both primary growth and secondary growth? Explain, providing evidence to support your answer.

Applying Your Knowledge

1. Cells of the epidermis frequently retain a capability for cell division. Why is this important? (*Hint:* What is their function?)

2. Why is the endodermis essential in the root but not in the stem?

Table 19.2
Structure and Function of Plant
Cells

Cell Type	Structure	Function	Plant Organ
Epidermis			
Guard cells			
Parenchyma			
Collenchyma			
Sclerenchyma			
Tracheids			
Vessels			
Sieve tubes			
Endodermis			
Primary meristems			
Vascular cambium			
Pericycle			
Periderm			
Ray parenchyma			

3. When lateral roots grow outward from the pericycle, what effect does this have on the cortex and the epidermis? (*Hint:* Review the structure of the root and the location of these tissues.)

4. In the summer of 1998, after extremely hot, dry weather, the Georgia corn harvest was expected to be reduced by at least 25%. Using your knowledge of the dual functions of guard cells relative to water retention and gas exchange, explain the reduction in photosynthetic productivity.

5. The belt buckle of a standing 20-year-old man may be a foot higher than it was when he was 10, but a nail driven into a 10-year-old tree will be at the same height 10 years later. Explain.

6. Explain, from a cellular point of view, how it is possible to determine the age of a tree.

7. The oldest living organisms on Earth are plants. Some bristlecone pines are about 4,600 years old, and a desert creosote bush is known to be 10,000 years old. What special feature of plants provides for this incredible longevity? How do plants differ from animals in their pattern of growth and development?

8. Plant cells have cell walls and animal cells do not. How does this difference relate to differences in plant and animal function?

Table 19.3
Adaptations of Plant Cells and Structures to the Land Environment

Environmental Factor	Adaptations to Land Environment
Desiccation	
Transport of materials between plant and environment	
Gas exchange	
Anchorage in substrate	
Transport of materials within plant body	
Structural support in response to gravity	
Sexual reproduction without water	
Dispersal of offspring from immobile parent	

9. Many of the structural features studied in this laboratory evolved in response to the environmental challenges of the terrestrial habitat. Complete Table 19.3 on this page, naming the cells, tissues, and organs that have allowed vascular plants to adapt to each environmental factor.

Investigative Extensions

1. The nut-and-bolt microtome can be used to separate a section of almost any part of a plant. You might grow your own plants from seeds and then embed small sections of each plant organ in paraffin and prepare slides for observation. Visualize the orientation of your material and sections before embedding.

2. Using the technique described in 1 or prepared slides, you can investigate plants that follow a different organization of tissues, including a group of angiosperms known as monocots. Stem sections and leaf sections should be different from those studied in lab.

References

Figure 19.3 and the idea for the nut-and-bolt microtome are from Dickey, J. *Laboratory Investigations for General Biology.* Redwood City, CA: Benjamin/Cummings, 1994. Used by permission.

Mauseth, J. D. *Botany: An Introduction to Plant Biology,* 2nd ed. Philadelphia, PA: Saunders College Publishing, 1995.

Moore, R., W. D. Clark, and D. S. Vodopich. *Botany,* 2nd ed. Boston, MA: WCB/McGraw-Hill, 1998.

Plant Growth

 This lab topic gives you another opportunity to practice the scientific process introduced in Lab Topic 1. Before going to lab, review scientific investigation in Lab Topic 1 and carefully read Lab Topic 20. Be prepared to use this information to design an experiment for plant growth.

Laboratory Objectives

After completing this lab topic, you should be able to:

1. Describe external and internal factors that influence the germination of angiosperm seeds.
2. Explain the effect of auxin on plant growth.
3. Explain the effect of gibberellins on the growth of dwarf corn seedlings.
4. Define and give examples of *phototropism* and *gravitropism*.
5. Design and execute an experiment testing factors that influence seed germination and plant growth.
6. Present the results of the experiment in oral or written form.

Introduction

In Lab Topic 16, Plant Diversity II, you studied the life cycle of angiosperms. You observed that fertilization of the egg in the female gametophyte results in an embryo protected in a **seed** consisting of the young embryonic sporophyte, food, and a protective seed coat. Seeds develop in the parent plant, and when they are mature, they are separated from the parent and dispersed. Most seeds go through a period of dormancy, but when a dormant seed finds a favorable environment, it will begin to **germinate;** that is, it renews its development and the embryo resumes its growth. Most plants continue to grow as long as they live, a condition known as **indeterminate growth.** Indeterminate growth is possible because of plant tissues called **meristems,** which remain embryonic as long as the plant lives. Seed germination and plant growth are regulated by external factors such as light, temperature, nutrients, and water availability. Plants respond to these environmental stimuli by internal mechanisms regulated by chemical messengers called **hormones.**

A hormone, whether it is found in plants or animals, is produced in small quantities in one part of the organism and transported to another site, where it causes some special effect.

In this lab topic, you will work in teams, investigating external stimuli and internal mechanisms that influence the germination of seeds and the growth of plants. You will be led through several brief introductory observational lab studies (Lab Study A of Exercises 20.1, 20.2, and 20.3); then your team will propose one or more testable hypotheses based on questions from the lab studies or your imagination. You will then design and carry out an independent investigation based on your hypotheses (Exercise 20.4). You may design an experiment that can be completed in the laboratory period. However, you should plan to make observations of your plants over several days or at the beginning of the next laboratory. Your instructor will tell you if you will be able to return to the lab to make observations or if you should carry your experiment elsewhere for observations. Before or during the first hour of the following laboratory period, you should have completed your observations and recorded your results. Your team should discuss the results and prepare an oral presentation. One member of your team will present your team's results to the class for discussion. This person should be prepared to persuade the class that your experimental design is sound and that your results support your conclusions. If required by the lab instructor, each of you will submit an independent laboratory report describing your experiment and results in the format of a scientific paper (see Appendix A).

 First complete Lab Study A in Exercises 20.1, 20.2, and 20.3. Then discuss possible questions for investigation with your research team. Be certain you can pose an interesting question from which you can develop a testable hypothesis. Design and initiate the experiment today. Complete the experiment and report your results during the following laboratory period.

Germinating Seeds and Growing Plants for Independent Investigations

Experimental Plants

You may choose plants used in the lab studies for your independent investigation. These include *Zea mays* (corn), *Phaseolus vulgaris* (pinto bean), *Phaseolus limensis* (lima bean), *Coleus blumei* (a common ornamental annual with colorful variegated leaves), and *Brassica rapa* (related to mustard and cabbage). If you decide to use different plant species, check with your laboratory instructor about the availability of additional plants.

Germinating Bean and Pea Seeds

Bean and pea seeds can be germinated by first submerging them in a 10% sodium hypochlorite solution for 5 minutes to kill bacteria and fungus spores on their surfaces. Follow this with a distilled water rinse and plant the seeds 1 cm deep in flats of vermiculite, a clay mineral that looks like mica and is frequently used as a starting medium for seeds. Add water or a test solution to the flats daily.

Growing Wisconsin Fast Plants

The *Brassica rapa* seeds used in this exercise were developed by Dr. Paul Williams of the Department of Plant Pathology, University of Wisconsin, Madison. Dr. Williams used traditional breeding techniques to produce plants, called Wisconsin Fast Plants™, that can complete an entire breeding cycle from seed to seed in 35 days (Figure 20.1). Because of the rapid growth and shortened breeding cycle of these plants, they are excellent investigative tools for use in plant growth experiments.

A. Seed Germination Exercises

Brassica rapa seeds can be germinated by placing them on wet filter paper in the lid of a petri dish. Stand the dish, tilted on its end, in a water reservoir such as the bottom of a 2-L soft-drink bottle (Figure 20.2a). The dish and reservoir should be placed under fluorescent lights. Germination begins within 24 hours, and observations can be made for several days. It is important to keep the filter paper moist by carefully adding water. If you wish to make quantitative measurements of seed germination, tape a transparent grid sheet marked in measured increments to the outside of the petri dish lid. Place the wet filter paper in the lid, as before, and plant the seeds at a particular position in relation to the grid. As the seeds germinate and grow, you can easily use the grid to measure their size (Figure 20.2b).

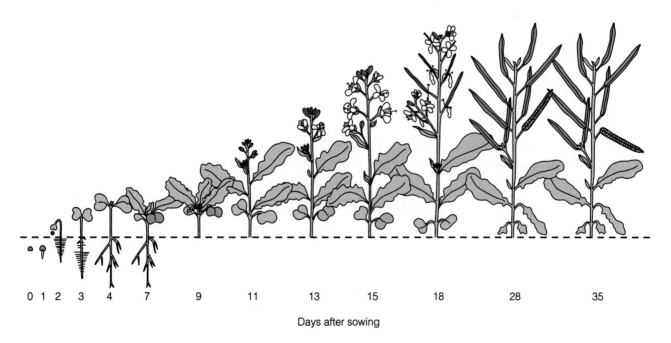

0 1 2 3 4 7 9 11 13 15 18 28 35

Days after sowing

Figure 20.1.
Life cycle of Fast Plant *Brassica rapa*. These plants can complete their entire life cycle from seed to seed in 35 days.

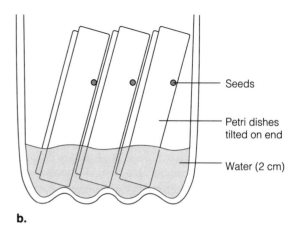

a.   **b.**

Figure 20.2.
Germinating *Brassica rapa* seeds in a petri dish. (a) Place the seeds on wet filter paper in the lid of a petri dish. Attach a grid to the outside of the lid for easy seedling measurement. (b) Stand the dishes on end in a water reservoir.

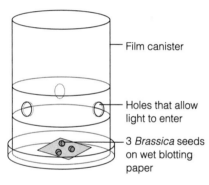

Figure 20.3.
Growing *Brassica rapa* plants in film canisters. Place seeds on moist blotting paper in the lid. Holes can be punched in the canister to allow light to enter the chamber.

B. Tropism Studies

Brassica rapa seeds can be germinated in empty 35-mm clear or black film canisters (Figure 20.3). The canisters can be used as is or black canisters can be modified by punching holes in the sides to allow light to enter the chamber. Place small, appropriately sized squares of wet blotting paper in the lid, and place two or three seeds on the blotting paper. (Do not use filter paper; it dries out too quickly.) Invert the canister and snap it into the lid. Holes in the canister can be covered with different-colored filters, and the size of the holes can be varied to alter the quality or quantity of light hitting the plants.

C. Growing Brassica rapa *Seedlings in Quads*

Scientists working with Wisconsin Fast Plants suggest germinating seeds in small, commercially available Styrofoam™ containers called *quads,* which contain four cells, or chambers. To germinate seeds in quads (Figure 20.4):

1. Add a wick to each cell to draw water from the source into the soil.
2. Add potting mix until each cell is about half full.
3. Add three fertilizer pellets.
4. Add more soil and press to make a depression.
5. Add two or three seeds to each cell and cover them with potting mix.
6. Carefully water each section using a pipette until water soaks through the potting mix and drips from the wick.
7. Place the quad on the watering tray under fluorescent lights.

After the seeds begin to germinate, you can manipulate the plants in many different ways to investigate plant growth.

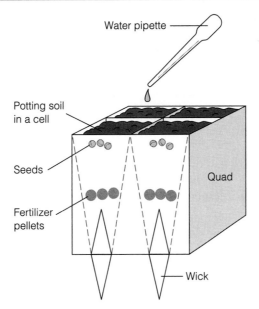

Figure 20.4.
Growing *Brassica rapa* plants in quads. Pull a wick through the hole in each cell. Add potting soil, fertilizer, and seeds. Initially, water using a pipette.

EXERCISE 20.1
Factors Influencing Seed Germination

Seeds are the means of reproduction, dispersal, and, frequently, survival for a plant. Plants are immobile and can colonize new habitats and escape inhospitable weather only through the dispersal and dormancy of seeds. *Dormancy* is a special condition of arrested growth in which the seed cannot germinate without special environmental cues. In this exercise, you will observe germinating bean and *Brassica rapa* seeds. The beans have been germinating in a moist environment for several days. The *Brassica rapa* seeds are germinating on wet filter paper in the lid of a petri dish.

Lab Study A. Germinating Bean and *Brassica rapa* Seeds

Materials

germinating bean seeds
petri dishes with germinating *Brassica rapa* seeds
stereoscopic microscope or hand lens

Introduction

In this lab study, you will examine seed and seedling morphology. Working individually, you will identify seed parts in two plants, a species of bean and *Brassica rapa*. As you investigate the morphology of seeds, consider the role of each structure in facilitating the function of the seed.

Procedure

1. Examine a germinating bean seed and identify the **seed coat, cotyledons** (seed leaves), and **embryo** consisting of the **radicle** (embryonic root),

Figure 20.5.
The structure of a bean seed. Add the labels: *seed coat, cotyledons, radicle, hypocotyl,* and *epicotyl.*

hypocotyl (plant axis below the cotyledons), and **epicotyl** with young leaves (plant axis above the cotyledons).

2. Secure a petri dish with germinating *Brassica rapa* seeds. Carefully examine the seeds using a hand lens or the stereoscopic microscope and identify the **seed coat** (which may have been shed), **cotyledons** (how many?), **hypocotyl, primary root, root hairs,** and **young shoot.**

Results

1. Label the parts of the bean seed in Figure 20.5 on the next page.
2. Draw and label several germinating *B. rapa* seeds in the margin of your lab manual.

Discussion

1. What is the function of the seed coat? From what does it develop?

2. What has happened to the endosperm that formed in the embryo sac of the developing ovule observed in Lab Topic 16, Plant Diversity II?

3. How have the cotyledons developed, and from what? (Check your text; see, for example, Campbell and Reece, 2002, Chapter 38.)

4. How does the structure of the seed facilitate the dispersal and survival of the plant?

Lab Study B. Additional Investigations of Seed Germination

Materials

seeds of *Brassica rapa*

various other seeds—beans, corn, radish, okra, lettuce

35-mm film canisters—clear plastic, black, or black with holes punched in the sides

small squares of blotting paper soaking in water

red, green, and blue cellophane sheets

tape

water baths, oven, refrigerator

grid sheets that fit the lids of petri dishes

reservoir

forceps

scissors

waterproof pen

agar plates

empty petri dishes

sandpaper

various pH solutions

hole punch

Introduction

If your team chooses to study seed germination for your independent investigation and report, use the available materials. Design a simple experiment to investigate factors involved in the germination of seeds.

Procedure

1. Collaborating with your research team, read the following questions, check your text and other sources for supporting information, and choose a question to investigate, using this list or your own imagination.

   a. Do seeds need light to germinate? What effect will germination in total darkness have on the process? Is germination better in alternating light and dark, as in nature?

   b. Is germination different in different wavelengths (colors) of light?

   c. What effect does scarification (scratching the seed coat) have on germination of various seeds? How does scarification occur in nature?

   d. What temperature regimens are optimum for seed germination? Is germination affected by alternating temperatures (as in nature)? Is a constant temperature favorable?

   e. Are there chemical promoters or hormones that influence germination? Check your text for possible test substances.

   f. What effect will salt solutions or acid solutions have on seed germination? Why would questions such as these be of interest?

   g. Does seed size have an effect on germination rates? On seedling size?

2. Design your experiment, proposing hypotheses, making predictions, and determining procedures as instructed in Exercise 20.4.

EXERCISE 20.2

Plant Growth Regulators: Auxin

Both plants and animals respond to environmental cues. Animals generally respond rapidly via the nervous system or more slowly via hormones secreted from endocrine glands. Plants lack a nervous system and respond to environmental stimuli via chemical messengers or hormones. Changes in these hormones lead to altered patterns of growth and development. **Auxin** is the name given to a complex of substances that promotes stem growth. The natural auxin, indoleacetic acid (IAA), is a hormone produced in apical meristems. It migrates down the stem from the zone of production. If the growing tip is removed, the stem will not elongate, but if the tip is replaced with a paste containing IAA, elongation will continue. IAA facilitates cell elongation and promotes growth by breaking linkages among cellulose fibers and loosening the cell wall. In this exercise, you will investigate the role of auxin in stem curvature in response to light and gravity.

Lab Study A. Gravitropic and Phototropic Curvature in *Coleus blumei*

Materials

(on demonstration)
Coleus plant placed on its side
Coleus plant in unilateral light
Coleus plant in upright position

Introduction

In this lab study, you will investigate the growth of the stem in response to two environmental stimuli, gravity and light. **Gravitropism** (or geotropism) is the response of a plant to gravity. **Phototropism** is the response of a plant to light. Three *Coleus blumei* plants are on demonstration in the lab room. One was placed on its side several days ago. Another has been growing in unilateral light for several days. The third, the control, was left undisturbed in the greenhouse until lab time.

Procedure

1. Study gravitropic curvature in *Coleus blumei*.
   a. Carry your lab notebook to the demonstration area and observe the *Coleus* plant placed on its side.
   b. Examine the plant, noting the appearance of different regions of the stems and roots (if visible). What part of each stem has curved? To what degree?
   c. Compare this plant with the control plant left in an upright position.
   d. Describe your observations and answer the questions in the Results section.
2. Study phototropic curvature in *Coleus blumei*.
   a. Examine the plant growing in unilateral light, noting the appearance of different regions of the stems.
   b. Compare the plant to the control plant, which has received light from all directions in the greenhouse.
   c. Record your observations and answer the questions in the Results section.

Results

1. Describe the appearance of the plant lying on its side. *Sketch* the plant in the margin of your lab manual. How does this compare with the appearance of the control plant?

2. What is the extent of the response to gravity? How could you measure or quantify the response?

3. Describe the appearance of the plant in unilateral light. Sketch the plant in the margin of your lab manual. Compare this plant with the control plant.

4. What is the extent of the response to the light? How could you measure or quantify the response?

5. What part of the plant specifically is being affected? (If you need to, review the anatomy of the apical meristem in Lab Topic 19, Plant Anatomy.) Can you explain why?

Discussion

1. What type of response would you expect to see if you reoriented the plant lying on its side? Explain.

2. How do plants detect the force of gravity (according to current theory)? Consult your text, if necessary.

3. Review with your team members the physiological basis for the growth response. How is auxin involved in gravitropism? Where is it produced? Consult your text, if necessary.

4. Is curvature of the stem in response to gravity and light the result of additional cell division or cell elongation? How do you know, or how could you investigate this?

5. What is the role of auxin in phototropism? How is directional light detected in the plant? Use your text and discuss these items with members of your research team.

Lab Study B. Additional Investigations of Auxins

Materials

auxin solutions in various
  concentrations
auxin in lanolin paste
lanolin with no auxin
scissors
Coleus plants
glass containers for planting
Brassica rapa seedlings in quads

corn and bean seedlings in pots or flats
lamps
toothpicks
protractor
spray bottles
cotton-tipped applicators
aluminum foil

Introduction

Having made observations of gravitropism and phototropism in the preceding lab study, discuss with your team members ways to use *Coleus*, *Brassica*, or corn or bean seedlings to further investigate these phenomena. If you choose to carry out your independent investigation with this system, the questions provided in the following Procedure section will be appropriate for your study. Using the materials available, design a simple experiment to investigate the role of auxin in plant growth or factors involved in phototropism and gravitropism.

Procedure

1. Collaborating with your research team, read the following questions, check your text and other sources for supporting information, and choose a question to investigate, using this list or your own imagination.

   a. If only some wavelengths stimulate phototropic response, which ones do and which do not?

   b. If the apical meristem is removed, will plants respond to unilateral light?

   c. If the tip of the root is removed, will roots respond to gravity? (Seedlings can be planted close to the wall in glass containers so that root growth can be viewed.)

   d. Can these tropisms be altered by applying auxin paste to the plant?

   e. What will happen if the tips of the plants (root or stem) are covered with aluminum foil?

   f. How else does auxin affect plants? How does auxin affect apical dominance? Can auxin be used as an herbicide? (In what concentrations? What is the effect on plants?) What concentration of auxin produces the largest roots on cut stems? (What horticultural application would this have?)

   g. Will seedlings growing in the dark respond to auxin applied to the side of the stem? At all locations on the stem?

2. Design your experiment, proposing hypotheses, making predictions, and determining procedures as instructed in Exercise 20.4.

EXERCISE 20.3
Plant Growth Regulators: Gibberellins

Gibberellins are another group of important plant growth hormones found in high concentrations in seeds and present in varying amounts in all plant parts. In some plants, gibberellins produce rapid elongation of stems; in others they produce **bolting,** the rapid elongation of the flower stalk. Produced near the stem apex, gibberellins work by increasing both the number of cell divisions and the elongation of cells produced by those divisions. The effects of gibberellins can be induced by artificially applying solutions to plant parts. Not all plants respond to the application of gibberellins, however, and in this exercise, you will investigate the effect of applying gibberellin solutions to normal and to dwarf (mutant) corn seedlings.

Lab Study A. Effects of Gibberellins on Normal and Dwarf Corn Seedlings

Materials

2 pots each with 4 tall (normal) corn seedlings
2 pots each with 4 dwarf (mutant) corn seedlings
calculator

Introduction

The seedlings used in this lab study are approximately the same age, but they exist in two phenotypes, tall and dwarf (Figure 20.6). The tall seedlings are wild type, or normal. A genetic mutation produces dwarf plants that lack gibberellins. Each team of students has four pots, each with four corn seedlings. Your instructor has previously treated the plants with either water

Figure 20.6.
Normal corn plants and recessive dwarf mutants.

or a gibberellin solution. In this lab study, you will investigate the effects of these treatments on the corn plants.

Procedure

1. Several days ago, your instructor sprayed the plants with either distilled water or a gibberellin solution, as follows:

Control	*Treated*
Pot 1: normal corn, water treatment	Pot 2: normal corn, gibberellin treatment
Pot 3: dwarf corn, water treatment	Pot 4: dwarf corn, gibberellin treatment

2. Observe the results of the treatments.
3. Measure the height of each of your plants and record these data in Table 20.1.

Table 20.1
Height of Normal and Dwarf Corn Seedlings with and Without Gibberellin Treatment

	Normal Control (Pot 1)	Normal Treated (Pot 2)	Dwarf Control (Pot 3)	Dwarf Treated (Pot 4)
Plant 1 Height				
Plant 2 Height				
Plant 3 Height				
Plant 4 Height				
Mean Height				

Results

1. Determine and record the mean height of plants in each category in Table 20.1.

2. Using the mean height for each category of plants, calculate the percentage difference in the mean height of treated normal plants and control normal plants. Then calculate the percentage difference in the mean height of treated dwarf plants and control dwarf plants. Use the given formula for your calculations:

$$\text{Normal \% difference} = \frac{\text{treated} - \text{control}}{\text{control}} \times 100 = \underline{\hspace{1.5cm}}\%$$

$$\text{Dwarf \% difference} = \frac{\text{treated} - \text{control}}{\text{control}} \times 100 = \underline{\hspace{1.5cm}}\%$$

3. Record your data for the average percentage difference in the mean values for both normal and dwarf plants from Table 20.1 on the class master sheet. Then calculate the average percentage differences for the entire class.

	Your Data	*Class Data*
Average % difference: normal	_____	_____
dwarf	_____	_____

Discussion

1. How do values for percentage difference compare for dwarf versus normal treated and untreated plants?

2. What is the action of gibberellins? Discuss your results with your group, and consult your text or other references in the laboratory.

Lab Study B. Additional Investigations of Gibberellins

Materials

normal and dwarf *Brassica rapa* seedlings
normal and dwarf corn seedlings
normal and dwarf pea seedlings
   (Little Marvel peas, *Pisum sativum*)

solutions of gibberellin
dropper bottles
sprayers
cotton-tipped applicators

Introduction

Having seen the effect of gibberellins on the growth of normal and dwarf corn seedlings in the preceding lab study, discuss with your team members possible questions for further study of this group of hormones. If you choose to carry out your independent investigation with this system, the questions provided in the following Procedure section will be appropriate for your study. Using the materials available, design a simple experiment to investigate the actions of gibberellins in plant growth or seed germination.

Procedure

1. Collaborating with your research team, read the following questions, check your text and other sources for supporting information, and choose a question to investigate, using this list or your own imagination.

   a. Plant scientists have discovered a mutant strain of *Brassica rapa* in which plants are dwarf. In these plants, the internodes do not elongate, and plants consist of a cluster of leaves spreading close to the soil. Flowers cluster close to the leaves. What could be the cause of this phenotype?

   b. Would other plant hormones produce the same response in dwarf corn seedlings as do gibberellins?

   c. In the demonstration experiment, the gibberellin solution was sprayed on all parts of the plant. If the gibberellin solution were added only to specific regions, such as the roots or apical meristem, would the effect be the same?

   d. Would the results in the corn experiment differ with different concentrations of gibberellin solution?

   e. What effect do gibberellins have on seed germination?

   f. What effect do gibberellins have on root growth on cut stems?

   g. Is the dwarf condition seen in certain strains of peas (Little Marvel peas) due to the lack of gibberellins?

2. Design your experiment, proposing hypotheses, making predictions, and determining procedures as instructed in Exercise 20.4.

EXERCISE 20.4
Designing Your Independent Investigation

Materials

See each Lab Study B materials list.

Introduction

Use Lab Topic 1 as a reference for designing and performing a scientific investigation. Be ready to assign tasks to members of your lab team. Be sure that everyone understands the techniques that will be used. Your experiment will be successful only if you plan carefully, cooperate with your team members, perform lab techniques accurately and systematically, and record and report data accurately.

 You and your lab partner are resonsible for the care and maintenance of your plants. Remember to check the water. The success of your investigation depends on the plants' survival.

Procedure

1. **Decide on one or more questions to investigate.** Review suggestions in Lab Study B of Exercises 20.1, 20.2, and 20.3. (Refer to Lab Topic 1, Exercise 1.1, Lab Study A. Asking Questions.)
   Question:

2. **Formulate a testable hypothesis.** (Refer to Exercise 1.1, Lab Study B. Developing Hypotheses.)
   Hypothesis:

3. **Summarize the experiment.** (Use separate paper.)
4. **Predict the results of your experiment based on your hypothesis.** (Refer to Lab Topic 1, Exercise 1.2, Lab Study C. Making Predictions.)
   Prediction: (If/then)

5. **Outline the procedures used in the experiment.** (Refer to Exercise 1.2, Lab Study B. Choosing or Designing the Procedure.)

   a. On a separate sheet of paper, list each step in your procedure in numerical order.

   b. Remember to include the number of repetitions (usually a minimum of five), levels of treatment, appropriate time intervals, and controls for each procedure.

   c. If you have an idea for an experiment that requires materials other than those provided, ask your laboratory instructor about their availability. If possible, additional supplies will be made available.

   d. When carrying out an experiment, remember to quantify your measurements when possible.

6. **Perform the experiment,** making observations and collecting data for analysis.

7. **Record observations and data** on a separate sheet of paper. Design tables and graphs, at least one of each. Be thorough when collecting data. Do not just write down numbers, but record what they mean as well. Do not rely on your memory for information that you will need when reporting your results.

8. **Prepare your discussion.** Discuss your results in light of your hypothesis.

   a. Review your hypothesis. Review your results (tables and graphs). Do your results support or falsify your hypothesis? Explain your answer, using your data for support.

   b. Review your prediction. Did your results correspond to the prediction you made? If not, explain how your results are different from your predictions, and why this might have occurred.

   c. If you had problems with the procedure or questionable results, explain how they might have influenced your conclusion.

   d. If you had an opportunity to repeat and expand this experiment to make your results more convincing, what would you do?

   e. Summarize the conclusion you have drawn from your results.

9. **Be prepared to report your results to the class.** Prepare to persuade your fellow scientists that your experimental design is sound and that your results support your conclusions.

10. If your instructor requires it, **submit a written laboratory report** in the form of a scientific paper (see Appendix A). Keep in mind that although you have performed the experiments as a team, you must turn in a lab report of *your original writing*. Your tables and figures may be similar to those, of your team members, but your paper must be the product of your own literature search and creative thinking.

Questions for Review

Having completed this lab topic, you should be able to define and use the following terms, providing examples when appropriate: *seed, seedling, seed coat, cotyledon, endosperm, radicle, hypocotyl, epicotyl, germination, dormancy, phototropism, gravitropism, apical dominance, auxin, gibberellins, bolting.*

Applying Your Knowledge

1. Auxin is directly or indirectly responsible for apical dominance in plants. In this phenomenon, the growth of lateral or axillary buds (described in Lab Topic 19, Plant Anatomy) is inhibited by the auxin that moves down the stem from the apical meristem. It has long been the practice of horticulturists to clip off the apical meristems of certain young house-plants. What impact should this practice have on subsequent plant growth and appearance?

2. Dormancy is often caused by various germination-inhibiting chemicals that may be present in seeds. These water-soluble inhibitors are more common in plants growing in regions with prolonged wet and dry seasons. Suggest an adaptive advantage of the presence of these inhibitors.

3. Heliotropism, or solar tracking, is a plant movement whereby some plants orient their leaves or flowers to follow the position of the sun over the course of the day. Based on your investigations, what hormone do you predict might be involved in solar tracking? Briefly describe an experiment to test whether a particular plant species demonstrates solar tracking.

References

Campbell, N., and J. Reece. *Biology,* 6th ed. Menlo Park, CA: Benjamin/Cummings, 2002.

Moore, R., W. D. Clark, and D. S. Vodopich. *Botany,* 2nd ed. Boston, MA: WCB/McGraw-Hill, 1998.

Taiz, L., and E. Zeiger. *Plant Physiology,* 2nd ed. Sunderland, MA: Sinauer, 1998.

Wisconsin Fast Plants Manual. Burlington, NC: Carolina Biological Supply, 1989.

Websites

Plant Hormones:
http://www.plant-hormones.bbsrc.ac.uk/

Wisconsin Fast Plants:
http://www.fastplants.org/

Vertebrate Anatomy I:
The Skin and Digestive System

Overview of Vertebrate Anatomy Labs
(Lab Topics 21, 22, and 23)

In Lab Topics 17 and 18, Animal Diversity I and II, you investigated several major themes in biology as illustrated by biodiversity in the animal kingdom. One of these themes is the relationship between form and function in organ systems. In this and the following two lab topics, you will continue to expand your understanding of this theme as you investigate the relationship between form, or structure, and function in vertebrate organ systems. For these investigations, you will be asked to view prepared slides and to dissect a representative vertebrate, the fetal pig. The purpose of these investigations is not to complete a comprehensive study of vertebrate morphology but rather to use several select vertebrate systems to analyze critically the relationship between form and function.

You will explore the listed concepts in the designated exercises.

1. The specialization of cells into tissues with specific functions makes possible the development of functional units, or organs (Exercise 21.1, Histology of the Skin).

2. Multicellular heterotrophic organisms must obtain and process food for body maintenance, growth, and repair (Exercise 21.3, The Digestive System in the Fetal Pig).

3. Because of their size, complexity, and level of activity, vertebrates require a complex system to transport nutrients and oxygen to body tissues and to remove waste from all body tissues (Exercise 22.1, Glands and Respiratory Structures of the Neck and Thoracic Cavity; Exercise 22.2, The Heart and the Pulmonary Blood Circuit; Exercise 23.1, The Excretory System).

4. Reproduction is the ultimate objective of all metabolic processes. Sexual reproduction involves the production of two different gametes, the bringing together of the gametes for fertilization, and limited or extensive care of the new individual (Exercise 23.2, The Reproductive System).

5. Complex animals with many organ systems must coordinate the activities of the diverse parts. Coordination is influenced by the endocrine and nervous systems. Integration via the endocrine system is generally slower and more prolonged than that produced by the nervous system, which may receive stimuli, process information, and elicit a response very quickly (Exercise 23.3, Nervous Tissue, the Reflex Arc, and the Vertebrate Eye).

Laboratory Objectives

After completing this lab topic, you should be able to:

1. Describe the four main categories of tissues and give examples of each.
2. Identify tissues and structures in mammalian skin.
3. Describe the function of skin. Describe how the morphology of skin makes possible its functions.
4. Identify structures in the fetal pig digestive system.
5. Describe the role played by each digestive structure in the digestion and processing of food.
6. Apply knowledge and understanding acquired in this lab to problems in human physiology.
7. Apply knowledge and understanding acquired in this lab to explain organismal adaptive strategies.

Introduction to Tissues

All animals are composed of **tissues**, groups of cells that are similar in structure and that perform a common function. During the embryonic development of most animals, the body is composed of three tissue layers: ectoderm, mesoderm, and endoderm. (Recall from Lab Topic 17, Animal Diversity I, that animals in the phylum Porifera lack true tissue organization and that animals in the phylum Cnidaria have only two tissue layers—ectoderm and endoderm.) It is from these embryonic tissue layers that all other body tissues develop. There are four main categories of tissues: epithelium, connective tissue, muscle, and nervous tissue. Organs are formed from these tissues, and usually all four will be found in a single organ.

Tissues are composed of cells and intercellular substances. The intercellular substances are secreted by the cells. **Epithelial tissue** has cells in close aggregates with little intercellular substance (see Figure 21.1). These cells may be in one continuous layer, or they may be in multiple layers. They generally cover or line an external or internal surface. If formed from single layers of cells, the epithelium is called **simple.** If cells are in multiple layers, the epithelium is called **stratified.** If epithelial cells are flat, they are called **squamous.** If they are cube-shaped, they are called **cuboidal.** Tall, prismatic cells are called **columnar.** Thus, epithelium can be stratified squamous (as in skin), simple cuboidal (as in kidney tubules), or in other combinations of characteristics. Epithelial layers may be derived from embryonic ectoderm, mesoderm, or endoderm.

In **connective tissue,** cells are widely separated by intercellular substances consisting of **fibers** embedded in an amorphous **ground substance,** which may be solid, gelatinous, or liquid (Figure 21.2). **Loose connective tissue,** embedded in a liquid ground substance, binds together other tissues and organs and helps hold organs in place. **Bone** and **cartilage** are specialized connective tissues found in the skeleton with, respectively, hard and gelatinous ground substances. **Blood** is a connective tissue with a liquid ground substance called **plasma.** Other connective tissues fill the spaces between various tissues, binding them together, storing fat, or performing other functions. Connective tissues are derived from mesoderm.

Epithelial tissue

a. Simple squamous

Simple
squamous
epithelial
cell

b. Simple cuboidal

Simple
cuboidal
epithelial
cell

Connective
tissue

c. Simple columnar

Connective
tissue

Simple
columnar
epithelial
cell

d. Stratified squamous

Stratified
squamous
epithelium

Figure 21.1.
Epithelial tissue. Epithelial tissue has closely packed cells with little intercellular matrix. Cells may be (a) squamous (flat), (b) cuboidal (cube-shaped),
or (c) columnar (elongated). They may be simple (in single layers) or
(d) stratified (in multiple layers).

Connective tissue

a. Loose connective tissue

Fiber

Cell

Ground substance

b. Bone

Cells

Ground substance

c. Cartilage

Ground substance

Cells

d. Blood

Ground substance

Cells

Figure 21.2.
Connective tissue. (a) In loose connective tissue, cells are embedded in a liquid fibrous matrix. (b) In bone, cells are embedded in a solid fibrous matrix. (c) In cartilage, cells are embedded in a gelatinous fibrous matrix. (d) In blood, cells are embedded in a liquid matrix.

Muscle tissue

a. Skeletal muscle

b. Cardiac muscle

c. Smooth muscle

Figure 21.3.
Muscle tissue. Muscle tissue is either striated or smooth. (a) Skeletal muscle is striated. (b) Cardiac muscle is also striated. (c) Smooth, or visceral, muscle is not striated.

Muscle tissue may be **striated,** showing a pattern of alternating light and dark bands, or **smooth,** showing no banding pattern (Figure 21.3). There are two types of striated muscle: **skeletal,** found in muscles that move the skeleton, and **cardiac,** found only in the wall of the heart. Smooth muscle, also called **visceral** muscle, is found in the skin and in the walls of organs such as the stomach, intestine, and uterus. Muscle, like connective tissue, is derived from mesoderm.

Nervous tissue is found in the central nervous system (brain and spinal cord) and in the peripheral nervous system consisting of nerves (Figure 21.4). Nervous tissue is found in every organ throughout the body. There are two basic cell types, neurons and glial cells. **Neurons** are capable of responding

Figure 21.4.
Nervous tissue. Neurons and glial cells.

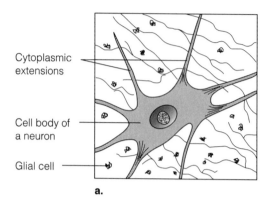

Cytoplasmic
extensions

Cell body of
a neuron

Glial cell

a.

b.

to physical and chemical stimuli by creating an **impulse**, which is transmitted from one locality to another. **Glial cells** support and protect the neurons. Nervous tissue is derived from ectoderm.

The organs that you will investigate in the following exercises are made up of the four basic tissues. The tissues, each with a specific function, are organized into a functional organ unit.

EXERCISE 21.1
Histology of the Skin

Materials

compound microscope
prepared slide of pig and/or monkey skin

Introduction

Tissues are structurally arranged to function together in **organs**, which are adapted to perform specific functions. Organs are found in all but the simplest animals. The largest organ of the vertebrate body, the skin, illustrates the organization of tissues, each with a specific function, into a functioning organ (Figure 21.5). The skin protects the body from dehydration and bacterial invasion, assists in regulating body temperature, and receives stimuli from the environment. As you work through this exercise, ask how the unique function of each tissue produces the functioning whole—the skin.

Procedure

1. Obtain a prepared slide of mammalian skin (pig or monkey). View it using the low and intermediate power objectives on the compound microscope.

2. Identify the two main layers of the skin. The thin outer layer, the **epidermis**, consists of **stratified squamous epithelium**; the thicker inner layer, the **dermis**, consists mainly of **dense connective tissue**

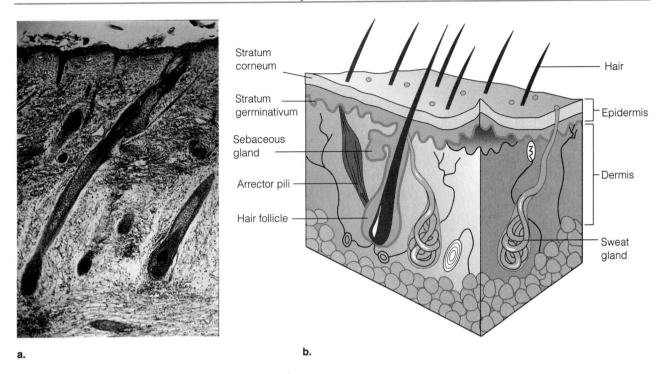

a.   b.

Figure 21.5.
Mammalian skin structure. (a) Photomicrograph of a cross section of the skin.
(b) A diagram detailing the skin structure.

and scattered **blood vessels.** The dermis merges into layers of loose
connective tissue and muscle, which are not considered part of the skin.

3. Locate **hair follicles** extending obliquely from the epidermis into the
   dermis. In the living animal, each follicle contains a hair, but the hair
   shaft may or may not be visible in every follicle on your slide, depending on the plane of the section through the follicle. The follicle is lined
   by epithelial cells continuous with the epidermis. Carefully observe several hair follicles. You may be able to find a band of smooth muscle cells
   attached to the side of a follicle. This muscle, called the **arrector pili,**
   attaches the hair follicle to the outermost layer of the dermis. When
   stimulated by cold or fright, it pulls the hair erect, causing "goose
   bumps." In furry animals this adaptation increases the thickness of the
   coat to provide additional temperature insulation. Clusters of secretory
   cells making up **sebaceous glands** are also associated with hair follicles.
   These are more obvious in monkey skin slides than in pig skin slides.

4. Focus your attention on the epidermis and locate the outermost layer,
   the **stratum corneum,** a layer of dead, keratinized cells, impermeable
   to water. This layer is continually exfoliated and replaced. The thickness
   of the stratum corneum varies, depending on the location of the skin.
   This layer is very thick on the soles of feet or palms of human hands.

5. The innermost layer of cells in the epidermis is called the **basal layer**
   or the **stratum germinativum.** These cells divide mitotically and produce new cells, which, as they mature, are pushed to higher and higher
   layers of the epidermis, until they fill with keratin and form the stratum

corneum. Scattered through the basal layer (though not seen on your slide) are cells called **melanocytes** that produce **melanin,** a pigment that produces brown or black hues in the skin. The melanin is inserted into newly forming epidermal cells as they are pushed outward. Regular exposure to sunlight stimulates melanocytes to produce more melanin, helping protect the body against the potentially harmful effects of sun exposure.

6. In addition to hair follicles, coiled tubular **sweat glands** lined with **cuboidal epithelium** extend from the epidermis into the dermis. They appear as circular clusters in cross section and may be easily located in pig skin but are less numerous or absent in furry animals, such as monkeys. The tubular secretory portion is convoluted into a ball, which connects with a narrow unbranched tube leading to the skin surface. It is unlikely that you will see an entire intact sweat gland in one section.

7. Look for connective tissue and blood vessels, which often contain red blood cells in the dermis. Look for fatty tissue below the dermis.

Results

In Table 21.1, list the tissues you have identified in the skin and indicate the specific function of each.

Discussion

1. How does the skin prevent dehydration?

2. How does the skin protect from bacterial invasion?

Table 21.1
Tissues of the Skin and Their Functions

Tissue	Function

3. Discuss how each of the following helps regulate body temperature: blood vessels in the dermis, sweat glands, fatty deposits below the dermis, hair, and hair follicles.

EXERCISE 21.2
Introduction to the Fetal Pig

Materials

preserved fetal pig   disposable gloves
dissecting pan   preservative

Introduction

Fetal, or unborn, pigs are obtained from pregnant sows being slaughtered for food. The size of your pig will vary, depending on its stage of gestation, a total period of about 112 to 115 days. After being embalmed in a formaldehyde- or phenol-based solution, pigs are stored in a preservative that usually does not contain formaldehyde, although the smell of formaldehyde may remain. Most preserving solutions are relatively harmless; however, they will dry the skin, and occasionally a student may be allergic to the solutions. For these reasons, you should not handle the pigs with your bare hands, and you should perform your dissections in a well-ventilated room.

 Wear disposable gloves when handling the pig and other preserved animals.

In this exercise, you will become familiar with the external anatomy of the fetal pig, noting the regions of its body and the surface structures. The skin, just studied in microscopic sections, will be the first organ observed.

Each student, working independently (unless otherwise instructed), will dissect a fetal pig; however, we encourage you to engage in collaborative discussions with your lab partner. Discuss results and conclusions and compare dissections.

Read carefully the rules and techniques for dissection in Appendix C before you begin your study of the fetal pig.

Procedure

1. Obtain a fetal pig and place it in a dissecting pan. Add a small amount of preservative to the pan. Do not allow the pig to dry out at any time. However, use the preservative, not water, to moisten the tissue unless otherwise instructed.

Your pig may have been injected with red and blue latex. The red was injected into arteries through one of the umbilical arteries; the blue was injected into veins through the external jugular vein through an incision in the neck.

2. Using information in Appendix C and collaborating with your lab partner, locate your pig's left and right, dorsal and ventral, and anterior (cranial) and posterior (caudal) regions. Use the terms *proximal* and *distal* to compare positions of several structures.

3. Locate the body regions on your pig. The pig has a **head, neck, trunk,** and **tail** (Figure 21.6a). The trunk is divided into an anterior **thorax,** encased by ribs, and a posterior **abdomen.** The thoracic and abdominal regions of the body house corresponding cavities that are divisions of the body cavity, or coelom. The **thoracic cavity** is in the thorax, and the **abdominal (peritoneal) cavity** is in the abdomen.

4. Examine the head with its concentration of sensory receptors. Identify the mouth; **external nostrils** on the end of the snout; ears, each with an external flap, the **auricle;** eyes with two eyelids, as in humans, and a third eyelid, the **nictitating membrane,** near the inside corner of each eye.

5. Examine the pig's skin and review its functions. In a fetal pig, an outer embryonic skin, the **epitrichium,** lies over the skin. You may find pieces of this layer on your pig. Is hair present on your pig?

6. Locate the cut **umbilical cord** on the ventral surface of the abdomen. Blood vessels pass from the placenta, attached to the wall of the mother's uterus, to the fetal pig through this cord. If your pig's umbilical cord is collapsed, use scissors to make a fresh transverse cut and examine the end more closely. Identify the cut ends of two round, thick-walled **umbilical arteries;** one larger, flattened **umbilical vein;** and one very small, round **allantoic stalk.** The arteries carry blood from the fetus to the placenta. The vein carries blood from the placenta to the fetus. The allantois is an extension of the urinary bladder of the fetus into the umbilical cord. Speculate about the nature of blood in the umbilical arteries and the umbilical vein. Explain your conclusions.

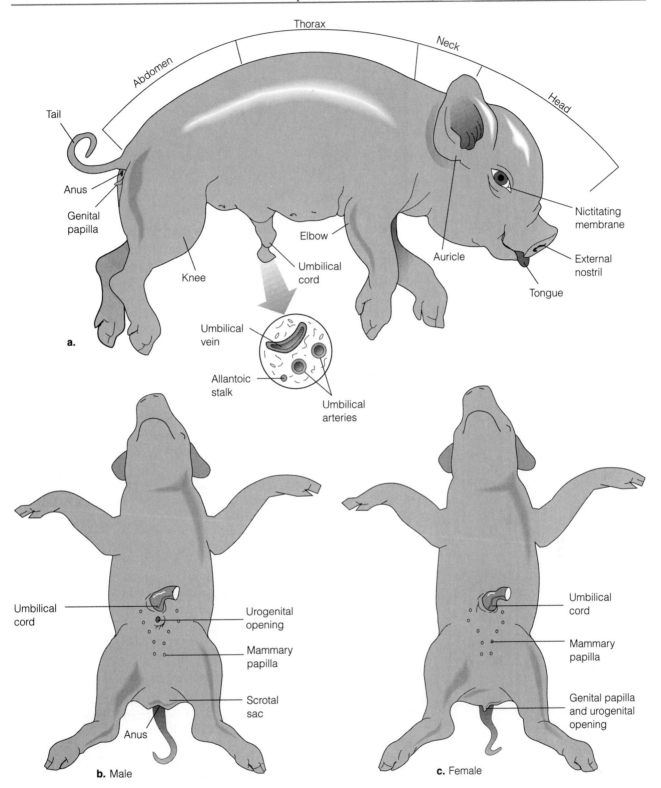

Figure 21.6.
Fetal pig. (a) Body regions and external structures of the fetal pig with an enlarged cross section of the umbilical cord. (b) Posterior region of male pig. (c) Posterior region of female pig.

a. Which vessel would carry blood *high* in oxygen (oxygen-rich blood)?

b. Which vessel would carry blood *low* in oxygen (oxygen-poor blood)?

c. Which vessel would carry blood high in nutrients?

d. Which vessel would carry blood high in metabolic waste?

7. Look just caudal to the umbilical cord to determine the sex of your pig. If it is a male (Figure 21.6b), you will see the **urogenital opening** in this position. This opening is located below the tail in the female. Locate the **anus** just ventral to the base of the tail in both sexes. In the male, **scrotal sacs** will be present ventral to the anus and caudal to the hind legs. In the female pig (Figure 21.6c), the **urogenital opening** is located ventral to the anus. Folds, or **labia**, surround this opening, and a small protuberance, the **genital papilla,** is visible just ventral to the urogenital opening. The urogenital opening is a common opening from the urinary and reproductive tracts. Notice that **mammary papillae** are present in pigs of both sexes. Locate a pig of the opposite sex for comparison. Having determined the sex of your pig, you are now ready to begin your dissection.

Results

1. List structures observed in the fetal pig that are no longer present in the pig after birth.

2. Modify Figure 21.6 or make a sketch in the margin of your lab manual with any additional details needed for future reference.

Discussion

Review the definition of the term *cephalization* defined in Lab Topics 17 and 18, Animal Diversity I and II, and describe how the pig demonstrates this phenomenon.

EXERCISE 21.3

The Digestive System in the Fetal Pig

Materials

supplies from Exercise 21.2
dissecting instruments
twine

plastic bag with twist tie and label
stereoscopic microscope or hand lens

Introduction

Most internal organs, including the entire digestive system, are located in
the body cavity, or coelom. A large muscular structure, the **diaphragm,**
divides the body cavity into the thoracic cavity and the abdominal cavity. Coelomic
epithelial membranes line these cavities and cover the surface of all organs.
Names of the epithelial linings are determined by their location. The epithelium lining the wall of the cavity is called **parietal** (L., *pariet,* "wall"). Thus,
the lining of the abdominal (peritoneal) cavity is **parietal peritoneum.** The
epithelium *covering organs* is called **visceral** (L., "internal organs"). Thus,
the coelomic epithelium covering organs in the peritoneal cavity is **visceral
peritoneum.** Use this convention to name coelomic linings as you open
each body cavity.

Recall from studies in Lab Topics 17 and 18, Animal Diversity I and II, that
the more complex animals have a tubular digestive system with an anterior
opening, the mouth, and a posterior opening, the anus. This pattern in the
digestive system allows specialization to take place along the length of the
tract, resulting in the development of specific organs that carry out specific
functions. As you investigate the digestive system in the fetal pig, ask how
each structure or region solves a particular problem in nutrition procurement
and processing. Remember that memorizing the names of structures is mean-
ingless unless you understand how the morphology is related to the function of the organ.

Procedure

1. Hold the pig ventral side up in the dissecting pan and use twine to tie
    the two anterior legs together and the two posterior legs together, leav-
    ing enough twine between to slip under the dissecting pan. The pig
    should be positioned "spread-eagle" in the pan, ventral side up.

2. To expose structures in the mouth cavity, use heavy, sharp-pointed scis-
    sors to cut at the corners of the mouth along the line of the tongue.
    Continue to cut until the lower jaw can be lowered, being careful not
    to cut into the tissues in the roof of the mouth cavity. Continue to cut,
    pulling down on the lower jaw until your cuts reach the muscle and
    tissue at the back of the mouth. Cut through this muscle until lower-
    ing the jaw exposes the back of the mouth cavity.

    a. Identify structures in the mouth cavity (Figure 21.7). Locate the
        teeth; the **tongue** covered with **papillae,** which house taste buds;
        and the roof of the mouth, composed of the **hard palate** and the **soft
        palate.** The hard palate is anterior to the soft palate and is marked
        by ridges.

Figure 21.7.

The mouth cavity. Openings into the pharynx in the rear of the mouth cavity lead to the respiratory system, the digestive system, and the nasal cavity. The tongue occupies the floor of the mouth, and the roof of the mouth consists of the hard and soft palates.

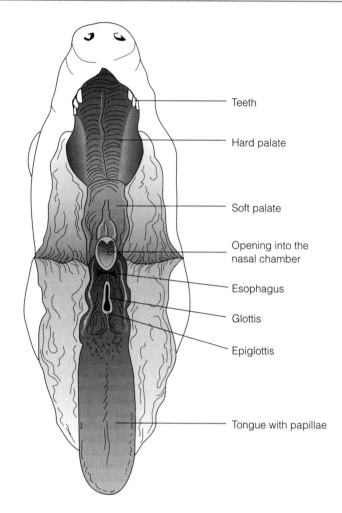

Teeth

Hard palate

Soft palate

Opening into the nasal chamber

Esophagus

Glottis

Epiglottis

Tongue with papillae

    b. Identify structures and openings at the rear of the mouth cavity: the **glottis,** the space in the beginning of the respiratory passageway; the **epiglottis,** a small flap of tissue that covers the glottis when swallowing; the **esophagus,** the beginning of the digestive tube (alimentary canal); and the **opening into the nasal chamber.** All these open into the **pharynx,** the chamber located posterior to the mouth.

    c. Probe into the nasal chamber through the opening at the rear of the soft palate, the esophagus just posterior and ventral to the opening into the nasal chamber, and the glottis. Notice that the opening into the esophagus lies dorsal to the opening into the respiratory tract.

3. Expose the digestive organs in the abdominal region by opening the posterior portion of the abdominal cavity.

    a. Begin the dissection by using the scalpel to make a shallow midventral incision from the base of the throat to the umbilical cord (Figure 21.8, incision 1). Cut lateral incisions (Figure 21.8, incision 2) around each side of the umbilical cord and continue the two incisions, one to the medial surface of each leg.

b. Now use the scissors to cut deep into one of the lateral incisions beside the cord until you penetrate into the abdominal cavity, piercing the parietal peritoneum. At this point, fluid in the cavity should begin to seep out. Use the scissors to cut through the body wall along the two lateral incisions to the legs and around the umbilical cord.

c. Pull lightly on the umbilical cord. If your dissection is correct, you will see that the umbilical cord and ventral wedge of body wall could be reflected, or pulled back, toward the tail, except for a blood vessel, the **umbilical vein.** This vein passes from the umbilical cord anteriorly toward a large brown organ, the liver. Cut through this vein, leaving a stub at each end. Tie a small piece of string around each stub so you can find them later. This should free the flap of body wall, which may now be reflected toward the tail, exposing the abdominal organs.

4. Open the anterior portion of the abdominal cavity.

a. Cut anteriorly through the body wall along the midventral incision until you reach the diaphragm, separating the thoracic and abdominal cavities.

b. Make four lateral cuts, two adjacent to the rib cage just posterior to the diaphragm (incision 3) and two at the posterior margin of the abdominal cavity (incision 4). This will produce two flaps of body wall that can be folded back like the lids of a box.

c. If your specimen contains coagulated blood or free latex from the injection, pull out the latex and rinse the body cavity under running water.

5. Identify the various structures in the abdominal cavity (Figure 21.9).

a. Shiny epithelial membranes line the cavity and cover the organs. The **parietal peritoneum** lines the cavity, and the **visceral peritoneum** covers the organs. Speculate about the contents of the space between these two membranes and its function.

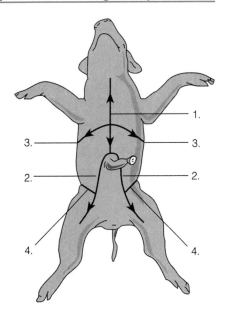

Figure 21.8.
Incisions to open the abdominal cavity. Incision 1 makes a shallow midventral incision from the base of the throat to the umbilical cord. Incision 2 cuts around the umbilical cord to the medial surface of each leg. Incision 3 cuts through the body wall laterally just posterior to the diaphragm. Incision 4 cuts laterally at the posterior margin of the abdominal cavity.

b. The **diaphragm** is a large domed muscle forming the transverse cranial wall of the abdominal cavity, separating this from the thoracic cavity. Only mammals have a diaphragm. The contraction and relaxation of this muscle and muscles between the ribs cause the thoracic cavity to expand and contract, changing the pressure in the cavity and lungs, thus facilitating movement of air into and out of the lungs.

c. The **liver** is the large brown organ that appears to fill the abdominal cavity. Notice that it consists of several lobes. Pull it cranially and locate the **gallbladder,** a small, thin-walled, paddle-shaped sac embedded in its ventral surface. The liver has many functions, including processing nutrients and detoxifying toxins and drugs. Its main digestive function is the production of **bile,** a substance that emulsifies fats. Bile is stored in the gallbladder until needed.

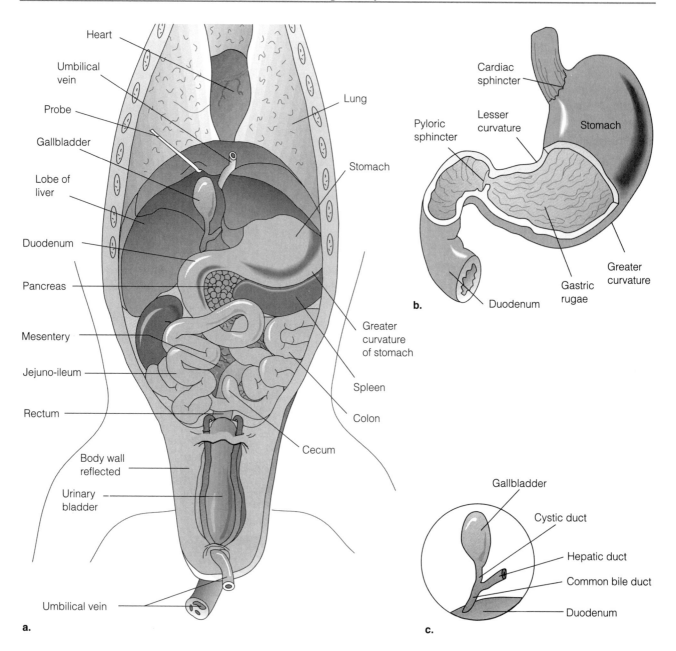

Figure 21.9.
Digestive organs of the abdominal cavity. (a) The liver is reflected cranially to
expose deeper-lying organs. The stomach leads into the duodenum of the small
intestine. The jejuno-ileum continues from the duodenum and empties into the
colon near the cecum. (b) Cutaway view of stomach showing internal gastric
rugae. (c) Enlargement of gallbladder and associated ducts.

d. The **stomach** is a large, saclike organ lying dorsal to the liver
(Figure 21.9b). Reflect the liver cranially to get a better view. The
larger upper-left portion of the stomach tapers down to a narrower
portion to the right. The **esophagus** passes through the diaphragm
and enters the upper medial border of the stomach. Locate the **spleen,**
a dark organ lying along the **greater curvature** of the stomach (the
lateral convex border). The spleen filters blood.

e. Cut into the stomach along the greater curvature. Rinse out the stomach contents and identify the numerous longitudinal folds, called **gastric rugae.** Speculate about the role played by these folds.

f. Food enters the stomach from the esophagus through the **cardiac valve,** or **cardiac sphincter.** A sphincter valve is a circular band of muscle that encircles an opening. Locate this valve between the esophagus and stomach and speculate about its function.

The stomach mechanically churns food and mixes it with water, mucus, hydrochloric acid, and protein-digesting enzymes.

g. From the stomach, food then passes into the **small intestine,** which joins the stomach at its extreme right narrow portion. Locate another valve, the **pyloric sphincter,** which lies between the stomach and small intestine. This sphincter is closed when food is present in the stomach, preventing food from entering the small intestine prematurely.

h. The **duodenum** is the portion of the small intestine connecting with the stomach (Figure 21.9b). The **pancreas,** an irregular, granular-looking gland, lies in a loop of the duodenum. As food passes through the duodenum, enzymes from the pancreas and the duodenal wall are added to it along with bile, which is produced in the liver and stored in the gallbladder. Using your forceps and a blunt probe to pick away surrounding tissue, locate and separate the **common bile duct,** which enters the duodenum. It is formed by the confluence of the **hepatic duct** passing from the liver and the **cystic duct** leading from the gallbladder (Figure 21.9c).

i. The **jejuno-ileum** is the extensive, highly convoluted portion of the small intestine extending from the duodenum to the colon (Figure 21.9a). Whereas the jejunum and the ileum are separate anatomical regions, macroscopically (without a microscope) it is difficult to distinguish between the two in the pig except by position. The duodenum joins the jejunum, which leads to the ileum. The ileum joins the colon.

Most digested food is absorbed into the circulatory system through the walls of the jejuno-ileum. The surface area of the lining of this organ is increased by the presence of microscopic **villi** and **microvilli,** greatly enhancing its absorbing capacity.

Spread apart folds in the jejuno-ileum and notice the thin membrane called **mesentery,** which supports the folds. Do you see blood vessels in this mesentery? Speculate about the relationship between these vessels and food processing.

j. Cut out a 1-cm-long segment of the jejuno-ileum and cut it open to expose the inner surface. Use a stereoscopic microscope or hand lens to examine this surface. Can you see villi?

k. Follow the ileum to its junction with the large intestine, or **colon.** The diameter of the colon is slightly greater than that of the small intestine, and it is tightly coiled and held together by mesentery. Look for a small outpocketing or fingerlike projection of the colon at its proximal end. This projection is the **cecum,** which is much larger in herbivores than in carnivores. In animals with a large cecum, it probably assists in digestion and absorption. In humans, a **vermiform** (wormlike) appendix extends from the cecum.

One of the important activities in the colon is the reabsorption of water that has been added, along with enzymes and mucus, to the food mass as it passes down the digestive tract. Water conservation is one of the most critical problems in terrestrial animals.

l. The distal portion of the colon is the **rectum,** which passes deep into the caudal portion of the abdominal cavity and to the outside of the body at the anus. Water reabsorption continues in the rectum.

6. After you complete the dissection, use an indelible pen to prepare two labels with your name, lab day, and room. Tie one label to your pig and place the pig in a plastic bag with the label in view. Add preservative from the lab stock and securely close the plastic bag. Tie the second label to the outside of the bag.

7. Using the compound microscope, study a prepared microscope slide of a section through a region of the jejuno-ileum (Figure 21.10, Color Plate 63).

a. Use the lowest power on the microscope and scan the section, finding the smooth outer surface and then the **lumen,** or central cavity, located within the intestine. Food passing through the intestine passes through the lumen. Sketch the outline of the section in the margin of your lab manual.

b. The fingerlike **villi** previously observed are now easily discernible, projecting into the lumen of the intestine. Switch to 10× magnification and focus on the **columnar epithelial** tissue lining each villus. This tissue functions in the absorption of nutrients into the circulatory system. Capillaries and lacteals (small lymph vessels) are located within each villus. These vessels are not usually visible.

c. Continue your observations, scanning outward toward the surface of the intestine. You will pass through regions with loose fibrous connective tissue containing many blood vessels. You may see large masses of cells that are lymphocytes in **lymph nodules.**

d. On the outer surface of the section, locate a thin layer of simple squamous epithelium, called the **visceral peritoneum,** or **serosa.** Two large bands of smooth muscle lie just inside the visceral peritoneum.

e. Locate the outermost muscle layer, composed of smooth muscle fibers extending longitudinally along the intestine. This muscle layer is

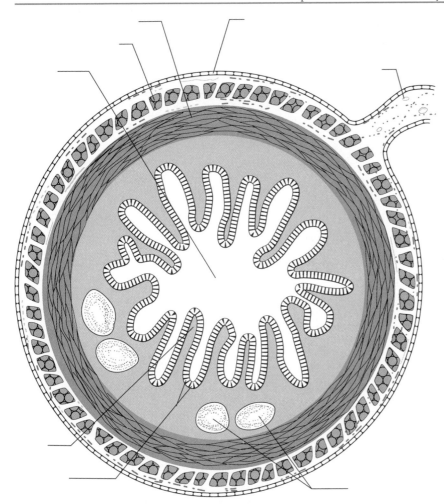

Figure 21.10.
Cross section through the pig jejuno-ileum. Label the cells and structures described in Exercise 21.3, Procedure section, step 7.

called the **longitudinal muscle layer.** Since this is a cross section, the longitudinal nature of the fibers will not be apparent. Look just inside the longitudinal muscle layer to see a wide band of muscle, the **circular muscle layer.** These muscle fibers encircle the intestine.

Imagine each band of muscle contracting as a unit, and speculate about the function of these muscles. Do you know the special name given to the waves of contraction of these muscles?

f. Turn to high power and locate nuclei in both the longitudinal and the circular muscle fibers.

g. Label Figure 21.10.

Table 21.2
Organs of the Pig Digestive Tract and Their Functions

Region/Organ	Function/Macromolecule Digested	Enzymes

Results

In Table 21.2, beginning with the mouth, list each region or organ through which food passes in the pig and describe for each the primary digestive functions, the enzymes active in that chamber, and the macromolecules affected, when appropriate. Consult your text if necessary.

Discussion

1. Conservation of water is a critical problem faced by terrestrial organisms. Given the water requirements for digestion, how is the digestive tract anatomy adapted to life on land?

2. Speculate about the outcome if food passes too slowly or too rapidly through the colon.

3. Consult a text and describe the process of food absorption in the small intestine, relating it to the structures observed in this exercise.

Applying Your Knowledge

1. The Peachtree Road Race is over, and you have just been awarded the coveted T-shirt. Your body is dripping wet and your skin appears bright red. Explain, from a physiological perspective, what is happening to your body.

2. What happens to your skin when you get a "sunburn"? Describe the process of "getting a tan." Relate these processes to skin histology.

3. The three most common forms of skin cancer are (1) basal cell carcinoma, (2) squamous cell carcinoma, and (3) malignant melanoma. Using your knowledge of skin histology, predict the skin layers and/or cells that are involved in each of these cancers.

4. In Lab Topics 17 and 18, Animal Diversity I and II, you investigated adaptation in invertebrates, which provided evidence for the concept that form is related to function. One might hypothesize that the digestive system would differ in mammals, which depend on different food sources. From your text and other sources, list examples of digestive structures that are modified for herbivory and carnivory.

Herbivores

Structure:
Modification:

Structure:

Modification:

Structure:
Modification:

Structure:
Modification:

Carnivores

Structure:
Modification:

Structure:
Modification:

Structure:
Modification:

Structure:
Modification:

References

Campbell, N., and J. Reece. *Biology*, 6th ed. Menlo Park, CA: Benjamin/Cummings, 2002.

Fawcett, D. W., and W. Bloom. *A Textbook of Histology*, 12th ed. Philadelphia, PA: Saunders College Publishing, 1994.

Walker, W. F., Jr. *Anatomy and Dissection of the Fetal Pig*, 5th ed. New York: W. H. Freeman, 1998.

Websites

Test yourself on fetal pig anatomy:
http://www.jburroughs.org/science/resources/pig/pig14.html

Photographs of fetal pig anatomy:
http://www.park.edu/bhoffman/courses/bi123/labs/fetalpig/htm

Vertebrate eye anatomy:
http://www.stlukeseye.com/anatomy.htm

Vertebrate eye anatomy:
http://www.discoveryfund.org/anatomyoftheeye.html

A Google search for "reflex arc" will yield many informative websites:
http://www.google.com

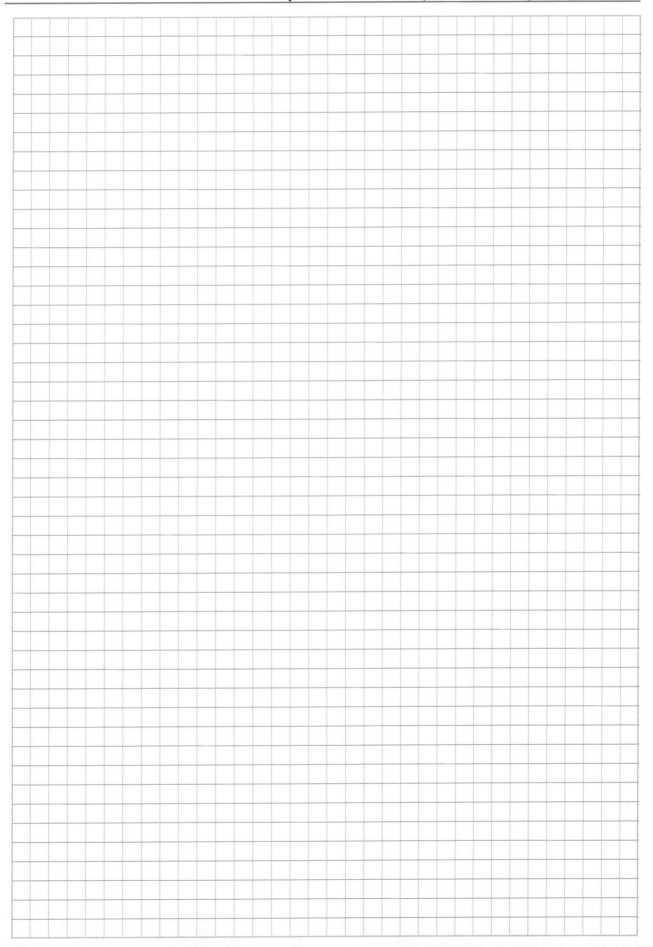

Vertebrate Anatomy II:
The Circulatory and Respiratory Systems

Laboratory Objectives

After completing this lab topic, you should be able to:

1. Identify and describe the function of the main organs and structures in the circulatory system and trace the flow of blood through the pulmonary and systemic circuits.

2. Identify and describe the function of the main organs and structures in the respiratory system and describe the exchange of oxygen and carbon dioxide in the lungs.

3. Describe how the circulatory and respiratory systems work together to bring about the integrated functioning of the body.

4. Apply knowledge and understanding acquired in this lab to problems in human physiology.

5. Apply knowledge and understanding acquired in this lab to explain organismal adaptive strategies.

Introduction

In Lab Topic 21, Vertebrate Anatomy I, you learned that nutrients are taken into the digestive tract, where they are processed: chewed, mixed with water and churned to a liquid, mixed with digestive enzymes, and finally digested into the component monomers, or building blocks, from which they were synthesized. For an animal to receive the benefits of these nutrients, these products of digestion must pass across intestinal cells and into the circulatory system to be transported to all the cells of the animal's body. Oxygen is necessary for the release of energy from these digested products. Oxygen from the atmosphere passes into the respiratory system of the animal, where it ultimately crosses cells in the lungs (in a terrestrial vertebrate) or gills (in an aquatic vertebrate) and enters the circulatory system for transport to cells of all organs, to be utilized in nutrient metabolism. Waste products of cellular metabolism—carbon dioxide and urea—are transported from the tissues that produce them via the blood and are eliminated from the body through the lungs of the respiratory system and the kidney of the excretory system, respectively. Thus, the circulatory, respiratory, and excretory systems function collectively, utilizing environmental materials, eliminating wastes, and maintaining a stable internal environment.

In this and the following lab topic, you will investigate the morphology of the circulatory, respiratory, and excretory systems in the fetal pig. As you dissect, relate the structure and specific function of each system to its role in the integrated body.

EXERCISE 22.1

Glands and Respiratory Structures of the Neck and Thoracic Cavity

Materials

These materials will be used for the entire lab topic.

fetal pig
dissecting pan
dissecting instruments
twine

disposable gloves
plastic bag with twist tie and labels
preservative

Introduction

To study the glands and respiratory structures of the neck, you must first open the thoracic cavity and then remove the skin and muscles in the neck region. This will expose several major glands that lie in the neck region in close proximity to the respiratory structures.

Procedure

 Wear disposable gloves when dissecting preserved animals.

1. Begin the dissection by opening the thoracic cavity, which houses the heart and lungs, and making an incision that extends to the jaw.

    a. Use scissors to deepen the superficial incision previously made anterior to the abdominal cavity, and continue deepening this incision to the base of the lower jaw.

    b. Cut through the body wall in the region of the thorax, clipping through the ribs slightly to the right or left of the **sternum** (the flat bone lying midventrally to which ribs attach).

    c. Continue the incision past the rib cage to the base of the lower jaw.

2. Using the blunt probe to separate tissues, carefully remove the skin and muscles in the neck region. You will expose the **thymus gland** on each side of the neck (Figure 22.1). This gland is large in the fetal pig and in young mammals, but regresses with age. It plays an important role in the development of the body's immune system.

3. Push the two thymus masses to the side to expose the **larynx** and **trachea** lying deep in the masses. Recall your knowledge about the **glottis**, observed in the dissection of the mouth in Lab Topic 21. The glottis leads into the larynx, an expanded structure through which air passes from the mouth to the narrower trachea. The larynx houses vocal cords.

4. A small reddish gland, the **thyroid gland**, covers the trachea. The thyroid gland secretes hormones that influence metabolism. Push this gland aside and observe the rings of cartilage that prevent the collapse of the trachea and allow air to pass to the lungs. Push aside the trachea to observe the dorsally located **esophagus**.

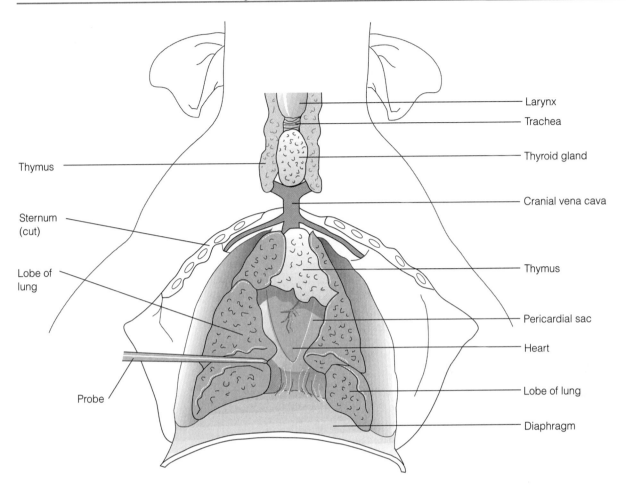

Figure 22.1.
Ventral view of the anterior region of the pig, showing structures in the neck region and the thoracic cavity. The pericardial sac encloses the heart.

5. Do not continue the dissection of the neck and thoracic regions at this time. To prevent damage to blood vessels, you will complete the dissection of the remainder of the respiratory system (Exercise 22.5) following the dissection of the circulatory system.

E X E R C I S E   2 2 . 2
The Heart and the Pulmonary Blood Circuit

The heart and lungs lie in the **pericardial** and **pleural** (Gk. for "rib") cavities, respectively, within the thoracic cavity. In your dissection of the heart and blood vessels, you will distinguish the two circulatory pathways found in mammalian circulation: the **pulmonary circuit,** which carries blood from the heart to the lungs in arteries and back to the heart in veins; and the

systemic circuit, which carries blood from the heart in arteries to all organs *but the lungs* and back to the heart in veins. This exercise investigates circulation in fetal and adult pig hearts and the pathway of blood to the lungs in the pulmonary circuit.

Materials

isolated adult pig heart dissected to show chambers and valves, demonstration only
supplies from Exercise 22.1

Procedure

Although, generally, veins contain blue latex and arteries contain red latex, the colors can vary and should not be used as guides to distinguish veins from arteries or vessels carrying oxygen-rich blood from vessels carrying oxygen-poor blood.

1. In the fetal pig, expose the heart lying in the **pericardial cavity** between the two pleural cavities. Gently push open the rib cage, using scissors and a probe to cut through muscle and connective tissue. Another lobe of the thymus gland will be seen lying over the **pericardial sac** housing the heart. The wall of the pericardial sac is a tough membrane composed of two fused coelomic epithelial linings, the **parietal pericardium** and the **parietal pleura.**

2. Cut into and push aside the pericardial sac. Carefully dissect away membranes adhering to the heart until you can identify the four chambers of the heart (Figure 22.2).

Figure 22.2.
Enlarged ventral view of a fetal heart, showing the four chambers and the major associated blood vessels. Compare this anatomy with that of an adult heart.

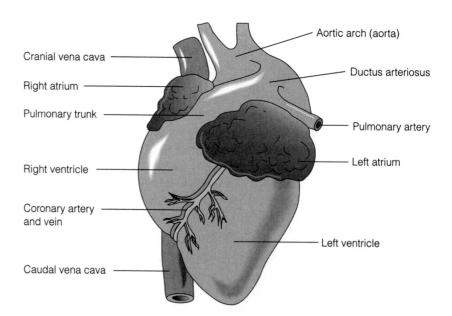

Cranial vena cava

Right atrium

Pulmonary trunk

Right ventricle

Coronary artery
and vein

Caudal vena cava

Aortic arch (aorta)

Ductus arteriosus

Pulmonary artery

Left atrium

Left ventricle

a. The **right atrium** and **left atrium** are small, dark, anteriorly located heart chambers that receive blood from the **venae cavae** and the pulmonary veins, respectively.

b. The **right ventricle** and **left ventricle** are large muscular heart chambers that contract to pump blood. A branch of the **coronary artery** may be seen on the heart surface where the left and right ventricles share a common wall.

What is the name of the epithelial lining adhering to the heart surface?

3. Trace the pulmonary circuit. As the heart contracts, blood is forced from the right ventricle into the **pulmonary trunk,** a large vessel lying on the ventral surface of the heart. Another large vessel, the **aorta,** lies just dorsal to the pulmonary trunk.

a. Use forceps to pick away tissue around the pulmonary trunk and trace the pulmonary trunk as it curves cranially, giving off three branches: the right and left **pulmonary arteries** and the **ductus arteriosus.**

b. Identify the ductus arteriosus and the left pulmonary artery (the right pulmonary artery is not readily visible).

The right and left pulmonary arteries are relatively small at this stage of development. They conduct blood to the right and left lungs, respectively. The ductus arteriosus is the short, large-diameter vessel that connects the pulmonary trunk to the aorta. Because the small right and left pulmonary arteries and compact lung tissue present an extremely resistant blood pathway, the greatest volume of blood will flow from the pulmonary trunk through the ductus arteriosus and directly into the aorta and systemic circulation, bypassing the pulmonary arteries and lungs. At the time of the fetus's birth, when air enters the lungs and the tissues expand, blood will more easily flow into the lungs. The ductus arteriosus closes off and eventually becomes a ligament.

4. Observe the isolated adult pig heart on demonstration and locate the dorsal and ventral surfaces (Figure 22.2).

a. Identify the **right atrium** with associated **cranial** and **caudal venae cavae** and the **left atrium** with associated **pulmonary veins.**

b. Locate the **right** and **left ventricles** and the **atrioventricular valves** between the atria and the ventricles.

c. Locate the **pulmonary trunk,** which carries blood from the right ventricle, and the **aorta,** carrying blood from the left ventricle. The first two small branches of the aorta are **coronary arteries.** Locate these vessels and the **coronary veins** lying on the surface of the heart between the left and right ventricles.

Results

Review the heart chambers, blood vessels, and organs in the pathway of the pulmonary circuit in the adult heart. To facilitate this review, fill in the blanks in the next paragraph.

Blood entering the heart passes first into the right atrium. From there it flows into the right ventricle. When the heart contracts, this blood is forced out of the ventricle into the _____ trunk. Branches of this trunk called _____ carry blood to the lungs. After birth, the blood will become oxygen-rich in the lungs. Blood from the lungs passes back to the heart through _____ , thus completing the circuit. It enters the left atrium of the heart.

Discussion

1. Define *artery*. Define *vein*.

2. Why would pulmonary arteries be relatively small at the fetal stage of development?

3. Although a pulmonary circuit exists, the heart in amphibians and most reptiles is made up of only three chambers—two atria and one ventricle. The latter receives blood from both atria. Speculate about possible disadvantages to this circulatory pathway.

EXERCISE 22.3
The Heart and the Systemic Circuit in the Thorax

Blood returning from the lungs collects in the left atrium and flows into the left ventricle. When the heart contracts, blood is forced out the **aorta,** the origin of which is obscured by the pulmonary trunk. The first branch from the aorta is the small **coronary artery,** previously identified, leading to the heart muscle. The larger volume of blood passes through the aorta to all organs of the body but the lungs. Blood returns to the heart from organs of the body through two large veins, the cranial and caudal venae cavae.

Procedure

1. Identify the venae cavae and their major branches.
    a. Push the heart to the pig's left to see two large veins entering the right atrium; these are the **cranial** and **caudal venae cavae** (Figure 22.3).

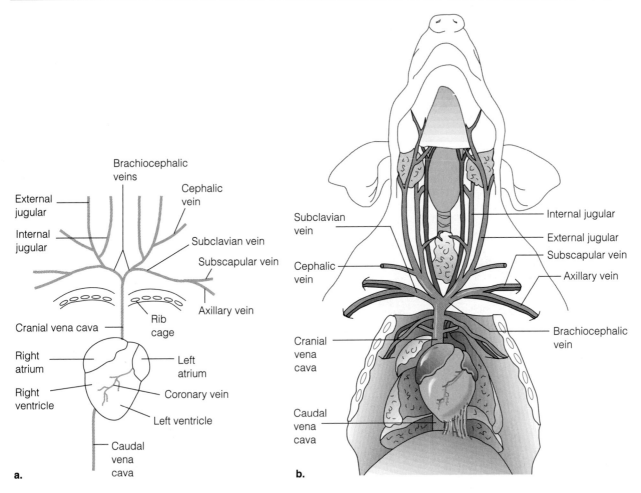

Figure 22.3.
Veins near the heart. The subclavian vein and the external and internal jugulars carry blood to the brachiocephalic veins, which unite into the cranial vena cava. The caudal vena cava carries blood from the posterior regions of the body.

b. Using the blunt probe to separate the vessels from surrounding tissues, follow the cranial vena cava toward the head and identify the two large **brachiocephalic veins**, which unite in the cranial vena cava.

c. Identify the three major veins that unite to form each brachiocephalic vein: the **external** and **internal jugulars** that carry blood returning from the head, and the **subclavian vein** that drains blood from the front leg and shoulder. Follow the subclavian vein into the front leg. Probe deep into the muscle covering the underside of the scapula (shoulder blade) and you should see the **subscapular vein**, draining blood from the shoulder region. The **axillary vein** carries blood from the front leg, becoming the subclavian vein at the subscapular branch. Occasionally, the subclavian vein is very short, and the subscapular and axillary veins unite close to the brachiocephalic vein. Another vein that is often injected and prominent in the shoulder area is the **cephalic vein.** This vein lies just beneath the skin on the upper front leg. It typically enters the external jugular near its base.

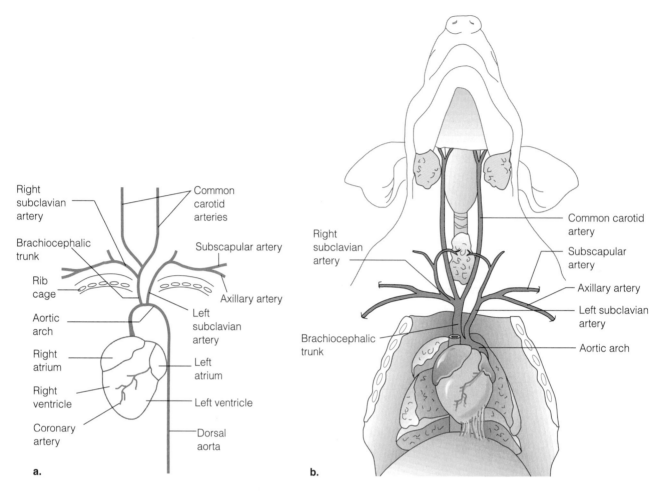

Figure 22.4.
Branches of the aorta. Branches from the aortic arch carry blood to the head and anterior limbs. The first branch, the brachiocephalic trunk, branches into the right subclavian artery to the right limb and two common carotid arteries to the head. The second branch is the left subclavian to the left limb.

2. Identify branches of the aorta near the heart (Figure 22.4).

   a. Push the pulmonary trunk ventrally and posteriorly to observe the curve of the aorta, the **aortic arch,** lying behind.

   b. Remove obscuring tissue and expose the first two major branches of the arch, which carry blood anteriorly. It may be necessary to remove the veins to do so. The larger of the branches, the **brachiocephalic trunk,** branches off first. The **left subclavian artery** branches off second.

   c. Identify the three major branches from the brachiocephalic trunk: the **right subclavian artery,** which gives off several branches that serve the right shoulder and limb area, and two **common carotid arteries,** which carry blood to the head. The common carotid arteries lie adjacent to the internal jugular veins.

   d. Trace the branches of the left subclavian artery into the left shoulder and front leg. The branch that passes deep toward the underside of the scapula is the **subscapular artery.** After the subscapular artery branches off, the left subclavian continues into the front leg as the left **axillary artery.** Additional branches of this artery complex may also be visible.

3. Pull the lungs to the pig's right side and trace the dorsal aorta as it extends posteriorly from the aortic arch along the dorsal thoracic wall. Notice again the **ductus arteriosus** connecting from the pulmonary trunk.

4. Note the small branches of the dorsal aorta carrying blood to the ribs. A large conspicuous vein, the **azygos vein,** lies near this region of the aorta. This vein carries blood from the ribs back to the heart.

Results

Modify Figures 22.3 and 22.4 or sketch additional details in the margin of your lab manual to indicate particular features of your pig's circulatory system for future reference.

EXERCISE 22.4

The Systemic Circuit in the Abdominal Cavity

The dorsal aorta passes into the abdominal cavity, where it branches into arteries supplying the abdominal organs, the legs, and the tail. In fetal circulation, it also branches into two large umbilical arteries to the placenta. Blood from the legs, tail, and organs collects in veins that ultimately join the caudal vena cava to return to the heart. Blood draining from organs of the digestive system passes through additional vessels in the hepatic portal system before emptying into the caudal vena cava.

Lab Study A. Major Branches of the Dorsal Aorta and the Caudal Vena Cava

In this lab study, you will identify the major blood vessels branching from the dorsal aorta and those emptying into the caudal vena cava.

Procedure

1. Identify branches of the dorsal aorta (Figures 22.5 and 22.7).

   a. The first large branch of the aorta in the abdominal cavity exits the aorta at approximately the level of the diaphragm. Clip the diaphragm where it joins the body wall, pull all the organs (lungs and digestive organs) to the pig's right, and search for the **coeliac artery,** which carries blood to the stomach and the spleen. You may have to pick away pieces of the diaphragm that are attached to the aorta to see this vessel.

   b. Once you have identified the coeliac artery, look for the next branch of the aorta, the **cranial mesenteric artery,** arising slightly caudal to the coeliac artery and carrying blood to the small intestine. The cranial mesenteric artery ultimately branches to the **mesenteric arteries** you observed when you studied the digestive system.

   c. Following the dorsal aorta posteriorly, identify the two **renal arteries** leading to the kidneys.

Coeliac artery

Cranial mesenteric artery

Caudal vena cava

Umbilical artery

Dorsal aorta

Renal artery and vein

Common iliac vein

External iliac artery and vein

Femoral artery and vein

Deep femoral artery and vein

Figure 22.5.
Branches of the aorta and caudal vena cava in the abdomen. Branches of the aorta supply blood to the stomach (the coeliac artery), the small intestine (the cranial mesenteric artery), the kidney (renal arteries), the hind limbs (iliac arteries), and the placenta (umbilical arteries). Branches of the caudal vena cava drain blood from the kidney (renal veins) and posterior limbs (common iliac veins).

✳ You will observe the posterior branches of the aorta after the dissection of the reproductive system.

d. The dorsal aorta sends branches into the hind legs (the **external iliac arteries**) and to the placenta (the **umbilical arteries**) through the umbilical cord.

e. Separate the muscles of the leg to see that the external iliac artery divides into the **femoral artery** and the **deep femoral artery**. The femoral artery carries blood to the muscles of the lower leg, and the deep femoral artery carries blood to the thigh muscles.

2. Identify branches of the caudal vena cava.

   a. Using Figure 22.5 as a reference, push the digestive organs to the pig's left and trace the caudal vena cava into the abdominal cavity. It lies deep to the membrane lining the wall of the abdominal cavity, the **parietal peritoneum.** Peel off this membrane to see the vena cava, the dorsal aorta, and the kidneys.

   b. Identify **renal veins** carrying blood from the kidneys. **Common iliac veins** (to be identified in Lab Topic 23) carry blood from the hind legs, and **hepatic veins** carry blood from the liver to the caudal vena cava. Hepatic veins are presented in Lab Study B.

Lab Study B. The Hepatic Portal System

In the usual pathway of circulation, blood passes from the heart to arteries, to capillaries in an organ, and to veins leading from the organ back to the heart (Figure 22.6a). In a few rare instances, a second capillary bed is inserted in a second organ in the circulation pathway (Figure 22.6b). When this

Figure 22.6.
Circulatory pathways. (a) General circulatory pathway; (b) circulation in a portal system; and (c) circulation in the hepatic portal system. Arteries are depicted in dark blue; veins are gray; portal veins are gray outlined in dark blue.

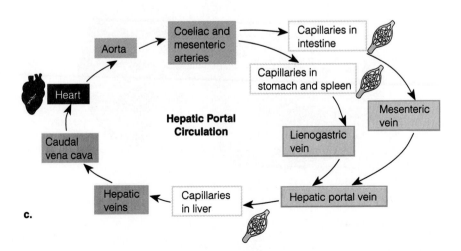

occurs, the circulatory circuit involved is called a **portal system.** Such a system of portal circulation exists in the digestive system (Figure 22.6c). An understanding of this circulation pathway will increase your understanding of the absorption and processing of nutrients.

You have previously exposed the coeliac and cranial mesenteric arteries, which send branches to the stomach, spleen, and small intestine. These arteries divide into smaller arteries, to arterioles, and, finally, to capillaries, thin-walled vessels that are the site of exchange between blood and the tissues of the organs. Arteries associated with the small intestine are called **mesenteric arteries;** veins leaving the small intestine are called **mesenteric veins,** and they unite to form one large **mesenteric vein.** Veins from the stomach and spleen unite to form the larger **lienogastric vein.** The mesenteric and lienogastric veins unite to form the **hepatic portal vein,** which enters the liver (Figure 22.7). In the fetal pig, small branches of the **umbilical vein** join the hepatic portal vein as it enters the liver. However, the greatest volume of blood in the umbilical vein passes directly through the liver into the caudal vena cava.

In the liver, the hepatic portal vein branches into a second capillary bed, where exchange takes place between blood and liver tissue. These capillaries reunite into **hepatic veins,** which join the caudal vena cava. To identify these vessels, begin by dissecting the veins.

Figure 22.7.
The hepatic portal system. Blood from the small intestine passes into the mesenteric vein, which unites with the lienogastric vein to form the hepatic portal vein. This vessel leads to the liver, where it breaks into a capillary bed. Blood leaves the liver through the hepatic veins.

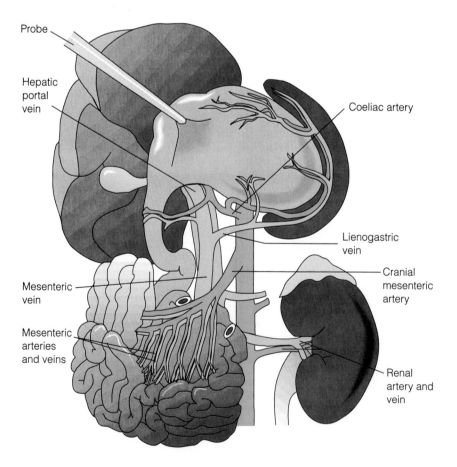

Probe

Hepatic portal vein

Coeliac artery

Lienogastric vein

Cranial mesenteric artery

Mesenteric vein

Mesenteric arteries and veins

Renal artery and vein

Procedure

1. Push the stomach and spleen anteriorly and dissect away the pancreas.

2. Use the blunt probe to expose a vein (it will probably not be injected) leading from the mesenteries of the small intestine. This is the **mesenteric vein.** It is joined by a vein leading from the stomach and spleen, the **lienogastric vein.** The two fuse to form the **hepatic portal vein,** which continues to the liver.

3. Review the flow of blood from the mesenteric arteries to the liver.

Results

Review the blood vessels and organs in the pathway of blood through the hepatic portal system of an adult pig with functioning digestive organs. Fill in the blanks in the next paragraph:

Blood that is poor in nutrients is carried from the aorta to the _____ _____ artery to smaller mesenteric arteries, which divide to a capillary bed in the wall of the _____, where, in the process of absorption, nutrients enter the blood. This nutrient-rich blood now flows into the _____ vein, which joins with the _____ vein from the spleen and stomach and becomes the_____ vein. This vein now carries blood to the liver, where it breaks into a second capillary bed. Capillaries in the liver converge into the _____ veins, which empty into the caudal vena cava for transport back to the heart.

Discussion

Referring to your text, review the function of the liver in nutrient metabolism and relate this to the function of the hepatic portal system. Include information on digestive products, drugs, and toxins.

EXERCISE 22.5

Fetal Pig Circulation

As you dissected the circulatory system in the fetal pig and observed the adult pig heart, you noted differences between the fetal heart and the adult heart, and you identified blood vessels found in the fetus but not in the adult. In this exercise you will review these vessels and structures, tracing blood flow through the fetal pig.

Procedure

1. Return the umbilical cord to the position it occupied before you began your dissection. Locate again the umbilical vein as it passes from the umbilical cord toward the liver. You cut through this vein when you opened the abdominal cavity. The umbilical vein carries blood from the umbilical cord into the liver. In the liver, small branches of this vein join the hepatic portal vein, passing blood into the liver tissue. However, the majority of the blood passes through a channel in the liver called the **ductus venosus** into the caudal vena cava. Would blood be *high* or *low* in oxygen in the caudal vena cava?

2. Review the anatomy of the heart, and retrace the flow of blood through the heart into the dorsal aorta by way of the *ductus arteriosus*. This represents one pathway of blood through the fetal heart.

3. A second pathway of blood through the heart is created by a structure in the fetal heart called the **foramen ovale.** To study this pathway, use your scalpel to open the pig heart by cutting it along a frontal plane, dividing it into dorsal and ventral portions. Begin at the caudal end of the heart and carefully slice along the frontal plane, cutting just through the ventricles, keeping the atria intact. Carefully lift the ventricles and look inside the heart for the wall between the two atria. Using your blunt probe, carefully feel along this wall for an opening between the two atria. This hole is the foramen ovale, which makes possible the second pathway of blood through the heart. How would this hole change the flow of blood through the heart?

   In fact, most blood coming into the heart from the caudal vena cava passes from the right atrium through this hole into the left atrium. After leaving the left atrium, where would blood go next?

4. Follow the dorsal aorta into the abdominal cavity to the umbilical artery branches. These branches pass through the umbilical cord to the placenta. Would blood in these branches be *high* or *low* in oxygen?

Results

Trace the pathway of blood from the umbilical vein to the umbilical artery by filling in the blanks in the next paragraph.

Blood from the umbilical vein passes through the liver and into the _____ _____ , which carries blood into the heart, specifically into the chamber called the _____ . In one circuit of blood flow, blood goes from this chamber into the right ventricle and out the _____ . A branch from this vessel, the _____ (present only in fetal circulation), carries most of this blood into the dorsal aorta. The dorsal aorta passes through the body, giving off branches to all organs of the body. Two large branches located near the tail lead into the umbilical cord and are called the _____ .

An alternate route carries blood from the right atrium through a fetal hole called the _____ into the heart chamber, the _____ . From this chamber, blood next goes into the left ventricle and out the _____ . Branches of this vessel lead to the head.

Discussion

1. What is the advantage of the circuit of fetal blood flow through the ductus arteriosus?

2. What is the advantage of fetal blood flow through the foramen ovale?

EXERCISE 22.6
Details of the Respiratory System

You have previously located several of the major structures of the respiratory system (Exercise 22.1). Direct your attention again to the neck region of the pig and complete the study of the respiratory system.

Procedure

1. Identify again the **larynx** and the **trachea** (Figure 22.8).
2. Follow the trachea caudally to the pleural cavities housing the lungs. The trachea branches into **bronchi** (sing., bronchus), which lead into the

lobes of the **lungs** (Color Plate 64). It will be necessary to push aside blood vessels to see this. *Take care not to destroy these vessels.*

3. Tease apart lung tissues to observe that the larger bronchi branch into smaller and smaller bronchi. When the tubes are about 1–2 mm in diameter, they are called **bronchioles.** Bronchioles continue to branch and ultimately lead to microscopic **alveoli** (not visible with the unaided eye), thin-walled, blind-ending sacs that are covered with capillaries. It is here that the exchange of oxygen and carbon dioxide takes place between the blood and the atmosphere.

4. Identify the epithelial lining of the pleural cavity. How would this epithelium be named?

5. After you complete this lab topic, return your pig to its plastic bag. Check that your labels are intact and that your name, lab room, and lab day are legible. Add preserving solution and securely close the bag.

Results

List, in order, the structures, tubes, and cellular barriers through which air passes as it travels from outside the body to the circulatory system of a pig, a terrestrial vertebrate.

Discussion

1. In terrestrial vertebrates, what is the advantage of having the surfaces for oxygen and carbon dioxide exchange embedded deep in lung tissue?

2. The capillaries that lie in close contact with alveoli are branches of what blood vessel?

3. The confluence of these capillaries forms what blood vessel?

4. Compare blood composition in adult circulation with reference to oxygen and carbon dioxide between capillaries approaching alveoli and capillaries leaving alveoli.

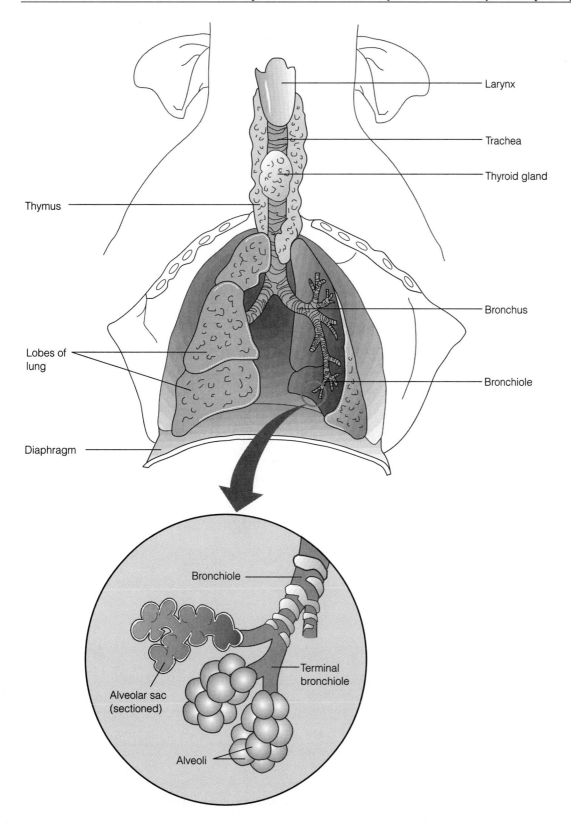

Figure 22.8.
The respiratory system of the fetal pig. Air passes through a succession of smaller and more numerous tubes: the larynx, trachea, bronchi, bronchioles, and ultimately, microscopic alveoli (see enlarged area).

5. Review the coelomic cavities, the organs contained within them, and the associated coelomic membranes by completing Table 22.1.

Table 22.1
Cavities, Organs, and Coelomic Membranes of the Mammalian Body

Cavity	Subdivision	Organ(s)	Membranes
Thoracic			
Abdominal (peritoneal)			

Applying Your Knowledge

1. The appearance of lung tissue differs in adult and fetal pigs. Predict differences in appearance and explain them.

2. Using materials provided in the lab, your text, library materials, or your previous knowledge, answer the following questions related to the effects of smoking on the structure and function of the human respiratory system.
    a. Describe changes in the cells and tissues of the lungs and describe the concomitant effects on function.

    b. Describe the effects and symptoms of each of the following diseases linked to cigarette smoking.

Disease	Effects and Symptoms
Chronic bronchitis	
Emphysema	
Lung cancer	

c. What effects does smoking during pregnancy have on the fetus?

3. The trachea is composed of rings of cartilage, while the nearby esophagus is composed of muscle and lacks cartilage. How are these structural differences related to the functions of each?

4. Scientists have concluded that a four-chambered heart is necessary to support the high metabolic rates seen in "warm-blooded" animals (endotherms)—that is, birds and mammals (see question 3, page 582). In 1998 scientists discovered that a 66-million-year-old dinosaur found in South Dakota appeared to contain a fossilized heart with two ventricles, as one would find in a four-chambered heart. What does this discovery suggest about the metabolism of this dinosaur and the position of this species of dinosaur in the evolutionary tree?

References

Burggren, W. "And the Beat Goes On—A Brief Guide to the Hearts of Vertebrates," *Natural History,* 2000, vol. 109, pp. 62–65.

Fisher, P. E., D. A. Russell, M. K. Stoskopf, R. E. Barrick, M. Hammer, and A. A. Kuzmitz. "Cardiovascular Evidence for an Intermediate or Higher Metabolic Rate in an Ornithischian Dinosaur," *Science,* 2000, vol. 288, pp. 503–505.

Marieb, E. N. *Human Anatomy and Physiology,* 5th ed. Menlo Park, CA: Benjamin/Cummings, 2001.

"What You Need to Know about Cancer," *Scientific American,* Special Issue, vol. 275, 1996.

Websites

Test yourself on fetal pig anatomy:

http://www.jburroughs.org/science/resources/pig/pig14.html

Photographs of fetal pig anatomy:

http://www.park.edu/bhoffman/courses/bi123/labs/fetalpig/htm

Vertebrate eye anatomy:

http://www.stlukeseye.com/anatomy.htm

Vertebrate eye anatomy:

http://www.discoveryfund.org/anatomyoftheeye.html

A Google search for "reflex arc" will yield many informative websites:

http://www.google.com

All About Smoking:

http://www.guess-what.com/ske_1.htm

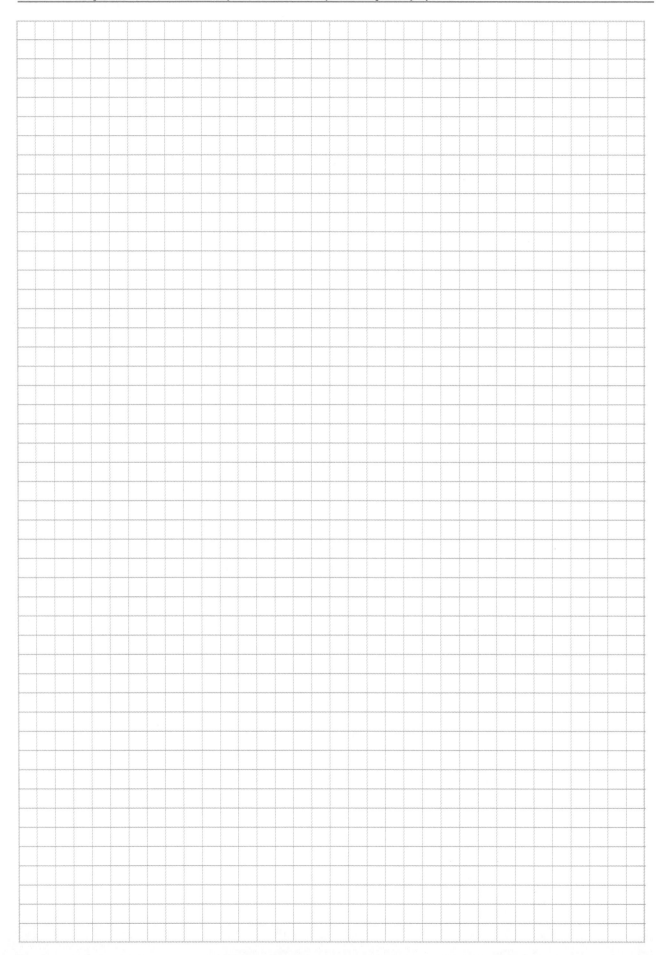

Vertebrate Anatomy III: The Excretory, Reproductive, and Nervous Systems

Laboratory Objectives

After completing this lab topic, you should be able to:

1. Identify and describe the function of all parts of the excretory system of the fetal pig, noting differences between the sexes and noting structures shared with the reproductive system.

2. Identify and describe the function of all parts of the reproductive systems of male and female fetal pigs and trace the pathway of sperm and egg from their origin out of the body.

3. Compare reproductive systems in pigs and humans.

4. Describe the structure of a neuron.

5. Describe the pathway of a simple reflex, relating this to the structure of the spinal cord.

6. Describe the structure of a representative sensory receptor, the eye.

7. Discuss the role played by the nervous and endocrine systems in integrating all vertebrate systems into a functioning whole organism.

Introduction

In Lab Topic 22, Vertebrate Anatomy II, you saw that, functionally, the excretory system is closely related to the circulatory and respiratory systems. Developmentally, however, the excretory system shares many embryonic and some adult structures with the reproductive system. In the first two exercises of this lab topic, you will investigate form and functional relationships in the excretory and reproductive systems. In the last exercise of this lab topic, you will study the nervous system, which keeps all organ systems functioning appropriately and in harmony.

The action and interaction of organ systems must be precisely timed to meet specific needs within the animal. Two systems in the body, the nervous system and the endocrine system, coordinate the activities of all organ systems. The nervous system consists of a **sensory component,** made up of **sensory receptors** that detect such stimuli as light, sound, touch, and the concentration of oxygen in the blood, and **sensory nerves,** which carry the data to the **central nervous system.** The central nervous system consists of the brain and spinal cord. It integrates information from all stimuli, external and internal, and, when appropriate, sends signals to the motor system. The **motor system** carries impulses along motor nerves to **effectors** such as glands, muscles, and other organs, bringing about the appropriate response. The nervous system provides rapid, precise, and complex control of body activities.

The endocrine system consists of endocrine glands, which respond to stimuli by secreting hormones into the blood to be transported to target tissues in the body. The target tissues then bring about the response. You have already observed several endocrine glands, including the thymus, thyroid, and pancreas. In this lab topic, you will study additional endocrine glands: ovaries and testes. Control mediated by hormones in the endocrine system is slower and less precise than nervous system control. The interaction of the nervous and endocrine systems brings about the coordination of physiological processes and the maintenance of internal **homeostasis**, the steady state condition in the vertebrate body.

EXERCISE 23.1
The Excretory System

Materials

preserved fetal pig
dissecting instruments

dissecting pan
disposable gloves

Introduction

Several important functions are performed by the vertebrate excretory system, including **osmoregulation**, the control of tissue water balance, and the elimination of excess salts and urea, a waste product of the metabolism of amino acids. In terrestrial animals, including most mammals, water conservation is an important function of the excretory system. Studying this system in the pig will reveal the organs and structures involved in producing and eliminating metabolic waste with minimal water loss.

 Wear disposable gloves when dissecting preserved animals.

Procedure

1. Locate the blood vessels serving the kidneys, exposed in the dissection of the circulatory system. The arteries branch from the dorsal aorta caudal to the cranial mesenteric artery. Blood enters the kidney through the **renal artery** and exits through the **renal vein.** Identify these vessels and the **kidneys** lying deep to the **parietal peritoneum** lining the abdominal cavity. This membrane was observed and removed in Lab Topic 22, Vertebrate Anatomy II.

2. Dissect the left kidney as follows. Leaving the kidney in the body and attached to all blood vessels and tubes, make a frontal section along the outer periphery, dividing it into dorsal and ventral portions (Figure 23.1a). Observe the **renal cortex, renal medulla, renal pyramids, renal pelvis,** and **ureter.**

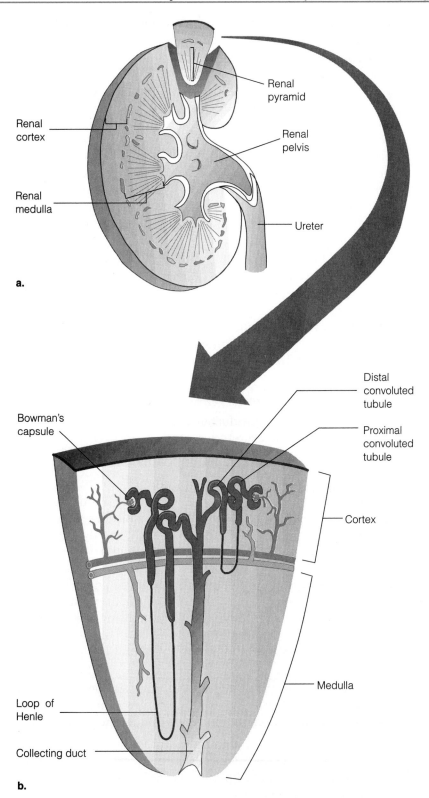

Figure 23.1.
Structure of the kidney.
(a) The kidney consists of three major regions: the cortex, the medulla, and the pelvis. Renal pyramids make up the medulla, and the pelvis is continuous with the ureter. (b) An enlarged wedge of the kidney, including the cortical region over one pyramid. Nephrons consisting of Bowman's capsule, a proximal convoluted tubule; the loop of Henle, a distal convoluted tubule; and a collecting duct extend over the cortical and medullary regions. Waste carried in the collecting duct ultimately passes into the pelvis and ureter.

Each kidney is made up of microscopic tubules, blood vessels, and thousands of nephrons (approximately 1 million in humans). A nephron (not visible in your dissections) consists of Bowman's capsule, a proximal convoluted tubule, the loop of Henle, a distal convoluted tubule, and a collecting duct (Figure 23.1b). (For details of nephron function, see your text.) Bowman's capsule, proximal and distal convoluted tubules, and associated blood vessels lie in the *renal cortex.* Loops of Henle and collecting ducts extend into *renal pyramids,* which make up the *renal medulla.* Both the loop of Henle and the collecting duct play a role in producing a concentrated urine, a significant adaptation for terrestrial vertebrates. The hypertonic urine passes into the collecting ducts, which ultimately empty into the renal pelvis, an expanded portion of the ureter into the kidney.

3. Using Figure 23.2 as a reference, follow the ureter as it exits the kidney at its medial border and turns to run caudally beside the dorsal aorta. The ureter then enters the **urinary bladder.** Also locate the ureter draining the right kidney and trace it to the urinary bladder. In the fetal pig, the urinary bladder is an elongate structure lying between the two **umbilical arteries** identified in Lab Topic 22, Vertebrate Anatomy II. It narrows into the small **allantoic stalk** identified in the study of the umbilical cord in Lab Topic 21, Vertebrate Anatomy I.

 Do not damage reproductive organs as you expose the structures of the excretory system.

4. Pull on the umbilical cord, extending the urinary bladder, and locate a single tube, the **urethra,** exiting the urinary bladder near the attachments of the ureters. At this stage, you will see only the end of the urethra near the entrance of the ureters. In male pigs (see Figure 23.2a), the urethra leads into the **penis.** This will be visible only after you have dissected the reproductive structures. In female pigs (Figure 23.3a), the urethra joins the **vagina,** forming a chamber, the **vaginal vestibule.** You will identify these structures after exposing the reproductive structures.

In male humans, the urethra is a tube in the penis. In female humans, the urethra does not join the vagina but empties to the outside of the body through a separate opening. The urethra becomes functional after birth when the umbilical cord and allantois wither and fall away. Waste stored in the bladder passes into the urethra, where it is carried to the outside of the body.

Results

Describe the pathway of metabolic waste from the aorta to the outside of the body in the fetal pig.

Discussion

How does the elimination of metabolic waste in the pig change after birth?

EXERCISE 23.2

The Reproductive System

Materials

items from Exercise 23.1

Introduction

Reproduction is perhaps the ultimate adaptive activity of all organisms. It is the means of transmitting genetic information from generation to generation. Less complex animals may reproduce sexually or asexually, but in general, vertebrates reproduce sexually. Sexual reproduction promotes genetic variation, which is important for species to adapt to changing environments. For evolution to occur, heritable variation must exist in populations. Although mutation is the source of variation, sexual reproduction promotes new and diverse combinations of genetic information. Ultimately, all sexual reproduction involves the production of gametes and the bringing together of gametes to enable fertilization to take place.

Lab Study A. Male Reproductive System

The male reproductive system consists of gonads, ducts, and glands. Testes, the male gonads, produce sperm and secrete testosterone and other male sex hormones. Sperm pass from the testes into the epididymis, where they mature and are stored. When ejaculation takes place, sperm pass from the epididymis through the ductus deferens—also called the *vas deferens*—to the urethra. The urethra leads to the penis, which carries the sperm to the outside of the body. As sperm pass through the male tract, secretions from the seminal vesicles, the prostate gland, and the bulbourethral glands are added, producing semen, a fluid containing sperm, fructose, amino acids, mucus, and other substances that produce a favorable environment for sperm survival and motility.

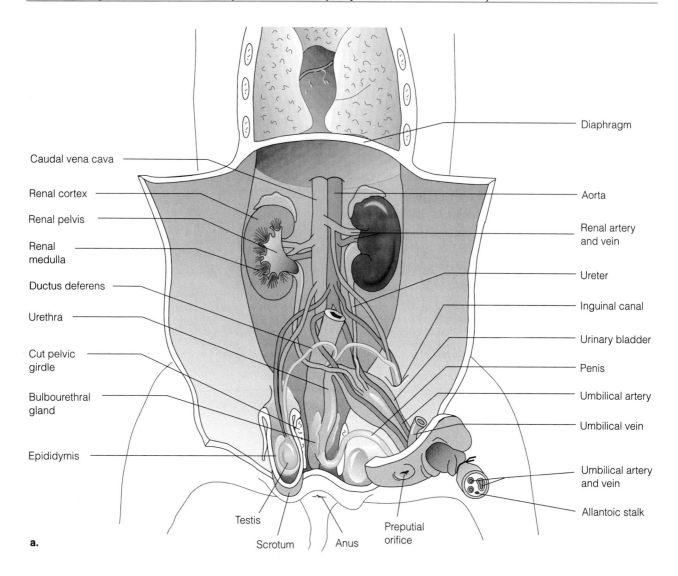

Caudal vena cava

Renal cortex

Renal pelvis

Renal medulla

Ductus deferens

Urethra

Cut pelvic girdle

Bulbourethral gland

Epididymis

Diaphragm

Aorta

Renal artery and vein

Ureter

Inguinal canal

Urinary bladder

Penis

Umbilical artery

Umbilical vein

Umbilical artery and vein

Allantoic stalk

Testis

Scrotum

Anus

Preputial orifice

a.

Figure 23.2a.
Organs of the excretory and reproductive systems in the male fetal pig. The ureters enter the urinary bladder between the umbilical arteries. The urethra exits the urinary bladder and leads to the penis. The penis leads to the preputial orifice. The testes lie in pouches in the scrotum. Sperm are produced in the testes, stored in the epididymis on the testis surface, and pass to the ductus deferens, which leads to the urethra.

Procedure

 You will dissect the reproductive system of only one sex. However, you should observe the dissection of a pig of the opposite sex and be able to identify and describe various structures of both sexes.

1. Expose the structures of the male reproductive system (Figure 23.2a). The penis is located in the flap of ventral body wall caudal to the umbilical cord. To prevent damage to this structure, locate it before you make

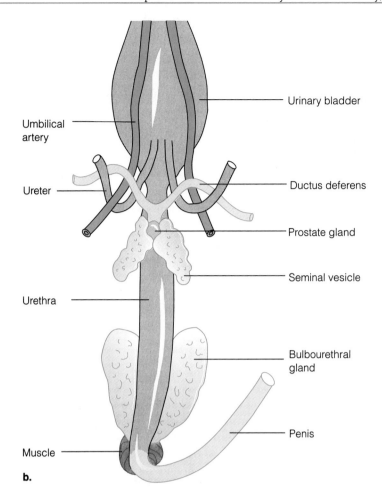

Figure 23.2b.
Enlarged dorsal view of male excretory and reproductive structures in the fetal pig. Seminal vesicles lie near the junction of the urethra and ductus deferens. Bulbourethral glands lie on either side of the urethra.

Umbilical artery

Ureter

Urethra

Muscle

b.

Urinary bladder

Ductus deferens

Prostate gland

Seminal vesicle

Bulbourethral gland

Penis

an incision. Hold the flap between your fingers and feel for the cord-like penis just below the skin. Once you locate the penis, using scissors, begin at the urogenital opening, the **preputial orifice** (identified in Lab Topic 21, Vertebrate Anatomy I), and make a longitudinal incision, extending caudally, just through the skin. Push aside the skin and use the probe to locate and expose the long penis from the orifice caudally until it turns dorsally to meet the urethra (see Figure 23.2b).

2. Next, begin to expose the testis, epididymis, and ductus deferens. To do this, locate the **ureters** (identified in Exercise 23.1) and observe the right and left **ductus deferentia** (sing., deferens), which loop over the ureters. Follow a ductus deferens outward and caudally to the **inguinal canal** leading into the **scrotum.** Use scissors to cut carefully along the canal to expose the **testis** lying in a membranous sac. Remove this sac and identify the various structures.

    a. Identify the **testis,** a bean-shaped gonad. The testes first develop in the abdominal cavity and descend before birth into the scrotal sacs.

    b. Identify the **epididymis,** a convoluted duct that originates at the cranial end of the testis, extends caudally along one side, then turns and continues cranially as the ductus deferens.

    c. Identify the **ductus deferens,** a duct that leads away from the epididymis back into the abdominal cavity, where it loops over the ureter and enters the urethra. Also locate the ductus deferens from the other testis.

3. Turn your attention again to the area where the penis turns dorsally to meet the urethra. Push the penis to one side and probe through the muscle between the legs to locate the pubic symphysis, the portion of the pelvic girdle that fuses in a position ventral to several of the reproductive structures and the rectum. *Being careful not to go too deep or to cut the penis,* use heavy scissors to cut the pubic symphysis from posterior to anterior beginning at the bend in the penis. Press the hind limbs apart and trim the ends of the symphysis. Use the probe to remove connective tissue, and expose the **urethra,** which continues anteriorly from the bend of the penis. The urethra continues into the **urinary bladder** lying between the umbilical arteries. Identify the two large **bulbourethral glands** lying on either side of the urethra anterior to its junction with the penis (see Figure 23.2b).

4. Pull on the umbilical cord, reflecting the urethra, and locate a pair of glands, the **seminal vesicles,** that lie on the dorsal surface of the urethra near the junction of the ductus deferens and the urethra. The **prostate gland** lies between the lobes of the seminal vesicles, but because of its immature stage of development, it is difficult to identify.

 At this time, complete the study of the branches of the dorsal aorta (Exercise 22.4, Lab Study A). Identify the **umbilical arteries** and the **external iliac arteries** to the legs and their branches, the **femoral** and **deep femoral arteries.** Also identify the **deep femoral, femoral,** and **common iliac veins,** which drain the legs and empty into the **caudal vena cava.**

5. After you conclude the study of the male pig, find someone with a female pig, and demonstrate the systems to each other.

6. Place your pig in its plastic bag, make sure the labels are legible, add preservative, secure the bag, and store it.

Results

In Table 23.1, list the organs and ducts through which sperm pass from their origin to the outside of the body. Describe what takes place in each organ or duct, and note glandular secretions when appropriate. Refer to your text if needed.

Discussion

1. Vasectomy is the most common form of human male sterilization used for birth control. Describe this process.

2. What structures identified are common to both reproductive and excretory systems?

Table 23.1
Pathway of Sperm

Organ/Duct	Activity and Glandular Secretion

3. The testes develop inside the abdominal cavity and descend through the inguinal canal into the scrotum before birth. Explain the significance of the external scrotum and external testes in mammals. Refer to your text if needed.

Lab Study B. Female Reproductive System

The female reproductive system consists of the ovaries (female gonads), short uterine tubes (also called *fallopian tubes,* or *oviducts*), the uterus, the vagina, and the vaginal vestibule. The vaginal vestibule is present in the pig but not in the human. In the pig, the uterus consists of a uterine body and two uterine horns in which embryonic pigs develop. In the human female, the uterus does not have uterine horns but consists of a dome-shaped portion, the fundus, which protrudes above the entrance of the fallopian tubes, and an enlarged main portion, the body of the uterus, where embryos develop.

Procedure

1. To study the female reproductive system (Figure 23.3a), use scissors and make a median longitudinal incision, cutting through the skin posterior to the umbilical cord. Push aside skin and muscles and probe in

the midline to locate the pubic symphysis, the portion of the pelvic girdle that fuses in a position ventral to many of the female reproductive
structures and the rectum. Being careful not to go too deep, use heavy
scissors to cut through the muscles and the symphysis. Press apart the
hind limbs and trim away the cut ends of the symphysis.

2. Begin observations by locating the **ovaries** in the abdominal cavity just
caudal to the kidneys (Figure 23.3a). They are a pair of small, bean-
shaped organs, one caudal to each kidney. (When the testes of the male
first develop, they are located in approximately the same position in
the abdominal cavity as the ovaries; however, the testes later descend,
becoming supported in the scrotal sacs.) A small convoluted tube, the
uterine tube, can be observed at the border of the ovary.

3. The reproductive structures form a long, continuous tract. Follow a
uterine tube from one ovary into the associated **horn of the uterus.**
Left and right horns join to form the **body of the uterus.** The body of

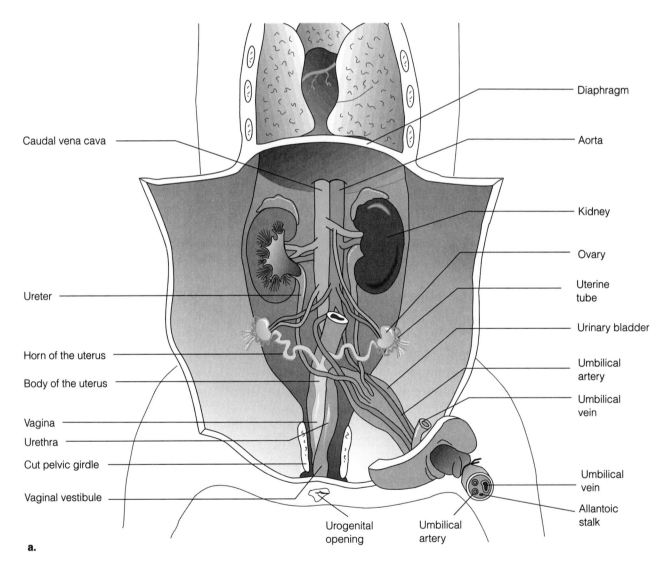

Figure 23.3a.
Organs of the excretory and reproductive systems in the female fetal pig.
The ureters enter the urinary bladder. The urethra exits the urinary bladder and
joins the vagina, forming the vaginal vestibule.

the uterus lies dorsal to the urethra. Push the urethra aside and use the probe to separate the urethra from the uterus. Notice that the urethra and the reproductive structures meet.

4. The body of the uterus leads into the **cervix** of the uterus, which leads into the **vagina.** To conclusively identify these regions, you must open the uterus. Without disturbing the junction of the urethra and the reproductive structures, use scissors to make a longitudinal, lateral incision in the reproductive structures and push back the sides, exposing the interior. Your dissection should resemble Figure 23.3b. Now you should be able to identify all parts of the uterus, the vagina, and the opening of the urethra into the reproductive tract. Identify the cervix, easily identified by the presence of internal ridges. The vagina, which joins the cervix, does not have these ridges. The vagina joins the urethra to form a common chamber, the **vaginal vestibule,** leading to the outside of the body. The outer opening is the **urogenital opening,** ventral to the anus (identified in Lab Topic 21, Vertebrate Anatomy I).

At this time, complete the study of the branches of the dorsal aorta (Exercise 22.4, Lab Study A). Identify the **umbilical arteries** and the **external iliac arteries** to the legs and their branches, the **femoral** and **deep femoral** arteries. Also identify the **deep femoral, femoral,** and **common iliac veins,** which drain the legs and empty into the **caudal vena cava.**

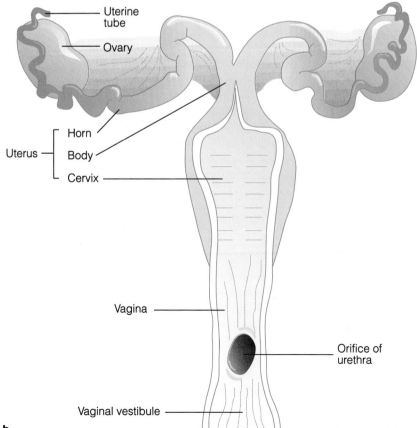

Figure 23.3b.
Enlarged view of the female reproductive system in a fetal pig. The cervix and vagina have been opened to show the ridges in the cervix, which are absent in the vagina. The vaginal vestibule is the common chamber formed by the confluence of the vagina and the urethra.

b.

5. After you conclude your study of the female pig, find someone with a male pig, and demonstrate the systems to each other.

6. Place your pig in its plastic bag, make sure your labels are legible, add preservative, secure the bag, and store it.

Results

Describe the pathway of an egg from the ovary to the outside of the body in a fetal pig, naming regions of organs when appropriate.

Lab Study C. The Pregnant Pig Uterus

On demonstration is an isolated pregnant pig uterus, which should include uterine horns and the body of the uterus. Ovaries and uterine tubes may be attached. Fetal pigs are located in the uterine horns. Each fetal pig is attached to the mother pig by means of the **placenta,** a structure consisting of tissue from the inner lining of the uterus (maternal tissue) and the **chorionic vesi- cle** (embryonic tissue). These tissues are convoluted, creating interdigitat- ing folds that increase the surfaces where the exchange of nutrients, oxygen, and wastes takes place between mother and fetus.

Procedure

1. Observe the uterus with one uterine horn partially opened (Figure 23.4). Some fetal pigs should be visible.

2. If it is not already dissected, using scissors, carefully cut into the **chorionic vesicle,** a saclike structure surrounding each fetal pig. Note that the chorionic vesicle is composed of two fused membranes, the outer **chorion** and the inner **allantois.** Blood vessels are visible lying within the thin allantois. In Lab Topic 21, Vertebrate Anatomy I, you identified the allantoic stalk, a small tube in the umbilical cord extending between the fetal pig's urinary bladder and the allantois. Speculate about the function of the allantois. The blood vessels are branches of which vessels?

3. Observe the **amnion,** a very thin, fluid-filled sac around the fetus. What function do you think this membrane performs?

4. Open the amnion and see the **umbilical cord** attaching each fetus to the fetal membranes.

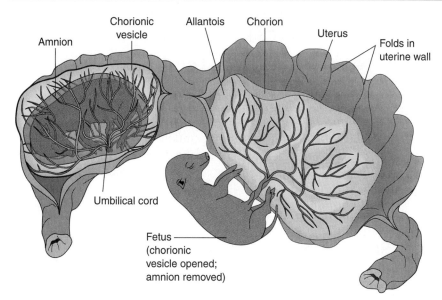

Amnion

Chorionic vesicle

Allantois

Chorion

Uterus

Folds in uterine wall

Umbilical cord

Fetus (chorionic vesicle opened; amnion removed)

Figure 23.4.
Section of uterine horn from an adult pig with two fetuses. Two saclike structures, an amnion and a chorionic vesicle, surround the fetus on the left. The chorionic vesicle around the other fetus has been opened and the amnion removed.

Results

Beginning with those membranes closest to the fetal pig, list in order all embryonic and maternal membranes and tissues associated with the fetal pig.

Discussion

1. Using your text if necessary, compare the female reproductive organs in a human and an adult pig with respect to the oviduct and uterus in the human and uterine tube, horns of the uterus, and body of the uterus in the pig. Speculate about the adaptive advantage of the differences.

2. Describe differences in the arrangement of the vagina and urethra in the fetal pig and human.

3. Tubal ligation is a common form of human female sterilization. Describe this process.

EXERCISE 23.3
Nervous Tissue, the Reflex Arc, and the Vertebrate Eye

In this exercise, you will study several components of the nervous system: the structure of neurons, the pathway of a reflex arc as it relates to the structure of the spinal cord, and the structure of a sensory receptor, the vertebrate eye.

Lab Study A. Nervous Tissue and the Structure of the Neuron

Materials

compound microscope
prepared slide of nervous tissue

Introduction

To understand the function of nervous tissue, review the structure of the **neuron,** the functional cell of nervous tissue. Neuron structure facilitates nervous impulse transmission. Each neuron has three parts: a **cell body,** which contains cytoplasm and the nucleus; **dendrites,** extensions from the cell body that transmit nervous impulses toward the cell body; and an **axon,** an extension that transmits nervous impulses away from the cell body to the next neuron or sometimes to a muscle fiber (Figure 23.5). Neurons are found in the brain and the spinal cord and in nervous tissue throughout the body. You will study the structure of nervous tissue and neurons in the spinal cord.

Procedure

1. Using the intermediate objective on your compound microscope, scan the prepared slide of nervous tissue provided. This is a smear preparation of tissue taken from the spinal cord. You will see hundreds of small, dark dots, which are the nuclei of **glial cells.** Glial cells are nonconducting cells that support and protect neurons.

Figure 23.5.
Structure of a neuron. Dendrites and an axon, cytoplasmic processes, extend from the cell body.

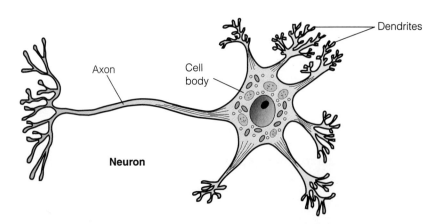

2. Look for large angular **cell bodies** of **motor neurons** scattered among the fibers and glial cells. Study one of these cell bodies on high power and locate the **nucleus,** usually with a prominent **nucleolus.** Try to identify the two types of **processes** extending from the cell body: the **axon** and **dendrites.** Although it is difficult to be certain, you may be able to differentiate between the single, broader axon and one or more slender dendrites extending from the cell body.

Lab Study B. The Reflex Arc and Structure of the Spinal Cord

Materials

stereoscopic microscope
compound microscope
prepared slide of a cross section of spinal cord

Introduction

By studying the anatomy of the spinal cord, you will be able to better envision the interaction of the three components of the nervous system: the sensory component with sensory receptors and sensory nerves; the central nervous system, consisting of the brain and the spinal cord; and the motor system, consisting of motor nerves and effectors. Each of these components plays a role in a simple reflex such as the knee-jerk reflex.

Procedure

1. Using the stereoscopic microscope, examine a prepared slide of a spinal cord cross section taken at a level that shows **dorsal** and **ventral roots.** The roots are collections of processes of neurons in spinal nerves.

2. Identify the dorsal and ventral surfaces of the spinal cord by locating the **ventral fissure** (Figure 23.6). Recall from Lab Topic 18, Animal Diversity II, that vertebrates have a tubular nervous system. Show this by locating the **central canal,** a small channel in the center of the cord.

3. Locate **gray** and **white matter.** In the spinal cord, white matter lies outside the butterfly-shaped gray matter. In sections through the spinal cord at the level where dorsal and ventral roots enter and exit the cord, you will be able to identify the **dorsal root ganglion,** in which cell bodies of sensory neurons lie. Look for the neuronal processes from these cell bodies. These processes continue into the tip of the dorsal "wing" of the gray matter. Sensory neurons receive impulses directly from the environment or from a specific sensory receptor.

4. Locate cell bodies of **motor neurons** in the ventral "wing" of the gray matter. These are best studied using lower powers on the compound microscope. Many of these cell bodies contain conspicuous nuclei and nucleoli. Whereas the simplest reflex involves only one sensory and one motor neuron, most reflexes involve many **interneurons,** lying between sensory and motor neurons. Motor neurons carry impulses to muscles or glands and bring about a **response.**

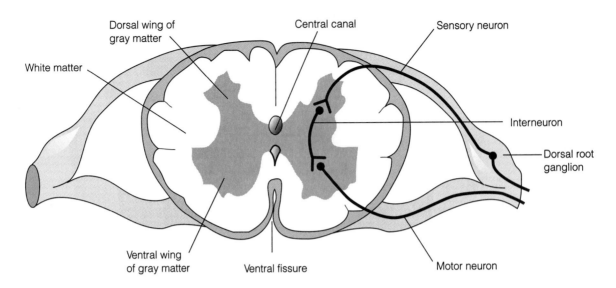

Figure 23.6.
Cross section of the spinal cord at the level of dorsal and ventral roots.
Sensory neurons enter the dorsal wing of the gray matter, and the cell bodies of motor neurons lie in the ventral portion of the gray matter. Interneurons may be present in simple reflex arcs. A simple reflex arc may include two neurons— one motor neuron and one sensory neuron—or three neurons if an interneuron is present.

5. Careful observations may reveal axons from motor neuron cell bodies coursing through the white matter and into the ventral root of the spinal nerve.

Results

Using information from the study of the spinal cord, list in sequence the structures or neurons involved in the simplest reflex.

Discussion

Most reflexes involve a specific sensory receptor (such as the eye, ear, or pain or touch receptors), several sensory neurons, several interneurons, several motor neurons, and effectors (muscles or glands). Propose a reflex arc that would result from your touching a hot plate in the lab.

Lab Study C. Dissection of a Sensory Receptor, the Eye

Materials

preserved cow or sheep eye
dissecting instruments

dissecting pan
disposable gloves

Introduction

The goal of this study is not to perform a comprehensive study of eye structure but rather to identify those structures in the eye that enable it to receive stimuli and transmit the signals in sensory nerves to the central nervous system for processing. After processing, the signals are sent through motor nerves to the effector, bringing about the response.

The vertebrate eye is a complex sensory organ containing nervous tissue capable of being stimulated by light to produce nervous impulses. Sensory neurons carry these impulses to the brain, where they are interpreted, resulting in the perception of sight. The light-sensitive, or photoreceptor, cells in the eye are called *rods* and *cones*. They are the sensory part of a multilayered tissue, the retina. Other structures in the eye protect the retina and regulate the amount and quality of light stimulating the photoreceptor cells.

As you dissect an isolated eyeball from a cow or sheep, determine the contribution of each structure to the production of sight.

Procedure

1. Examine the isolated eye and notice that it is covered with fatty tissue and muscle bands except in the region of the **cornea**, a tough, transparent layer that allows light to enter the eye (Figure 23.7a).

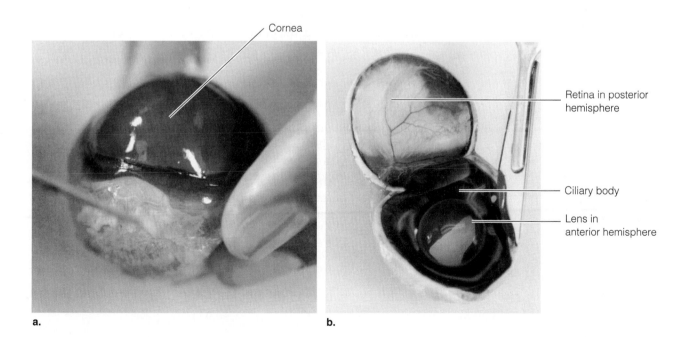

a.

b.

Figure 23.7.

(a) Isolated cow eye and (b) cow eye opened to show internal structures.

2. Search through the fatty tissue on the eye sphere approximately opposite the cornea and locate the round stub of the **optic nerve** exiting the eyeball.

3. Use forceps and scissors to trim away all fat and muscle on the eye surface, taking care to leave the optic nerve undisturbed.

4. Once the fat is removed, you will see that the cornea is the anterior portion of the tough, outer layer of the eyeball, the **fibrous tunic.** The posterior portion of this layer is the white **sclera.** The fibrous tunic protects the internal eye structures.

5. Use scissors to cut the eye in half, making an equatorial incision and separating the anterior hemisphere (with the cornea) from the posterior hemisphere (bearing the optic nerve). Open the eye by placing it, nerve down, in the dissecting tray and lifting off the front hemisphere. Place this hemisphere in the tray with the cornea down. Your dissection should look like Figure 23.7b.

6. Identify the various structures in the anterior hemisphere.

   a. Identify the **lens,** a hard, oval-shaped structure that focuses the light on the retina. In life, this is transparent. Surrounding and attached to the lens may be a jellylike clear substance, the vitreous humor, described in step 8.

   b. Identify the **ciliary body,** a dark, ridged, muscular structure surrounding and attached to the lens by thin ligaments. The ciliary body is a component of the second tunic of the eye, the darkly pigmented **vascular tunic.** Contraction of muscle fibers in the ciliary body changes the shape of the lens. What role does this process play in eye function?

7. Carefully remove the lens and observe that the ciliary body merges anteriorly into another component of the vascular tunic, the **iris.** The iris surrounds an opening, the **pupil.** The pupil allows light to pass through the vascular tunic to the lens. The iris is a sphincter muscle. What is its function?

8. Turn your attention to the posterior hemisphere of the eye. If dissected as described, this hemisphere should hold the **vitreous humor,** which holds the retina in place and is the major internal support of the eye.

9. Using forceps, carefully remove the vitreous humor and identify the pale, delicate **retina,** the third tunic of the eye. The retina contains microscopic rods and cones. What is the function of the retina?

10. The retina lies on the inside surface of the pigmented **choroid layer**, another component of the vascular tunic. The choroid layer absorbs extraneous light rays passing through the retina. Gently push the retina aside and notice that it appears to be attached to the choroid layer in only one spot. This point of attachment is actually where processes from sensory neurons exit the retina as fibers of the **optic nerve.** You may notice a semicircular area of rainbow-colored tissue in the choroid layer. This is the **tapetum lucidum,** a tissue found in the choroid of some animals that enhances vision in limited light.

Results

Complete Table 23.2, naming the three tunics of the eye and their subdivisions, if appropriate. Give the function of each subdivision.

Table 23.2
Eye Tunics and Their Functions

Tunic	Subdivision	Function

Discussion

1. Using your text or library sources, describe each listed functional impairment of the eye.

   myopia (nearsightedness):

   hyperopia (farsightedness):

astigmatism:

cataracts:

2. Which of the above impairments is (are) most likely to occur as a result of aging?

Applying Your Knowledge

1. Individuals with high blood pressure are often placed on a salt-restricted diet. Explain the relationship between the amount of salt in the blood and kidney function, urine volume, and blood pressure. Refer to your text if necessary.

2. Define *homeostasis*. Describe disorders or diseases that may result when homeostasis is disrupted owing to problems in the respiratory, digestive, circulatory, or excretory system.

3. A person who has lost a limb may experience phantom pain, feeling pain in the part of the body that is gone. Suggest an explanation for this phenomenon.

4. Both the eye and a camera focus an image using a lens, but the mechanisms differ. How does the eye lens focus light on the retina? How is this different in a camera?

5. As humans age, the lens loses its elasticity. How would this affect its ability to focus light on the retina?

6. Occasionally in a human male, one or both testes do not descend into the scrotal sacs before birth but remain in the body cavity (a condition known as *cryptorchidism*). What functional abnormalities could result from this condition?

References

Fawcett, D. W., and W. Bloom. *A Textbook of Histology*, 11th ed. Philadelphia, PA: Saunders College Publishing, 1986.

Marieb, E. N. *Human Anatomy and Physiology*, 5th ed. Menlo Park, CA: Benjamin/Cummings, 2001.

Rust, T. G. *A Guide to Biology Lab*. San Antonio, TX: Southwest Educational Enterprises, 1983.

Websites

Test yourself on fetal pig anatomy:
http://www.jburroughs.org/science/resources/pig/pig14.html

Photographs of fetal pig anatomy:
http://www.park.edu/bhoffman/courses/bi123/labs/fetalpig/htm

Vertebrate eye anatomy:
http://www.stlukeseye.com/anatomy.htm

Vertebrate eye anatomy:
http://www.discoveryfund.org/anatomyoftheeye.html

A Google search for "reflex arc" will yield many informative websites:
http://www.google.com

Animal Development

Laboratory Objectives

After completing this lab topic, you should be able to:

1. Describe early development in an echinoderm (sea star), amphibian (frog or salamander), fish (zebrafish), and bird (chicken).
2. List the events in early development that are common to all organisms.
3. Compare early development in the organisms studied, speculating about factors causing differences.
4. Relate the events of early development in vertebrates to the formation of a dorsal nerve cord.
5. Discuss the effects of large amounts of yolk on the events of early development.

Introduction

The development of a multicellular organism involves many stages in a long process beginning with the production and fusion of male and female gametes, continuing with the development of a multicellular embryo, the emergence of larval or juvenile stages, growth and maturation to sexual maturity, and the process of aging, and eventually ending with the death of the organism. A range of biological processes functions in development, including **cell division; differentiation,** where cells, tissues, and organs become specialized for a particular function; and **morphogenesis,** the development of the animal's shape, or body form, and organization.

Fifty years ago, developmental biologists primarily studied **morphology,** or form, to describe the process of development, asking questions about the forces involved in morphogenesis. More recently, developmental biologists ask questions about the genetic control of development and the processes involved in activating different genes in different cells. Before these questions can be pursued, however, it is important to have a basic understanding of early development.

In this lab topic, you will investigate major morphological events that take place early in an organism's development. These events include **gameto-genesis,** the production of gametes; **fertilization,** the union of male and female gametes; **cleavage** and **blastulation,** the production of a multicellular blastula; **gastrulation,** the formation of three primary germ layers—ectoderm, mesoderm, and endoderm; **neurulation,** the formation of the nervous system in chordates; and **organogenesis,** the development of organs from the three primary germ layers. Although you may observe all of these developmental stages, you will study primarily cleavage and blastulation, gastrulation, neurulation, and organogenesis.

Figure 24.1.

Egg types based on amount and distribution of yolk. (a) Isolecithal eggs have small amounts of evenly distributed yolk. (b) Telolecithal eggs have large amounts of yolk concentrated at one end.

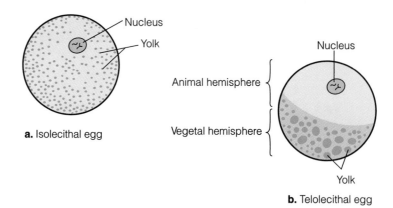

a. Isolecithal egg

b. Telolecithal egg

Overview of Stages in Early Development

Stage 1: Preparation of the Egg, Fertilization, and Cleavage

Development begins as sperm and egg prepare for fertilization. Sperm develop a flagellum, which propels the cell containing the haploid genetic complement of the paternal parent to the egg, which contains the haploid maternal genetic complement. The egg builds up food reserves called **yolk**, which is composed of protein and fat, to be utilized by the early embryo.

When egg and sperm come into contact, their nuclei, each containing a haploid set of chromosomes, combine to form one diploid cell, the **zygote.** The mitotic cell divisions of cleavage rapidly convert the zygote to a multicellular ball, or disc, called the **blastula.** The cells of the blastula are called **blastomeres.** A cavity, the **blastocoel,** forms within the ball of cells. The blastocoel is centrally located in embryos developing from isolecithal eggs. In embryos developing from telolecithal eggs, the blastocoel is associated with the dividing cells in the animal hemisphere.

Egg Types

Because early events in development are affected by the amount of yolk present in the egg, the classification of eggs is based on the amount and distribution of yolk. Eggs with small amounts of evenly distributed yolk are called **isolecithal** eggs (Figure 24.1a). Eggs containing large amounts of yolk concentrated at one end are called **telolecithal** eggs (Figure 24.1b). Some species are moderately telolecithal, whereas others are strongly telolecithal. Eggs may also be classified as **centrolecithal** (yolk in the center of the egg) or **alecithal** (no significant yolk reserves). Neither of these conditions will be studied in this lab topic.

Figure 24.2. (☞)

Cleavage types based on amount and distribution of yolk.
(a) In isolecithal eggs, cleavage is holoblastic, and the blastocoel is centrally located. (b) In moderately telolecithal eggs, cleavage is holoblastic, and the blastocoel develops in the animal hemisphere. (c) In strongly telolecithal eggs, cleavage is meroblastic. Only the active cytoplasm divides, producing a cap of cells, the blastoderm. The blastocoel forms within the blastoderm.

Holoblastic cleavage

Meroblastic cleavage

a. Isolecithal egg

b. Moderately telolecithal egg

c. Strongly telolecithal egg

Cleavage plane I

Zygote

Zygote

Yolk

Blastodisc

2-cell stage

Cleavage plane II

2-cell stage

2-cell stage

Cleavage furrows

4-cell stage

Cleavage plane III

4-cell stage

4-cell stage

8-cell stage

8-cell stage

8-cell stage

Blastoderm

16-cell stage

16-cell stage

Yolk

Section through blastoderm and yolk

Blastocoel

Blastocoel

In strongly telolecithal eggs, the nucleus is surrounded by **active cytoplasm,** which is relatively devoid of yolk. This nuclear-cytoplasmic region is called the **blastodisc.** The blastodisc is displaced toward the pole of the egg where polar bodies budded from the cell in meiosis. This pole is designated the **animal pole.** The half of the egg associated with the animal pole is the **animal hemisphere.** In these eggs, the yolk is concentrated in the other half of the egg, designated the **vegetal hemisphere.** The pole of this hemisphere is the **vegetal pole.**

Cleavage Types

Although the end result of cleavage, the formation of the blastula, is the same in all organisms, the pattern of cleavage can differ. One factor that influences the pattern of cleavage is the amount of yolk present. In total, or **holoblastic,** cleavage, cell divisions pass through the entire fertilized egg. This type of cleavage takes place in isolecithal eggs, where the impact of yolk is minimal (Figure 24.2a). In these eggs, the blastocoel forms in the center of the blastula. In moderately telolecithal eggs, the yolk will retard cytoplasmic divisions and affect the size of cells. However, if the entire egg is cleaved, cleavage is considered holoblastic (Figure 24.2b). In this case, the blastocoel develops in the animal hemisphere. Cells in this hemisphere will be smaller and have less yolk than cells in the vegetal hemisphere.

In a strongly telolecithal egg, only the active cytoplasm is divided during cleavage. This process is called **meroblastic** cleavage, and it produces a cap of cells called a **blastoderm** (Figure 24.2c). In meroblastic embryos, the blastocoel forms between two layers of cells within the blastoderm.

Stage 2: Gastrulation

Gastrulation transforms the blastula, the hollow ball of cells (in holoblastic cleavage) or cap of cells (in meroblastic cleavage), into a **gastrula** made up of three embryonic, or germ, layers: endoderm, ectoderm, and mesoderm (Figure 24.3). Whereas cleavage is characterized by cell division, gastrulation is characterized by cell movement. Surface cells migrate into the interior of the embryo in a process called **involution.** The involuted cells form a new internal cavity, the **archenteron,** lined by the **endoderm,** the embryonic germ layer that ultimately forms the digestive tract. The archenteron opens to the outside through the **blastopore,** which in deuterostomes becomes the anus. In protostomes, the blastopore becomes the mouth.

Figure 24.3.
Gastrulation. The blastula is converted to a three-layer embryo. Ectoderm and endoderm germ layers form first. Mesoderm forms later between the ectoderm and endoderm.

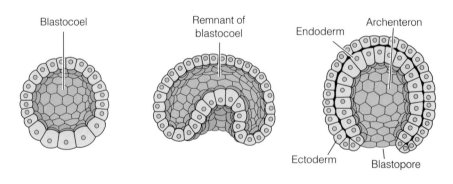

a. Blastula   **b.** Early gastrula   **c.** Late gastrula

The cells that remain on the surface of the embryo become the **ectoderm.** A third layer of cells, the **mesoderm**, develops between ectoderm and endoderm.

Stage 3: Neurulation

Late in gastrulation, neurulation, the formation of a dorsal, hollow neural tube, begins (Figure 24.4). In this strictly chordate process, certain ectodermal cells flatten into an elongated **neural plate** extending from the dorsal edge of the blastopore to the anterior end of the embryo. The center of the plate sinks, forming a **neural groove**. The edges of the plate become elevated to form **neural folds,** which approach each other, touch, and eventually fuse, forming the hollow **neural tube.** The anterior end of the tube develops into the brain, while the posterior end develops into the nerve (spinal) cord.

Stage 4: Organogenesis

After the germ layers and nervous system have been established, organogenesis, the formation of rudimentary organs and organ systems, takes place. Ectoderm, the source of the neural tube in chordates, also forms skin and associated glands. In chordates, somites and the notochord (see Lab Topic 18, Animal Diversity II) develop early from mesodermal cells. Later, muscles, the skeleton, gonads, the excretory system, and the circulatory system develop from mesoderm. Nonchordate animals lack somites and the notochord, but their muscles and organs of the excretory, circulatory, and reproductive systems develop from mesoderm. The endoderm develops into the lining of the digestive tract and such associated organs as the liver, pancreas, and lungs.

Today's lab will be a comparative study of early development in four organisms: (1) the sea star, an echinoderm and invertebrate; (2) the salamander, an amphibious vertebrate; (3) the fish, an aquatic vertebrate; and (4) the chick, a terrestrial vertebrate.

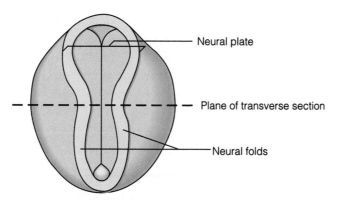

a. Dorsal view of frog embryo

Figure 24.4.
Neurulation. (a) Dorsal view of the entire frog embryo, showing the ectodermal neural plate with edges elevated, forming the neural folds. (b) Seen in transverse section, the neural folds meet and fuse, forming the neural tube.

b.

EXERCISE 24.1

Development in an Echinoderm: The Sea Star

Materials

compound microscope
prepared slide of whole sea star embryos in different stages
   of development

Introduction

The sea star (starfish) is classified in the phylum Echinodermata, the invertebrate group that is phylogenetically closer to chordates than any other. Male and female sea stars release large numbers of gametes into the sea, and fertilization is external. Early development leads to a larval stage that is free-swimming and free-feeding. In this exercise, you will observe a slide that contains an assortment of whole embryos in various stages of development. You will identify each developmental stage and determine the type of egg and cleavage pattern of the echinoderm.

Procedure

1. View the prepared slide of sea star embryos using low and intermediate powers on the compound microscope.

 Use only low and intermediate powers. Using the high power objective to view this slide will destroy the slide!

2. Find examples of all stages of development. When you find a good example of each of the stages described, make a careful drawing of that stage in the appropriate square in Figure 24.5. (See Color Plate 65 for photomicrographs of various developmental stages in an echinoderm.)

Unfertilized Egg

By the time sea star eggs leave the body of the female, meiosis I and II are completed. The nucleus, called the *germinal vesicle,* is conspicuous because the nuclear envelope is intact. A nucleolus is usually distinct. The plasma membrane surrounding the egg cytoplasm closely adheres to a thin external membrane known as the **vitelline layer.** The vitelline layer contains species-specific sperm receptors.

Fertilized Egg

The fertilized egg, or **zygote,** has no visible nuclear envelope, giving this cell a uniform appearance. Look on the zygote surface for a **fertilization membrane,** most easily seen using phase-contrast microscopy. This membrane forms as a result of sperm–egg fusion, and helps prevent multiple fertilizations, or *polyspermy.* Two sequential processes prevent polyspermy, the *fast block* and the *slow block.* When a sperm first fuses with an egg, the permeability of the egg plasma membrane immediately changes, allowing an influx of sodium ions. The sodium ions change the electric potential across the cell membrane and, within a second or so, create a *fast block to polyspermy.* A second block to multiple fertilization takes about 20 to 30 seconds. This *slow block to polyspermy* involves the fusion of egg cytoplasmic vesicles with the egg plasma membrane. These vesicles lie in the cortex, or outer portion of the egg cytoplasm, and are called *cortical vesicles.* When they fuse with the egg membrane, their contents are expelled to the egg surface. Enzymes from the vesicles break bonds between the vitelline layer and the egg plasma membrane, and water flows between the two layers. The vitelline layer rises up from the egg membrane and becomes the fertilization membrane. Some time after the egg and sperm cells fuse, the egg and sperm nuclei, called **pronuclei,** move toward the center of the egg, where they fuse and almost immediately begin to prepare for the first mitotic division of cleavage. Pronuclei are usually not visible in these preparations.

Early Cleavage

Cleavage begins with the zygote and converts this single cell into a multicellular embryo. Find two-, four-, and eight-cell stages. Is the entire zygote involved in early cleavage?

The fertilization membrane remains intact around the embryo until the gastrula stage. What is happening to the size of the cells as cleavage takes place and cell numbers increase?

Late Cleavage

As cleavage continues, a cavity, the **blastocoel,** forms in the center of the cell cluster. The end product of cleavage will be a hollow ball of cells, the **blastula.** Locate and study a blastula. How does the size of individual cells compare with the size of the fertilized egg?

How does the overall size of the blastula compare with that of the fertilized egg?

Early Gastrulation

Gastrulation converts the blastula into the gastrula, an embryo composed of three primary germ layers. The early gastrula can be recognized by a small bubble of cells protruding into the blastocoel. These cells push into the blastocoel through a region on the embryo surface called the **blastopore.** As cells continue to invaginate, or move inward, a tube called the archenteron forms. The archenteron eventually becomes the adult gut. Which embryonic germ layer lines the archenteron?

Middle Gastrulation

The archenteron continues to grow across the blastocoel. It takes on a bulb-like appearance as the advancing portion swells.

Late Gastrulation

Cells at the leading edge of the advancing archenteron extend pseudopodia that attach to a specific region across the blastocoel. These cells continue to pull the archenteron across the blastocoel. As the tip of the archenteron approaches the opposite wall of the embryo, it bends to one side and fuses with surface cells. The site of fusion will eventually become the mouth of the embryo. What will be formed from the blastopore at the opposite end of the archenteron?

What is the germ layer of cells on the surface of the embryo called?

The amoeboid cells that attach the archenteron to the embryo wall are called *mesenchyme cells.* These cells later detach from the archenteron, proliferate, and form a layer of cells lining the old blastocoel, now divided by the archenteron. This layer of cells will become the mesodermal germ layer.

Bipinnaria Larval Stage

The archenteron of the gastrula differentiates into a broad **esophagus** leading from the **mouth** to a large oval **stomach** and on to a small, tubular **intestine.** All these structures will be visible in the bilaterally symmetric bipinnaria larva. Locate these structures in larvae on your slide and in Color Plate 66. The larva is now self-feeding and begins to grow. It will later be transformed into the radially symmetric adult sea star.

Results

Draw stages of sea star development in the appropriate boxes in Figure 24.5.

Discussion

1. What is the advantage of species-specific sperm receptors in the vitelline layer of the egg?

a. Unfertilized egg	**b.** Fertilized egg
c. Early cleavage	**d.** Late cleavage
e. Early gastrulation	**f.** Middle gastrulation
g. Late gastrulation	**h.** Bipinnaria larva

Figure 24.5.
Early stages of development in the sea star.

2. What type of egg does the sea star have? What evidence have you observed that supports your answer?

3. Describe the pattern of cleavage seen in the sea star and give the name for this type of cleavage.

EXERCISE 24.2
Development in an Amphibian

Materials

video or film of early development in a salamander or some other
   amphibian

Introduction

Amphibians are vertebrates that lay jelly-coated eggs in water or in moist areas on land. Common examples include frogs and salamanders. For most species, fertilization is external, with the male depositing sperm over the eggs after the female releases them. Internal fertilization takes place in some amphibians, however, in which cases the young are born in advanced developmental stages. Early development is similar in all species. After fertilization, the zygote begins cleavage followed by gastrulation, neurulation, and organogenesis.

In this exercise, you will study early development in an amphibian by observing a video or film presentation of some species such as the salamander *Triturus alpestris*. The film or video shows dramatic time-lapse photography of cleavage, gastrulation, and neurulation.

Procedure

1. Before viewing the film or video, complete Table 24.1 by defining terms commonly used when describing early embryos. (You may need to refer to your text.)
2. Read the questions in the Results section, view the film or video, and then answer the questions.

Results

1. Would you describe the amphibian egg as isolecithal, moderately telolecithal, strongly telolecithal, or alecithal?

Table 24.1
Common Terms Used in Embryology

Term	Definition
Animal pole	
Animal hemisphere	
Equator	
Vegetal hemisphere	
Vegetal pole	

2. Describe the cleavage pattern. Is it holoblastic or meroblastic? Are cleavages synchronous or irregular? Can you detect any particular pattern in the cleavage? Where is the second cleavage plane in relation to the first?

3. Does the size of the embryo change as cleavage progresses?

4. Visually follow surface cells during gastrulation. Do they all move at the same rate? Describe gastrulation, comparing the process with that in the sea star. Notice the position of the blastopore and the yolk plug located in the blastopore.

5. During neurulation, do the neural ridges (folds) meet and fuse simultaneously along the entire length of the neural tube or do they close like a zipper?

Discussion

1. Name at least two major differences in early development between the salamander and the sea star and describe factors responsible for these differences.

2. Compare the video of amphibian development with Figure 24.6. Label the following in the appropriate figure: **animal pole**, **vegetal pole**, **blastocoel**, **blastopore**, **yolk plug**, **neural plate**, and **neural folds**.

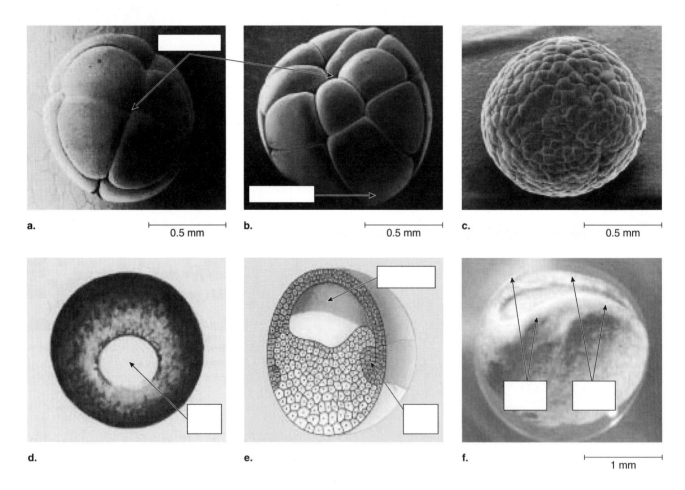

a. 0.5 mm b. 0.5 mm c. 0.5 mm

d. e. f. 1 mm

Figure 24.6.
Early amphibian development. (a) and (b) Early cleavage. (c) Surface view of the hollow blastula in late cleavage. (d) Surface view of a gastrula. (e) Cross section of a gastrula. (f) Surface view of a neurula.

EXERCISE 24.3

Development in the Zebrafish

Materials

small petri dishes
depression slides
embryo-rearing solution
clean toothpicks

fish embryos in various developmental stages (some on ice)
stereoscopic microscope
compound microscope

Introduction

In this portion of the laboratory, you will observe living embryos in early developmental stages using a freshwater fish commonly known as the zebrafish, or zebra danio (*Brachydanio rerio*). This fish is a native of streams in India. Male and female fish are similar in appearance, but the male is generally smaller, with a streamlined body shape. The female is larger and broader than the male, especially when carrying eggs. (See Color Plate 65.)

In nature, zebrafish are stimulated to reproduce when days consist of approximately 16 hours of light and 8 hours of dark. This photoperiod corresponds to favorable weather and food supplies for developing embryos. By artificially creating this photoperiod in the laboratory, we can produce conditions that stimulate the zebrafish to spawn. After only 2 or 3 days on a cycle of 16 hours of light and 8 hours of dark, female fish will lay eggs, and male fish will deposit sperm for external fertilization.

The embryos you will observe today were collected from zebrafish on the artificial schedule. Newly spawned embryos were placed in embryo-rearing solution in petri dishes. Some embryos were maintained at room temperature, while others were placed on ice to retard development. The petri dishes were labeled to indicate the approximate stage of development. Because some embryos have been kept on ice, and because not all female fish lay their eggs at exactly the same time, a variety of early developmental stages should be available for your study. Neurulation and organogenesis stages are available from yesterday's spawning.

The approximate schedule of development at 25°C is described in Table 24.2. Use this schedule to predict the approximate stage of development for eggs collected at 8 A.M. and maintained at room temperature (approximately 23°C).

Procedure

1. Obtain a petri dish with an embryo in embryo-rearing solution from the lab supply. View it using the stereoscopic microscope. Gently roll the embryo using a toothpick to see the embryo from several angles.

2. Read the description (following) of each stage of development, and determine the stage of the embryo. Remember that these are living embryos, and the stage of development may have changed from that indicated on the petri dish label.

3. Using a pipette, carefully transfer the embryo and rearing solution to a depression slide and view it on the lowest power of the compound microscope.

Table 24.2
Developmental Schedule for Zebrafish at 25°C

Hour	Time	Comments
0	8 A.M.	Lights on. Fish stimulated to spawn. Fish begin to dart back and forth, depositing eggs and sperm (spawning) close to the bottom of the aquarium. Fertilization takes place, forming the zygote. Cleavage begins in 35 minutes.
1	9 A.M.	Cleavage continues. Some embryos are collected and placed on ice to slow development.
2	10 A.M.	Embryos are in midblastula stage (approximately 64 cells).
4	12 noon	Late blastula.
5	1 P.M.	Early gastrula.
6	2 P.M.	Midgastrula.
12	8 P.M.	Gastrulation completed; neurulation taking place.
18	2 A.M.	Neurulation completed; organogenesis beginning.
24	8 A.M.	Second day begins; organogenesis continues.
96	8 A.M.	Day 4 begins; embryos hatch.

4. Remembering that these are living embryos, watch carefully to observe cells dividing. You may observe a two-cell embryo changing to a four-cell embryo or a late blastula beginning gastrulation. With careful and patient observations, you may be fortunate enough to see the developmental stages unfolding.

5. Make drawings in the margin of your lab manual so that you will be able to refer to them later.

6. Using the pipette, return the embryo to the petri dish. Then return the petri dish to the lab supply.

7. Obtain a petri dish with an embryo in a different stage of development and repeat steps 1 to 6. Continue your observations until you have seen all listed stages of development.

Unfertilized Egg

Because most eggs are immediately fertilized after spawning, you may not find any unfertilized eggs. The unfertilized egg is about 0.5 mm in diameter. It is spherical, with yolk granules evenly distributed. There is a membrane, the **chorion**, around the egg.

Fertilized Egg (Zygote)

A thin **fertilization membrane** forms after fertilization. The yolk granules condense, and the active cytoplasm migrates to the **animal pole,** where it becomes the **blastodisc,** or germinal disc. The blastodisc is visible as a bulge in the otherwise spherical cell. The future embryo will develop from the blastodisc, and the yolk will serve as the nutrient supply.

Cleavage

Cleavage takes place in the blastodisc. Cells resulting from cleavage are called **blastomeres.** The blastodisc divides into 2, then 4, 8, and 16 cells of equal size.

Blastula

By the 64-cell stage, the blastula appears as a high dome of cells at the animal pole (Figure 24.7a). This dome of cells is called the **blastoderm.** As cleavage continues, the cells become more compact, and the interface between the blastoderm and the yolk flattens out (Figure 24.7b).

Gastrula

Gastrulation in the zebrafish is strikingly different from the process in the sea star and the salamander, because cleavage is restricted to the blastodisc. The surface cells of the blastula spread over the entire yolk mass toward the vegetal pole in a process called **epiboly.** The surface cells produce the ectoderm. When the advancing blastoderm cells have covered approximately one-half of the yolk, a type of cell movement called **involution** begins when cells move into the interior of the embryo in a ring at the edge of the advancing blastoderm. These involuting cells will eventually form mesoderm and endoderm. Figure 24.7c and d illustrate early and late gastrulation.

Neurulation

The antero/posterior, dorso/ventral embryonic axes are first obvious during neurulation. As neurulation takes place, ectodermal cells form the neural plate and eventually the neural tube. In the whole embryo, the region of the neural tube appears as a ridge on the dorsal surface. With careful investigation, you can discern that one end of the neural tube is enlarged. This enlarged portion is the **brain** developing at the anterior end of the embryo. The posterior end of the neural tube develops into the **nerve (spinal) cord.** As development progresses, a supportive rod, the **notochord,** forms from mesoderm beneath the neural tube. The notochord is later replaced by vertebrae. Blocks of tissue called **somites** form from mesoderm along each side of the nerve cord (Figure 24.7e).

Organogenesis

In organogenesis, formation of rudimentary organs and organ systems takes place. In the fish, the brain, eyes, somites, spinal cord, and tail bud are visible. The rhythmic beating of the heart and circulating blood are seen.

Among other things, somites develop into skeletal muscles, and older embryos will be actively twisting and turning in the fertilization membrane. Developing **pigmentation** will be visible in the skin and eye.

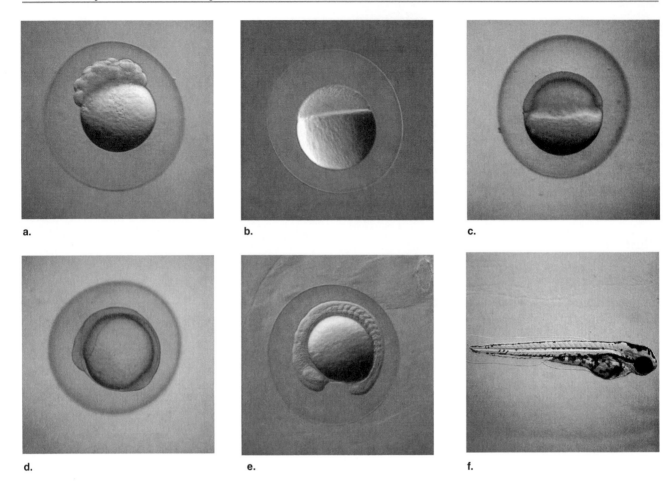

a. b. c.

d. e. f.

Figure 24.7.
Development in the zebrafish. (a) The 64-cell blastula. (b) Late blastula in side view. (c) The early gastrula. Surface cells move over the yolk mass. When they cover approximately one-half of the yolk, they begin to involute at the blasto- pore. (d) The late gastrula. (e) Neurulation and organogenesis. Ectodermal cells form the neural tube, which eventually develops into the anterior brain and posterior spinal cord. (f) Newly hatched embryo.

Hatching

As organogenesis continues, embryos grow and develop, and after 4 days, the eggs hatch (Figure 24.7f).

Results

In the margin of your lab manual, draw the stages of development. Include at least two stages in early cleavage (2-cell, 4-cell, 8-cell, 16-cell) and label the animal pole, vegetal pole, blastomere, and fertilization membrane.

Discussion

1. What type of egg does the zebrafish have?

2. Is cleavage in the zebrafish holoblastic or meroblastic?

3. Compare the size of the blastodisc and the size of cells before and after cleavage.

E X E R C I S E   2 4 . 4
Development in a Bird: The Chicken

Materials

compound microscope	finger bowl
stereoscopic microscope	warm 0.9% NaCl
unincubated egg (demonstration)	flat-tipped forceps
prepared slide of 16-hour chick	sharp-pointed scissors
prepared slide of 24-hour chick	watch glass
living egg incubated 48 hours	disposable pipette
living egg incubated 96 hours	pipette bulb

Introduction

Immature eggs, or **oocytes,** develop within follicles in the single ovary of the adult female bird. (Two ovaries begin to develop in birds, but the second ovary degenerates.) In the sexually mature bird, hormonal stimulation brings about **ovulation,** the release of oocytes into a single oviduct. An oocyte consists of active cytoplasm, called the **blastodisc,** or germinal disc, floating on a huge amount of food reserve, the yolk, surrounded by a plasma membrane. At the time of ovulation, chromosomes in the large oocyte nucleus have just completed the first maturation division of meiosis (meiosis I). At ovulation in chickens, the oocyte nucleus measures approximately 0.5 mm and the oocyte measures approximately 35 mm in diameter.

Fertilization is internal in birds. If sperm are present in the oviduct at ovulation, they will penetrate each oocyte (one per oocyte), stimulating the completion of meiosis in the oocyte nucleus. The sperm nucleus and the now mature egg nucleus fuse, producing the zygote nucleus, which begins to divide by mitosis followed by cytoplasmic cleavage. As this developing embryo continues its passage down the oviduct, albumin, shell membranes, and finally a calcareous shell are deposited on its surface. In chickens, passage down the oviduct takes about 25 hours. This means that a freshly laid chicken egg, if it has been fertilized, has completed about 25 hours of development. The cleaved blastodisc is now called the **blastoderm,** or **blastula.** Development continues in the blastoderm, giving rise to all parts of the embryo, with yolk containing carbohydrates, proteins, lipids, and vitamins serving as the food reserves.

In this exercise, you will observe an unincubated egg and incubated eggs in several stages of development. As you study the embryos, identify developing structures and compare bird development with that of the sea star, salamander, and zebrafish.

Procedure

1. Refer to Figure 24.8 and observe the unincubated chicken egg on demonstration.

   Most eggs sold for human consumption are purchased from commercial egg farms where hens are not allowed contact with roosters. The egg you are studying may or may not have been fertilized.

   a. Observe the broken calcareous **shell** with outer and inner **shell membranes** just inside. The shell and membranes are porous, allowing air to pass through to the embryo inside. You have probably noticed an air chamber at one end of a hard-boiled egg, between the two membranes.

   b. Observe the watery, proteinaceous **egg albumin** (egg white) and the yellow yolk. The layers of albumin closest to the yolk are more viscous and stringy than the outer albumin. As the yolky egg passes down the oviduct, it rotates, twisting the stringy albumin into two whitish strands on either end of the yolk. Called **chalaza**, these strands suspend the yolk in the albumin.

   c. Locate the **cytoplasmic island**, a small whitish disc lying on top of the yolk. This is larger in a fertilized egg because of the development that has taken place. Remember that this island is called the *blastodisc* before cleavage begins and the *blastoderm* after cleavage has begun. If you are studying a fertilized egg, cleavage is completed. Cleavage is restricted to the blastoderm; the yolk does not divide.

   As cleavage takes place, the blastoderm, now a mass of cells, becomes elevated above the yolk. Subsequent horizontal cleavages create three or four cell layers in the blastoderm, and a space, the blastocoel, forms within these layers.

2. Study the prepared slide of the 16-hour egg (the gastrula). Refer to Figure 24.9a, a surface view of the embryo.

 Use only low and intermediate powers when viewing this slide. The high power objective will break the slide!

Figure 24.8.
The unincubated chicken egg.
The chalaza suspends the yolk in the albumin.

a.

Figure 24.9.
Chick gastrulation. (a) Surface view of chick blastoderm after 16 hours of incubation, the gastrula stage. The primitive streak is visible. (b) Cross section of blastoderm after 16 hours of incubation. Cells turn in at the primitive streak, initiating the formation of mesodermal tissues.

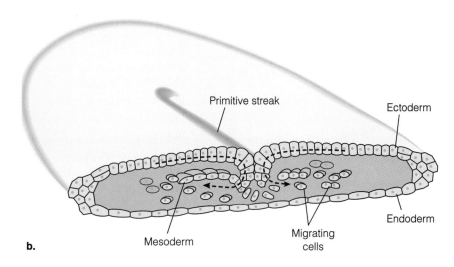

Primitive streak

Ectoderm

Endoderm

Mesoderm

Migrating cells

b.

a. Using low and then intermediate powers on the compound microscope, view a prepared slide of the whole chick embryo after about 16 hours of incubation. At this stage, cells in the blastoderm have separated into an upper layer forming ectoderm and an inner layer forming endoderm. These layers are visible only in sections of the embryo.

b. Locate a dark, longitudinal thickening, the **primitive streak.** Surface cells migrate toward the primitive streak and then turn under, through the primitive streak. By 18 hours, they have spread out and initiated the formation of mesodermal tissues (Figure 24.9b). The notochord is one of the first structures to develop in the mesodermal layer.

3. Study the prepared slide of the 24-hour chick (neurulation). Refer to Figure 24.10.

Use only low and intermediate powers to view this slide. The high power objective will break the slide!

Figure 24.10.
The chick after 24 hours of incubation (neurulation). Edges of the ectodermal neural plate elevate, forming neural folds. The depressed center is the neural groove. The neural folds eventually fuse, forming the neural tube.

a. Use the low and then intermediate powers on the compound microscope to view the prepared slide of a chick after 24 hours of incubation. At this stage, the neural tube is forming anterior to the primitive streak in a process similar to neurulation in fish.

b. Look for a longitudinal ectodermal **neural plate** with elevated edges called **neural folds** and a depressed center called the **neural groove.** The margins of the neural folds, which appear as a pair of dark longitudinal bands, become elevated and approach each other until they touch and eventually fuse. This fusion of the folds forms the neural tube. The anterior end of the neural tube becomes the brain; the posterior end becomes the spinal, or nerve, cord.

c. Label the following on Figure 24.10: neural folds, neural groove, developing brain, spinal cord region of the neural tube, and primitive streak.

 Study the next two stages of development using living chick embryos and the materials listed at the beginning of the exercise. Work in pairs. One student will open the 48-hour chick; the other will open the 96-hour chick. Collaborate as you observe both eggs.

4. Prepare each egg to study the 48- and 96-hour chicks.

a. Pour warm (heated to about 38°C) 0.9% NaCl solution into a clean finger bowl.

b. Obtain an egg and carry it to your desk, keeping it oriented with the "top" up as it has been in the incubator. Crack the "down" side of the egg on the edge of the finger bowl. Hold the egg, cracked side down, in the NaCl solution, and carefully open the shell, allowing the egg to slide out of the shell.

c. Observe the embryo on the surface of the yolk. The embryo should either be on top of the yolk or it should float to the top. The embryo is in the center of the vascularized **blastoderm.**

d. Using broad-tipped forceps and sharp scissors, remove the embryo from the yolk surface by carefully snipping outside the vascularized region of the embryo. Use the forceps to hold the blastoderm as you cut. Do not let go or you may lose the embryo in the mass of yolk.

e. Hold a watch glass under the NaCl solution and carefully pull the blastoderm away from the surface of the yolk into the watch glass. Carefully lift the watch glass and embryo out of the solution and pipette away excess solution until only a small amount remains.

f. Wipe the bottom of the watch glass, place on the stereoscopic microscope, and observe.

5. Study the 48-hour chick (early organogenesis). Refer to Figure 24.11.

Figure 24.11.
The chick after 48 hours of incubation. Identify the heart (atrium and ventricle), vitelline blood vessels, the brain, an eye, the spinal cord, and somites.

a. Identify structures in the circulatory system. In the living embryo, the **heart** is already beating at this stage, pumping blood through the **vitelline blood vessels,** which emerge from the embryo and carry food materials from the yolk mass to the embryo. If the heart is still beating, you should be able to see blood passing from the **atrium** into the **ventricle.** The atrium lies behind the ventricle, which is a larger, U-shaped chamber.

b. Identify structures in the nervous system. The anterior part of the neural tube has formed the **brain. Eyes** are already partially formed. Follow the tube posteriorly to the **spinal cord.**

c. Observe **somites,** blocks of tissue lying on either side of the **spinal cord.** Somites develop into body musculature and several other mesodermal organs.

d. Label Figure 24.11.

e. Swap chick embryos with your lab partner.

6. Study the 96-hour chick (later organogenesis). Refer to Figure 24.12 on the next page.

a. Notice that the 96-hour chick has a strong **cervical flexure,** bending the body into a C configuration. Several organs are noticeably larger than in the 48-hour chick.

b. Locate the developing **brain, eyes,** and **ears.**

c. Identify the conspicuous **heart.**

d. Locate one of the two **anterior limb buds** just behind the heart. Anterior limb buds develop into wings.

e. Locate the **posterior limb buds** near the tail. These limb buds grow into legs.

f. Identify one of four **extraembryonic membranes,** the **allantois,** which protrudes outward from the hindgut near the posterior limb bud (see Figure 24.13). Extraembryonic membranes are derived from embryonic tissue, but are found outside the embryo proper. These membranes are important adaptations for land-dwelling organisms like reptiles, birds, and mammals. They help solve problems such as desiccation, gas exchange, and waste removal in the embryo. The large saclike allantois will continue to grow until it lies close inside the porous shell. It functions to bring oxygen to the embryo, carry away carbon dioxide, and store liquid wastes.

g. Look for a second extraembryonic membrane, the **amnion,** a thin, transparent membrane that encloses the embryo in a fluid-filled sac.

h. Using the broad-tipped forceps, carefully lift the embryo to observe the yolk stalk and **yolk sac,** a third extraembryonic membrane that surrounds the yolk. The fourth extraembryonic membrane, the **chorion,** is not easily observed.

i. Label Figure 24.12.

j. Swap chick embryos with your lab partner.

Figure 24.12.
The chick after 96 hours of incubation. A strong cervical flexure has developed. Limb buds, allantois, ears, and tail are visible.

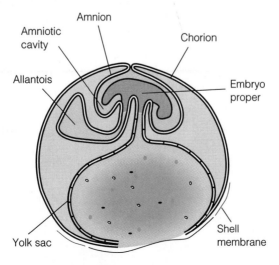

Amniotic cavity

Amnion

Allantois

Chorion

Embryo proper

Yolk sac

Shell membrane

Figure 24.13.
Extraembryonic membranes in a chick between 96 and 120 hours of incubation. (The shell is not shown.) The allantois protrudes from the gut near the posterior limb bud. The amnion surrounds the embryo proper, creating a fluid-filled amniotic cavity; the yolk sac surrounds the yolk; and the chorion grows until it eventually fuses with the shell membrane.

Results

Label Figures 24.10, 24.11, and 24.12 and make additional sketches in the margin of your lab manual for future reference.

Discussion

1. What type of egg is the chicken egg?

2. This egg undergoes what type of cleavage?

3. Collaborating with your lab partner, describe major differences between the 48-hour and 96-hour chicken embryos.

Questions for Review

1. Having completed this lab topic, define and describe the following terms, giving examples when appropriate: *cleavage, blastula, gastrula, involution, archenteron, blastocoel, blastopore, isolecithal, telolecithal, alecithal, meroblastic, holoblastic, bipinnaria, epiboly, neurulation, organogenesis, animal pole, vegetal pole, blastodisc, blastoderm, ectoderm, mesoderm, endoderm, neural plate, neural groove,* and *neural fold.*

2. List the embryonic germ layers and the organs derived from each.

3. Differentiate between epiboly and involution.

Applying Your Knowledge

1. Review the stages of early development in animals. How are these stages similar in the animals you have studied? How do they differ? Complete Table 24.3.

Table 24.3
Comparison of Stages of Early Development in the Sea Star, Salamander, Fish, and Chick

Organism	Cleavage	Gastrulation	Neurulation	Organogenesis
Sea star				
Salamander				
Fish				
Chick				

2. What is yolk? What is its function in development? Do mammals have yolk? Explain.

3. Giving examples from organisms studied, explain how the amount of yolk affects cleavage and gastrulation.

4. How do the differences in development lead to adaptations to the particular lifestyles of these organisms? (Some are aquatic, others terrestrial, and so on.)

5. What are the important events that commonly occur in gastrulation for all organisms observed in this lab?

6. Eggs of reptiles, birds, and a few primitive mammals are laid on land, usually away from water and independent sources of food. What features of the land egg (chick) allow this type of early development?

7. Name the four extraembryonic membranes in the chick and, using your text as a reference if necessary, give their respective functions, relating these to adaptation to the land environment.

References

Beams, H. W., and R. G. Kessel. "Cytokinesis: A Comparative Study of Cytoplasmic Division in Animal Cells," *American Scientist,* 1976, vol. 64, pp. 279–290. Scanning electron micrographs of development in zebrafish.

Campbell, N., and J. Reece. *Biology,* 6th ed. Menlo Park, CA: Benjamin/Cummings, 2002.

Gilbert, S. F. *Developmental Biology,* 5th ed. Sunderland, MA: Sinauer Associates, 1997.

Hisaoka, K. K., and C. F. Firlit. "Further Studies on the Embryonic Development of the Zebra Fish, *Brachydanio rerio* (Hamilton-Buchanan)." *Journal of Morphology,* 1960, vol. 107, pp. 205–226.

Patten, B. M. *Early Embryology of the Chick,* 5th ed. New York, NY: McGraw-Hill, 1971.

Westerfield, M. (ed.). *The Zebrafish Book; A Guide for the Laboratory Use of Zebrafish (Brachydanio rerio).* Eugene, OR: University of Oregon Press, 1989.

Exercise 24.3, Development in the Zebrafish, is based on an exercise by John Pilger, Professor of Biology, Agnes Scott College, Decatur, GA, and a workshop presented by Robert R. Cohen, Professor of Biology, Metropolitan State College, Denver, at a meeting of the American Society of Zoologists. Used by permission.

Website

The Fish Net:
http://zfin.org/index.html

Ecology I: Terrestrial Ecology

Laboratory Objectives

After completing this lab topic, you should be able to:

1. Describe the trophic levels of an ecosystem and provide examples from field experience.
2. Describe the environmental factors that are important components of the ecosystem.
3. Calculate density, frequency, dominance, and species diversity.
4. Describe the relative importance of particular species in the ecosystem as determined by their density, size, or role in the ecosystem.
5. Construct an illustrative model of the ecosystem components.

Introduction

Organisms are influenced by their physical environment and by interactions with other living organisms. The study of the relationships of organisms with their environment (both physical and biological) is called **ecology**. Ecological investigations may address questions at several hierarchical levels: **individuals, populations** (organisms of the same species that share a common gene pool and occur in the same area), **communities** (populations of different species that inhabit the same area), and **ecosystems** (the community of plants and animals plus the physical environment). A physiological ecologist studies the effects of the environment on individual organisms. A population ecologist might be interested in questions about the reproductive biology of a population of endangered plant species. The community ecologist might investigate the sequence of species composition changes in a forest following a disturbance. And the ecosystem ecologist might question how the interactions among members of different trophic levels (feeding levels) are influenced by environmental conditions.

An ecosystem can be divided into **biotic** components (living organisms) and **abiotic** components (physical features). In a forest ecosystem, the abiotic components include the climatic factors, soil type, water availability, and landscape features. The biotic components of the forest include trees, shrubs, wildflowers, squirrels, foxes, caterpillars, eagles, spiders, millipedes, and fungi on the forest floor and in the soil (Figure 25.1). The biotic components can be further characterized based on **trophic structure**, the ecological role of organisms in the food chain. Plants and some protists are categorized as **primary producers** (autotrophic organisms), capable of transforming light energy into chemical energy stored in carbohydrates

Figure 25.1.

Forest ecosystem. A simplified forest system showing trophic (feeding) relationships among primary producers, consumers, detritivores, and decomposers.

through the process of photosynthesis. The amount of energy available for all other trophic levels is dependent on the photosynthetic ability of the primary producers. **Consumers** are animals and heterotrophic protists, which literally consume the primary producers or each other or both. They may be divided into **primary consumers** (**herbivores**, which consume plants) and **secondary** and **tertiary consumers** (**carnivores**, which eat other consumers). Rarely do ecosystems support additional levels of consumers. In general, only 10–20% of the energy available at one trophic level is transferred to the next trophic level. The number of organisms that can be supported at subsequent higher trophic levels is limited by the available energy.

Detritivores obtain their nutrients and energy from dead organisms and waste materials, and **decomposers** (fungi and bacteria) absorb nutrients from nonliving organic material.

With the assistance of your lab partner, match each of the following trophic levels with an example of an organism from the forest system just described. Remember that the trophic level reflects who is eating whom.

Primary producers:

Primary consumers:

Secondary consumers:

Tertiary consumers:

Detritivores:

Decomposers:

Note that some organisms fit into more than one trophic level—because, like many humans, some are omnivores, eating whatever is available.

Stating the Problem

In this lab topic, you will investigate the structure and function of a local ecosystem. The exercise is designed for a forest ecosystem but can be adapted easily for use in grasslands or even a weedy urban lot. (An outline for adapting the lab for use in a weedy field is included at the end of the lab topic.) The study site has been selected in advance by your instructor, who may have prepared an introductory description for you.

In the field, spend 5 minutes observing the features of your study site, both biotic and abiotic. Based on your observations and the information provided by your instructor, write in the space below a brief description of the study site, including its physical and biological features.

Study Site

You will work as teams of ecologists to determine the components of the ecosystem. Each team, composed of six to eight students, will sample one plot, thus providing three or four replicate samples, depending on the number

Suggested Organization of Student Teams

Exercise	Sampling	No. of Students
Exercise 25.1	Biotic Components	
A	Trees	2
B	Shrubs, saplings, and vines	2
C	Seedlings and herbaceous vegetation	2
D	Macroinvertebrates	2
E	Microinvertebrates	2
F	Microorganisms	2*
G	Other forest animals	All
Exercise 25.2	Abiotic Components	2*

*Two students can complete both Exercise 25.2 and Field Study F in Exercise 25.1.

of teams. Within teams, each student will have specific assigned responsibilities, as suggested below and fully described in the following exercises.

Following the field sampling, you will share results with other teams, make calculations, pool and analyze data, and develop a model of the ecosystem. Students should read assignments for all field studies.

EXERCISE 25.1

Biotic Components

As you begin your observations of the forest, note the vertical layers of the forest from the forest floor up to the tallest and largest trees, which form a canopy. The forest vegetation can be subdivided arbitrarily into categories according to the structural pattern of the forest (Figure 25.2): forest **trees** (woody plants with a diameter at breast height (DBH) of >10 cm); **shrubs, saplings,** and **vines** (DBH 2.5–10 cm); and **seedlings** and **herbaceous plants** (DBH < 2.5 cm). (Note that DBH is measured at a height of 1.5 m from the base of the tree.) Microorganisms and small animals can be sampled from the forest floor, **litter** (fallen leaves, for example), and soil, with large vertebrates observed directly or indirectly by animal signs (nest sites, feces, tracks).

In your student teams, you will sample part of the study site using circular plots to estimate the abundance of plants and animals in each of the categories described above. The size of the circular plots varies according to the size and abundance of the organisms (Table 25.1). Thus, trees are sampled using the largest plot, while the herbs of the forest floor are sampled in small plots. Imagine the difficulty of sampling trees in plots of only 1 m² or counting all the nonwoody plants in a plot with a diameter of over 10 m!

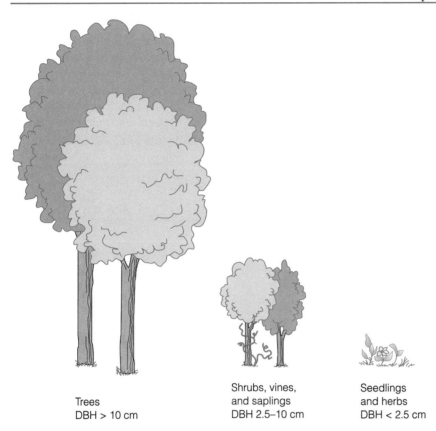

Figure 25.2.
Vertical stratification of the forest.
The forest can be divided into layers:
the trees (DBH > 10 cm); shrubs,
saplings, and vines (DBH 2.5–10 cm);
and seedlings and herbaceous plants
(DBH < 2.5 cm).

Trees
DBH > 10 cm

Shrubs, vines,
and saplings
DBH 2.5–10 cm

Seedlings
and herbs
DBH < 2.5 cm

Table 25.1
Sampling Design for Determining the Biotic
Components of a Forest Ecosystem

Organisms	Plot Size
Trees (DBH > 10 cm)	100 m^2
Shrubs, saplings, and vines (DBH 2.5–10 cm)	50 m^2
Seedlings and herbs (DBH < 2.5 cm)	0.50 m^2
Litter macroinvertebrates	0.50 m^2
Microinvertebrates from litter and soil samples	—
Microorganisms from litter and soil samples	—
Large vertebrates observed by all	—

Avoid contact with poison ivy. Your instructor will identify the plant for you. After completing the fieldwork, thoroughly wash all areas of exposed skin with soap and water. Avoid contact with your clothing if you think you have come into contact with poison ivy. Notify your instructor if you are allergic to bee stings or other plants and animals that you might encounter outdoors.

Field Study A. Trees

Materials

3 lines, 5.64 m long, with a clip on one end and a stake on the other end of each
center post
mallet

DBH measuring tape
index cards
permanent marker
plastic bags and rubber bands

Introduction

Trees form the uppermost layer, or canopy, of the forest. They influence the physical environment, such as the quality and quantity of light reaching all other vegetation, water availability, and temperature. A forest description is usually based on the largest and most abundant species of trees.

Procedure

1. Determine the sample plot location based on recommendations from your instructor.
2. Locate the center of the sample plot and hammer the center post into the ground at that location.
3. Clip one end of a line to the center post. Extend the line, keeping it straight and taut, and hammer the stake into position (Figure 25.3, line 1).
4. Attach and secure lines 2 and 3 at an angle forming two wedge-shaped sections A and B (see Figure 25.3). Each wedge should be equal to approximately one-fifth of the plot.
5. Identify and measure DBH (>10 cm) for all trees in sections A and B (see Figure 25.3). The number of DBH measurements will also provide a record of abundance. If a tree is on the outer perimeter of the plot, it should be counted in the plot if at least 50% of the tree is within the plot.

Diameter at breast height (DBH) is measured 1.5 m above the base of the tree. Measure or estimate this height on your body to ensure that you determine DBH in a consistent fashion. If DBH measuring tapes are not available, measure trees with a circumference of > 32 cm.

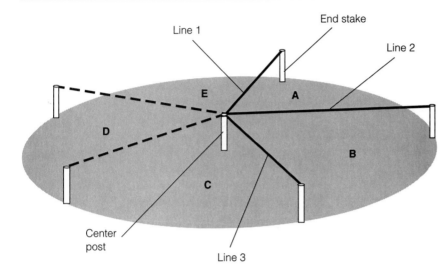

Figure 25.3.
Establishing and sampling a circular plot. Locate the center post and attach three lines (1, 2, 3) to form two wedge-shaped sections, A and B. After sampling A and B, move line 2 to form section C. After sampling C, move line 3 to form sections D and E.

6. If you cannot identify a tree, assign a number to that type of tree. Collect a leaf sample, if possible, for later identification. Label the sample by attaching a numbered card or by writing the number on the leaf blade. If leaves are not available, write a brief description.

7. Before moving any lines, check with the shrub, sapling, and vine group to be sure they have completed their sampling. Their plot is smaller and lies within the boundary of the tree plot.

8. Do not move line 1. Detach line 2 and move it into position to form the boundary between sections C and D (the first dotted line in Figure 25.3).

9. Identify and measure DBH for all trees in section C (see Figure 25.3).

10. Detach line 3 and move it into position to form the boundary between sections D and E (the second dotted line in Figure 25.3).

11. Identify and measure DBH for all trees in sections D and E (see Figure 25.3).

Results

1. Record your data in Table 25.2 on the next page.

2. In Exercise 25.3, Data Analysis, you will calculate:
   DBH (if measurements were taken of circumference rather than DBH)
   Density and relative density
   Frequency and relative frequency
   Basal area, dominance, and relative dominance
   Importance value

Field Study B. Shrubs, Saplings, and Vines

Materials

circular plot established for trees
    in Field Study A; the radius
    lines should be flagged conspi-
    cuously at 4 m for the SSV plot

plastic bags and rubber bands
calipers
permanent marker
index cards

Table 25.2
Sampling Results for **Trees** (DBH > 10 cm)

Locality: _____ Plot ID #: _____ Plot size: _____ Date: _____

Students: _____ Instructor: _____

Species:	Circumference (cm)	DBH (cm) = $\frac{Circumference}{\pi}$	Basal Area (cm²) = 0.7854 (DBH)²

(Form table repeated in six blocks, each headed by "Species:" with columns Circumference (cm), DBH (cm) = Circumference/π, and Basal Area (cm²) = 0.7854 (DBH)²)

Introduction

Lower vertical layers of the forest are inhabited by young trees of the types seen in the upper levels, trees and shrubs unique to this layer, and some vines. The shrub, sapling, and vine (SSV) plot is located within the tree plot (Figure 25.4). Therefore, each line should be boldly marked to indicate the radius for 50 m².

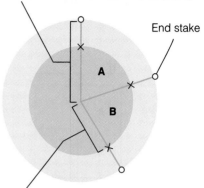

Radius = 5.64 m for 100-m² plot (trees)

End stake

A

B

Radius = 4 m for 50-m² plot (SSV)

Figure 25.4.
Placement of circular plot for shrubs, saplings, and vines. A circular plot with a smaller diameter is marked within the boundary of the large tree plot. Radius lines are clearly marked to indicate the outer perimeter for the plot (Xs).

 Coordinate your sampling with the tree group, Field Study A.

Procedure

1. Locate the circular plot established by your team members sampling trees. Restrict your sampling to the smaller plot located within the tree plot. The radius of the smaller plot should be marked clearly with flagging or tape along each line. Sample vines and other woody plants with a DBH of 2.5–10 cm within the SSV plot.

2. Begin sampling in section A (see Figure 25.3). Identify and measure each individual in the SSV category for all sections of the plot. If available, use calipers, rather than a meter tape, to determine DBH.

 Diameter at breast height (DBH) is measured 1.5 m above the base of the woody plant. Measure or estimate this height on your body to ensure that you determine DBH in a consistent fashion. If DBH measuring tapes are not available, measure plants with a circumference of 8–32 cm.

3. If you cannot identify a woody plant, assign a number to that type of plant. Collect a leaf sample, if possible, for later identification. Label the sample by attaching a numbered card or writing the number on the leaf blade. If leaves are not available, write a brief description.

Results

1. Record your data in Table 25.3 on the next page.
2. In Exercise 25.3, Data Analysis, you will calculate:
   DBH (if measurements were taken of circumference rather than DBH)
   Density and relative density
   Frequency and relative frequency
   Basal area, dominance, and relative dominance
   Importance value

Table 25.3
Sampling Results for **Shrubs**, **Saplings**, and **Vines** (DBH 2.5–10 cm)

Locality: _____ Plot ID #: _____ Plot size: _____ Date: _____

Students: _____ Instructor: _____

Species:	Circumference (cm)	DBH (cm) = $\frac{\text{Circumference}}{\text{ }}$	Basal Area (cm^2) = 0.7854 (DBH)^2	Species:	Circumference (cm)	DBH (cm) = $\frac{\text{Circumference}}{\text{ }}$	Basal Area (cm^2) = 0.7854 (DBH)^2	Species:	Circumference (cm)	DBH (cm) = $\frac{\text{Circumference}}{\text{ }}$	Basal Area (cm^2) = 0.7854 (DBH)^2

Field Study C. Seedlings and Herbaceous Vegetation

Materials

circular 0.50-m² plot   plastic bags and rubber bands
compass   permanent marker
index cards

Introduction

Tree seedlings and herbaceous plants appear near the forest floor. These plants may be difficult to count, and, in some cases, it may be almost impossible to determine what is actually one individual. Because of this, the abundance of these plants is estimated based on the percent cover.

The seedling and herb plot is not located within the larger plots but should be placed near the tree plot at a predetermined position.

Procedure

1. Place a 0.50-m² plot just outside the tree plot. Determine the exact location for the plot before beginning. For example, it might always be 1 m away from the tree plot at a compass heading of due north.
2. Identify and estimate the abundance of each species by estimating the percent of the plot area covered by the species. Sketching the plot may help determine cover and ensure consistency in your estimates.
3. If you cannot identify a plant, assign a number to that type of plant. Collect a leaf or flower sample if possible for later identification. Label the sample by attaching a numbered card or by writing the number on the leaf blade. If leaves are not available, write a brief description.

Results

1. Record results in Table 25.4 on the next page.
2. In Exercise 25.3, Data Analysis, you will calculate average percent cover, frequency, and relative frequency.

Field Study D. Macroinvertebrates

Materials

circular 0.50-m² plot   vials with 70% alcohol
thin plastic sheet   labeling tape
forceps   permanent marker
dissecting probes   compass

Introduction

Large invertebrates—for example, grasshoppers, ants, and spiders—can be surveyed by sifting through the dead leaves or litter on the forest floor. These animals may fit into any of the consumer trophic levels. For example, grasshoppers are primary consumers, spiders are secondary consumers, and ants are omnivores.

Table 25.4
Sampling Results for **Seedlings** and **Herbaceous Vegetation** (DBH < 2.5 cm)

Locality: _____ Plot ID #: _____ Plot size: _____ Date: _____			
Students: _____ Instructor: _____			
Species	**Percent Cover**	**Species**	**Percent Cover**

Procedure

1. Carefully place a 0.50-m² circular plot on the ground in an undisturbed spot outside and near the large vegetation plot. This should be a pre-selected spot; for example, it might always be 1 m away from the large plot at a compass heading of due south. Avoid disturbing the animals present. Quickly cover the plot with plastic to discourage "escapees."

2. Carefully remove all animals from the vegetation and litter at ground level.

3. Sort animals into similar groups in the field. Place the organisms into vials of 70% alcohol according to their group. If you cannot identify an animal, assign a number to that type of animal. Preserve the animal in alcohol and label the sample using tape and a permanent marker.

Results

1. Record results in Table 25.5.
2. In Exercise 25.3, Data Analysis, you will calculate density for the groups.

Table 25.5
Sampling Results for **Consumers, Detritivores,** and **Decomposers**

Locality: _____	Plot ID #: _____	Date: _____
Students: _____	Instructor: _____	

Macroinvertebrates		Microinvertebrates
Species/Group	No. of Individuals	Groups Observed

Microorganisms:

Vertebrates:

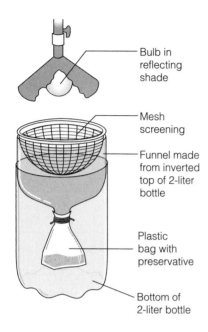

- Bulb in reflecting shade
- Mesh screening
- Funnel made from inverted top of 2-liter bottle
- Plastic bag with preservative
- Bottom of 2-liter bottle

Figure 25.5.
Berlese-Tullgren funnel used for the extraction of microinvertebrates from litter and soil. The samples are placed on screening beneath a light. The light and heat drive the animals down into the small sampling bag containing preservative.

Field Study E. Microinvertebrates

Materials

circular 0.50-m^2 plot
index cards
self-sealing plastic bags
Berlese-Tullgren funnels

light sources
soil sample collected in
    Exercise 25.2, Field Study A

Introduction

A variety of invertebrates, including mites and springtails, inhabit the litter layer and the upper layers of the soil. Many of these animals are not easily seen with the naked eye and would be impossible to collect by inspecting samples. These consumers and detritivores can be sampled by collecting soil and litter and placing these in Berlese-Tullgren funnels (Figure 25.5). The animals move away from the light and heat source into a small sampling vial. The animals can then be identified in the laboratory using a dissecting microscope. You may be asked to collect samples for extraction later in the lab, or your instructor may have already collected the samples and started the extractions.

Procedure

1. Place the 0.50-m^2 plot in an undisturbed location. Carefully remove half the litter (discard sticks) and place it into the bag provided. Include a card with the plot number in your sample bag. Close the bag securely.

2. Upon return to the lab, extract the microinvertebrates using a Berlese-Tullgren funnel. A soil sample will also be collected by the soil group (see Exercise 25.2, Field Study A), and microinvertebrates will be extracted using the same procedure.

    a. Place the soil or litter sample on wire mesh in a large funnel under a lightbulb. The soil samples can be wrapped in a layer of cheese-cloth to prevent soil particles from sifting into the collection vials.

    b. The light and heat force the animals down the funnel into the collecting vial containing 70% alcohol. (See Figure 25.5 for extraction funnel setup.)

3. After 24 to 48 hours, the organisms can be sorted and identified using the dissecting scope. Refer to the illustrated key to common microinvertebrates in Figure 25.6.

Results

1. Record in Table 25.5 the microinvertebrates present.
2. Sketch the most common organisms in the margin of your lab manual if they are not represented in the illustrated key.

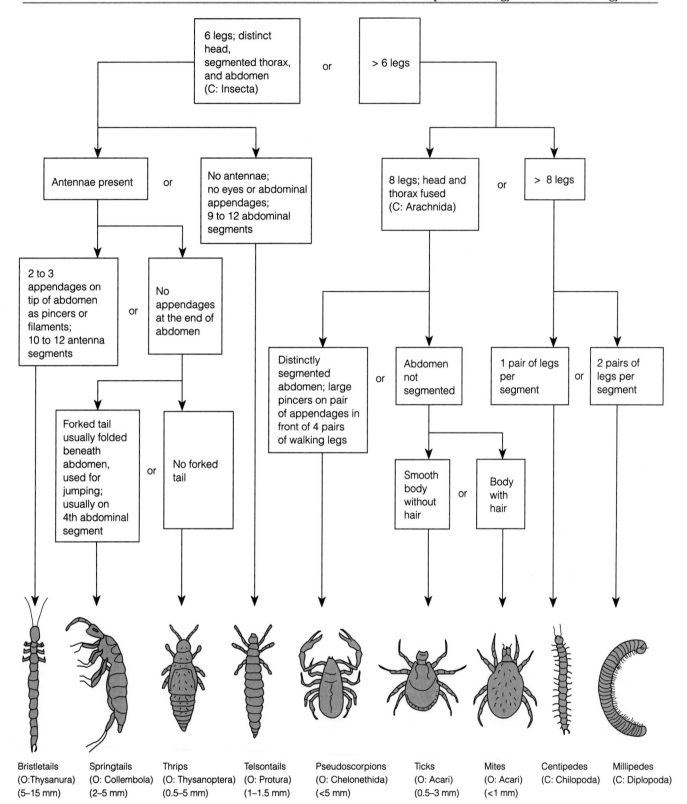

Figure 25.6.
Picture key to microinvertebrates commonly found in litter and soil samples.
C: class; O: order.

Field Study F. Microorganisms

Materials

petri dishes of nutrient agar
soil sample collected in Exercise 25.2, Field Study A
litter sample collected in Exercise 25.1, Field Study E

Introduction

Microorganisms in the litter and soil are important decomposers, the primary functions of which are soil building and nutrient recycling. Your instructor may have collected the samples in advance and begun the cultures. If not, you will need to obtain a small portion of the soil sample from the students sampling the abiotic components and some litter from the microinvertebrate group. You will prepare cultures for later evaluation.

Procedure

1. Upon returning to the lab, place small samples of leaf litter and soil on separate agar plates and incubate them at room temperature for several days until bacterial and fungal growth are abundant. Refrigerate them to prevent further growth.
2. Observe the diversity of colonies present after 2 or 3 days.

Results

Record the presence of different bacterial colony types and fungi in Table 25.5. Refer to Lab Topic 13, Bacteriology, for help with describing organisms.

Field Study G. Other Forest Animals

Materials

binoculars
field guides

Introduction

You will not trap forest vertebrates in this field study, but all students will need to make observations of these larger but often secretive animals. Observe the activities of these animals as well as their calls, tracks, nest sites, and feces. Think about their role in the ecosystem.

Procedure

1. After completing your field sampling, survey the surrounding forest for birds, mammals, reptiles, and amphibians.
2. Record observations of animals sighted, plus any tracks, nests, burrows, carcasses, feces, owl pellets, songs, or calls. Field guides are provided to assist with identification.

Results

Record your observations in Table 25.5.

EXERCISE 25.2
Abiotic Components

Abiotic components include the physical features of the environment that influence the biotic components and in turn may be influenced by the organisms inhabiting the area. You will record the climatic conditions both for the local environment and for the smaller scale microenvironment within the ecosystem. Two students in each team will measure and record all abiotic features.

Field Study A. Soil

Materials

soil thermometer	trowel
soil auger	diagram of soil profile
self-sealing plastic bags	soil map of the area
index cards	soil test kit
permanent marker	

Introduction

The soil contains biotic and abiotic components of the ecosystem. You will determine the soil type and collect samples to be used in extracting microinvertebrates (Exercise 25.1, Field Study E) and microorganisms (Exercise 25.1, Field Study F).

Procedure

1. Read about soil temperature (Field Study A) and air temperature (Field Study B); then place thermometers in appropriate locations to equilibrate while you begin your other work.

2. Remove the vegetation from a small undisturbed area near the tree plot. Place the soil thermometer in the soil and allow it to equilibrate for 10 to 15 minutes before recording the temperature.

3. Carefully remove the leaf litter. Using the soil auger, remove two soil cores approximately 30–45 cm long.

4. Sketch the profile of the soil layers in the margin of your lab manual. (See an example of a soil profile in your materials.) Note changes in color and texture. How much sand or clay or dark organic matter appears to be present?

5. Place each soil sample in a separate plastic (self-sealing) bag. Follow the directions provided with the soil test kit. Determine the soil pH and any other characteristics suggested by your instructor for one sample. Instructions are included with the soil test kit. Save the other sample to share with your team.

6. Remove a third sample of soil to be used for determining the presence and types of microinvertebrates and microorganisms. Collect this sample by using a trowel to dig some of the upper loose dirt. Seal this sample in a third plastic bag. Label it "organisms" with the plot number. The organisms will be extracted as described in Exercise 25.1, Field Studies E and F.

7. Study the soil association map of this general area and determine the type of soil typical of this region.

Results

1. Record the soil temperature and pH in Table 25.6.
2. Sketch the soil profile in the margin of your lab manual.
3. Record in Table 25.6 the soil type and other pertinent information from soil maps.

Field Study B. Climatology

Materials

NOAA climatological data sheets   light meter
sling psychrometer (with directions)   thermometers
min/max thermometer   wind anemometer
   (with directions)   (with directions)

Introduction

The climatic conditions of the environment can be viewed on the local level or on a smaller scale (microclimate) within the forest ecosystem. Not only does the microclimate affect the organisms that are present, but the process is mutual: Organisms will influence the microclimatic conditions as well. For example, the air temperature above bare ground and open grassland may differ significantly owing to differences in water loss and the shading effect of the vegetation.

Procedure

1. *Local climate.* For general climate patterns in your area, consult the local climatological data sheets provided. You should record in Table 25.6 the average annual rainfall for this month, temperature averages, and the relative humidity at 1300 hours (1 P.M.).

2. *Microclimate.* Variation in microclimate due to such factors as elevation, slope, and shade can result in temperatures, humidities, and light intensities quite different from those of surrounding areas only a few meters away. For example, the microclimate conditions near ground level will be different from those a few meters above the surface. Measure the following microclimate conditions and record your results in Table 25.6.

    a. *Air temperature.* Record the temperature at the soil surface and 2 m or so above the ground for a sunny spot and a shady spot. Allow 5 to 10 minutes for the thermometer to equilibrate at each position. Record the minimum and maximum temperature for the previous 24 hours if a min/max thermometer was left in the forest overnight.

    b. *Light.* Using a light meter, measure the light intensity in the forest and in full sunlight. Calculate the percentage of full sun that reaches the forest floor.

    c. *Humidity.* Humidity refers to the amount of water vapor in the air. It has important biological effects on respiration, transpiration, and evaporation. **Relative humidity** (the most common measurement)

Table 25.6
Characteristics of the Physical Environment

Locality: _____ Plot ID #: _____ Date: _____
Students: _____ Instructor: _____
Soil
Temperature (°C):   pH: Other: Description:
Local Climate
Annual rainfall: Annual average temperature: Relative humidity:
Microclimate

Temperature
 	
   Soil surface: sun: _____ shade: _____
 	
   2 m above surface: sun: _____ shade: _____
 	
   Min _____
 	
   Max _____
 Light
 	
   Forest _____
 	
   Full sun _____
 	
   % full sun _____
 Relative humidity _____
 Wind speed _____

Topography   **Disturbance**   **Comments**

is the actual amount of water vapor in the air divided by the total possible water vapor (or saturation vapor) in the air at its temperature. Refer to the directions provided and measure relative humidity with a **sling psychrometer.** Do not hit anyone with the psychrometer!

d. *Wind.* Using the **wind anemometer,** measure the wind speed in the sampling area. What factors can you suggest that affect wind speed?

Results

Record in Table 25.6 the results of your measurements for air temperature, light, humidity, and wind.

Field Study C. Topographic Features

Materials

field notebook
pencil

Introduction

Before completing your study of the abiotic components, you should stand back and observe the general features of the landscape that are difficult to measure but that may influence other physical factors and the organisms as well.

Procedure

Observe the topography of the sampling site. Is the area sloping, eroded, on a hillside, or cut by a stream or ditch? Record in Table 25.6 indications of past or present disturbance—for example, scarring from past fires, cut stumps, old fences, or terracing.

Results

1. Record the results of your observations in Table 25.6.
2. In the margin of your lab manual, sketch the topographic features that appear to influence your sample site.

E X E R C I S E 2 5 . 3
Data Analysis

Materials

summary of all student data
calculator

Introduction

Students will need to pool data with team members and other teams. You may determine the abundance (density or cover), distribution (frequency), overall size (dominance), and importance (the sum of relative density, frequency, and dominance) for each species in the sampling categories (trees, SSV, and so on).

Density, the number of individuals per unit area, provides a summary of abundance by species. (**Percent cover** is the measure of abundance used for seedlings and herbaceous plants.) However, the density of a species does not necessarily reflect the distribution of the species on the landscape. **Frequency** provides information on the distribution of a species and is calculated as the percent of plots sampled that have at least one individual of the species present. **Dominance** is a measure of the influence of a species based on the size of individuals. (Dominance is determined from the area, called basal area, calculated from DBH measurements.) Adding the relative values for each of these measures provides an estimate of overall **importance**, which includes abundance, distribution, and size. The equations for calculating these parameters are provided in Table 25.7 on the next page.

Procedure

Trees, Shrubs, Saplings, and Vines

1. If circumference was measured for trees and shrubs, saplings, and vines, then calculate DBH for individuals in each sample plot and record the results in Tables 25.2 and 25.3, respectively.

2. Calculate basal area for each tree and shrub, sapling, and vine. Record your results in Tables 25.2 and 25.3, respectively.

3. Pool the data for all sample plots and record for each species the total number of individuals, number of plots in which a species was present, and total basal area. Summarize tree data in Table 25.8, SSV data in Table 25.9.

4. Calculate density. Total the densities for all species and calculate the relative density of each species.

5. Calculate frequency. Total the frequencies for all species and calculate the relative frequency of each species.

6. Calculate dominance. Total the dominance for all species and calculate the relative dominance of each species.

7. Calculate importance value by totaling the relative density, relative frequency, and relative dominance for each species.

Table 25.7
Calculating Density, Frequency, Dominance, and Importance
Values for the Biotic Components of the Ecosystem

DBH = $\dfrac{\text{circumference}}{\pi}$	**Basal area** = $0.7854 \, (\text{DBH})^2$
Dominance = $\dfrac{\text{total basal area}}{\text{total area sampled}}$	
Relative dominance = $\dfrac{\text{dominance for a species}}{\text{total dominance for all species}} \times 100$	
Density = $\dfrac{\text{no. of individuals}}{\text{total area sampled}}$	
Relative density = $\dfrac{\text{density for a species}}{\text{total density for all species}} \times 100$	
Frequency = $\dfrac{\text{number of plots in which species recorded}}{\text{total number of plots sampled}}$	
Relative frequency = $\dfrac{\text{frequency for a species}}{\text{total frequency for all species}} \times 100$	
Average percent cover = $\dfrac{\text{total percent cover}}{\text{total area sampled}}$	
Importance value = relative density + relative dominance + relative frequency	

Seedlings and Herbs

1. Pool the data for all sample plots and record in Table 25.10 the percent cover for each species and the number of plots in which a species was present.
2. Calculate average percent cover.
3. Calculate frequency. Sum the frequencies for all species and calculate the relative frequency of each species.

Macroinvertebrates

1. Pool the data for all sample plots and record in Table 25.11 the total number of individuals for each species and the number of plots in which a species was present.
2. Calculate density. Sum the densities for all species and calculate the relative density of each species.
3. Calculate frequency. Sum the frequencies for all species and calculate the relative frequency of each species.

Abiotic Components

Pool the data for all sample plots and record it in Table 25.12.

Results

1. Record all summary results for *trees* in Table 25.8 and those for *shrubs, saplings,* and *vines* in Table 25.9.

2. List in the spaces provided the three most important tree species and the three most important shrub, sapling, and vine species.

   Trees:

   Shrubs, saplings, and *vines:*

3. Record the summary results of *seedlings* and *herbs* in Table 25.10.

4. List in the space provided the three most common species based on their abundance.

   Seedlings and *herbs:*

5. Record summary results for *macroinvertebrates* in Table 25.11.

6. List in the space provided the three most common macroinvertebrate species based on abundance. Indicate, if possible, the appropriate trophic level: *primary* (1°) or *secondary* (2°) *consumers,* or *detritivores* (D) by placing the appropriate letter or number by each. To make these determinations, observe mouthparts or other body structures. Consult reference books or handouts provided in the laboratory or from the library. See "Who Eats What" (Hogan, 1994).

   Macroinvertebrates:

Table 25.8
Summary of Results for **Trees**

Locality: _____ Size class: Trees Date: _____

No. of plots sampled: _____ Total area sampled: _____

Species	Total No. of Individuals	Density	Relative Density	No. of Plots Present	Frequency	Relative Frequency	Total Basal Area	Dominance	Relative Dominance	Importance Value
Totals			100			100			100	

Table 25.9
Summary of Results for **Shrubs**, **Saplings**, and **Vines**

Locality: _____ Size class: SSV Date: _____

No. of plots sampled: _____ Total area sampled: _____

Species	Total No. of Individuals	Density	Relative Density	No. of Plots Present	Frequency	Relative Frequency	Total Basal Area	Dominance	Relative Dominance	Importance Value
Totals			100			100			100	

Table 25.10
Summary of Results for **Seedlings** and **Herbaceous Vegetation**

Locality: _____ Size class: S/Herb Date: _____

No. of plots sampled: _____ Total area sampled: _____

Species	Average Percent Cover	No. of Plots Present	Frequency	Relative Frequency
Totals				100

Table 25.11
Summary of Results for **Macroinvertebrates**

Locality: _____ Size class: Macroinvert. **Date:** _____

No. of plots sampled: _____ Total area sampled: _____

Species	Total No. of Individuals	Density	Relative Density	No. of Plots Present	Frequency	Relative Frequency
Totals			100			100

7. List in the space below the five most common *microinvertebrates* observed in all plots. Indicate, if possible, the appropriate trophic level: *primary* (1°), *secondary* (2°), or *tertiary* (3°) *consumers*, or *detritivores* (D) by placing the appropriate letter or number by each. To determine trophic level, observe mouthparts and other body structures. Consult reference books or handouts provided in the laboratory or from the library. See "Who Eats What" (Hogan, 1994).

   Microinvertebrates:

8. What types of microorganisms grew in your agar plates? Did you observe fungal hyphae (filaments)? Did you observe bacterial colonies? Describe them briefly. (Refer to Lab Topic 13, Bacteriology.)

9. Record the summary results for all *abiotic* components in Table 25.12.

10. List the abiotic features that appear to be important influences in the ecosystem.

11. Describe any summary information not included in the tables.

Table 25.12
Summary of Results for **Physical Environment**

	Plot				
	1	**2**	**3**	**4**	**5**
Soil					
Description					
pH					
Temperature					
Climate					
Annual rainfall					
Annual avg. temp.					
Microclimate					
Temperature					
°C soil surface					
°C 2 m above					
°C min					
°C max					
Light intensity					
Forest					
Full sun					
% full sun					
Relative humidity					
Wind speed					
Topography					
Comments					

Figure 25.7.
Profile diagram of a typical forest system. Using your results, label the important species in each of the vertical layers of the forest, from trees to herbs on the forest floor.

Discussion

1. Prepare ecosystem profiles. Using the results from your study of the forest, label the profile diagram provided in Figure 25.7. Label the trees, shrubs, saplings, vines, and herbs to illustrate the species composition of each vertical layer of the forest ecosystem. If you are not investigating a forest system, construct a profile diagram that will illustrate the specific composition and patterns of your study site. Refer to Figure 25.7.

2. Incorporating all components of the ecosystem, complete the model of the ecosystem in Figure 25.8, indicating the trophic levels and interactions observed in the forest. Provide examples for each trophic level, from producers to top carnivores to decomposers.

3. Write a one-page discussion of your results. Characterize the forest by vegetation type. Describe trophic levels and provide examples, using your model as an illustration. Propose features of the physical environment that appear to influence or be influenced by the biotic community.

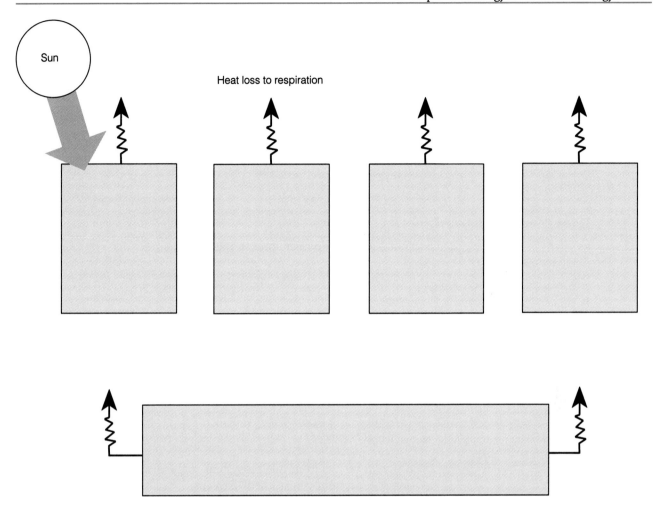

Figure 25.8.
Compartmental model for trophic relationships in an ecosystem. Heat losses
to respiration are represented by zigzag arrows. Label the trophic levels and add
arrows to represent energy flow from trophic level to trophic level. For each
trophic level, list examples from organisms observed in this laboratory.

Questions for Review

1. What are the factors that determine the importance of species in the
   tree category?

2. Are the same species important in the tree and SSV categories?

3. What are the advantages and disadvantages of using cover as a measure of abundance for herbaceous plants?

4. Which group of consumers, primary or secondary, had the highest density?

5. What are the top carnivores in this ecosystem?

   Explain the relatively low density of carnivores (for example, hawks, owls, or snakes) in this ecosystem.

6. Do your results from this ecosystem analysis adequately represent the forest ecosystem you studied? Explain.

Applying Your Knowledge

1. To investigate the structure and function of ecosystems, ecologists may construct a microcosm using organisms and materials from the ecosystem. Properly constructed, these model systems should be self-sustaining. If you remove the primary producers from the microcosm, would you predict that your model would continue to be self-sustaining? Explain.

If you remove the decomposers and detritivores, would the microcosm be self-sustaining? Explain.

2. Using your knowledge of ecosystem structure and function, compare the trophic structure of a desert to that of a temperate hardwood forest. Include the relative number of organisms and energy availability for the different trophic levels.

3. Design a sampling regimen to answer the following question: Are there differences in the abundance and species composition of microinvertebrates found in the tree litter from forests of different ages? Include the types of plots, organisms, and physical features to be measured and the selection of sample sites.

4. Using examples from your study, explain the different information provided by density, frequency, and dominance. How do these three estimates overlap in providing information? How are they related?

5. Horizontal pattern in a forest appears to be related to dispersion of organisms and environmental factors. What factors appear to be influencing the biological community studied in this lab?

OPTIONAL EXERCISE 25.1
Biotic Components: Weedy Lots or Fields

If a forest system is not accessible for study, small and more numerous plots can be used to study weedy fields, which are ubiquitous in both urban and rural environments. The scale for environmental factors can also be reduced and will require sampling at intervals that correspond to the smaller plot sizes. If the weedy field has woody vegetation, then refer to the plot sizes recommended earlier for the forest ecosystem. If only a few woody plants are present, consider recording the presence of these in the general description of the study site, but do not sample them. If the field has only seedlings or nonwoody (herbaceous) vegetation (or both), then use 0.50-m^2 plots to sample the vegetation and invertebrates.

It may be necessary to modify your field studies to correspond to the ecosystem being studied.

Students should work in teams of four: two for seedlings, herbaceous plants, and macroinvertebrates, and two for microinvertebrates and abiotic factors. A class of 24 could sample 6 to 12 plots.

Suggested Outline for Weedy Fields

Exercise 25.1, Biotic Components
    Field Study C. Seedlings and Herbaceous Plants
             D. Macroinvertebrates
             E. Microinvertebrates
             F. Microorganisms
             G. Other Forest Animals

Exercise 25.2, Abiotic Components
    Field Study A. Soil
             B. Climatology

Exercise 25.3, Data Analysis

Complete sections that are appropriate to the biotic components sampled.

References

Barbour, M., J. H. Burk, and W. D. Pitts. *Terrestrial Plant Ecology,* 3rd ed. Menlo Park, CA: Addison Wesley Longman, 1999.

Brower, J. E., and J. H. Zar. *Field and Laboratory Methods for General Ecology.* Dubuque, IA: William C. Brown, 1972. This edition is more comprehensive than later editions.

Cox, G. W. *Laboratory Manual of General Ecology,* 7th ed. Dubuque, IA: William C. Brown, 1996.

Hogan, K. "Who Eats What," *Eco-Inquiry,* Appendix A. Dubuque, IA: Kendall-Hall Publishing, 1994, pp. 355–382.

Meuller-Dombois, D., and H. Ellenberg. *Aims and Methods of Vegetation Ecology.* New York: Wiley, 1974.

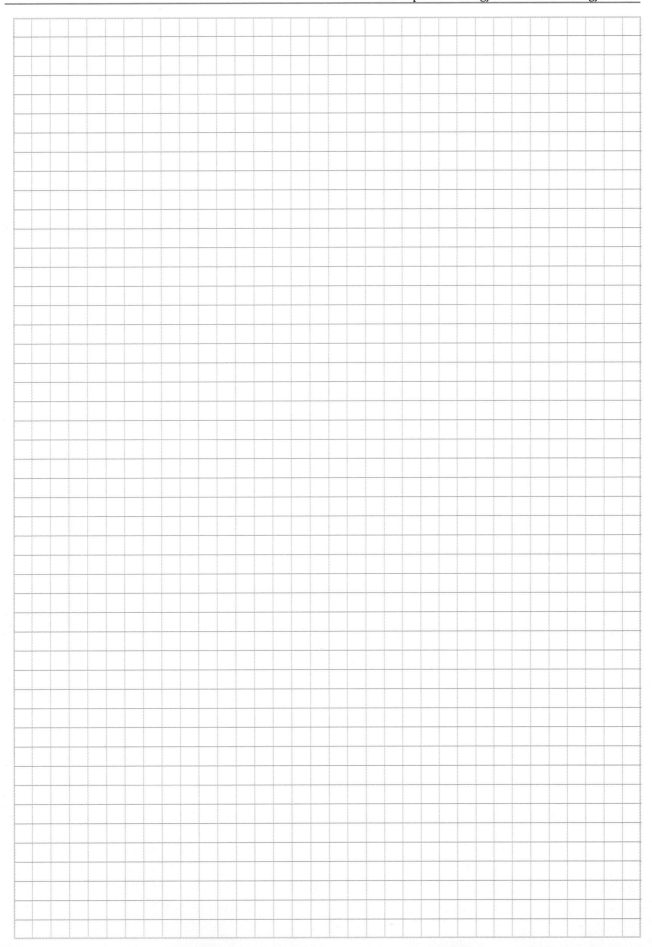

Ecology II: Computer Simulations of a Pond Ecosystem

Laboratory Objectives

After completing this lab topic, you should be able to:

1. Develop a computer model to investigate a pond ecosystem.
2. Calibrate the model using information from field investigations.
3. Determine the steady-state values for the model ecosystem.
4. Answer questions and test hypotheses using a computer model.
5. Evaluate the effects of disturbance on the model ecosystem.
6. Apply the results of computer simulations to predict the results in real ecosystems.

Introduction

Ecosystems are difficult to investigate using the experimental method because they are so large and complex. Scientists are nevertheless studying ecosystem structure and function in a selected number of systems across the United States as part of the Long Term Ecological Research Program, effectively implementing experiments at the landscape level in places such as the Okefenokee Swamp in Georgia, Konza Prairie in Kansas, and the hardwood forest of Coweeta Hydrological Station in North Carolina. However, to understand these complex systems and to make predictions concerning their responses to disturbance (both natural and human), ecologists often depend on computer models that correspond to the ecosystem of interest. Information obtained in field investigations is used to determine the structure of the model, the appropriate interactions among components, and the actual values used in the model.

You have already worked with models in other laboratory topics, including the bead models of cellular reproduction and population genetics and the diagrammatic models in terrestrial ecology. Models generally provide a simplified and amplified (or reduced) view of the phenomenon of interest. In this lab topic, you will actually construct a computer model of a simple ecosystem, the pond. As you develop your model, you can simulate a variety of conditions, including the effects of disturbance.

If you have completed Lab Topic 25, Ecology I: Terrestrial Ecology, you should be able to construct a compartmental model of a forest ecosystem and develop a general model based on the trophic levels present in ecosystems. Before continuing this lab, complete Table 26.1, providing definitions and examples. Refer to Lab Topic 25 and your textbook if necessary.

Table 26.1
Definitions of Ecological Terms

Primary producer:
Consumer:
Trophic level:
Ecosystem:
Biotic component:
Abiotic component:
Food chain:

The Pond Ecosystem

The primary producers in a pond are generally the algae floating in the surface layers and some plants growing at the pond edge, or margin. These autotrophic organisms convert the energy of sunlight into chemical energy stored in organic compounds. The producers, in turn, are consumed by primary consumers (herbivores such as aquatic invertebrates), which are ingested by secondary consumers (carnivores such as sunfish) and even tertiary consumers (carnivores such as bass) (Figure 26.1). The movement of energy through these systems is called **energy flow** (energy does not cycle), and at each trophic level, the amount of available energy is reduced. All organisms expend some energy in the activities of life, and this energy is dissipated as heat. The efficiency of transfer from one level to another is only about 10%.

The rate at which light energy is converted to chemical energy is called **primary productivity.** Productivity is measured as the amount of **biomass,** or organic matter, added to the system per unit area per unit time (for example, $kg/m^2/yr$). In tropical rain forests, for example, the primary productivity is 2.2 $kg/m^2/yr$; in temperate grassland, 0.6 $kg/m^2/yr$; and in lakes and streams, 0.25 $kg/m^2/yr$ (Campbell and Reece, 2002). **Secondary productivity** is the rate at which consumers and detritivores accumulate new biomass from organic matter that was consumed. In the computer model of the pond, the changes in each trophic level will be measured as biomass.

Refer to the food web in Figure 26.1, and in the margin of your lab manual, sketch a compartmental model of a pond ecosystem. (See also the example of a compartmental model in Figure 25.8.) Indicate connections between compartments (inputs and outputs).

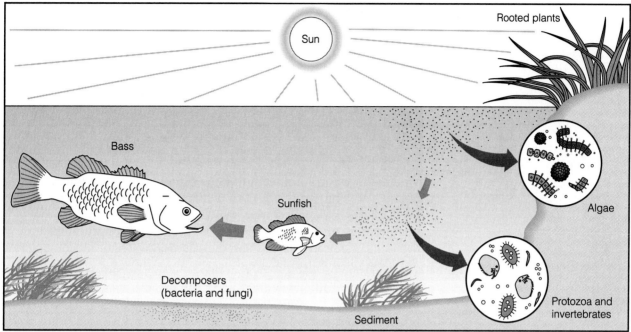

Figure 26.1.
The food web of a pond ecosystem. The primary producers (algae) are consumed by primary consumers (protozoa and invertebrates), which in turn are consumed by secondary consumers (sunfish and bass). In this pond, bass also may be tertiary consumers.

EXERCISE 26.1
Computer Model of the Pond Ecosystem

The computer model of an ecosystem must be based on observations of the natural ecosystem in the field. Your compartmental model, which includes biotic components and interactions, represents the first step in constructing a model. You must also determine the biomass associated with each compartment based on data collected from field investigations. These data are used to **calibrate** the model—that is, to set the starting values for each component.

In this exercise, you will construct and calibrate a computer model for a pond ecosystem. You will run an initial simulation to determine the **steady-state,** or stable, values for your pond, then compare your results with those expected from a field study. In the process, you will practice changing components of the model, graphing, and printing your results. Once you have determined that your model adequately represents a natural ecosystem, you can begin to ask questions, formulate hypotheses and predictions, and test these using the model ecosystem. This process will continue as you adjust the model, analyze your results, and simulate conditions.

Experiment A. Constructing and Calibrating the Model

Materials

computer software (Environmental Decision Making)
Macintosh computer with mouse
printer

Introduction

Working in groups of three, using the computer software Environmental Decision Making, written by E. C. Odum, H. T. Odum, and N. S. Peterson for the BioQUEST project, you will develop a compartmental model for a pond ecosystem. You will calibrate the model and run the simulation to determine the steady-state values, the values at which the model stabilizes.

The 1-hectare (= 2.47 acres) pond that you are modeling is inhabited by a variety of **pond life,** including such small organisms as algae, micro- and macroinvertebrates, plants, and animals and microbes that inhabit the pond bottom. Two species of fish are present: **sunfish,** which feed primarily off the pond life, and **bass,** which eat the sunfish. Each component of the ecosystem is represented by an icon (Figure 26.2).

Procedure

Your instructor will review how to use the computer, including use of the mouse, and guidelines for use of the computer facilities. Enviromental Decision Making is now available in both Mac and Windows™ versions. Depending on the version you are using, the screens may be slightly different.

1. Open the program by double-clicking on the icon Environmental Decision Making (EDM), then double-click on *Pond Worksheet.* (Double-click on *Pondwork* in the Windows version.) Click on the *Extend* screen. You should see an empty window with the plotter icon in the corner with the label "Quantity."

2. Construct the model to incorporate pond life, sunfish, and bass.

    a. Choose BioQUEST Library from the Library menu, and then choose Sunlight from the submenu. (Choose BIOQULIB.LIX from the Library menu if using the Windows version.)

    b. When you select an icon and hold down the mouse button, the pointer changes to a hand that allows you to move the icon. Move the sunlight icon to the left of the window.

    c. Choose Pond Life from the BioQUEST Library submenu and position it to the right of the sunlight icon.

Figure 26.2.
Icons for the components of the model ecosystem.

d. To connect the sunlight and pond life components, draw a line from one icon to another, connecting the small boxes on each icon. To do this, move the pointer over the small dark box by the sunlight icon. The pointer changes to a pen. Drag the pen from the dark box of the sunlight icon to the open box of pond life (Figure 26.3). Release the button. The line should connect the dark box of the sunlight icon (indicating flows out of this component) with the open box of the pond life icon (indicating flows into the second component). For example, sunlight provides the energy input to the ecosystem through pond life. Therefore, the dark box of sunlight is connected to the open box of pond life.

e. Connect the pond life to the plotter (Figure 26.4) by drawing a line connecting the upper dark box of the pond life icon to the first open box on the plotter. The plotter can connect up to four components.

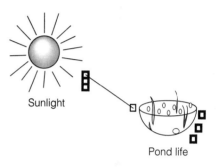

Figure 26.3.
Drawing lines with the mouse to connect icons. Position the mouse over the dark box, click the mouse, and hold. A pen will appear, and you can draw a connecting line.

 To erase an icon, move the pointer to the icon, and a hand should appear. Select the icon and press *Delete.*

To erase a line, move the pointer to the line and click it to select it. Press *Delete.*

---

f. Choose Sunfish from the BioQUEST Library and position it to the right of the pond life icon. Connect the open box of the sunfish icon to a dark box of the pond life icon. Connect the upper dark box of the sunfish to the second box of the plotter.

g. Choose Bass from the BioQUEST Library and position the icon to the right of the sunfish icon. Connect one of the open boxes of the bass icon to one of the dark boxes of the sunfish icon. Connect the

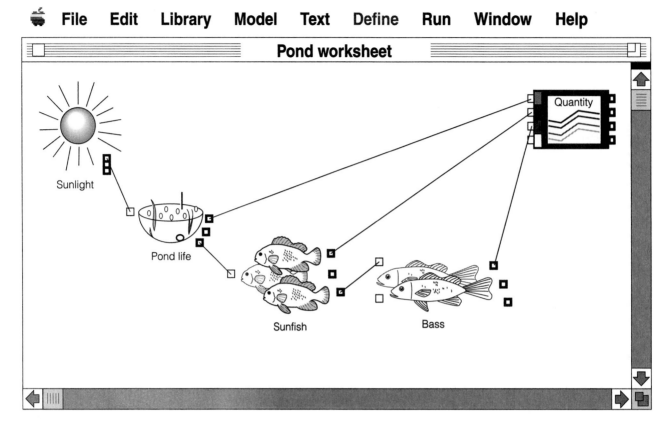

Figure 26.4.
An example of the model ecosystem.

upper dark box of the bass icon to the third box of the plotter. Beginning on the left side of the screen, you should have sunlight connected to pond life; pond life should in turn be connected to sunfish, which consume the pond life. Finally, the bass should be connected to the sunfish. All the organisms should be connected to the plotter (Figure 26.4). What trophic level is represented by the bass?

3. Calibrate the model by determining the starting values for the components of the ecosystem: sunlight, pond life, sunfish, and bass.

   a. Refer to the map of solar radiation for the United States (Figure 26.5). Determine the solar energy for your location in kilocalories per meter squared. If your location is not included on the map, ask your instructor for appropriate values to use.

   b. Double-click on the sunlight icon. A box, called a *dialog box,* should appear on the screen. Calibrate the model by entering the appropriate energy values in the box and click on OK.

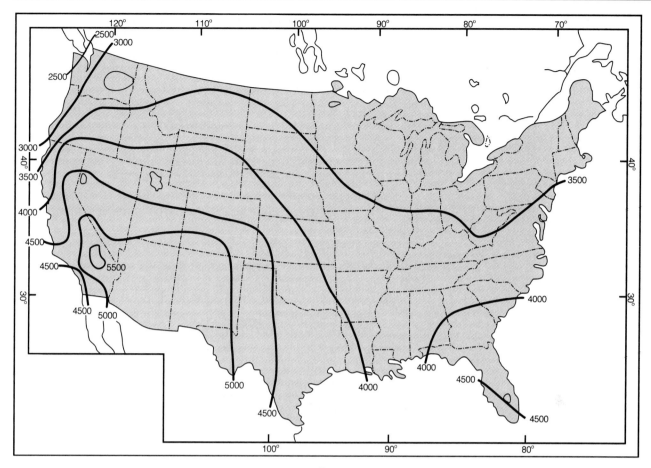

Figure 26.5.
Solar radiation for regions of the United States. Select the kilocalories of solar radiation for your location.

   c. Double-click on the pond life icon. Enter *1,000 kg/ha (kilograms per hectare) for your starting value.* Click on OK.

   d. Double-click on the sunfish icon and enter the total biomass of sunfish in kilograms in the dialog box. An appropriate starting value for sunfish might be 500 sunfish for a 1-ha pond. (*Assume 10 sunfish per kilogram, or 50 kg/ha.*) Click on OK.

   e. Double-click on the bass icon and enter the total biomass of bass in kilograms in the dialog box. *The starting value for bass might be 10 large bass, 1 kg each, or 10 kg/ha.* Click on OK.

   f. Record the starting values for all components in Table 26.2.

4. To calibrate the plotter, choose Simulation Setup from the Run menu. In the time dialog box that appears, change the time to end the simulation to 2 years (730 days). Enter *730* in the first box and click on OK.

5. Run the simulation: Choose Run Simulation from the Run menu. The simulation should run and the simulation graph, similar to the screen shown in Figure 26.8, should be plotted.

   a. Check the lines on the graph. There should be three, representing pond life, sunfish, and bass. If not, the icons on the model are not correctly attached to the plotter or each other. Return to the model by closing the Pond System window. Correct the model and run the simulation again.

   b. Check the axes of the graph. You can modify the graph and table, if needed, to accommodate all the components of the ecosystem and to scale axes appropriately. To change the values on the axes, click on the lower or upper value for the axis. Type in the new number and press *Return*.

   c. Label the axes for your graph. The controls for changing the features of the graph appear in a bar at the top of the screen. You may want to experiment with these in a later simulation. (Refer to Figure 26.6.) Click on the icon in the first box of the display bar. A palette showing the variables in the graph will appear. Pond life should appear in the first box (Figure 26.7). Click in the second box and type in *Sunfish kg/ha*. Then click in the next box and type in *Bass kg/ha*. To read the small values for the bass, you will use a different scale on the right axis (Y2). Click on the graph icon (eighth column) on the same row for Bass. The graph icon should now be reversed, indicating that the right axis is selected. Click on the Close box to make the variable palette disappear and return to the graph. Click in the space above the right-hand axis. Type in *kg/ha*. Press *Enter*. Change the right axis values by clicking on the upper value and typing in *100*. Press *Enter*. Click and type *1* as the lower value. Press *Enter*.

Figure 26.6.
Display bar for graph. Select the graph icon to adjust the axes and labels for the simulation graph.

Sets graph variables

Figure 26.7.
Example of palette for modifying graph variables. Modify the axes and labels by entering information in this palette.

☐ **Delay changes until close**

Pond life..				∿	·	General	⌐	▣	⇧
Sunfish...				∿	·	General	⌐	▣	
Bass kg/..				∿	·	General	⌐	▣	
				∿	·	General	⌐	▣	⇩

d. The graph will run again with the new graph features. Make additional changes as needed.

Figure 26.8.
Example of reading values from a simulation graph. To determine the values
at any point on the graph, move the cursor to the position. Read the values on
the top row of the table below the graph. The cursor line is at 5,225 kg/ha of
pond life on day 30.

Results

1. On the simulation graph, note the point at which biomass levels off for
    the ecosystem components. These various points indicate the steady
    state values for the energy levels used in your model, showing that the
    system has stabilized. To read values from the graph, move the cursor
    to the point of interest (for example, the steady-state point) and read the
    corresponding biomass in the table at the bottom of the graph (Figure 26.8).
    The top row of the table should show the time and biomass at the posi-
    tion on the graph indicated by the cursor line. By moving along the
    graph, you can follow the values on the top row, indicating increases,
    decreases, and relative stability. Other values and times are listed in
    the table.

2. Record the steady-state values and the time it took to reach steady state in Table 26.2.

Table 26.2
Starting and Steady-State Values for Computer Simulation, Exercise 26.1

Component	Starting Value	Steady-State Value
Sunlight		
Pond life		
Sunfish		
Bass		
Time to steady state:		

3. Choose *Print* from the File menu. If you want to print only the graph, then click on the *Top Plot Only* radio button. If *Plot Data Tables* is selected (an *X* appears in the box), then click on this box to remove the table option. Click on *Print*.

4. Close the simulation window.

Discussion

1. Describe the changes in the biomass of each component of the ecosystem over time.

    Pond life:

    Sunfish:

    Bass:

2. Did the highest and lowest values for the three components occur at the same time? Explain why or why not.

3. What do you predict would happen to the steady-state values if you increased or decreased the amount of sunlight available?

Experiment B. Steady-State Model

Materials

computer software (Environmental Decision Making)
Macintosh computer with mouse
printer

Introduction

Your initial calibration was based on data from field observations and investigations. Having run the model, you should have estimates for the steady-state values. In this simulation, you will calibrate and run the model using the steady-state values from Experiment A.

Hypothesis

State a hypothesis for changes in the components of the ecosystem at steady state.

Predictions

Based on your hypothesis, predict the appearance of the simulation.

Procedure

1. Calibrate the model. (Refer to Experiment A, Procedure step 3.) Double-click on each of the icons and set the starting value for each component at the steady-state value (see Table 26.2).
2. Run the simulation.

Results

1. Compare the graph of this simulation with the results from the first simulation (Experiment A). If the starting values for this experiment are not similar to the ending steady-state values from the first simulation, check the starting value for each component. Rerun the simulation if necessary.
2. If necessary, modify Table 26.2 to reflect new steady-state values.

3. Print the graph. Choose *Print* from the File menu.

4. Label each line on your graph.

Discussion

1. Did your results match your predictions? If not, explain.

2. Were the values you set for this simulation actually at steady state? If not, consider using new steady-state values from this simulation and repeat the simulation.

3. The steady-state value for each component represents the biomass that can be sustained by this ecosystem. This is referred to as the **carrying capacity** for each component of the ecosystem. At carrying capacity, how many bass can be sustained by this pond system? (*Hint:* The values used in the model are biomass.)

4. Does the biomass increase or decrease as you move from producers to the secondary and tertiary consumers? Would you ever expect the pond biomass to be the same in all the components? Explain.

EXERCISE 26.2
Effects of Disturbance
on the Pond Ecosystem

Materials

computer software (Environmental Decision Making)
Macintosh computer with mouse
printer
3.5-in. computer disk

Introduction

In this exercise, you will discuss questions that interest your group and design experiments to determine the effects of disturbance on the components of the pond ecosystem. You will run a series of three or more simulations.

In groups of three, discuss with your teammates possible options for *simulating disturbance of the pond ecosystem.* Using Environmental Decision Making, you can change a number of factors. Consider the following options as you discuss your ideas:

1. Change the starting values of one or more components.
2. Change interactions among components of the system (inputs and outputs).
3. Change the amount of solar radiation.
4. Add a component. (Another fish, the gar, is available. Gar eat sunfish but not bass.)
5. Remove a component.

The questions you pose should have a biological basis; that is, they should be meaningful questions based on your understanding of ecosystems, particularly pond ecosystems. Just because you can change the model does not mean the question is appropriate. If necessary, consult your textbook or additional readings supplied by your instructor.

List the questions of interest to your group.

Questions

You will run three computer simulations of your own design. You may choose to pursue one or more questions, depending on your results. With a computer model, you can make any number of changes easily, but, depending on what you do, you may have difficulty in stating predictions and interpreting your results. It is best to begin with one change at a time, increasing the level of complexity in subsequent simulations.

In the third simulation (Experiment C), you will investigate the effects of fishing on the components of the pond ecosystem. You may choose to add fishing to one of your previous models or design an entirely new simulation model.

Be prepared to describe one of your questions, explain the model, and present your results at the end of the lab period.

Experiment A. Computer Simulation 1

Choose one question that you want to pursue. Formulate a hypothesis and make a prediction for your computer simulation.

Question

Hypothesis

Formulate a hypothesis about the effects of disturbance on the pond ecosystem.

Prediction

State a prediction based on your hypothesis. (This is an if/then statement that predicts the results of changes in the steady-state model in Exercise 26.1.)

Test your prediction using the computer simulation model.

Procedure

1. In Table 26.3 on the next page, describe the disturbance problem you have chosen to simulate. Record the selected starting values for your model and indicate, by circling, the values that differ from the steady-state model.

2. Note any other changes in the model—for example, changes in interactions, solar radiation, or addition or removal of components.

3. Calibrate the model based on your changes. Modify the model according to your problem. You should be able to make changes in the model based on your experience in Exercise 26.1, Experiment A, Procedure step 2. For additional help, refer to the EDM manual provided with the software.

4. Run the simulation until steady-state values are reached. At steady state, the biomass for each component should change only slightly or not at all.

5. Modify the graph features if necessary.

Results

1. Record the new steady-state values and the time to steady state in Table 26.3.

Table 26.3
Starting and Steady-State Values for Exercise 26.2, Experiment A

Problem:		
Component	**Starting Value**	**Steady-State Value**
Sunlight		
Pond life		
Sunfish		
Bass		
Time to steady state:		

2. Print the simulation graph.
3. If instructed to do so, save your model on a 3.5-in. disk. Refer to the following instructions for assistance.

To Save a Model

a. Insert your formatted disk into the disk drive. (Ask your instructor for assistance if your disk is not formatted.)

b. Click on *File* and pull down to *Save Model As*. Enter the name of the file, which might be, for example, your name and the experiment number (Stef1.A). Select the formatted disk. (Ask for assistance if the disk does not appear on the screen.) Click on *Save*. The file is saved on your disk.

c. If the file has been saved previously, click on *File* and *Save*. The current version of the file will be saved with the existing name. Save your files to a disk for future use. You may choose to save each model for Experiments A to D with a different name. Ask your instructor.

Discussion

1. Describe the interactions among the trophic levels in the pond ecosystem.

2. Do your results match your predictions? Discuss any differences between results and predictions.

3. How did the disturbance simulated in this experiment affect the pond ecosystem? How might these results be applied to a natural ecosystem?

Experiment B. Computer Simulation 2

Your research group should evaluate the questions you listed earlier in light of the results from your first computer simulation. Select a related question or pose new or modified questions that you want to pursue in this simulation. An appropriate choice might be to increase the disturbance factor or to add another level of complexity to the first simulation. State the question of interest below.

Question

Hypothesis

Formulate a hypothesis about the effects of disturbance on the pond ecosystem.

Prediction

State a prediction based on your hypothesis. (This is an if/then statement that predicts the results of changes in the steady-state model in Exercise 26.1.)

Test your prediction using the computer simulation model.

Procedure

1. In Table 26.4, describe the disturbance problem you have chosen to simulate. Record the selected starting values for your model and indicate, by circling, the values that differ from the steady-state model.

2. Note any other changes in the model, such as changes in interactions, solar radiation, or addition or removal of components.

3. Calibrate the model based on your changes. Modify the model according to your problem.

4. Run the simulation until steady-state values are reached. At steady state, the biomass for each component should change only slightly or not at all.

5. Modify the graph features if necessary.

Results

1. Record the new steady-state values and the time to steady state in Table 26.4.

Table 26.4
Starting and Steady-State Values for Exercise 26.2, Experiment B

Problem:		
Component	**Starting Value**	**Steady-State Value**
Sunlight		
Pond life		
Sunfish		
Bass		
Time to steady state:		

2. Print the simulation graph.
3. If instructed to do so, save your model on a 3.5-in. disk. Refer to the instructions in Experiment A for assistance.

Discussion

1. Describe the interactions among the trophic levels in the pond ecosystem.

2. Do your results match your predictions? Discuss any differences between results and predictions.

3. How did the disturbance simulated in this experiment affect the pond ecosystem? How might these results be applied to a natural ecosystem?

Experiment C. Simulation of Fishing Activities

Although we often think of our human activities as being separate from natural ecosystems, we can have a dramatic effect on these systems. Ponds support not only carnivores such as bass, but also humans, who fish selectively. In this simulation, you will add fishing as a component to the model. Your objective might be to allow fishing at levels that will maintain a stable pond ecosystem. You might choose to challenge the system by increasing fishing on one or more species. You do not have to begin with the original steady-state model but can choose to add fishing to one of your previous models. Consider what type of fish will be caught—sunfish, bass, or gar. Is it possible to catch more than one type of fish? Does fishing compound disturbance factors that you may have introduced in previous simulations?

Hypothesis

State a hypothesis about the effect of fishing on the pond ecosystem.

Prediction

State a prediction based on your hypothesis.

Test your prediction using the computer simulation model.

Procedure

1. In Table 26.5, describe the problem you have chosen to simulate. Record the selected starting values for your model.

2. Record in the space provided the proposed changes to the model. What fish will be caught? Are any other interactions being changed?

3. Modify the model. Select Fishing from the Library. Connect the open box for fishing to the dark box for the fish of choice. Connect the dark box for catch to the fourth plotter line.

4. Calibrate the model based on your changes. The level for fishing is set at 1 hour of fishing per day. Begin with this level. You may adjust the model according to your hypothesis.

5. Run the simulation until steady-state values are reached. At steady state, the biomass for each component should change only slightly or not at all.

6. You will need to modify the graph features. Fishing should now be displayed on the right (Y2) axis. Select the first box on the display bar over the graph. In the fourth row, type in *Fishing kg/ha/d* and select the right axis by clicking in the eighth column. Return to the graph and adjust the right axis values as needed. The right axis label is now *Catch/day* (for fishing) and *kg/ha* (for bass). Refer to the Procedure section for the first simulation for additional assistance. (See also Figures 26.7 and 26.8.)

Results

1. Record the new steady-state values and the time to steady state in Table 26.5.
2. Print the simulation graph.
3. If instructed to do so, save your model on a 3.5-in. disk. Refer to the instructions in Experiment A for assistance.

Discussion

1. Describe the interactions among the trophic levels in the pond ecosystem.

Table 26.5
Starting and Steady-State Values for Exercise 26.2, Experiment C (Fishing)

Problem:		
Component	Starting Value	Steady-State Value
Sunlight		
Pond life		
Sunfish		
Bass		
Fishing		
Time to steady state:		

2. Do your results match your predictions? Discuss any differences between results and predictions.

3. Discuss the effects of fishing on the pond ecosystem. How might these results be applied to a natural ecosystem?

Experiment D. Computer Simulation of an Invasive Species

Problem

Jake, a fish farmer, counted the number of dead striped bass in his net. Twenty more today! He skillfully cut one open, exposing intestines and the mottled mass of muscles riddled with worms. "I'm not sure I can even harvest enough stripers to cover my expenses, much less make a profit. At this rate, it looks like the worm has turned. They're eatin' my fish instead of the other way 'round." Bud, the fishery's technician, suggested, "Can't you just kill those worms? You know, worm the fish." Jake countered, "I can't kill the worms because they reproduce in the snails. I can't kill the snails, because every chemical I could use would also kill the fish and contaminate my fish farm." "How about a biological control, like we use grass carp to keep the plants down in the pond?" suggested Bud. Jake thought about this idea. He knew that black carp would eat the snails. No snails, no worms. But he remembered that black carp is considered an invasive species, when it escapes from ponds into streams and lakes. Maybe he should find out more before investing in snail-crunching black carp.

News Focus from *Science:*

"Will Black Carp Be the Next Zebra Mussel?" by Dan Ferber, vol. 292. pp. 203–204, April 13, 2001.

> *There's good reason to worry about black carp, says ichthyologist Jim Williams of the U.S. Geological Survey (USGS) Caribean Research Center in Gainesville, Florida. In a detailed 1996 risk assessment of the fish, Williams and USGS colleague Leo Nico concluded that black carp would survive and reproduce in U.S. rivers, consuming native mollusks and competing with native mollusk-eating fish such as redear sunfish and freshwater drum.*

Additional Information

If Jake adds black carp to his pond and they escape to a natural pond, there could be problems. The structure and function of the pond ecosystem would change. Black carp will eat the snails (part of the pond life in the computer model). The bass prefer to eat the sunfish, because carp are too bony. Therefore, black carp would be competing with the sunfish for food, but with little or no predation by bass. (Assume no bass predation.)

Questions

What might be the consequences if black carp were to escape to a nearby natural pond? What do you think would happen to the pond life, sunfish, and bass in a natural pond?

Hypothesis

Formulate a hypothesis about the effects of introducing black carp to the pond ecosystem.

Test your hypothesis using the computer simulation model.

Prediction

State a prediction based on your hypothesis. (This is an if/then statement that predicts the results of changes in the model.)

Test your prediction using the computer simulation model.

Procedure

1. In Table 26.6, describe the components of the model you will simulate. Record the selected starting values for your model. The starting value for black carp should be small relative to sunfish. For example, if sunfish is 30 kg/ha, then black carp might be 10 kg/ha.

2. Note below any other changes to the model, such as changes in interactions or additions or removal of components.

3. Calibrate the model based on your changes. Modify the model according to your problem. Select a new fish icon from the Library menu to represent the black carp. (Black carp does not appear as an icon, so you should select the gar icon or add another sunfish icon.) Connect the dark box of pond life to the open box of the new fish icon. Connect the new icon to the plotter. Double-click on the new icon to set the starting value for black carp (Table 26.6). Remember, the starting value for carp should be less than for sunfish. (You may want to check the starting values for all components at this time.) The carp should not be connected to bass.

4. Run the simulation until steady-state values are reached.

5. You will need to modify the graph features. Select the first box on the display bar over the graph. In the fourth row, type in *Black carp kg/ha* and select the right axis by clicking in the eighth column. Return to the graph and adjust the right axis as needed. Refer to the Procedure section of the first simulation for additional assistance. (See also Figures 26.7 and 26.8.)

Results

1. Record the new steady-state values and the time to steady state in Table 26.6.

Table 26.6
Starting and Steady-State Values for Exercise 26.2, Experiment D

Problem:		
Component	**Starting Value**	**Steady-State Value**
Sunlight		
Pond life		
Sunfish		
Bass		
Black carp		
Time to steady state:		

2. Print the simulation graph.
3. If instructed to do so, save your model on a 3.5-in. disk. Refer to the instructions in Experiment A for assistance.

Discussion

1. Describe the interactions among the trophic levels in the pond ecosystem.

2. Do your results match your predictions? Discuss any differences between results and predictions.

3. Do you think that Jake should add black carp to his pond? Why or why not? Remember that Jake wants to increase his yield of striped bass (after all, he is a fish farmer). Should the federal government ban the sale of black carp, given your prediction of what will happen if black carp invade natural aquatic ecosystems?

Questions for Review

1. Define *model* and provide examples from several areas in biology. Consider areas of biology other than those studied in the laboratory.

2. Critique the computer model used in this lab topic. In what ways is it an appropriate model of the pond ecosystem? In what ways does it fail to model the pond adequately?

3. Even when you adjust the starting values for components in the model, the steady-state values remain the same. However, if you change the energy from the sun, new steady-state values will emerge. Explain.

4. Which disturbance factors had the greatest effect on the pond ecosystem? How are you measuring the effect?

Applying Your Knowledge

1. Where would you expect more primary productivity in a pond, in Georgia or in Michigan? Why? What factors would be limiting in these two environments?

2. In 1997, nonnative and invasive Asian swamp eels were collected in Florida for the first time at two sites near Tampa and Miami. These fish are extremely adaptable to a wide range of freshwater habitats, from wetlands to streams and ponds. They are predators that feed on worms, insects, crayfish, frogs, and other fishes, including bluegill and bass. Swamp eels have the ability to gulp air, which allows them to survive in only a few inches of water and to move over land to a nearby body of water. Scientists are tracking their movements and increasing numbers in the Southeast. In one pond, several species of fish have been completely eliminated.

   Based on your understanding of the pond ecosystem, predict the effect of introducing swamp eels on the following components of the pond.

   Bluegill:

   Bass:

   Pond life:

3. Using your knowledge of ecosystem structure and function, propose a plan of action for eliminating the swamp eels (described in question 2 above) from the pond before they eliminate the other organisms. You cannot use toxins, since the local anglers fish in this pond.

4. A local television news bulletin urges you not to eat fish caught in nearby Lake Ketchum because water levels of the pollutant PCB have reached 0.0001 part per million (ppm). With such a small reading, why should you be concerned?

Investigative Extension

Environmental Decision Making has two other ecosystem models, Grasslands and Forestry and Logging, as well as an option for creating your own model using general symbols. These programs can be used to pursue additional topics, including ecosystem dynamics and management.

References

Campbell, N., and J. Reece. *Biology*, 6th ed. Menlo Park, CA: Benjamin/Cummings, 2002.

Cox, G. W. *Alien Species in North America and Hawaii*, Washington, DC: Island Press, 1999.

Mack, R. N., D. Simberloff, W. M. Lonsdale, H. Evans, M. Clout, and F. Bazzaz. "Biotic Invasions: Causes, Epidemiology, Global Consequences and Control," *Issues in Ecology*, 2000, No. 5, Spring.

Odum, E. C., H. T. Odum, and N. S. Peterson. *Environmental Decision Making, The BioQUEST Library Volume V.* San Diego, CA: Academic Press, 2001. Lab written to correspond to software by permission of publisher.

Odum, H. T., and E. C. Odum. *Computer Minimodels and Simulation Exercises,* Gainesville, FL: Center for Wetlands, Phelps Laboratory, University of Florida, 1989. Examples using BASIC with program listings for Apple II, PC, and Macintosh.

SOS for America's Streams (video). Gaithersburg, MD: Izaak Walton League of America, 1990. See the Preparation Guide for ordering information.

Website

The BioQUEST Curriculum Consortium:
http://bioquest.org

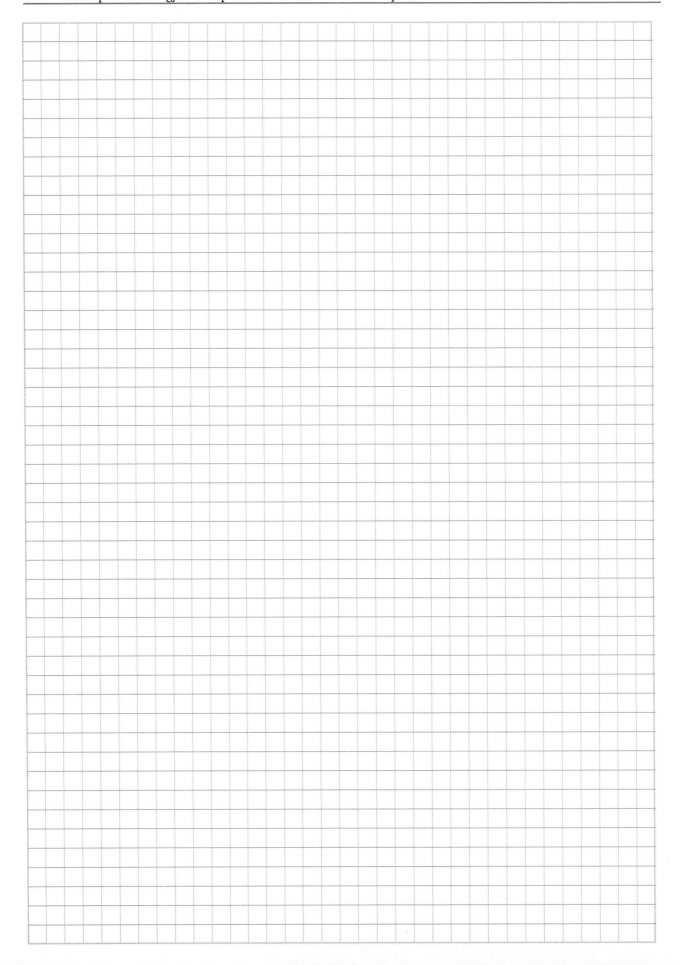

Laboratory Objectives

After completing this lab topic, you should be able to:

1. Define *ethology*.
2. Define and give an example of *taxis, kinesis, agonistic behavior,* and *reproductive behavior.*
3. State the possible adaptive significance of each of these behaviors.
4. Propose hypotheses, make predictions, design experiments to test hypotheses, collect and process data, and discuss results.
5. Present the results of your experiments in a scientific paper.

Introduction

Behavior, broadly defined, is the sum of the responses of an organism to stimuli in its environment. In other words, behavior is what organisms do. **Ethology** is the study of animal behavior in the context of the evolution, ecology, social organization, and sensory abilities of an animal (Gould, 1982). Ethologists concentrate on developing accurate descriptions of animal behavior by carefully observing and experimentally analyzing overt behavior patterns and by studying the physiology of behavior (Barnett, 1981).

Explaining a particular behavior in the broad, multivariable context of evolution or ecology can become a complex undertaking. It is often necessary, therefore, to study behavior in animals that have a limited range of behaviors and for which more is known about their evolution, ecology, and sensory abilities. Understanding simple and isolated behaviors is important in unraveling more complex behaviors.

There are two basic categories of behavior: **learned** and **innate** (inherited) behavior. Experimental evidence suggests that the basis of both lies in the animal's genes. As with all genetically controlled features of an organism, behavior is subject to evolutionary adaptation. As you study animal behavioral activities in this lab topic, think in terms of both **proximate causes,** the immediate physiological events that led to the behavior, and **ultimate causes,** the adaptive value and evolutionary origin of the behavior. To illustrate, a fiddler crab will respond to human intrusion into its feeding area by running into its burrow. The proximate cause of this behavior might be the vibration caused by footsteps stimulating sensory receptors and triggering nervous impulses. The nervous impulses control muscle contractions in the crab's legs. Ultimate causes are the adaptive value of retreating from predators to avoid being eaten.

Note that you will be asking **causal** questions in your investigations. It is inappropriate to ask **anthropomorphic** questions—that is, questions that ascribe human attributes to the animal. Consider, for example, a behavior that places an animal in its best environment. An anthropomorphic explanation for this behavior would be that the animal makes a conscious choice of its environment. There is no way for us to come to this conclusion scientifically. The causal explanation would be that the animal is equipped with a sensory system that responds to environmental stimuli until the favorable environment is reached.

Ethologists have categorized behavioral patterns based on the particular consequence of that behavior for the organism. **Orientation behaviors** place the animal in its most favorable environment. Two categories of orientation behaviors are **taxis** (plural, **taxes**) and **kinesis.** A taxis is movement directly toward or away from a stimulus. When the response is toward a stimulus, it is said to be *positive;* when it is away from the stimulus, it is *negative.* Prefixes such as *photo, chemo,* and *thermo* can be added to the term to describe the nature of the stimulus. For example, an animal that responds to light may demonstrate positive phototaxis and is described as being *positively phototactic.*

A kinesis differs from a taxis in that it is undirected, or random, movement. A stimulus initiates the movement but does not necessarily orient the movement. The intensity of the stimulus determines the rate, or velocity, of movement in response to that stimulus. If a bright light is shined on an animal and the animal responds by moving directly away from it, the behavior is a taxis. But if the bright light initiates random movement or stimulates an increase in the rate of turning with no particular orientation involved, the behavior is a kinesis. The terms *positive* and *negative* and the prefixes mentioned earlier are also appropriately used with *kinesis.* An increase in activity is a positive response; a decrease in activity is a negative response.

Another complex of behaviors observed in some animals is **agonistic behavior.** In this case, the animal is in a conflict situation where there may be a threat or approach, then an attack or withdrawal. Agonistic behaviors in the form of force are called **aggression;** those of retreat or avoidance are called **submission.** Often the agonistic behavior is simply a display that makes the organism look big or threatening. It rarely leads to death and is thought to help maintain territory so that the dominant organism has greater access to resources such as space, food, and mates.

Mating, or **reproductive behavior,** can involve a complex sequence of activities, sometimes spectacular, that facilitate finding, courting, and mating with a member of the same species. It is an adaptive advantage that reproductive behaviors are species-specific. Can you suggest reasons why?

For the first hour of lab, you will perform Experiment A in each of the exercises that follow, briefly investigating the four behaviors just discussed: taxis in brine shrimp, kinesis in pill bugs, agonistic behavior in Siamese fighting fish, and reproductive behavior in fruit flies. After completing every Experiment A, your team will choose one of the systems discussed and perform Experiment B in that exercise. To begin Experiment B, you will propose one or more testable hypotheses and design a simple experiment by which to test your hypotheses. Then you will spend the remainder of the laboratory period carrying out your experiments.

Near the end of the laboratory period, several of you may be asked to present your team's results to the class for discussion. One part of the scientific process involves persuading your colleagues that your experimental design is sound and that your results support your conclusions (either negating or supporting your hypothesis). Be prepared to describe your results in a brief presentation in which you will use your experimental evidence to persuade the other students in your class.

You may be required to submit a laboratory report describing your experiment and results in the format of a scientific paper (see Appendix A). You should discuss results and come to conclusions with your team members; however, you must turn in an originally written lab report. Your Materials and Methods section and your tables and figures may be similar, but your Introduction, Results, and Discussion sections must be the product of your own library research and creative thinking.

Remember, first complete Experiment A in each exercise. Then discuss with your research team a possible question for your original experiment, choosing one of the animals investigated in Experiment A as your experimental organism. Be certain you can pose an interesting question from which you can develop a testable hypothesis. Then turn to Experiment B in the exercise for your chosen organism and design and execute an experiment.

EXERCISE 27.1

Taxis in Brine Shrimp

Brine shrimp (*Artemia salina*) are small crustaceans that live in salt lakes and swim upside down using 11 pairs of appendages. Their sensory structures include two large compound eyes and two pairs of short antennae (Figure 27.1). They are a favorite fish food and can be purchased in pet stores.

Figure 27.1.
Brine shrimp (*Artemia salina*) magnified about 20×. A type of fairy shrimp, brine shrimp live in inland salt lakes such as the Great Salt Lake in Utah.

Experiment A. Brine Shrimp Behavior in Environments with Few Stimuli

Materials

brine shrimp   1 small finger bowl
2 large test tubes   salt water
black construction paper   dropper

Introduction

In this experiment, you will place brine shrimp in a test tube of salt water similar to the water of their normal environment. You will not feed them or disturb them in any way. You will observe their behavior in this relatively stimulus-free environment. Notice their positions in the test tube. Are they in groups, or are they solitary? Are they near the top or near the bottom? You should make careful observations of their behavior, asking questions about possible stimuli that might initiate taxes in these animals.

Hypothesis

Hypothesize about the behavior of brine shrimp in an environment with few stimuli.

Prediction

Predict the result of your experiment based on the hypothesis (if/then).

Procedure

1. Place six brine shrimp in a test tube filled two-thirds with salt water. Rest the test tube in the finger bowl in such a way that you can easily see all six shrimp. You may need to use black construction paper as a background.

2. Describe the behavior of the brine shrimp in the Results section; for example, are they randomly distributed throughout the test tube or do they collect in one area?

3. Record your observations in the Results section.

Results

1. By describing the behavior of brine shrimp in an environment with relatively few stimuli, which component of experimental design are you establishing?

2. Describe the behavior of the brine shrimp.

Discussion

On separate paper, list four stimuli that might initiate taxes in brine shrimp and predict the response of the animal to each. What possible adaptive advantage could this behavior provide?

Experiment B. Original Investigation of Brine Shrimp Behavior

Materials

supplies from Experiment A	dropper bottles—solutions of
piece of black cloth	sugar, egg albumin, acid,
lamp	and base

Introduction

If your team chooses to perform your original experiment investigating taxes in brine shrimp, return to this experiment after you have completed all the introductory investigations (Experiment A of each exercise). Using the materials available and collaborating with other members of your research team, design a simple experiment to investigate taxes in brine shrimp.

Hypothesis

State the hypothesis that you will investigate.

Prediction

Predict the results of your experiment based on your hypothesis (if/then).

Procedure

 Allow a conditioning period of several minutes after the shrimp have been disturbed or stimulated. If you add something to the water in one experiment, begin additional experiments with fresh water and shrimp.

1. On separate paper, list in numerical order each step of your procedure. Remember to include the number of repetitions, levels of treatment, the duration of each stimulus, and other time intervals when appropriate (see Lab Topic 1).

2. If you have an idea for an experiment that requires materials other than those available, ask your laboratory instructor. If possible, additional supplies will be made available.

3. Quantify your data whenever possible (count, weigh, measure, time).

Results

On separate paper, record your data and describe your results. You should design at least one table and figure.

Discussion

1. Among members of your team, discuss your results in light of your hypothesis. If possible, come to conclusions about the behaviors you have been investigating. Record your conclusions on a separate paper.

2. You may be asked to report the results of your experiments to the class.

EXERCISE 27.2
Kinesis in Pill Bugs

Kinesis can be studied using a crustacean in the order Isopoda (called *isopods*). These animals are also called *pill bugs, sow bugs,* and *roly-polies* (Figure 27.2). Although most crustaceans are aquatic, pill bugs are truly terrestrial, and much of their behavior is involved with their need to avoid desiccation. They are easily collected in warm weather under flowerpots, in leaf litter, or in woodpiles. They often respond to mechanical stimuli by rolling up into a ball.

Experiment A. Pill Bug Behavior in Moist and Dry Environments

Materials

pill bugs
2 large petri dishes

filter paper
squirt bottle of water

Figure 27.2.
Pill bugs magnified about 15×.
These terrestrial isopods are also called
sow bugs and *roly-polies*.

Introduction

In this experiment, you will investigate pill bug behavior in moist and dry environments by observing the degree of their activity, that is, the number of times they circle and turn. As you observe their behavior, ask questions about possible stimuli that might modify this behavior.

Hypothesis

Hypothesize about the degree of activity of pill bugs in moist and dry environments.

Prediction

Predict the results of the experiment based on your hypothesis (if/then).

Procedure

1. Prepare two large petri dishes, one with wet filter paper, the other with dry filter paper.
2. Place five pill bugs in each dish.
3. Place the dishes in a dark spot, such as a drawer, for 5 minutes.
4. After 5 minutes, carefully observe the pill bugs in the petri dishes. Before you open the drawer or uncover the petri dishes, assign each of the following procedures to a member of your team.

    a. Count the number of pill bugs moving in each dish.

    b. Choose one moving pill bug in each dish and determine the rate of locomotion by counting revolutions per minute (rpm) around the petri dish.

c. Determine the rate of turning by counting turns (reversal of direction) per minute for one pill bug in each dish.

Results

Record your results in Table 27.1.

Table 27.1
Kinesis in Pill Bugs: Response to Wet and Dry Environments

Environmental Condition	Number Moving	Rate of Locomotion (rpm)	Rate of Turning (turn/min)
Moist			
Dry			

Discussion

1. Kinetic response to varying moisture in the environment is called *hygrokinesis*. What other environmental factors might influence the behavior of pill bugs?

2. On separate paper, list four factors that might initiate kineses in pill bugs and predict their response to each. What possible adaptive advantage could this behavior provide?

Experiment B. Original Investigation of Pill Bug Behavior

Materials

supplies from Experiment A
white enamel pan
wax pencils
beaker of water

construction paper
manila folder
large pieces of black cloth

Introduction

If your team chooses to perform your original experiment investigating kineses in pill bugs, return to this experiment after you have completed all the introductory investigations (Experiment A of each exercise). Using the materials available and collaborating with other members of your research team, design a simple experiment to investigate kineses in pill bugs.

Hypothesis

State the hypothesis that you will investigate.

Prediction

Predict the results of the experiment based on your hypothesis (if/then).

Procedure

1. On separate paper, list in numerical order each step of your procedure. Remember to include the number of repetitions, the levels of treatment, the duration of stimulus, and other time intervals where appropriate (see Lab Topic 1).

2. If you have an idea for an experiment that requires materials other than those available, ask your laboratory instructor. If possible, additional supplies will be made available.

3. Quantify your data whenever possible (count, weigh, measure, time).

Results

On separate paper, record your data and describe your results. You should design at least one table and figure.

Discussion

1. Among members of your team, discuss your results in light of your hypothesis. If possible, come to conclusions about the behaviors you have been investigating. Record your conclusions on a separate paper.

2. You may be asked to report the results of your experiments to the class.

EXERCISE 27.3

Agonistic Display in Male Siamese Fighting Fish

The innate agonistic behavior of the male Siamese fighting fish (*Betta splendens*) has been widely studied (Simpson, 1968; Thompson, 1969). The sight of another male *Betta* or even its own reflection in a mirror will stimulate a ritualized series of responses toward the intruder. If two fish are placed in the same aquarium, their agonistic behavior usually continues until one fish is defeated or subordinated (see Color Plate 67).

Experiment A. Display Behavior in Male Siamese Fighting Fish

Materials

male Siamese fighting fish in a 1- to 2-L flat-sided fishbowl
mirror

Introduction

The purpose of this experiment is to describe the ritualized agonistic display of a male Siamese fighting fish after being stimulated by its own reflection in a mirror. Before you begin the experiment, become familiar with the fish's anatomy, identifying its dorsal fin, ventral fin, pectoral fin, gill cover, and tail (Figure 27.3 and Color Plate 68).

When you begin the experiment, you will be looking for several possible responses: frontal approach (facing intruder), broadside display, undulating movements, increased swimming speed, fin elevation (dorsal, ventral, or pectoral), gill cover extension (angle may vary), tail expansion, and enhanced coloration in tail, fin, or body.

Hypothesis

Hypothesize about the response of the fish to its image in the mirror.

Prediction

Predict the result of the experiment based on your hypothesis (if/then).

Figure 27.3.
**Male Siamese fighting fish
(*Betta splendens*).**

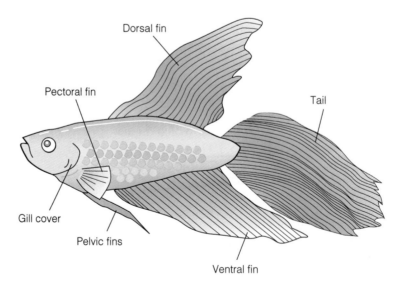

Procedure

1. Plan your strategy.

   a. Be ready with your pencil and paper to record your observations. Behaviors can happen very quickly. Your entire team should observe and record them.

   b. Each team member should be responsible for timing the duration of particular responses (listed in the Introduction). You might also take turns observing different behaviors, alternating from one behavior to another every 30 seconds.

2. Place the mirror against the fishbowl.

3. As the fish reacts to its reflection, list, in order and using the appropriate terminology, the series of responses. Be as quantitative as possible; for example, you might record "gill cover extended 90° for 30 seconds" or "broadside display for 60 seconds."

4. Compare collective results.

5. In the Results section, make a *sequential* list of the recognizable responses involved in the display.

6. Note in the Results section those responses that take place simultaneously.

Results

1. Record your sequential list.

2. Record the responses that take place simultaneously.

Discussion

1. Collaborating with your teammates, write a descriptive paragraph, as quantitative and detailed as possible, describing the agonistic display elicited in the Siamese fighting fish in response to its reflection.

2. What is the obvious adaptive advantage of complex agonistic displays that are not followed by damaging fights? Are there advantages that are not so obvious?

3. Name several other animals that demonstrate a strong display that is seldom followed by a damaging fight.

4. Name several animals that do engage in damaging fights.

Experiment B. Original Investigation of Siamese Fighting Fish Behavior

Materials

supplies from Experiment A
colored pencils
index cards

fish of different species in
    fishbowls
female Siamese fighting fish

Introduction

If your team chooses to perform your original experiment investigating agonistic behavior in Siamese fighting fish, return to this experiment after you have completed all the introductory investigations (Experiment A of each exercise). Using the materials available and collaborating among your research team, design a simple experiment to investigate this behavior.

Discuss with your team members possible investigations that might be carried out. Several questions follow that might give you ideas.

1. What is the simplest stimulus that will initiate the response? Is color important? Size? Movement?

2. Is the behavior "released" by a specific stimulus or by a complex of all the stimuli?

3. Will another species of fish initiate the response?

4. Will a female *Betta* fish initiate the response, and, if so, how does the response compare with the response to a fish of a different species?

5. Is the response all or none—that is, are there partial displays with different stimuli?

6. Does the fish become "conditioned"—that is, after repeated identical stimuli, does the duration of the display change, or does the display cease?

7. Could chemical stimulation contribute to the response? (Transfer water from one fishbowl to another.)

Hypothesis

After your team has decided on one or more questions to investigate, formulate a testable hypothesis.

Prediction

Predict the results of the experiment based on your hypothesis (if/then).

Procedure

1. On separate paper, list in numerical order each step of your procedure. Remember to include the number of repetitions, the levels of treatment, the duration of a stimulus, and other time intervals where appropriate (see Lab Topic 1).

2. If you have an idea for an experiment that requires materials other than those available, ask your laboratory instructor. If possible, additional supplies will be made available.

3. Quantify your data whenever possible (count, weigh, measure, time).

Results

On separate paper, record your data and describe your results. You should design at least one table and figure.

Discussion

1. Among members of your team, discuss your results in light of your hypothesis. If possible, come to conclusions about the behaviors you have been investigating. Record your conclusions on a separate paper.

2. You may be asked to report the results of your experiments to the class.

EXERCISE 27.4

Reproductive Behavior in Fruit Flies

Spieth (1952, described in Marler, 1968) has classified the mating behavior of the fruit fly *Drosophila melanogaster* as being a complex of at least fourteen behaviors. Described below are ten of the most common and easily recognized of these behaviors. Read the list carefully and become familiar with the behaviors you will be required to recognize. Six of the behaviors are seen in males, four in females. The behavior sequence begins as the male orients his body toward the female (Figure 27.4a).

Male Behaviors

1. *Tapping.* The forelegs are extended to strike or tap the female (Figure 27.4b).
2. *Waving.* The wing is extended and held 90° from the body, then relaxed without vibration (Figure 27.4c).
3. *Wing vibration.* The male extends one or both wings from the resting position and moves them rapidly up and down (Figure 27.4c).
4. *Licking.* The male licks the female's genitalia (on the rear of her abdomen) (Figure 27.4d).
5. *Circling.* The male postures and then circles the female, usually when she is nonreceptive.
6. *Stamping.* The male stamps forefeet as in tapping but does not strike the female.

Female Behaviors

1. *Extruding.* A temporary, tubelike structure is extended from the female's genitalia.
2. *Decamping.* A nonreceptive female runs, jumps, or flies away from the courting male.
3. *Depressing.* A nonreceptive female prevents access to her genitalia by depressing her wings and curling the tip of her abdomen down.
4. *Ignoring.* A nonreceptive female ignores the male.

If the behavior display is successful, the flies will copulate (Figure 27.4e, f).

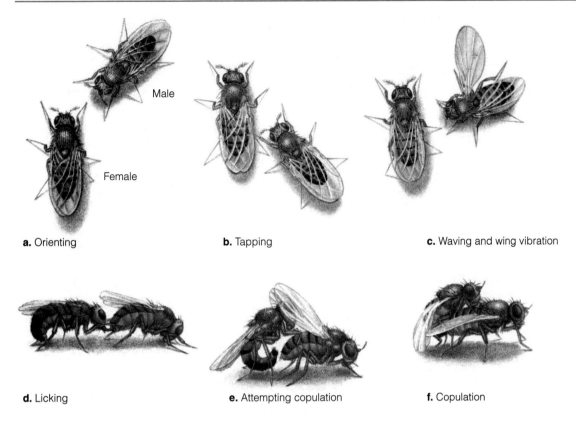

a. Orienting   **b.** Tapping   **c.** Waving and wing vibration

d. Licking   **e.** Attempting copulation   **f.** Copulation

Figure 27.4.
Mating behavior in fruit fly, *Drosophila melanogaster.*

Experiment A. Reproductive Behavior in *Drosophila melanogaster*

Materials

stereoscopic microscope
fly vials with 2 or 3 virgin female *D. melanogaster* flies
fly vials with 2 or 3 male *D. melanogaster* flies

Introduction

In this experiment, you will place virgin female *D. melanogaster* flies in the same vial with male flies and observe the behavior of each sex. Working with another student, discuss the behaviors described in the introduction to this exercise and plan the strategy for your experiment. Identify mating behaviors of *D. melanogaster* and record their sequence and duration (when appropriate). As you observe the behavior of the flies, discuss possible original experiments investigating reproductive behavior in flies.

Hypothesis

Hypothesize about the presence of flies of the opposite sex in the same vial.

Prediction

Predict the results of the experiment based on your hypothesis (if/then).

Procedure

1. Set up the stereoscopic microscope.
2. Have paper and pencil ready. The behaviors can happen very rapidly. One person should call out observations while the other person records.
3. Obtain one vial containing virgin females and one vial containing males, and gently tap the male flies into the vial containing females.
4. Observe first with the naked eye. Once flies have encountered each other, use the stereoscopic microscope to make observations.

Results

1. Describe, in sequence, the response of the male to the female and the female to the male. Quantify your observations. To do this, you may consider counting the number of times a behavior takes place and timing the duration of behaviors.

2. Describe rejection if this takes place.

3. In the margin of your lab manual, note any behaviors that can be analyzed quantitatively.

Discussion

Speculate about the adaptive advantage of elaborate courtship behaviors in animals.

Experiment B. Original Investigation of Reproductive Behavior in Fruit Flies

Materials

supplies from Experiment A
fly vials with 2 or 3 virgin females
of an alternate fly species (other
than *D. melanogaster*)

fly vials with 2 or 3 males of
the alternate species

Introduction

If your team chooses to perform your original experiment investigating reproductive behavior in fruit flies, continue with this experiment after you have completed all the introductory investigations (Experiment A of each exercise). Using the materials available and collaborating with your research partner, design a simple experiment to investigate reproductive behavior. Several questions follow that might provide ideas.

1. Will reproductive behavior in another species be identical to that in *D. melanogaster*?
2. Will males placed in the same vial demonstrate courtship behaviors?
3. Will males respond to dead females?
4. What is the response of a male *D. melanogaster* to females of a different species?
5. Do males compete?

Quantify your observations. To do this, you may consider counting the number of times a behavior takes place or timing the duration of behaviors.

Hypothesis

After your team has decided on one or more questions to investigate, formulate a testable hypothesis.

Prediction

Predict the results of your experiment based on your hypothesis (if/then).

Procedure

1. On a separate paper, list in numerical order each step of your procedure. Remember to include the number of repetitions, the levels of treatment, the duration of stimulus, and other time intervals where appropriate (see Lab Topic 1).
2. If you have an idea for an experiment that requires materials other than those available, ask your laboratory instructor. If possible, additional supplies will be made available.
3. Quantify your data whenever possible (count, weigh, measure, time).

Results

On a separate paper, record your data and describe your results. You should design at least one table and figure.

Discussion

1. Within your team, discuss your results in light of your hypothesis. If possible, come to conclusions about the behaviors you have been investigating. Record your conclusions on a separate paper.

2. You may be asked to report the results of your experiments to the class.

Questions for Review

Define, compare, and give examples for each item in the following pairs:

1. Learned behavior—innate behavior
2. Proximate cause of behavior—ultimate cause of behavior
3. Causal explanation for a behavior—anthropomorphic explanation for a behavior
4. Taxis—kinesis

Applying Your Knowledge

1. Based on your understanding of ethology and scientific methodology, critique the following explanation of graylag goose behavior.

   A behavioral biologist places an egg near the nest of a graylag goose. The goose notices the egg and wants to add it to her clutch of eggs. She uses her bill to retrieve the egg.

2. Propose an explanation for the following behavior.

   The female praying mantis (*Mantis religiosa*) frequently eats her smaller mate after breeding or even before if she is hungry enough.

3. Adult male European robins have red feathers on their breasts. A male robin will display aggressive behavior and attack another male robin that invades his territory during mating season. Immature male robins with all brown feathers do not elicit this behavior in the adult robin.

How could you explain this behavior? Design an experiment to test your explanation (hypothesis).

4. In May 2001, Diana Reiss of Columbia University and Lori Marino of Emory University reported results of experiments performed with bottlenose dolphins. These researchers found that dolphins apparently display "self-recognition" behaviors in which they appear to demonstrate self-awareness when seeing their reflection in a mirror (see "News in Brief," *Scientific American* online at http://www.sciam.com/news/050101/3.html). Read this *Scientific American* report or the complete May 2001 article in *Proceedings of the National Academy of Science* (see References section).

   Review behavioral responses of Siamese fighting fish to their reflections in a mirror. Do you think this response could be "self-recognition"? Why or why not? How could you design an experiment to test this question?

References

Campbell, N., and J. Reece. *Biology,* 6th ed. Menlo Park, CA: Benjamin/Cummings, 2002.

Gould, J. L. *Ethology.* New York, NY: Norton, 1982.

Greenspan, R. J. "Understanding the Genetic Construction of Behavior," *Scientific American,* 1995, vol. 272, no. 4, p. 72.

Grier, J. W., T. Burk. *Biology of Animal Behavior,* 2nd ed. St. Louis, MO: Mosby Year Book, 1992.

Johnson, R. N. *Aggression in Man and Animals.* Philadelphia, PA: Saunders College Publishing, 1972.

Marler, P. "Mating Behavior of *Drosophila.*" In *Animal Behavior in Laboratory and Field,* editor A. W. Stokes. San Francisco: Freeman, 1968.

Raham, G. "Pill Bug Biology," *The American Biology Teacher,* 1986, vol. 48, no. 1.

Reiss, D., and L. Marino. "Mirror self-recognition in the bottlenose dolphin: A case of cognitive convergence." *Proc. Natl. Acad. Sci. USA,* 2001, vol. 98, pp. 5937–5942.

Simpson, M. J. A. "The Threat Display of the Siamese Fighting Fish, *Betta splendens,*" *Animal Behavior Monograph,* 1968, vol. 1, p. 1.

Thompson, T. "Aggressive Behavior of Siamese Fighting Fish," in *Aggressive Behavior,* editors S. Garattini and E. B. Sigg. Proceedings of the International Symposium on the Biology of Aggressive Behavior. New York, NY: Wiley, 1969.

Scientific Writing

For the scientific enterprise to be successful, scientists must communicate their work. Major scientific findings are never kept secret. Instead, scientists share their ideas and results with other scientists, encouraging critical review and alternative interpretations from colleagues and the entire scientific community. Communication, both verbal and written, occurs at every step along the research path. While working on projects, scientists present their preliminary results for comments from their coworkers at laboratory group meetings and in written research reports. At a later stage, scientists report the results of their research activities as a poster or oral presentation at a scientific meeting. Then the final report is prepared in a rather standard scientific paper format and submitted for publication in an appropriate scientific journal. At each stage in this process, scientists encourage and require critical review of their work and ideas by their peers. The final publication in a peer-reviewed journal generally promotes additional research and establishes this contribution to current knowledge.

One of the objectives of every lab topic in this manual is to develop your writing skills. You will generate and write hypotheses, results, observations, answers to questions, and more, as one way of learning biology. Also, you will practice writing in a scientific paper format and style to communicate the results of your investigations. By the time you have completed the lab topics in this manual, you will have written the equivalent of at least two complete scientific papers.

As you investigate the different lab topics, you will make observations, ask questions, and propose hypotheses. You will design and conduct experiments using procedures of your own design or following procedures in the manual. You will record results, designing tables and graphs to present your data in a logical and organized format. You will then interpret results and come to conclusions based on your hypotheses. This process is reflected in the design of a scientific paper and the format you will use for your laboratory papers. Each paper will be divided into sections that reflect these activities.

A scientific paper usually includes the following parts: a **Title** (statement of the question or problem), an **Abstract** (short summary of the paper), an **Introduction** (background and significance of the problem), a **Materials and Methods** section (report of exactly what you did), a **Results** section (presentation of data), a **Discussion** section (interpretation and discussion of results), and **References Cited** (books and periodicals used). A **Conclusion** (concise restatement of conclusions) and **Acknowledgments** (recognition of assistance) may also be included.

We propose that you practice writing throughout the biology laboratory program by submitting individual sections of a scientific paper. Although your instructor will determine which sections you will write for a given lab topic, we outline a sample writing program below.

Scientific Writing Program

Examples of Individual Sections of a Scientific Paper for Suggested Lab Topics:

> Title Page and Materials and Methods for Lab Topic 1, Scientific Investigation
>
> Results for Lab Topic 2, Enzymes
>
> Discussion for Lab Topic 4, Diffusion and Osmosis
>
> Results plus Discussion for Lab Topic 5, Cellular Respiration and Fermentation
>
> Introduction and References Cited for Lab Topic 6, Photosynthesis

Your instructor will evaluate each of these sections, pointing out areas of weakness and suggesting improvements. By the time you have completed these assignments, you will have submitted the equivalent of one scientific paper.

Having practiced writing each section of a scientific paper in the first half of the laboratory program, you will then write one or two complete laboratory papers in scientific paper format during the second half of the laboratory program, reporting the results of experiments, preferably those that you and your research team have designed and performed. Because performing the experiment will be a collaborative effort, you and your teammates will share information for the Materials and Methods and Results sections of your reports. However, the Introduction, Discussion, and References Cited (or References) sections must be the product of your own personal library research and creative thinking. If you are not certain about the level of independence and what constitutes plagiarism in this laboratory program, ask your instructor to clarify the class policy. *In the most extreme case of plagiarism, a student presents another student's report as his or her own. However, representing another person's ideas as your own without giving that person credit is also plagiarism and is a serious offense.*

A more detailed description of each section of a scientific paper follows. As you write your paper, clearly label each section (except the title page), placing the title of the section against the left margin on a separate line.

Title Page and Title

The title page is the first page of the paper and includes the title of the paper, your name, the course title, your lab time or section, your instructor's name, and the due date for the paper. *The title should be as short as possible and as long as necessary to communicate to the reader the question being answered in the paper.* For example, if you are asking a question about the inheritance patterns of the gene for aldehyde oxidase production in *Drosophila melanogaster,* a possible title might be "Inheritance of the Gene for Aldehyde Oxidase in *Drosophila melanogaster.*" Something like "Inheritance in Fruit Flies" is too general, and "A Study of the Inheritance of the Enzyme Aldehyde Oxidase in the Fruit Fly *Drosophila melanogaster*" is too wordy. The words "A Study of the" are superfluous, and "Enzyme" and "Fruit Fly" are redundant. The suffix -*ase* indicates that aldehyde oxidase is an enzyme, and most scientists know that *Drosophila melanogaster* is the scientific name of a common fruit fly species. However, it is appropriate to include in the title both common and scientific names of lesser known species.

Place the title about 7 cm from the top of the title page. Place "by" and your name in the center of the page, and place the course name, lab section, instructor's name, and due date, each on a separate centered line, at the bottom of the page. Leave about 5 cm below this information.

Abstract

The abstract, if one is requested by the instructor, is placed at the beginning of the second page of the paper, after the title page. *The abstract concisely summarizes the question being investigated in the paper, the methods used in the experiment, the results, and the conclusions drawn.* The reader should be able to determine the major topics in the paper without reading the entire paper. The abstract should be no more than 250 words, and fewer if possible. Compose the abstract after the paper is completed.

Introduction

The introduction has two functions: (1) to provide the context for your investigation and (2) to state the question asked and the hypothesis tested in the study. Begin the introduction by reviewing background information that will enable the reader to understand the objective of the study and the significance of the problem, relating the problem to the larger issues in the field. Include only information that directly prepares the reader to understand the question investigated. Most ideas in the introduction will come from outside sources, such as scientific journals or books dealing with the topic you are investigating. All sources of information must be referenced and included in the References Cited (or References) section of the paper, but the introduction must be in your own words. Refer to the references when appropriate. Unless otherwise instructed, place the author of the reference cited and the year of publication in parentheses at the end of the sentence or paragraph relating the idea; for example, "(Finnerty, 1992)." Additional information on citing references is provided on p. 756, References Cited. Do not use citation forms utilized in other disciplines. Do not use footnotes and avoid the use of direct quotes.

As you describe your investigation, include only the question and hypothesis that you finally investigated. Briefly describe the experiment performed and the outcome predicted for the experiment. Although these items are usually presented after the background information near the end of the introduction, you should have each clearly in mind before you begin writing the introduction. It is a good idea to write down each item (question, hypothesis, prediction) before you begin to write your introduction.

Write the introduction in the past tense when referring to your experiment; but when relating the background information, use the present tense as you refer to another investigator's published work. Previously published work is considered established in the present body of knowledge.

Throughout your paper, we encourage you to use the active voice whenever possible. Doing so makes the paper easier to read and more understandable. In biology, editors of scientific journals are now suggesting or requiring use of the active voice.

In general, the Introduction is written before the Discussion; however, some authors prefer to write the Introduction last. Remember to revise the Introduction after completing your paper.

Materials and Methods

The Materials and Methods section describes your experiment in such a way that it can be repeated. This section should be a narrative description that integrates the materials with the procedures used in the investigation. Do not list the materials and do not list the steps of the procedure. Rather, write the Materials and Methods section concisely in paragraph form in the past tense. Be sure to include levels of treatment, numbers of replications, and controls. If you are working with living organisms, include the scientific name and the sex of the organism if that information is relevant to the experiment. If you used computer software or any statistical analyses, include these in the Materials and Methods section.

The difficulty in writing this section comes as you decide the level of detail to include in your paragraphs. You must determine which details are essential for another investigator to repeat the experiment. For example, if in your experiment you incubated potato pieces in different concentrations of sucrose solution, it would not be necessary to explain that the pieces were incubated in plastic cups labeled with a wax marking pencil or to provide the numbers of the cups. In this case, the molarity of the sucrose solutions, the size of the potato pieces and how they were obtained, and the amount of incubation solution are the important items to include. Do not include failed attempts unless the technique used may be tried by other investigators. Do not try to justify your procedures in this section.

The Materials and Methods section is often the best place to begin writing your paper. The writing is straightforward and concise, and you will be reminded of the details of the work.

Results

The Results section consists of at least four components: (1) one or two sentences reminding the reader about the nature of the research, (2) one or more paragraphs that describe the results, (3) figures (graphs, diagrams, pictures), and (4) tables. *The Results is the central section of a scientific paper.* Therefore, you should think carefully about the best way to present your results to the reader. The data included in tables and graphs should be summarized and emphasized in the narrative paragraph. Draw the reader's attention to the results that are important. Describe trends in your data and provide evidence to support your claims. This section also is written in the past tense.

Before writing the Results section, prepare the tables and figures. Remember to number figures and tables consecutively throughout the paper (*see Lab Topic 1, Scientific Investigation, for instructions on creating figures and tables and their presentation).* Refer to figures and tables within the paragraph as you describe your results, using the word Figure or Table, followed by its number; for example, "(Figure 1)." If possible, place each figure or table at the end of the paragraph in which it is cited.

If you have performed a statistical analysis of your data, such as chi-square, include the results in this section.

Report your data as accurately as possible. Do not report what you expected to happen in the experiment nor whether your data supported your hypothesis. Do not discuss the meaning of your results in this section. Do not critique the results. Any data you plan to include in the Discussion section must be presented in the Results. Conversely, do not include data in the Results that you do not mention in the Discussion.

Write the Results section before attempting the Discussion section. This will ensure that the results of your investigation are clearly organized, logically presented, and thoroughly understood before they are discussed. For this reason, some scientists begin with the Results section when writing a paper.

Discussion

In the Discussion section, you will analyze and interpret the results of your experiment. Simply restating the results is not interpretation. The Discussion must provide a context for understanding the significance of the results. Explain why you observed these results and how these results contribute to our knowledge. Your results either will support or confirm your hypothesis or will negate, refute, or contradict your hypothesis; but the word *prove is* not appropriate in scientific writing. If your results do not support your hypothesis, you must still state why you think this occurred. Support your ideas from other work (books, lectures or outside reading of scientific literature). State your conclusions in this section.

Complete your Introduction and Results sections before you begin writing the Discussion. The figures and tables in the Results section will be particularly important as you begin to think about your discussion. The tables allow you to present your results clearly to the reader, and graphs allow you to visualize the effects that the independent variable has had on the dependent variables in your experiment. Studying these data will be one of the first steps in interpreting your results. As you study the information in the Introduction section and your data in the Results section, write down relationships and integrate these relationships into a rough draft of your discussion.

The following steps, modified from Gray, Dickey, and Kosinski (1988), may be helpful to you as you begin to organize your discussion and before you write the narrative:

1. Restate your question, hypothesis, and prediction.
2. Answer the question.
3. Write down the specific data, including results of statistical tests.
4. State whether your results did or did not confirm your prediction and support or negate your hypothesis.
5. Write down what you know about the biology involved in your experiment. How do your results fit in with what you know? What is the significance of your results?

6. How do your results support or conflict with previous work? Include references to this work.

7. Clearly state your conclusions.

8. List weaknesses you have identified in your experimental design that affected your results. List any problems that arose during the experiment itself that affected your results. The weaknesses of the experiment should not dominate the Discussion. Include one or two sentences only if these problems affected the results. Remember the focus of the Discussion is to convey the significance of the results.

9. You are now ready to write the narrative for the Discussion. Integrate all of the information into several simple, clear, concise paragraphs. Discuss the results; do not simply restate the data. Refer to other work to support your ideas.

References Cited (or References)

A References Cited section lists only those references cited in the paper. A References section (bibliography), on the other hand, is a more inclusive list of all references used in producing the paper, including books and papers used to obtain background knowledge that may not be cited in the paper. For your paper you should have a References Cited section that includes only those references cited in the paper. The format for the References Cited section differs slightly from one scientific journal to the next. How does an author know which format to use? Every scientific journal provides "Instructions to Authors" that describe specific requirements for this important section and all other aspects of the paper. You may use the format used in this lab manual and provided in the examples below, select the format in a scientific journal provided by your instructor, or use another accepted format for listing your references. Your instructor may provide additional instructions. Be sure to read the references that you cite in your paper.

Examples of Reference Citations

Journal article, one author:

> Whittaker, R. H. "New Concepts of Kingdoms of Organisms." *Science,* 1969, vol. 163, pp. 150–160.

Journal article, two or more authors:

> Watson, J. D., and F. H. Crick. "Molecular Structure of Nucleic Acids: A Structure for Deoxyribose Nucleic Acid." *Nature,* 1953, vol. 171, pp. 737–738.

Book:

> Darwin, C. R. *On the Origin of Species.* London: John Murray, 1859.

Chapter or article in an edited book:

> Baker, H. G. "Characteristics and Modes of Origin of Weeds" in *Genetics and Colonizing Species,* eds. H. G. Baker and G. L. Stebbins. New York: Academic Press, 1965, pp. 147–152.

Government publication:

> Office of Technology Assessment. *Harmful Non-indigenous Species in the United States.* Publication no. OTA-F-565. Washington, D.C.: U.S. Government Printing Office, 1993.

In the text of the paper, cite the references using the author's name and the year. For example: "The innate agonistic behavior of the male Siamese fighting fish has been widely studied (Simpson, 1968)." "Simpson (1968) has described the agonistic behavior of the male Siamese fighting fish." If there are more than two authors, use the first author's name followed by *et al.* (and others). For example: (Simpson *et al.,* 1968).

Using Information Sources from the Web

The Web can provide access to online reference resources including *Biological Abstracts, Current Contents, Medline,* and *Annual Reviews* among many others. These search tools provide access to a wide range of published papers, some of which may be available online as full text journals. For suggestions and examples of how to locate sources using the Web, see Pechenik (2001). Scientific papers published in professional journals have gone through an extensive review process by other scientists in the same field. Most scientific articles have been revised based on comments by the reviewers and the editors. Sources of information that lack this critical review process do not have the same validity and authority.

The World Wide Web (WWW) is an exciting, immediate, and easily accessible source of information. However, unlike traditional bibliographic resources in the sciences, the WWW includes websites with material that has not been critically reviewed. Your instructor may prefer that you use the WWW only for locating peer-reviewed resources or as a starting point to promote your interest and ideas. You may not be allowed to use WWW sources at all. Consult your instructor concerning use of online information.

If you do use the WWW to locate information, you should be prepared to evaluate these sites critically. Remember always to record the online address for any site you use as a reference. Tate and Alexander (1996) suggest the following five criteria for evaluating WWW sources:

1. **Authority.** Determine the author and sponsor for the WWW site. What is the professional affiliation of the author? Are phone numbers and addresses included? Is there a link to the sponsor's home page? Does the author list his or her qualifications? If the material is copyrighted, who owns the copyright?

2. **Accuracy.** Look for indications of professional standards for writing, citations, figures, and tables. Are there typographical, spelling, and grammatical errors? Are sources of information cited? Are the data presented or simply summarized?

3. **Objectivity.** Is the site provided as a public service, free of advertising? If advertising is present, is it clearly separate from the information? Does the site present only the view of the sponsor or advertiser?

4. **Currency.** Determine the date of the site and whether it is regularly revised. How long has the site existed? When was it last updated? Are figures and tables dated? Some WWW sites disappear overnight. Always record the date that you visited the site and retrieved information.

5. **Coverage.** Is the information offered in a complete form or as an abstract or summary of information published elsewhere? Is the site under construction? When was the site last revised?

We have included one suggested format for citing online information in the References Cited section of your paper. Also see the examples at the end of many lab topics in this manual. Other formats may be suggested by your instructor or librarian.

Author. *Title.* [online] available http://www.address, date accessed.

For example: Manning, G. *The Drosophila Virtual Library.* [online] available http://www.ceolas.org/fly/, 1998.

Reminders

Scientific writing should be clear and concise. This requires critical thinking and repeated revision. You should read background information carefully and critically in preparation for designing your investigation and to provide a context for your work. As you complete your investigation, you must think critically about your results and the best way to present your results. Scientific writing involves using evidence from your work and that of others to make a clear and logical argument. To be successful you must plan time for researching your topic, analyzing your results, and then revising your writing. For suggestions and examples of how to revise your work, see Chapter 5, "Revising," in Pechnik (2001).

As you begin writing your paper, refer to the following list for hints on how to make your writing stronger:

1. Write clearly in short and logical, but not choppy, sentences.

2. Use the past tense in the Abstract, Materials and Methods, and Results sections. Also use the past tense in the Introduction and Discussion sections when referring to your experiment.

3. Write in grammatically correct English.

4. When referring to the scientific name of an organism, the genus and species should be in italics or underlined. The first letter of the genus is capitalized, but the species is written in all lowercase letters; for example, *Drosophila melanogaster.*

5. Use metric units. Use numerals when reporting measurements, percentages, decimals, and magnifications. When beginning a sentence, write the number as a word. Numbers of ten or less, that are not measurements, are written. Numbers greater than ten are given as numerals.

6. The word "data" is plural.

7. Record the citation information for any references, including online sources, at the time you read the information. Refer to the citation format to record the complete citation.

8. Save a copy of your work on a disk and print a copy of your paper before turning in the original.

9. Begin writing early to allow time for revision. Simplify your writing. Delete unnecessary words. Adjectives and adverbs have limited use in describing your work.

10. Carefully proofread your work, even if your word processor has checked for grammatical and spelling errors. These programs cannot distinguish between your and you're, for example.

References

The following sources are recommended to give additional help and examples in scientific writing:

Gray, L. S., J. Dickey, and R. Kosinski. *Writing Guide.* Clemson, SC: Clemson University, 1988.

McMillan, V. E. *Writing Papers in the Biological Sciences.* New York, NY: St. Martin's Press, 1988.

Moore, R. *Writing to Learn Biology.* New York, NY: Saunders College Publishing, 1992.

Pechenik, J. A. *A Short Guide to Writing about Biology,* 4th ed., New York, NY: Addison Wesley, 2001.

Tate, M., and J. Alexander. "Teaching Critical Evaluation Skills for World Wide Web Resources." *Computers in Libraries,* Nov/Dec 1996, pp. 49–55.

Websites

Bibliography on Evaluating Internet Resources: http://refserver.lib.vt.edu/libinst/critTHINK.HTM, 1998.

Biologist's Guide to Library Resources: www.ase.tufts.edu/biology/bguide/, 2000.

Chi-Square Test

Chi-square is a statistical test commonly used to compare observed data with data we would expect to obtain according to a specific scientific hypothesis. For example, if according to Mendel's laws, you expect 10 of 20 offspring from a cross to be male and the actual observed number is 8 males out of 20 offspring, then you might want to know about the "goodness of fit" between the observed and the expected. Were the deviations (differences between observed and expected) the result of chance, or were they due to other factors? How much deviation can occur before the investigator must conclude that something other than chance is at work, causing the observed to differ from the expected? The chi-square test can help in making that decision. The chi-square test is always testing what scientists call the **null hypothesis,** which states that there is no significant difference between the expected and the observed result.

The formula for calculating chi-square (χ^2) is:

$$\chi^2 = \Sigma(o - e)^2 / e$$

That is, chi-square is the sum of the squared difference between observed (*o*) and expected (*e*) data (or the deviation, *d*), divided by the expected data in all possible categories.

For example, suppose that a cross between two pea plants yields a population of 880 plants, 639 with green seeds and 241 with yellow seeds. You are asked to propose the genotypes of the parents. Your scientific hypothesis is that the allele for green is dominant to the allele for yellow and that the parent plants were both heterozygous for this trait. If your scientific hypothesis is true, then the predicted ratio of offspring from this cross would be 3:1 (based on Mendel's laws), as predicted from the results of the Punnett square (Figure B.1). The related null hypothesis is that there is no significant difference between your observed pea offspring and offspring produced according to Mendel's laws. To determine if this null hypothesis is rejected or not rejected, a χ^2 value is computed.

To calculate χ^2, first determine the number expected in each category. If the ratio is 3:1 and the total number of observed individuals is 880, then the expected numerical values should be 660 green and 220 yellow ($\frac{3}{4} \times 880 = 660$; $\frac{1}{4} \times 880 = 220$).

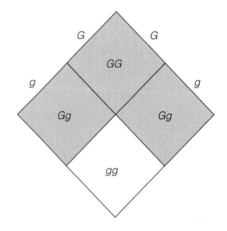

Figure B.1.
Punnett square. Predicted offspring from cross between green- and yellow-seeded plants. Green (*G*) is dominant (3/4 green; 1/4 yellow).

 Chi-square analysis requires that you use numerical values, not percentages or ratios.

Then calculate χ^2 using the formula, as shown in Table B.1. Note that we get a value of 2.673 for χ^2. But what does this number mean? Here's how to interpret the χ^2 value:

1. Determine **degrees of freedom** (df). Degrees of freedom can be calculated as the number of categories in the problem minus 1. For example, if we had four categories, then the degrees of freedom would be 3. In our example, there are two categories (green and yellow); therefore, there is 1 degree of freedom.

2. Determine a relative standard to serve as the basis for rejecting the hypothesis. Scientists allow some level of error in their decision making for testing their hypotheses. The relative standard commonly used in biological research is $p < 0.05$. The **p value** is the *probability* of rejecting the null hypothesis (that there is no difference between observed and expected), when the null hypothesis is true. In other words, the p value gives an approximate value for the error of falsely stating that there is a significant difference between your observed numbers and the expected numbers, when there is *not* a significant difference. *When we pick $p < 0.05$, we state that there is less than a 5% chance of error of stating that there is a difference when, in fact, there is no significant difference.* Although scientists and statisticians sometimes select a lower significance value, in this manual we will assume a value of 0.05.

3. Refer to a chi-square distribution table (Table B.2). Using the appropriate degrees of freedom, locate the value corresponding to the p value of 0.05, the error probability that you selected. If your χ^2 value is *greater* than the value corresponding to the p value of 0.05, then you reject the null hypothesis. You conclude that the observed numbers are significantly different from the expected. In this example your calculated value, $\chi^2 = 2.673$, is not larger than the table χ^2 value of 3.84 (df = 1, $p = 0.05$). *Therefore, your observed distribution of plants with green and yellow seeds is not significantly different from the distribution that would be expected under Mendel's laws. Any minor differences between your offspring distribution and the expected Mendelian distribution can be attributed to chance or sampling error.*

Step-by-Step Procedure for Testing Your Hypothesis and Calculating Chi-Square

1. State the hypothesis being tested and the predicted results.

2. Gather the data by conducting the relevant experiment (or, if working genetics problems, use the data provided in the problem).

3. Determine the expected numbers for each observational class. Remember to use numbers, not percentages.

 Chi-square should *not* be calculated if the expected value in any category is less than 5.

4. Calculate χ^2 using the formula. Complete all calculations to three significant digits.

Table B.1
Calculating Chi-Square

	Green	Yellow
Observed (o)	639	241
Expected (e)	660	220
Deviation ($o - e$)	−21	21
Deviation² (d^2)	441	441
d^2/e	0.668	2.005
$\chi^2 = \Sigma d^2/e = 2.673$		

Table B.2
Chi-Square Distribution

Degrees of Freedom (df)	Probability (p)										
	0.95	0.90	0.80	0.70	0.50	0.30	0.20	0.10	0.05	0.01	0.001
1	0.004	0.02	0.06	0.15	0.46	1.07	1.64	2.71	3.84	6.64	10.83
2	0.10	0.21	0.45	0.71	1.39	2.41	3.22	4.60	5.99	9.21	13.82
3	0.35	0.58	1.01	1.42	2.37	3.66	4.64	6.25	7.82	11.34	16.27
4	0.71	1.06	1.65	2.20	3.36	4.88	5.99	7.78	9.49	13.28	18.47
5	1.14	1.61	2.34	3.00	4.35	6.06	7.29	9.24	11.07	15.09	20.52
6	1.63	2.20	3.07	3.83	5.35	7.23	8.56	10.64	12.59	16.81	22.46
7	2.17	2.83	3.82	4.67	6.35	8.38	9.80	12.02	14.07	18.48	24.32
8	2.73	3.49	4.59	5.53	7.34	9.52	11.03	13.36	15.51	20.09	26.12
9	3.32	4.17	5.38	6.39	8.34	10.66	12.24	14.68	16.92	21.67	27.88
10	3.94	4.86	6.18	7.27	9.34	11.78	13.44	15.99	18.31	23.21	29.59
	Nonsignificant								Significant		

Source: R. A. Fisher and F. Yates, *Statistical Tables for Biological, Agricultural, and Medical Research*, 6th ed., Table IV, Longman Group UK Ltd., 1974.

5. Use the chi-square distribution table to determine the significance of the value.

   a. Determine the degrees of freedom, one less than the number of categories. Locate that value in the appropriate column.

   b. Locate the χ^2 value for your significance level ($p = 0.05$ or less).

   c. Compare this χ^2 value (from the table) with your calculated χ^2.

6. State your conclusion in terms of your hypothesis.

   a. If your calculated χ^2 value is greater than the χ^2 value for your particular degrees of freedom and p value (0.05), then *reject the null hypothesis* of no difference between expected and observed results. *You can conclude that there is a significant difference between your observed distribution and the theoretical expected distribution* (for example, under Mendel's laws).

   b. If your calculated χ^2 value is less than the χ^2 value for your particular degrees of freedom and p value (0.05), then *fail to reject the null hypothesis* of no difference between observed and expected results. *You can conclude that there does not seem to be a significant difference between your observed distribution and the theoretical expected distribution* (for example, under Mendel's laws). *You can conclude that any differences between your observed results and the expected results can be attributed to chance or sampling error.* (Note: It is incorrect to say that you "accept" the null hypothesis. Statisticians either "reject" or "fail to reject" the null hypothesis.)

The chi-square test will be used to test for the goodness of fit between observed and expected data from several laboratory investigations in this lab manual.

Reference

Motulsky, M. *Intuitive Biostatistics*. New York: Oxford University Press, 1995.

Terminology and Techniques for Dissection

Orientation Terminology

Orientation terminology used with quadrupeds (four-legged animals such as the fetal pig) differs from terminology used with bipeds (such as humans). Become familiar with the following terms, which refer to quadrupeds (Figure C.1).

Right/left: always refer to the animal's right or left, not yours.

Anterior, cranial: toward the head.

Posterior, caudal: toward the tail.

Dorsal: backside; from the Latin *dorsum,* meaning "back."

Ventral: bellyside; from the Latin *venter,* meaning "belly."

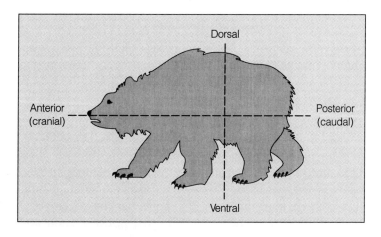

Figure C.1.
Orientation terminology for quadrupeds.

Terms Relating to Position in the Body

Proximal: near the trunk, attached portion, or point of reference, for example: "The pig's elbow is *proximal* to its wrist."

Distal: farther from the trunk, attached portion, or point of reference, for example: "The toes are *distal* to the ankle."

Superficial: lying on top or near the body surface.

Deep: lying under or below.

Figure C.2.
Sections of an organism.

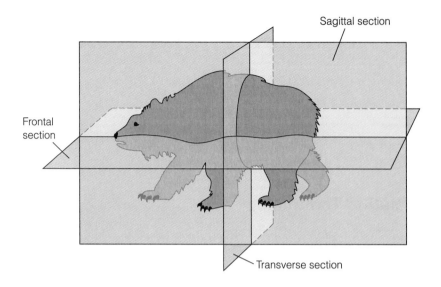

Planes and Sections

A **section** is a cut through a structure. A **plane** is an imaginary line through which a section can be cut. Anatomists generally refer to three planes or sections (Figure C.2).

Sagittal section: divides the body into left and right portions or halves. This is a longitudinal or lengthwise section from anterior to posterior.

Frontal section: A longitudinal or lengthwise section from anterior to posterior, this divides the body into dorsal and ventral portions or halves.

Transverse section: Also called a **cross section,** this divides the body into anterior and posterior portions or cuts a structure across its smallest diameter.

Dissection Techniques

When studying the anatomy of an organism, the term **dissection** is perhaps a misnomer. *Dissection* literally means to cut apart piece by piece. In lab, however, it is usually more appropriate to expose structures rather than dissect them. Initial incisions do require that you cut into the body, but after body cavities are opened, you will usually only separate and expose body parts, using dissection rarely. Accordingly, you will use the scalpel when you make initial incisions into the body wall of large animals, but seldom when studying small animals or organs of large animals.

Scissors are used to deepen initial cuts made by the scalpel in large animals and to cut into the bodies of smaller animals. When using scissors, direct the tips upward to prevent gouging deeper organs. Once the animal's body is open, use forceps and the blunt probe to carefully separate organs and to pick away connective tissue obstructing and binding organs and ducts. Needle probes are only minimally useful. Never cut away an organ or cut through a blood vessel, nerve, or duct unless given specific instructions to do so.

Producing a good dissection takes time and cannot be rushed. As you study the anatomy of animals, your goal should be to expose all parts so that they can be easily studied and demonstrated to your lab partner or instructor.

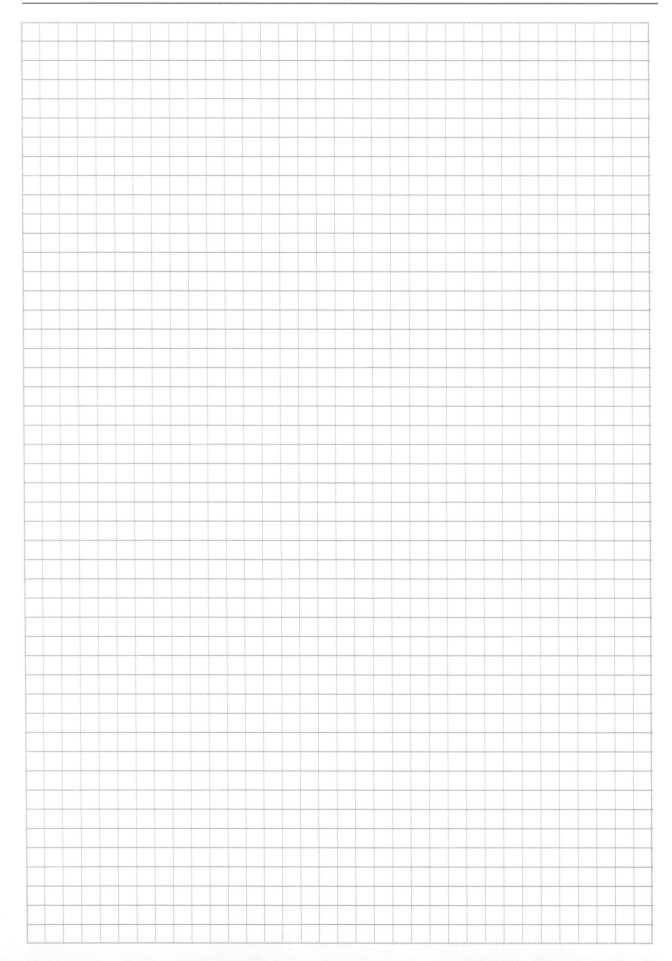

List of Color Plates

1 Amoeba moves and ingests using pseudopodia (Lab Topic 3).

2 *Trichonympha* inhabits termite intestines (Lab Topic 3).

3 *Protococcus,* a green alga with cells in aggregates, lives on tree bark (Lab Topic 3).

4 *Scenedesmus,* an aquatic alga, occurs in simple colonies of four cells (Lab Topic 3).

5 *Volvox.* Individual cells in this complex colony are connected by cytoplasmic strands to form a sphere. Small spheres within the larger sphere are daughter colonies (Lab Topic 3).

6 *Elodea,* a multicellular plant, has a large central vacuole surrounded by cytoplasm (Lab Topic 3).

7 Human epithelial cells, thin, flat cells that line the cheek (Lab Topic 3).

8 Human red blood cells. The star-shaped cell in the center has lost water and crenated (Lab Topic 4).

9 The electromagnetic spectrum (Lab Topic 6).

10 *Coleus* leaves with green and pink pigments (Lab Topic 6).

11 Human chromosomes (Lab Topic 7).

12 Two mating types of *Sordaria fimicola* growing on agar (Lab Topic 7).

13 Wild-type *Brassica rapa* seedlings. Anthocyanin may be seen in the leaf stems (Lab Topic 8).

14 Yellow-green mutant *Brassica rapa* seedlings in the right half of each quad (wild-type in the left half) (Lab Topic 8).

15 *Talinum,* a succulent commonly found in shallow soils on rock outcrops (Lab Topic 12).

16 Bacterial colonies isolated using the streak technique (Lab Topic 13).

17 Fungi growing on an agar plate. Note the filamentous fungal body, the mycelium (Lab Topic 13).

18 *Staphylococcus aureus* growing on blood agar (Lab Topic 13).

19 A common bacterium, *Bacillus cereus* (Lab Topic 13).

20 Gram-positive coccus bacteria (purple) and gram-negative rod-shaped bacteria (pink) (Lab Topic 13).

21 Radiolarians, protozoa that move using pseudopodia, have skeletons of silicon dioxide (Lab Topic 14).

22 Photosynthetic diatoms, with cell walls of silica, are found in two forms, pennate and centric (Lab Topic 14).

23 The kelp *Macrocystis,* a brown alga (Lab Topic 14).

24 A red alga, *Palmaria* (Lab Topic 14).

25 *Ulva,* sea lettuce, is an edible green alga (Lab Topic 14).

26 The green algae, *Chara,* and land plants may share a common ancestor (Lab Topic 14).

27 The vegetative plasmodium of the slime mold, *Physarum* (Lab Topic 14).

28 Fruiting bodies of a slime mold (Lab Topic 14).

29 Ecuadorian poison frog in cup fungus (Lab Topic 14).

30 In a moss, spores develop in sporangia at the end of the sporophyte growing out of the gametophyte (Lab Topic 15).

31 Liverworts. Gemmae cups on the surface of this bryophyte function in asexual reproduction (Lab Topic 15).

32 *Lycopodium.* This club moss is a living member of the division Lycophyta (Lab Topic 15).

33 This *Selaginella* species lives in moist habitats, but other species may survive in a desert (Lab Topic 15).

34 Sporangia are seen on stems of the whisk fern, *Psilotum* (Lab Topic 15).

35 Horsetail stems are seen here with sporangia, or strobili, on their tips (Lab Topic 15).

36 Fern fronds are the sporophyte stage of the life cycle. The fiddleheads in the inset are young fronds ready to unfurl (Lab Topic 15).

37 Fern frond with sori. The sorus in the inset has an indusium covering the sporangia (Lab Topic 15).

38 Coniferophyta. First, second, and third-year cones of bristlecone pine (Lab Topic 16).

39 Cycadophyta (Lab Topic 16).

40 Ginkgophyta. Ginkgo leaves shown with ovules (Lab Topic 16).

41 Ginkgophyta. Male strobili, pollen-producing structures, cluster at the base of leaves (Lab Topic 16).

42 Gnetophyta. Mormon tea occurs in the deserts of North and Central America (Lab Topic 16).

43 Close-up of a tulip showing reproductive structures (Lab Topic 16).

44 Wind pollinated flower (Lab Topic 16).

45 Flowers pollinated by bees may be irregular in shape (Lab Topic 16).

46 Hummingbirds pollinate red tubular flowers (Lab Topic 16).

47 A bat pollinating night-blooming flowers (Lab Topic 16).

48 An ovule containing an eight-nucleate embryo sac (not all nuclei are visible) (Lab Topic 16).

49 Pollen tubes growing from pollen grains (Lab Topic 16).

50 Sponge. Needlelike spicules of calcium carbonate protrude from the osculum and surface of the sponge body (Lab Topic 17).

51 Red finger sponges (Lab Topic 17).

52 *Hydra.* This freshwater cnidarian reproduces by budding (Lab Topic 17).

53 *Dugesia,* a freshwater planarian (Lab Topic 17).

54 Roundworm, in the phylum Nematoda, has a smooth body with no segments (Lab Topic 17).

55 *Nereis.* This segmented clamworm is an annelid that bears fleshy appendages called parapodia (Lab Topic 17).

56 *Donax,* a molluscan species, seen here with the foot and two siphons extended (Lab Topic 18).

57 *Cambarus.* The freshwater crayfish is a member of the phylum Arthropoda (Lab Topic 18).

58 Grasshopper with segmented body and jointed appendages (Lab Topic 18).

59 *Branchiostoma.* The lancelet is a small chordate that lives in coastal waters (Lab Topic 18).

60 Xylem vessels in longitudinal section (Lab Topic 19).

61 Cross section of a sunflower, a herbaceous stem (Lab Topic 19).

62 A woody stem seen in cross section (Lab Topic 19).

63 Cross section of the small intestine. Villi project into the intestinal lumen. Lymph nodules are visible between villi and the circular muscle layer (Lab Topic 21).

64 Arteries and bronchi (Lab Topic 22).

65 Sea star early developmental stages (Lab Topic 24).

66 Sea star bipinnaria larva (Lab Topic 24).

67 Zebrafish are important organisms for developmental studies (Lab Topic 24).

68 *Betta splendens.* The male Siamese fighting fish displays agonistic behavior (Lab Topic 27).

COLOR PLATES

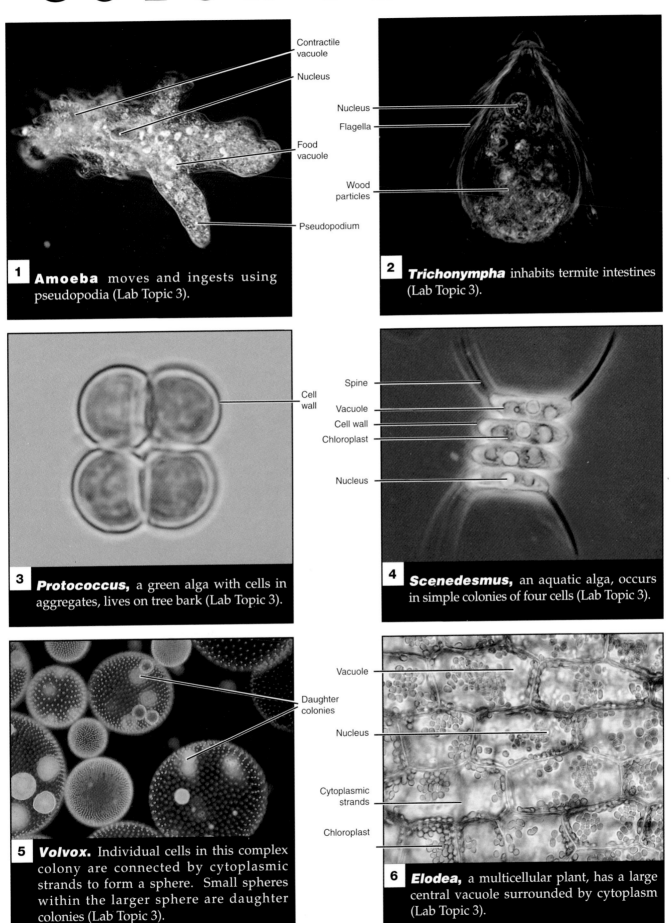

Contractile vacuole
Nucleus
Food vacuole
Pseudopodium

1 **Amoeba** moves and ingests using pseudopodia (Lab Topic 3).

Nucleus
Flagella
Wood particles

2 **Trichonympha** inhabits termite intestines (Lab Topic 3).

Cell wall

3 **Protococcus,** a green alga with cells in aggregates, lives on tree bark (Lab Topic 3).

Spine
Vacuole
Cell wall
Chloroplast
Nucleus

4 **Scenedesmus,** an aquatic alga, occurs in simple colonies of four cells (Lab Topic 3).

Daughter colonies

5 **Volvox.** Individual cells in this complex colony are connected by cytoplasmic strands to form a sphere. Small spheres within the larger sphere are daughter colonies (Lab Topic 3).

Vacuole
Nucleus
Cytoplasmic strands
Chloroplast

6 **Elodea,** a multicellular plant, has a large central vacuole surrounded by cytoplasm (Lab Topic 3).

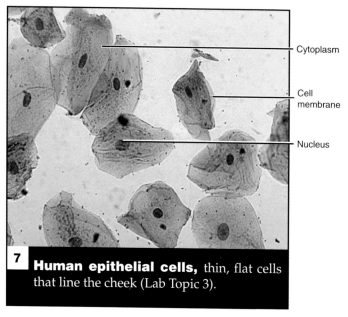

7 **Human epithelial cells,** thin, flat cells that line the cheek (Lab Topic 3).

Cytoplasm

Cell membrane

Nucleus

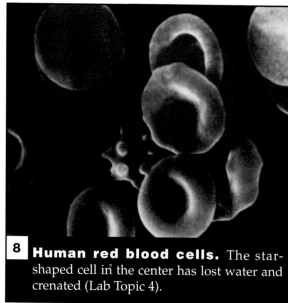

8 **Human red blood cells.** The star-shaped cell in the center has lost water and crenated (Lab Topic 4).

| 10^{-5}nm | 10^{-3}nm | 1 nm | 10^{3}nm | 10^{6}nm | 1 m (10^{9}nm) | 10^{3}m |

| Gamma rays | X-rays | UV | Infrared | Microwaves | Radio waves |

Visible light

380 nm   450 nm   500 nm   550 nm   600 nm   650 nm   700 nm   750 nm

Wavelength increases →
← Energy increases

9 **The electromagnetic spectrum** (Lab Topic 6).

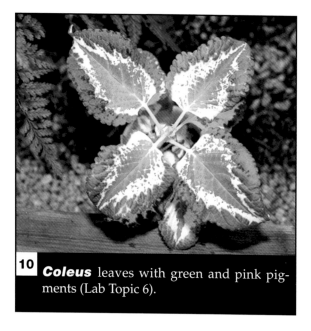

10 *Coleus* leaves with green and pink pigments (Lab Topic 6).

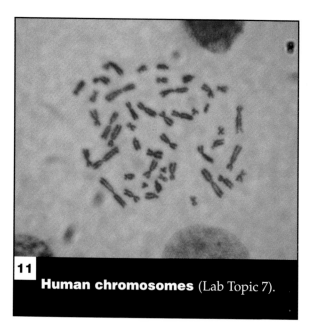

11 **Human chromosomes** (Lab Topic 7).

12 Two mating types of **_Sordaria fimicola_** growing on agar (Lab Topic 7).

13 Wild-type **_Brassica rapa_** seedlings. Anthocyanin may be seen in the leaf stems (Lab Topic 8).

14 Yellow-green mutant **_Brassica rapa_** seedlings in the right half of each quad (wild-type in the left half) (Lab Topic 8).

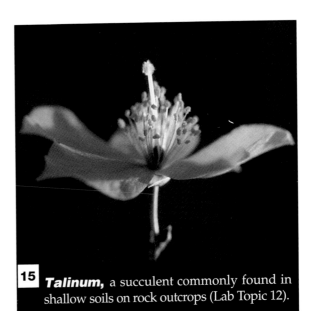

15 **_Talinum,_** a succulent commonly found in shallow soils on rock outcrops (Lab Topic 12).

16 **Bacterial colonies** isolated using the streak technique (Lab Topic 13).

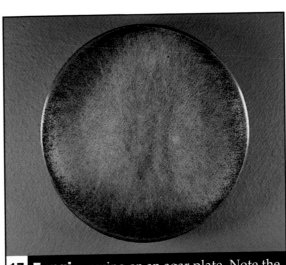

17 **Fungi** growing on an agar plate. Note the filamentous fungal body, the mycelium (Lab Topic 13).

18 Colonies of the bacterium ***Staphylococcus aureus*** growing on blood agar (Lab Topic 13).

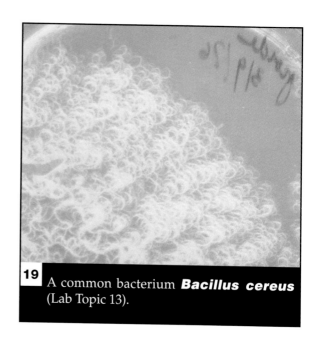

19 A common bacterium ***Bacillus cereus*** (Lab Topic 13).

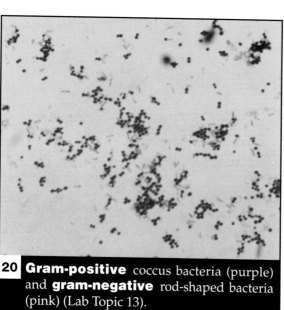

20 **Gram-positive** coccus bacteria (purple) and **gram-negative** rod-shaped bacteria (pink) (Lab Topic 13).

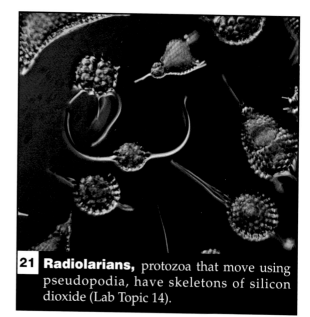

21 **Radiolarians,** protozoa that move using pseudopodia, have skeletons of silicon dioxide (Lab Topic 14).

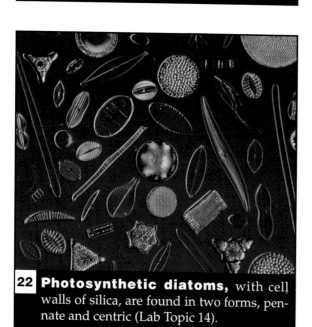

22 **Photosynthetic diatoms,** with cell walls of silica, are found in two forms, pennate and centric (Lab Topic 14).

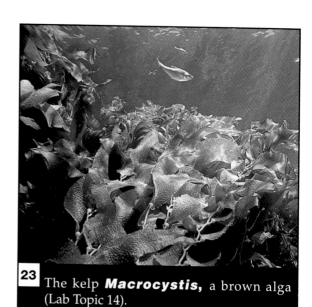

23 The kelp ***Macrocystis,*** a brown alga (Lab Topic 14).

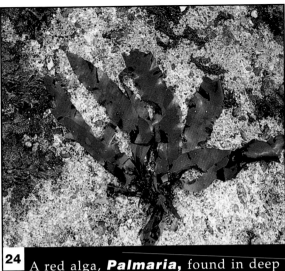

24 A red alga, **_Palmaria_,** found in deep marine waters (Lab Topic 14).

25 **_Ulva_,** sea lettuce, is an edible green alga (Lab Topic 14).

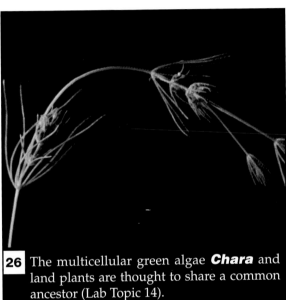

26 The multicellular green algae **_Chara_** and land plants are thought to share a common ancestor (Lab Topic 14).

27 **The slime mold _Physarum_.** The vegetative plasmodium is a multinucleate mass of protoplasm (Lab Topic 14).

28 **Fruiting bodies of a slime mold** are shown magnified about 50 times (Lab Topic 14).

29 **Ecuadorian poison frog in cup fungus** (Lab Topic 14).

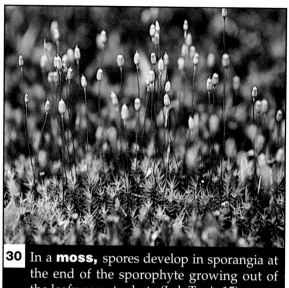

30 In a **moss,** spores develop in sporangia at the end of the sporophyte growing out of the leafy gametophyte (Lab Topic 15).

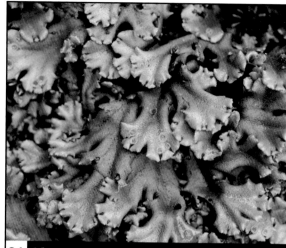

31 **Liverworts.** Gemmae cups on the surface of this bryophyte function in asexual reproduction (Lab Topic 15).

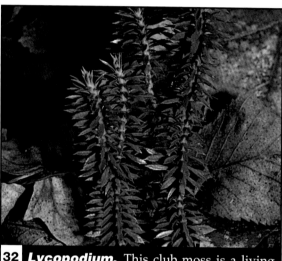

32 *Lycopodium.* This club moss is a living member of the division Lycophyta (Lab Topic 15).

33 This *Selaginella* species lives in moist habitats, but other species may survive in a desert (Lab Topic 15).

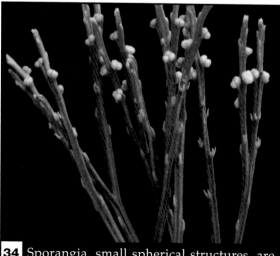

34 Sporangia, small spherical structures, are seen on stems of the **whisk fern,** *Psilotum* (Lab Topic 15).

35 **Horsetail stems** are seen here with strobili containing sporangia (Lab Topic 15).

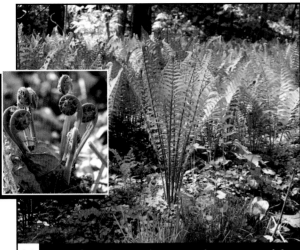

36 **Fern fronds** are the sporophyte stage of the life cycle. The fiddleheads in the inset are young fronds ready to unfurl (Lab Topic 15).

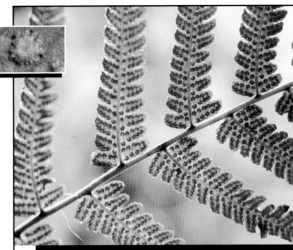

37 **Fern frond** with clusters of sporangia in sori. The sorus in the inset has an indusium covering the sporangia (Lab Topic 15).

38 **Coniferophyta.** First, second, and third-year cones of bristlecone pine. Some bristlecone pines are more than 4,000 years old. (Lab Topic 16).

39 **Cycadophyta.** Pollen is produced in male cones, seeds in female cones in cycads (Lab Topic 16).

40 **Ginkgophyta.** These ginkgo leaves are shown with ovules (Lab Topic 16).

41 **Ginkgophyta.** Male strobili, pollen-producing structures, cluster at the base of leaves (Lab Topic 16).

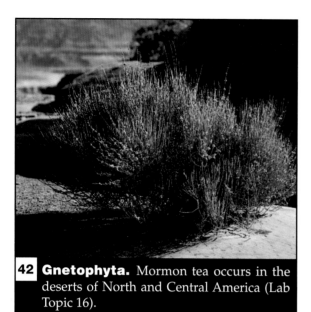

42 Gnetophyta. Mormon tea occurs in the deserts of North and Central America (Lab Topic 16).

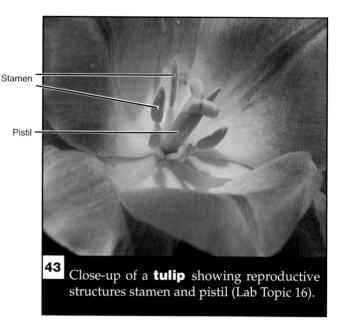

Stamen

Pistil

43 Close-up of a **tulip** showing reproductive structures stamen and pistil (Lab Topic 16).

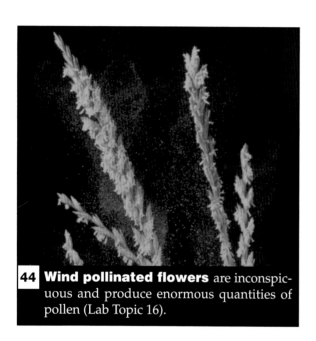

44 Wind pollinated flowers are inconspicuous and produce enormous quantities of pollen (Lab Topic 16).

45 Flowers pollinated by bees may be irregular in shape (Lab Topic 16).

46 Hummingbirds pollinate red tubular flowers (Lab Topic 16).

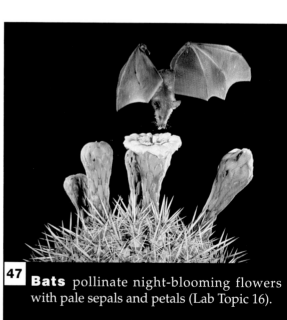

47 Bats pollinate night-blooming flowers with pale sepals and petals (Lab Topic 16).

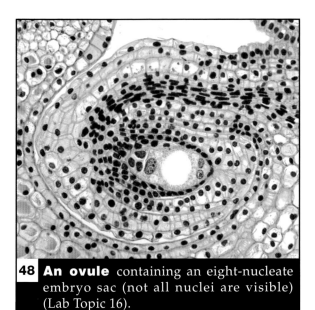

48 **An ovule** containing an eight-nucleate embryo sac (not all nuclei are visible) (Lab Topic 16).

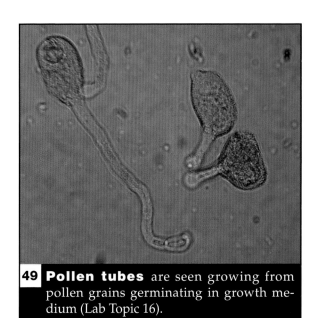

49 **Pollen tubes** are seen growing from pollen grains germinating in growth medium (Lab Topic 16).

50 **Sponge.** Needlelike spicules of calcium carbonate protrude from the osculum and surface of the sponge body (Lab Topic 17).

51 **Red finger sponges** (Lab Topic 17).

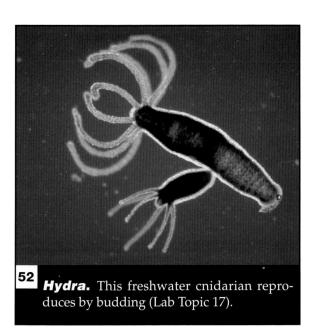

52 ***Hydra.*** This freshwater cnidarian reproduces by budding (Lab Topic 17).

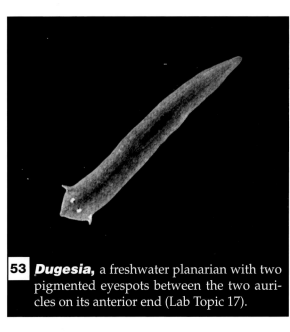

53 ***Dugesia,*** a freshwater planarian with two pigmented eyespots between the two auricles on its anterior end (Lab Topic 17).

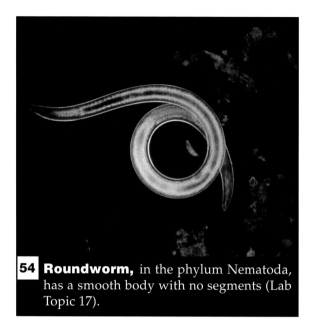

54 **Roundworm,** in the phylum Nematoda, has a smooth body with no segments (Lab Topic 17).

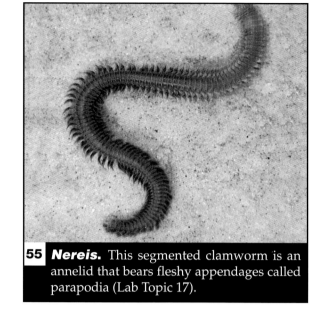

55 *Nereis.* This segmented clamworm is an annelid that bears fleshy appendages called parapodia (Lab Topic 17).

56 *Donax,* a molluscan species, seen here with the foot and two siphons extended (Lab Topic 18).

57 *Cambarus.* The freshwater crayfish is a member of the phylum Arthropoda (Lab Topic 18).

58 The segmented body and jointed appendages are visible in this **grasshopper,** a terrestrial anthropod (Lab Topic 18).

59 *Branchiostoma.* The lancelet is a small chordate that lives in coastal waters (Lab Topic 18).

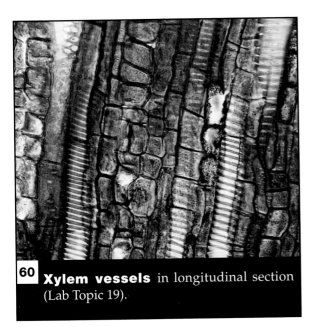

60 **Xylem vessels** in longitudinal section (Lab Topic 19).

61 Cross section of a sunflower, a **herbaceous stem** (Lab Topic 19).

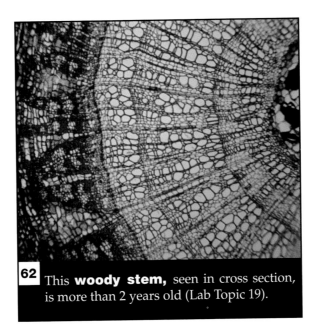

62 This **woody stem,** seen in cross section, is more than 2 years old (Lab Topic 19).

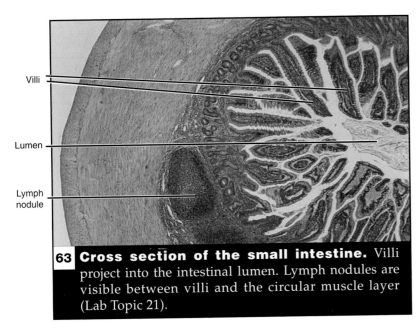

Villi

Lumen

Lymph nodule

63 **Cross section of the small intestine.** Villi project into the intestinal lumen. Lymph nodules are visible between villi and the circular muscle layer (Lab Topic 21).

64 **Arteries** (red) and **bronchi** (clear) in a resin cast of lung tissue (Lab Topic 22).

Trachea

Bronchi

Pulmonary artery

65 **Early development in the sea star.** a. Unfertilized egg with germinal vesicle. b. Early cleavage. c. A blastula with blastocoel. d. An early gastrula with archenteron forming (Lab Topic 24).

Blastocoel

Archenteron

66 **Sea star bipinnaria larva.** Identify mouth, esophagus, stomach, intestine, and anus (Lab Topic 24).

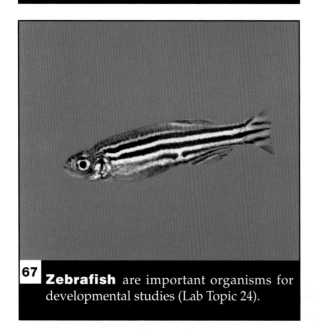

67 **Zebrafish** are important organisms for developmental studies (Lab Topic 24).

68 *Betta splendens.* The male Siamese fighting fish displays agonistic behavior (Lab Topic 27).